ECOLOGY AND CONSERVATION OF GRASSLAND BIRDS OF THE WESTERN HEMISPHERE

Peter D. Vickery and James R. Herkert
Editors

Proceedings of a Conference
Tulsa, Oklahoma
October 1995

Sponsor:

Association of Field Ornithologists

Studies in Avian Biology No. 19
A PUBLICATION OF THE COOPER ORNITHOLOGICAL SOCIETY

Cover photograph of Greater Rheas (*Rhea americana*) in the Pampas of Argentina by Juan Carlos Reboreda.

STUDIES IN AVIAN BIOLOGY

Edited by

John T. Rotenberry
Department of Biology
University of California
Riverside, California 92521

Studies in Avian Biology is a series of works too long for *The Condor,* published at irregular intervals by the Cooper Ornithological Society. Manuscripts for consideration should be submitted to the editor. Style and format should follow those of previous issues.

Price $25.00 for soft cover and $39.50 for hard cover including postage and handling. All orders cash in advance; make checks payable to Cooper Ornithological Society. Send orders to Cooper Ornithological Society, ℅ Western Foundation of Vertebrate Zoology, 439 Calle San Pablo, Camarillo, CA 93010.

ISBN: 1-891276-11-5 (cloth)   ISBN: 1-891276-08-5 (paper)

Library of Congress Catalog Card Number: 99-74812
Printed at Allen Press, Inc., Lawrence, Kansas 66044
Issued: 10 September 1999

CONTENTS

LIST OF AUTHORS

CHARLES D. ARDIZZONE
Department of Biological Sciences
State University of New York College at Brockport
Brockport, NY 14420
(present address: 1011 East Tudor Road
Anchorage, AK 99503)

ROBERT A. ASKINS
Department of Zoology
Connecticut College
New London, CT 06320

GIANFRANCO D. BASILI
Department of Wildlife Ecology
University of Wisconsin
Madison, WI 53706
(present address: Florida Audubon Society
1331 Palmetto Avenue
Winter Park, FL 32789)

BARRY C. BENNETT
Department of Environmental, Population, and
    Organismic Biology
University of Colorado
Boulder, CO 80309-0334

LOUIS B. BEST
Department of Animal Ecology
Iowa State University
Ames, IA 50011

CARL E. BOCK
Department of Environmental, Population, and
    Organismic Biology
University of Colorado
Boulder, CO 80309-0334

JANE H. BOCK
Department of Environmental, Population, and
    Organismic Biology
University of Colorado
Boulder, CO 80309-0334

RANDALL B. BOONE
Department of Wildlife Ecology
Nutting Hall
University of Maine
Orono, ME 04469

ROBERTO B. CAVALCANTI
Departamento de Zoologia
Universidade de Brasília
70910-900 Brasília, D.F., Brazil

GERARDO CEBALLOS
Instituto de Ecología
Universidad Nacional Autónoma de México, C.U.
Apartado Postal 70-275
México, D.F., C.P. 04510
Mexico

STEPHEN K. DAVIS
Saskatchewan Wetland Conservation Corporation
202-2050 Cornwall Street
Regina, SK S4P 2K5
Canada

MARTHA J. DESMOND
Department of Forestry, Fisheries and Wildlife
University of Nebraska
Lincoln, NE 68583-0819
(present address: Caesar Kleberg Wildlife Research
    Institute
Texas A&M University
Kingsville, TX 78363)

DAVID C. DUNCAN
Saskatchewan Wetland Conservation Corporation
202-2050 Cornwall Street
Regina, SK S4P 2K5
Canada

WILLIAM R. EVANS
Cornell Laboratory of Ornithology
159 Sapsucker Woods Road
Ithaca, NY 14850
(present address: P.O. Box 46
Mecklenburg, NY 14863)

BRICK M. FEVOLD
Department of Wildlife Ecology
University of Wisconsin
Madison, WI 53706

FABIÁN MARCELO GABELLI
Laboratorio de Biología del Comportamiento
Instituto de Biología y Medicina Experimental
Obligado 2490
1428 Buenos Aires, Argentina and
Facultad de Psicología
Universidad de Buenos Aires
Buenos Aires, Argentina

WILLIAM D. GLASS
Illinois Department of Natural Resources
Division of Natural Heritage
P. O. Box 88
Wilmington, IL 60481

ANDREW J. HANSEN
Fish & Wildlife Management Program
Biology Department
Montana State University
Bozeman, MT 59717

KATHLEEN HARTMAN
Department of Biological Sciences
State University of New York College at Brockport
Brockport, NY 14420

JAMES R. HERKERT
Illinois Endangered Species Protection Board
524 South Second Street
Springfield, IL 62701

C. STUART HOUSTON
853 University Drive
Saskatoon, SK S7N 0J8
Canada

MALCOLM L. HUNTER, JR.
Department of Wildlife Ecology
Nutting Hall
University of Maine
Orono, ME 04469

LAWRENCE D. IGL
Northern Prairie Wildlife Research Center
U.S. Geological Survey, Biological Resources
    Division
8711 37th Street SE
Jamestown, ND 58401

M. ALAN JENKINS
George M. Sutton Avian Research Center
P.O. Box 2007
Bartlesville, OK 74005-2007

DOUGLAS H. JOHNSON
Northern Prairie Wildlife Research Center
U.S. Geological Survey, Biological Resources
    Division
8711 37th Street SE
Jamestown, ND 58401

MALCOLM T. JONES
Department of Wildlife Ecology
Nutting Hall
University of Maine
Orono, ME 04469

STEVEN T. KNICK
USGS Forest and Rangeland Ecosystem Science
    Center
Snake River Field Station
970 Lusk Street
Boise, ID 83706

FRITZ L. KNOPF
U.S. Geological Survey, Biological Resources
    Division
4512 McMurry Avenue
Fort Collins, CO 80525-3400

ROLF R. KOFORD
Northern Prairie Wildlife Research Center
U.S. Geological Survey, Biological Resources
    Division
8711 37th Street SE
Jamestown, ND 58401
(present address: Iowa Cooperative Fish and Wildlife
    Research Unit
Science Hall II
Iowa State University
Ames, IA 50011)

T. BRUCE LAUBER
Department of Wildlife Ecology
Nutting Hall
University of Maine
Orono, ME 04469
(present address: Department of Natural Resources
Fernow Hall
Cornell University
Ithaca, NY 14853)

RURIK LIST
Department of Zoology, Oxford University
South Parks Road
Oxford OX1 3PS
United Kingdom

ELIZABETH M. MADDEN
Fish & Wildlife Management Program
Biology Department
Montana State University
Bozeman, MT 59717
(present address: J. Clark Salyer National Wildlife
    Refuge
P.O. Box 66
Upham, ND 58789)

PATRICIA MANZANO-FISCHER
Department of Zoology, Oxford University
South Parks Road
Oxford OX1 3PS
United Kingdom
(present address: Apartado Postal 32-F
Toluca, México 50190
Mexico)

KATHY MARTIN
Centre for Applied Conservation Biology
Department of Forest Sciences
#270-2357 Main Mall
University of British Columbia
Vancouver, BC V6T 1Z4
Canada
(present address: Canadian Wildlife Service
5421 Robertson Road, R.R. 1
Delta, BC V4K 3N2
Canada)

DAVID K. MELLINGER
Cornell Laboratory of Ornithology
159 Sapsucker Woods Road
Ithaca, NY 14850
(present address: Monterey Bay Aquarium Research
    Institute
7700 Sandholdt Road
Moss Landing, CA 95039-0628)

ANDREW J. MURPHY
North American Waterfowl Management Plan
c/o Ducks Unlimited Canada
#8, 5580-45th Street
Red Deer, AB T4N 1L1
Canada

KARI J. NELSON
Centre for Applied Conservation Biology
Department of Forest Sciences
#270-2357 Main Mall
University of British Columbia
Vancouver, BC V6T 1Z4
Canada
(present address: 1895 Sea Lion Crs.
Nanoose Bay, BC V9P 9J3
Canada)

CHRISTOPHER J. NORMENT
Department of Biological Sciences
State University of New York College at Brockport
Brockport, NY 14420

RAYMOND J. O'CONNOR
Department of Wildlife Ecology
Nutting Hall
University of Maine
Orono, ME 04469

LAURA K. PAINE
Department of Agronomy
University of Wisconsin
Madison, WI 53706

DUSTIN W. PERKINS
Department of Forestry and Wildlife Conservation
Holdsworth Natural Resource Center
University of Massachusetts
Amherst, MA 01003

BRUCE G. PETERJOHN
U.S. Geological Survey, Biological Resources
  Division
Patuxent Wildlife Research Center
12100 Beech Forest Road
Laurel, MD 20708

KENNETH L. PETERSEN
Department of Environmental Studies
Dordt College
Sioux Center, IA 51250

A. TOWNSEND PETERSON
Natural History Museum
University of Kansas
Lawrence, KS 66045

DAVID R. C. PRESCOTT
Land Stewardship Centre of Canada
13 Mission Avenue
St. Albert, AB T8N 1H6
Canada
(present address: Alberta Conservation Association
P.O. Box 40027, Baker Centre Postal Outlet
Edmonton, AB T5J 4M9
Canada)

DAN L. REINKING
George M. Sutton Avian Research Center
P.O. Box 2007
Bartlesville, OK 74005-2007

MARK B. ROBBINS
Natural History Museum
University of Kansas
Lawrence, KS 66045

RONALD W. ROHRBAUGH, JR.
George M. Sutton Avian Research Center
P.O. Box 2007
Bartlesville, OK 74005-2007
(present address: Cornell Laboratory of Ornithology
159 Sapsucker Woods Road
Ithaca, NY 14850)

KENNETH V. ROSENBERG
Cornell Laboratory of Ornithology
159 Sapsucker Woods Road
Ithaca, NY 14850

JAY J. ROTELLA
Fish & Wildlife Management Program
Biology Department
Montana State University
Bozeman, MT 59717

JOHN T. ROTENBERRY
Natural Reserve System and Department of Biology
University of California
Riverside, CA 92521

JEFFERY R. RUPERT
U.S. Geological Survey, Biological Resources
  Division
4512 McMurry Avenue
Fort Collins, CO 80525-3400

DAVID W. SAMPLE
Bureau of Research
Wisconsin Department of Natural Resources
Monona, WI 53716

JOHN R. SAUER
U.S. Geological Survey, Biological Resources
  Division
Patuxent Wildlife Research Center
12100 Beech Forest Road
Laurel, MD 20708

JULIE A. SAVIDGE
Department of Forestry, Fisheries and Wildlife
University of Nebraska
Lincoln, NE 68583-0819

JOSEF K. SCHMUTZ
Department of Biology
University of Saskatchewan
112 Science Place
Saskatoon, SK S7N 5E2
Canada

STEVE K. SHERROD
George M. Sutton Avian Research Center
P.O. Box 2007
Bartlesville, OK 74005-2007

W. GREGORY SHRIVER
Department of Forestry and Wildlife Conservation
Holdsworth Natural Resource Center
University of Massachusetts
Amherst, MA 01003
(present address: College of Environmental Science
  and Forestry
State University of New York
1 Forestry Drive
Syracuse, NY 13210)

JOSÉ MARIA CARDOSO DA SILVA
Universidade Federal de Pernambuco
Centro de Ciências Biologicas
Departamento de Zoologia
Av. Prof. Morais Rego, 1235
50670-420 Recife, PE
Brazil

STANLEY A. TEMPLE
Department of Wildlife Ecology
University of Wisconsin
Madison, WI 53706

PABLO LUIS TUBARO
Laboratorio de Biología del Comportamiento
Instituto de Biología y Medicina Experimental
Obligado 2490
1428 Buenos Aires
Argentina

DANIEL J. UNDERSANDER
Department of Agronomy
University of Wisconsin
Madison, WI 53706

PETER D. VICKERY
Department of Wildlife Ecology
Nutting Hall
University of Maine
Orono, ME 04469
(present address: Center for Biological Conservation
Massachusetts Audubon Society
Lincoln, MA 01773 and
Department of Forestry and Wildlife Conservation
University of Massachusetts
Amherst, MA 01003)

JEFFREY V. WELLS
Cornell Laboratory of Ornithology
159 Sapsucker Woods Road
Ithaca, NY 14850
(present address: National Audubon Society
Cornell Laboratory of Ornithology
159 Sapsucker Woods Road
Ithaca, NY 14850)

MAIKEN WINTER
Department of Behavioral Physiology
University-Tübingen
72072 Tübingen
Germany
(present address: 611 Winston Court, Apt. #4
Ithaca, NY 14850-1953)

DONALD H. WOLFE
George M. Sutton Avian Research Center
P.O. Box 2007
Bartlesville, OK 74005-2007

Studies in Avian Biology No. 19:1, 1999.

PREFACE

This book had its genesis in 1994, when the Council of the Association of Field Ornithologists and the staff of the George M. Sutton Avian Research Center recognized the need to convene a conference on the ecology, status, and conservation of grassland birds in the Western Hemisphere. This two-day conference, convened in Tulsa, Oklahoma, in October 1995, reflected the deep concern held by many avian biologists that populations of many grassland bird species are declining throughout the Western Hemisphere. Generous support from the U.S. Fish and Wildlife Service, the Association of Field Ornithologists, the Sutton Avian Research Center, and the National Fish and Wildlife Foundation made it possible to invite a broad international contingent, especially from South America. Steve Sherrod and the Sutton Avian Research Center staff facilitated conference arrangements and field trips for this productive meeting.

The Council of the Association of Field Ornithologists, notably presidents Greg Butcher, Elissa Landre, and Charles Duncan, provided leadership and support throughout this process. The commitment of the AFO council to both the conference and the publication of this volume is warmly and gratefully acknowledged. We also thank Steve Lewis and the Office of Migratory Bird Management of the U.S. Fish and Wildlife Service for their financial support of this volume. The Center for Biological Conservation of the Massachusetts Audubon Society, especially Christopher Leahy, and the Illinois Endangered Species Protection Board provided logistical support and encouragement to Vickery and Herkert, respectively.

We thank the more than 40 reviewers whose insights measurably improved the manuscripts in this volume. We also thank Andrea Jones, Dustin Perkins, Jan Pierson, Vanessa Rule, and Greg Shriver for their help and suggestions on a variety of issues. Elizabeth Pierson meticulously copyedited the entire manuscript and brought greater clarity to every manuscript herein; that she was able to do this with wit and grace and without offending anyone seems remarkable. We thank Eugenia Wheelwright, who translated all abstracts into Spanish, and Rosita Moore, who provided assistance with graphics. We are immeasurably grateful to Barbara, Simon, and Gabriel Vickery and to Linda, Nathan, and Nicholas Herkert for their collective patience and support. We especially thank John Rotenberry, editor of the Studies in Avian Biology series, for his cheerful guidance, encouragement, and good counsel throughout.

This volume is dedicated to John A. Wiens, whose research on grassland and shrubsteppe birds has had a profound influence not only on both of us but on countless other ecologists of many different disciplines. John's ecological perspicacity and intellectual brilliance continue to inspire and serve as a model. This volume is also dedicated to our children and their millions of cohorts throughout this hemisphere, that they may all have the opportunity to admire prairie-chickens and buntings, or rheas, canasteros, and seedeaters, in wonder, joy, and we hope, curiosity.

Peter D. Vickery
Center for Biological Conservation
Massachusetts Audubon Society
Lincoln, Massachusetts

James R. Herkert
Illinois Endangered Species Protection Board
Springfield, Illinois

Studies in Avian Biology No. 19:2–26, 1999.

CONSERVATION OF GRASSLAND BIRDS IN THE WESTERN HEMISPHERE

PETER D. VICKERY, PABLO L. TUBARO, JOSÉ MARIA CARDOSO DA SILVA, BRUCE G. PETERJOHN, JAMES R. HERKERT, AND ROBERTO B. CAVALCANTI

"The sweeping vista of the world's natural grasslands—be they steppes, savannas, rangelands, punas or prairies—occupy nearly seven billion hectares; over half of the earth's land surface. Add to that figure the vast area converted to . . . habitats of low intensity agriculture and grasslands become second only to the oceans in terms of direct dominance of the planet's ecosystems. They govern, directly, the livelihoods of hundreds of millions of people."
—C. Imboden (1988:vii).

Research on and interest in grassland birds have increased considerably in the past 20 yr. There are several reasons for this heightened interest. Foremost, it is clear that populations of many grassland birds have declined sharply throughout the Western Hemisphere (e.g., Bucher and Nores 1988, Cavalcanti 1988, Fjeldså 1988, McNicholl 1988, Knopf 1994, Peterjohn and Sauer 1999). In North America, populations of at least 13 species of grassland birds declined significantly between 1966 and 1995 (Peterjohn and Sauer 1999). And as a group, North American grassland birds have experienced "steeper, more consistent, and more geographically widespread declines than any other behavioral or ecological guild," largely because of habitat loss and degradation (Knopf 1994:251). Similar declines are also occurring in South America, where species such as Pampas Meadowlark (*Sturnella defilippii*; Tubaro and Gabelli 1999), Saffron-cowled Blackbird (*Agelaius flavus*; Fraga et al. 1998), and *Sporophila* seedeaters (Silva 1999) have declined in the past 20 yr. Indeed, Collar et al. (1992:35) describe the "near-total destruction of open grasslands in south-east Brazil . . . and in the vast central planalto . . . as one of the great ecological catastrophes in South America."

Another reason for the increased research interest in grassland birds is changing agricultural practices. For example, the U.S. Department of Agriculture's Conservation Reserve Program (CRP), which has taken more than 14 million ha of cropland out of production under 10-yr contracts, has made it possible to examine regional, and even continental, effects of changing landscapes on grassland birds (e.g., Lauber 1991, Reynolds et al. 1994, Herkert 1998). Additionally, the CRP has provided excellent opportunities to study bird colonization, habitat use, and nesting success in different regions and under different ecological conditions. Finally, grassland birds are also fascinating from ecological and evolutionary perspectives. Distinctive or un-

usual adaptations, such as large body size and cursorial habits, have evolved in grassland birds. And the ability to readily observe many behaviors makes these species ideal for research (e.g., Wheelwright and Mauck 1998).

GRASSLAND HABITATS IN THE WESTERN HEMISPHERE

Grassland ecosystems occur in a variety of forms and are affected by geology, geography, moisture, soil type, elevation, climate, and disturbance regime (Kantrud 1981, Vickery et al. in press). In this volume, we define a grassland habitat as any extensive area that is dominated by more than 50% grass (Poaceae) or sedge (Cyperaceae) cover and that generally has few scattered shrubs (< 4 m high) and trees. We have generally excluded habitats that are dominated by more than 50% shrub cover, such as chaparral.

In addition to such obvious grassland habitats as tallgrass and shortgrass prairies, pampas, and Patagonian grassland, we include sedge-dominated tundra, alpine ridges and barrens, puna, and paramo. We also include the longleaf pine (*Pinus palustris*) ecosystems of the southeastern United States and the pine (*Pinus* spp.) forests and savannas of Mexico because it is clear that several species of birds, among them Bachman's Sparrow (*Aimophila aestivalis*), Striped Sparrow (*Oriturus superciliosus*), and Sierra Madre Sparrow (*Xenospiza baileyi*), have adapted to the graminoid ground cover beneath these forests. Although these ecosystems are generally viewed as forests, the above species appear to occupy them as a form of grassland, not forest, habitat. Bachman's Sparrow, for example, continues to occupy clear-cut glades after forest removal (Dunning 1993). In North America, we also include as grassland wet-mesic upland habitats where the soil is often saturated but not inundated for long periods; we do not include freshwater, brackish, and saltwater wetlands where

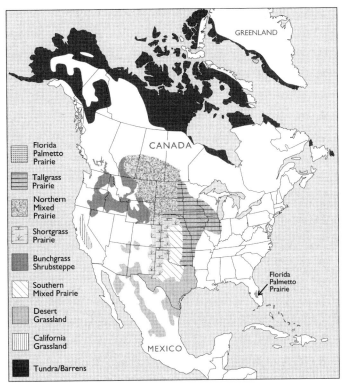

FIGURE 1. Distribution of major grassland ecosystems in North America and Mexico prior to European settlement. Alpine zones above tree line have not been depicted. This map was adapted and modified from two primary sources, Risser et al. 1981 and Environment Canada 1998.

standing water is present for long periods, however.

Native grasslands in the Western Hemisphere extend from high-arctic sedge meadows in the tundra of North America to pampas and Patagonian grasslands in southern South America (Figs. 1 and 2). In North America, a mosaic of tundra/barrens habitats forms the northernmost grassland component. In the temperate region, the most extensive grasslands historically included the shortgrass prairie and southern mixed prairie of the western Great Plains and the tallgrass prairie and northern mixed prairie of the midwestern United States and Canada (Knopf 1988; Fig. 1). Although they were less extensive, bunchgrass shrubsteppe (including palouse prairie) and California grasslands in the west, desert grasslands in the southern United States and Mexico, and palmetto (*Serenoa repens*) dry prairie in Florida were historically all major grassland types in North America (Fig. 1).

In South America, major native grassland ecosystems include high-altitude paramo and puna grasslands (listed as Andean grasslands; Fig. 2) and mid-elevation monte grasslands (Fig. 2). Low-elevation grasslands include Patagonian grasslands in southern Argentina and Chile and pampas in eastern Argentina, Uruguay, and southernmost Brazil. Brushier savanna grasslands include chaco, cerrado (particularly "campo limpo" and "campo sujo" in central Brazil), Beni savannas, Amazonian savannas, Guianan savannas, and espinal. Native South American grasslands also include such mesic ecosystems as the llanos of Venezuela and Colombia and the Pantanal of southwestern Brazil, where seasonal flooding for several months each year is followed by pronounced dry seasons when most surface water disappears (Soriano 1991, Dinerstein et al. 1995, Stotz et al. 1996; Fig. 2).

DEFINING GRASSLAND BIRDS

"The difficulty . . . in defining grassland species . . . results from the fact that grassland itself is not easy to define precisely. How small may a prairie be before it is a mere opening? Where does grassland stop and very open woodland begin? . . . How much sage is required before grassland becomes some form of desert scrub?"

—R. M. Mengel (1970:283)

Few would argue that species such as Lesser Rhea (*Rhea pennata*), Sprague's Pipit (*Anthus*

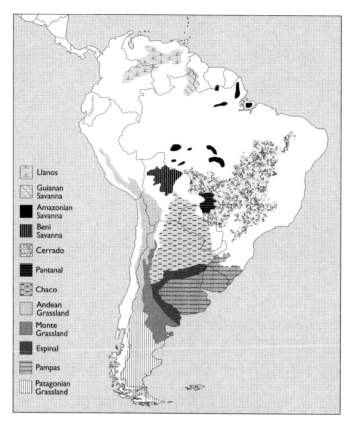

FIGURE 2.   Distribution of major grassland ecosystems in South America prior to European settlement. Puna and paramo grasslands have been classified as Andean grasslands. This map was adapted and modified from two primary sources, Cabrera and Willink 1980 and Dinerstein et al. 1995.

spragueii), McCown's Longspur (*Calcarius mccownii*), and Wedge-tailed Grass-Finch (*Emberizoides herbicola*) are completely adapted to grassland habitats and should be considered grassland specialists. Classification seems obvious in these cases, as all of these species use grassland habitat for all their life-history needs. But for many other species, determining which ones should be considered grassland birds quickly becomes complicated and invariably somewhat subjective. Are Western Kingbirds (*Tyrannus verticalis*), Red-winged Blackbirds (*Agelaius phoeniceus*), and Blue-black Grassquits (*Volatinia jacarina*), for instance, also grassland birds? What about jaegers (*Stercorarius* spp.)? Although each of the three jaeger species spends 9 mo a year on the open ocean, all require open tundra for nesting. And nest success in Pomarine Jaegers (*S. pomarinus*), as in Snowy Owls (*Nyctea scandiaca*), depends strongly on collared lemming (*Dicrostonyx torquatus*) populations (Pitelka et al. 1955).

Mengel (1970) recognized the difficulties inherent in trying to define grassland birds. He realized that grasslands extend along a moisture gradient—from arid prairies to wet meadows and marshes—and that defining the limits of this gradient in relation to the birds that occupy these habitats can be, and is, somewhat arbitrary. In addition, he noted that grassland ecosystems frequently intergrade with forested and other habitat types, making it difficult to define the limits of some grassland types. In the Cerrado of central Brazil, for example, "campo limpo," or open grasslands, are interspersed with "campo sujo," or grasslands with scattered trees and shrubs; and campo sujo may blend into "cerradão," which is even more densely forested (Eiten 1972). In the United States, tallgrass prairie intergrades into oak (*Quercus*) savannas in the Midwest, and in the Southeast the dry palmetto prairies of central Florida merge into longleaf pine savannas, called "flatwoods." Consequently, it is often difficult to delineate where grassland ends and forest begins. Furthermore, different species of birds may respond differently to the same ecotone. In Florida, Grasshopper Sparrows (*Ammodramus savannarum floridan-*

us) breed only on treeless palmetto prairies and do not occupy savanna flatwoods. Bachman's Sparrows, however, breed commonly in both habitats. From the perspective of these two sympatric grassland sparrows, the definition of grassland habitat is quite different.

This process is further complicated by the fact that some grassland species use different habitats in different parts of their ranges. Savannah Sparrows (*Passerculus sandwichensis*) are known to use an extraordinary array of open habitats throughout their extensive range (Wheelwright and Rising 1993). In eastern Texas, Bachman's Sparrows typically breed in open pine forests, but in central Florida they commonly breed on treeless palmetto prairies (Dunning 1993, Shriver et al. 1999). Although there are similarities in these habitats, notably the predominant graminoid ground cover, the differences are also obvious and striking.

Finally, the fact that so many grassland habitats have been severely altered by modern agricultural practices further complicates efforts to define grassland birds. Many grassland species in the Western Hemisphere are presently occupying artificial habitats that did not exist 200–300 yr ago. For example, Northern Harriers (*Circus cyaneus*), Short-eared Owls (*Asio flammeus*), Henslow's Sparrows (*Ammodramus henslowii*), and many other grassland birds now breed on reclaimed surface coal mines in western Pennsylvania, West Virginia, Ohio, and Indiana. These newly created "prairies" did not exist 100 yr ago, but they appear to be providing important refugia for threatened species in these regions (D. Brauning, pers. comm.). Conversely, some steppe or forest birds are invading open habitats because as early settlers cleared the land for agriculture, they provided the perches and refuges these species require (Gochfeld 1979, McNicholl 1988). Thus, it is necessary to have some understanding of habitat preferences prior to European settlement to determine whether present-day habitat use reflects long-term evolutionary patterns.

Given the complexities in defining grassland habitats, how does one define the birds that use this variety of habitats? Are there common threads that help define grassland birds? And are these similarities consistent spatially and across taxa?

In midwestern North America, Mengel (1970) recognized two groups of grassland birds based on distribution and habitat selection. He relied on limited geographic range and endemism to determine "primary" grassland birds, which were restricted to the central Great Plains. He identified as "secondary" grassland birds those species that had "strong affinities with the grasslands, although [were] not restricted to them" (Mengel 1970:283). This geographic emphasis created ecological inconsistencies. Wilson's Phalarope (*Phalaropus tricolor*) and Franklin's Gull (*Larus pipixcan*), for instance, were considered "primary" grassland species, but the ecological connections to grassland habitat for either species are limited. Wilson's Phalarope, for example, generally breeds along the edges of prairie potholes and open marshes but makes little use of the surrounding grassland habitat.

We prefer an ecological basis for defining grassland birds. We thus define a grassland bird as any species that has become adapted to and reliant on some variety of grassland habitat for part or all of its life cycle, be it breeding (either nesting or feeding), migration, or wintering. Grassland birds often, but not necessarily, nest on the ground. Thus, we consider Swainson's Hawk (*Buteo swainsoni*), Mountain Plover (*Charadrius montanus*), and Long-billed Curlew (*Numenius americanus*) to be grassland birds, despite the fact that Swainson's Hawks nest in trees and that curlews often use a variety of intertidal habitats in the nonbreeding seasons. Along the moisture gradient, we include as grassland birds four species of South American geese (*Chloephaga* spp.), Sedge Wren (*Cistothorus platensis*), Henslow's Sparrow, and Le Conte's Sparrow (*Ammodramus leconteii*), but we exclude birds that normally breed over or adjacent to standing water, among them Swamp Sparrow (*Melospiza georgiana*), Nelson's Sharp-tailed Sparrow (*Ammodramus nelsoni*), Seaside Sparrow (*A. maritima*), some waterfowl (Anatidae), and most rails (Rallidae) and herons (Ardeidae; but see Sample and Mossman 1997 for a different perspective). Along the shrub gradient, we consider Rufous-winged Sparrow (*Aimophila carpalis*) and Lark Sparrow (*Chondestes grammacus*) to be grassland birds but not Brewer's Sparrow (*Spizella breweri*). We exclude species that occur commonly in grassland habitats but do not use the graminoid components of these habitats; examples include Pinyon Jay (*Gymnorhinus cyanocephalus*), which feeds almost exclusively on shrub seeds, and aerial insectivores such as swifts (Apodidae) and swallows (Hirundinidae), which only feed over grasslands.

Finally, we include species that occupy wetland, shrub, and forest edges adjacent to grassland habitats only when they make regular use of the grassland habitat away from edge (> 100 m). For example, we consider the American Bittern (*Botaurus lentiginosus*), which nests in prairie fragments and fields, and the various puddle ducks that nest in upland fields far from wetlands to be grassland birds.

OBLIGATE AND FACULTATIVE GRASSLAND BIRDS

Within our ecological definition of grassland birds, two groups can be reasonably separated. Obligate grassland specialists are species that are exclusively adapted to and entirely dependent on grassland habitats and make little or no use of other habitat types. Examples include Lesser Rhea, Baird's Sparrow (*Ammodramus bairdii*), and Pampas Meadowlark (Tables 1 and 3). Obligate grassland birds would almost certainly become extinct without the appropriate grassland habitat.

Facultative grassland specialists use grasslands as part of a wider array of habitats. In general, these species are not entirely dependent on grasslands but use them commonly and regularly. If the appropriate types of grassland habitat were destroyed, populations of some facultative grassland birds would diminish but probably would not completely disappear. Examples of facultative grassland birds include Barn Owl (*Tyto alba*), Loggerhead Shrike (*Lanius ludovicianus*), Clay-colored Sparrow (*Spizella pallida*), and Blue-black Grassquit (Tables 2 and 4).

The number of obligate species found in grasslands is not especially great compared with other habitats. In North America, Mexico, and the Caribbean, for example, there are 59 species of obligate grassland species from 35 genera (Table 1) compared with more than 180 species of obligate forest-dwelling species. With 124 species from 59 genera (Table 3), South America supports many more obligate grassland species than do North America, Mexico, and the Caribbean. Not surprisingly, facultative grassland species are more numerous than obligates; there are 97 species of facultative grassland birds in North America, Mexico, and the Caribbean (Table 2) and 164 in South America (Table 4).

DISTRIBUTION OF GRASSLAND BIRDS

Obligate grassland specialists have a wide geographic distribution. They occur from north of the Arctic Circle to the southern tip of Argentina and Chile and as far offshore as the Islas Malvinas (Falkland Islands) and, 1770 km east of Tierra del Fuego, South Georgia Island (Tables 1 and 3). As a genus, pipits (*Anthus* spp.) have the widest breeding range of any Western Hemisphere passerines, extending from arctic Canada (American Pipit [*A. rubescens*]) to South Georgia Island (South Georgia Pipit [*A. antarcticus*]).

Only three obligate grassland species are widely distributed across the Americas, however. The Short-eared Owl breeds discontinuously from the arctic regions of Canada and Alaska to Tierra del Fuego; the Burrowing Owl (*Athene cunicularia*) breeds from southern Canada and Florida to the southern pampas of Argentina; and the Sedge Wren, currently classified as a single, widely distributed species, occurs from eastern North America to southern South America (AOU 1998). Only seven obligate grassland species in North America breed in both arctic/alpine and temperate regions (Table 1).

Although there are differences between arctic/alpine breeders in North America (e.g., ptarmigan [*Lagopus* spp.], jaegers, and buntings [*Plectrophenax* spp.]) and temperate or steppe breeders (e.g., prairie-chickens [*Tympanuchus* spp.], sparrows [*Aimophila* spp.], and meadowlarks [*Sturnella* spp.]), the similarities between grassland birds of these regions are pronounced. Many genera are shared between the arctic/alpine and temperate regions, despite the fact that the breeding ranges of most species are restricted to either the arctic/alpine or temperate region (Table 1). For example, McCown's Longspurs and Chestnut-collared Longspurs (*Calcarius ornatus*), both of which occur in shortgrass and mixed prairies, are replaced by Smith's Longspurs (*C. pictus*) and Lapland Longspurs (*C. lapponicus*) farther north. The same allopatric relationships are found among hawks (*Buteo* spp.), falcons (*Falco* spp.), plovers (*Charadrius* spp.), curlews (*Numenius* spp.), godwits (*Limosa* spp.), shrikes (*Lanius* spp.), and pipits.

In South America, taxonomic affinities between high-altitude and lowland temperate birds occur in hawks (*Buteo* spp.), caracaras (*Phalcoboenus* spp.), seedsnipes (*Attagis* and *Thinocorus* spp.), doves (*Metriopelia* and *Zenaida* spp.), tyrant flycatchers (Tyrannidae), and seedeaters (Emberizinae). It should be noted that the geographic scope of research in this volume is limited to birds that breed in the temperate regions of North, Central, and South America.

In North America, the geographic separation between arctic/alpine and temperate breeders largely disappears in the nonbreeding season. Although a few species such as ptarmigan are largely resident, many arctic/alpine species migrate medium to long distances and can be found wintering with temperate grassland breeding birds. A few arctic breeders, such as American Golden-Plovers (*Pluvialis dominicus*) and Eskimo Curlews (*Numenius borealis*), join more temperate breeders such as Upland Sandpipers (*Bartramia longicauda*) and Bobolinks (*Dolichonyx oryzivorus*) to winter on the pampas in Argentina and southern Brazil.

LOSS OF GRASSLAND HABITAT

Since the early 1800s, most grassland ecosystems in North America have been profoundly altered by agricultural activities, and many are now among the continent's most endangered ecosystems (Table 5; Noss et al. 1995). In most areas, habitat loss has exceeded 80% (Samson and Knopf 1994, Noss et al. 1995), and where soil and topography are well suited for crops, less than 0.1% of native prairie remains (Samson and Knopf 1994). Since 1850, for example, the decline of tallgrass prairie (estimated to be 88–99%) exceeds that reported for any other major ecosystem in North America (Samson and Knopf 1994, Noss et al. 1995). Similarly, in Florida only 19% of the original palmetto dry prairie remains, with most of this habitat having been converted to citrus groves and improved cattle pastures since about 1950 (Shriver and Vickery 1999).

Native temperate grasslands in the Western Hemisphere have experienced major, sometimes profound, losses from agriculture, range management, and urban development. Some grassland species, however, notably Picazuro Pigeon (*Columba picazuro*), Spot-winged Pigeon (*C. maculosa*), Eared Dove (*Zenaida auriculata*), Grasshopper Sparrow, Dickcissel (*Spiza americana*), Bobolink, and meadowlarks have adapted successfully to these modified landscapes (Graber and Graber 1963, Bucher and Nores 1988, Rodenhouse et al. 1995, O'Connor et al. 1999). In the midwestern United States, agricultural lands have provided adequate breeding habitat for many species, but in the past 50 yr conversion of pastures and hayfields into rowcrops (e.g., corn [*Zea mays*] and soybeans [*Glycine max*]) and shortened cutting rotations of hay have made much of this habitat unsuitable and have become major threats to grassland bird populations (Herkert 1991, 1997; Warner 1994; Herkert et al. 1996).

In Canada, approximately 25% of native grasses remain, but losses continue; 570,000 ha, or approximately 6% of what remained, were lost between 1991 and 1996 (Statistics Canada 1997). Southeastern Alberta and southwestern Saskatchewan contain much of the remaining native prairie, and several grassland bird species, among them Baird's Sparrow and Sprague's Pipit, are abundant there (Price et al. 1995). Grazing pressure has generally increased on remaining native grasslands (Gayton 1991).

In South America, modernization and mechanical changes in agricultural practices have had similarly adverse effects on breeding birds (Bucher and Nores 1988, Cavalcanti 1999b, Tubaro and Gabelli 1999). Horses and cattle were introduced to the Pampas in 1535, and by 1750 feral populations were so common that they supported a growing industry of exporting hides. The effects of grazing and burning to improve

pastures and to deter aboriginal Indians transformed the Pampas and were commented on by Darwin (1876). The most profound changes, however, occurred after 1890 with the expansion of agriculture in South America. During the first quarter of the twentieth century, the negative effect of agriculture on grassland species such as the Strange-tailed Tyrant (*Alectrurus risora*) became evident (Wilson 1926). Since 1970, increased use of agrochemicals and technology has contributed to the intensive use of grasslands. In the northern Pampas, silviculture is also reducing grassland area.

In Brazil, more than 50% of the Cerrado has been converted for human uses since 1950 (Silva 1995), and today the region is seen as a promising area for "carbon bank" mitigation (planting trees to absorb and convert carbon dioxide) against deforestation in Amazonia (Cavalcanti 1999a). The trend in the Cerrado is an ever-growing rate of destruction of natural habitats. Recent estimates indicate that approximately 75% of this biome can be converted to pastures and agriculture fields to produce about 100 million ton of crops and meat annually (Macedo 1994). An analysis of satellite images from 1987 to 1993 covering the entire Cerrado region showed that 67% of the land surface (excluding non-Cerrado habitats) was in a disturbed or highly disturbed condition as a result of human activity (Mantovani and Pereira 1998).

In the Pampas, less than 5% of the land was used for agriculture in 1890, but in high, mesic areas that figure is now greater than 50%. In the more arid and lowland areas of the Pampas, tillage agriculture represents less than 10% of the land use, but cattle grazing over seeded or natural pastures is widespread (Leon et al. 1984).

It is clear that similar rates of habitat loss have taken place elsewhere in Central and South America, from northern Mexico (Manzano-Fischer et al. 1999) to Argentina (Collar et al. 1992, Dinerstein et al. 1995, Tubaro and Gabelli 1999). It is distressing that conversion of native grasslands for agricultural purposes in South America has been "so utterly neglected as an international conservation issue" (Collar et al. 1992:35). In Brazil, remnants of native grassland are now largely restricted to national parks (Collar et al. 1992). In Argentina, there is no national park protecting a representative sample of pampas (Burkart and Valle Ruiz 1994). Moreover, a recent attempt to create a national park in the Pampas failed because the landowner plowed and destroyed the grassland on his hacienda when he realized the government was considering appropriating the area (P. Tubaro, pers. comm.). The most acutely imperiled grasslands in Central and South America are the Cerrado,

TABLE 1. Obligate grassland birds of North America, Mexico, and the Caribbean

Family		Breeding distribution			
		Arctic/ alpine	Temperate	Sub- tropical/ Mexico	Caribbean
Hawks	Accipitridae				
Northern Harrier	Circus cyaneus	✓	✓		
Swainson's Hawk	Buteo swainsoni		✓	✓	
Ferruginous Hawk	Buteo regalis		✓		
Rough-legged Hawk	Buteo lagopus	✓	✓		
Falcons	Falconidae				
Aplomado Falcon	Falco femoralis			✓	
Partridge, grouse, Old World quail	Phasianidae				
Rock Ptarmigan	Lagopus mutus	✓			
White-tailed Ptarmigan	Lagopus leucurus	✓			
Sharp-tailed Grouse	Tympanuchus phasianellus		✓		
Greater Prairie-Chicken	Tympanuchus cupido		✓		
Lesser Prairie-Chicken	Tympanuchus pallidicinctus		✓		
New World quail	Odontophoridae				
Montezuma Quail	Cyrtonyx montezumae			✓	
Ocellated Quail	Cyrtonyx ocellatus			✓	
Stone curlews	Burhinidae				
Double-striped Thick-knee	Burhinus bistriatus			✓	
Plovers, lapwings	Charadriidae				
American Golden-Plover	Pluvialis dominica	✓			
Pacific Golden-Plover	Pluvialis fulva	✓			
Mountain Plover	Charadrius montanus		✓		
Shorebirds	Scolopacidae				
Upland Sandpiper	Bartramia longicauda	✓	✓		
Eskimo Curlew*	Numenius borealis	✓			
Bristle-thighed Curlew	Numenius tahitiensis	✓			
Long-billed Curlew	Numenius americanus		✓		
Marbled Godwit	Limosa fedoa		✓		
Baird's Sandpiper	Calidris bairdii	✓			
Buff-breasted Sandpiper	Tryngites subruficollis	✓			
Gulls, jaegers	Laridae				
Pomarine Jaeger	Stercorarius pomarinus	✓			
Parasitic Jaeger	Stercorarius parasiticus	✓			
Long-tailed Jaeger	Stercorarius longicaudus	✓			
Owls	Strigidae				
Snowy Owl	Nyctea scandiaca	✓			
Burrowing Owl	Athene cunicularia		✓	✓	✓
Long-eared Owl	Asio otus		✓	✓	
Short-eared Owl	Asio flammeus	✓	✓		✓
Larks	Alaudidae				
Horned Lark	Eremophila alpestris	✓	✓	✓	
Wrens	Troglodytidae				
Sedge Wren	Cistothorus platensis		✓	✓	
Pipits	Motacillidae				
American Pipit	Anthus rubescens	✓	✓		
Sprague's Pipit	Anthus spragueii		✓		
Emberizids	Emberizidae				
Ruddy-breasted Seedeater	Sporophila minuta			✓	
Saffron Finch	Sicalis flaveola				✓
Grassland Yellow-Finch	Sicalis luteola			✓	✓

TABLE 1.   CONTINUED

Family		Breeding distribution			
		Arctic/ alpine	Temperate	Sub- tropical/ Mexico	Caribbean
Cassin's Sparrow	*Aimophila cassinii*			√	
Bachman's Sparrow	*Aimophila aestivalis*		√		
Botteri's Sparrow	*Aimophila botterii*			√	
Striped Sparrow**	*Oriturus superciliosus*			√	
Vesper Sparrow	*Pooecetes gramineus*		√		
Lark Bunting	*Calamospiza melanocorys*		√		
Savannah Sparrow	*Passerculus sandwichensis*	√	√	√	
Grasshopper Sparrow	*Ammodramus savannarum*		√	√	√
Baird's Sparrow	*Ammodramus bairdii*		√		
Henslow's Sparrow	*Ammodramus henslowii*		√		
Le Conte's Sparrow	*Ammodramus leconteii*		√		
Sierra Madre Sparrow**	*Xenospiza baileyi*			√	
McCown's Longspur	*Calcarius mccownii*		√		
Lapland Longspur	*Calcarius lapponicus*	√			
Smith's Longspur	*Calcarius pictus*	√			
Chestnut-collared Longspur	*Calcarius ornatus*		√		
Snow Bunting	*Plectrophenax nivalis*	√			
McKay's Bunting	*Plectrophenax hyperboreus*	√			
Cardinals and allies	Cardinalidae				
Dickcissel	*Spiza americana*		√		
Meadowlarks, blackbirds	Icteridae				
Bobolink	*Dolichonyx oryzivorus*		√		
Eastern Meadowlark	*Sturnella magna*		√	√	√
Western Meadowlark	*Sturnella neglecta*		√	√	

Note: This list was derived from numerous sources, including Bond 1971; Johnsgard 1981; Hayman et al. 1986; Raffaele 1989; Howell and Webb 1995; AOU 1998; and J. L. Dunn, pers. comm.
* Possibly extinct.
** Autecology poorly known.

chaco savannas, Pampas, and Beni savannas (Bolivia), and more regionally, the savannas near Veracruz and Tehuantepec, Mexico (Dinerstein et al. 1995).

Although habitat loss is frequently viewed primarily as conversion to cropland or other uses, it also includes more subtle forms of degradation, among them unnatural grazing regimes, planting of exotic grasses, and succession to shrublands (Vickery et al. in press). In Patagonia, overgrazing by sheep has degraded tallgrass habitats (Fjeldså 1988), and in the western pampas of Argentina it is contributing to the spread of chañar trees (*Geoffroea decorticans*; Anderson 1977). In North America, shortgrass prairie is adapted to intensive grazing by native herbivores, but contemporary cattle management emphasizes rotations that maintain moderate ground cover, which is less suitable for some rare species such as Mountain Plover (Knopf and Rupert 1999).

THE IMPETUS FOR GRASSLAND BIRD AND HABITAT CONSERVATION

Habitat loss and degradation have been the two most important factors influencing the decline of grassland birds in North and South America (Collar et al. 1992, Knopf 1994, Herkert et al. 1996, Stotz et al. 1996, Vickery et al. in press). In South America, excessive hunting and illegal trapping have also contributed to some grassland bird declines (Bucher and Nores 1988, Collar et al. 1992, Fraga et al. 1998).

In North America, most grassland bird populations have been declining for half a century (Askins 1993, Peterjohn and Sauer 1999). Populations of at least 13 grassland species declined significantly between 1966 and 1996, whereas populations of only 3 species are known to have increased during that period (Peterjohn and Sauer 1999). There is additional concern because these declines have prevailed across much of the continent. It is unlikely that there is a single underlying cause of these declines; instead, multiple causes are probably responsible. It is clear, however, that these declines are not local, isolated phenomena (Peterjohn and Sauer 1999).

Similar declines have taken place throughout South America, especially in lowland grasslands (Bucher and Nores 1988, Fjeldså 1988, Caval-

TABLE 2. FACULTATIVE GRASSLAND BIRDS OF NORTH AMERICA, MEXICO, AND THE CARIBBEAN

Family		Breeding distribution			
		Arctic/ alpine	Temperate	Sub- tropical/ Mexico	Caribbean
Herons	Ardeidae				
American Bittern	*Botaurus lentiginosus*		✓		
Cattle Egret	*Bubulcus ibis*		✓	✓	✓
Storks	Ciconiidae				
Jabiru	*Jabiru mycteria*			✓	
New World vultures	Cathartidae				
Turkey Vulture	*Cathartes aura*		✓	✓	✓
Lesser Yellow-headed Vulture	*Cathartes burrovianus*			✓	
Waterfowl	Anatidae				
Greater White-fronted Goose	*Anser albifrons*	✓			
Emperor Goose	*Chen canagica*	✓			
Snow Goose	*Chen caerulescens*	✓			
Ross's Goose	*Chen rossii*	✓			
Canada Goose	*Branta canadensis*	✓	✓		
Brant	*Branta bernicla*	✓			
Gadwall	*Anas strepera*		✓		
American Wigeon	*Anas americana*		✓		
Mallard	*Anas platyrhynchos*		✓		
Blue-winged Teal	*Anas discors*		✓		
Northern Shoveler	*Anas clypeata*		✓		
Northern Pintail	*Anas acuta*		✓		
Green-winged Teal	*Anas crecca*	✓	✓		
Falcons	Falconidae				
Crested Caracara	*Carcara plancus*			✓	✓
American Kestrel	*Falco sparverius*		✓	✓	✓
Merlin	*Falco columbarius*	✓	✓		
Gyrfalcon	*Falco rusticolus*	✓			
Peregrine Falcon	*Falco peregrinus*	✓	✓	✓	
Prairie Falcon	*Falco mexicanus*		✓	✓	
Partridge, grouse, Old World quail	Phasianidae				
Gray Partridge*	*Perdix perdix*		✓		
Ring-necked Pheasant*	*Phasianus colchicus*		✓		
Willow Ptarmigan	*Lagopus lagopus*	✓	✓		
New World quail	Odontophoridae				
Scaled Quail	*Callipepla squamata*			✓	
Elegant Quail	*Callipepla douglasii*			✓	
Northern Bobwhite	*Colinus virginianus*		✓	✓	✓*
Black-throated Bobwhite	*Colinus nigrogularis*			✓	
Crested Bobwhite	*Colinus cristatus*			✓	
Rails	Rallidae				
Yellow Rail	*Coturnicops noveboracensis*		✓		
Cranes	Gruidae				
Sandhill Crane	*Grus canadensis*	✓	✓		✓
Whooping Crane	*Grus americana*		✓		
Plovers, lapwings	Charadriidae				
Black-bellied Plover	*Pluvialis squatarola*	✓			
Killdeer	*Charadrius vociferus*		✓		✓
Shorebirds	Scolopacidae				
Lesser Yellowlegs	*Tringa flavipes*		✓		
Willet	*Catoptrophorus semipalmatus*		✓		
Whimbrel	*Numenius phaeopus*	✓			

TABLE 2.   CONTINUED

Family		Arctic/ alpine	Temperate	Sub- tropical/ Mexico	Caribbean
			Breeding distribution		
Hudsonian Godwit	*Limosa haemastica*	√			
Surfbird	*Aphriza virgata*	√			
Red Knot	*Calidris canutus*	√			
Sanderling	*Calidris alba*	√			
Semipalmated Sandpiper	*Calidris pusilla*	√			
Western Sandpiper	*Calidris mauri*	√			
Least Sandpiper	*Calidris minutilla*	√	√		
White-rumped Sandpiper	*Calidris fuscicollis*	√			
Pectoral Sandpiper	*Calidris melanotos*	√			
Purple Sandpiper	*Calidris maritima*	√			
Rock Sandpiper	*Calidris ptilocnemis*	√			
Dunlin	*Calidris alpina*	√			
Short-billed Dowitcher	*Limnodromus griseus*	√			
Long-billed Dowitcher	*Limnodromus scolopaceus*	√			
Common Snipe	*Gallinago gallinago*	√	√		√
Wilson's Phalarope	*Phalaropus tricolor*		√		
Gulls	Laridae				
Franklin's Gull	*Larus pipixcan*		√		
Doves	Columbidae				
Mourning Dove	*Zenaida macroura*		√		√
Common Ground-Dove	*Columbina passerina*			√	√
Barn Owls	Tytonidae				
Barn Owl	*Tyto alba*		√	√	√
Owls	Strigidae				
Striped Owl	*Pseudoscops clamator*			√	
Goatsuckers	Caprimulgidae				
Lesser Nighthawk	*Chordeiles acutipennis*			√	
Common Nighthawk	*Chordeiles minor*		√	√	
Common Poorwill	*Phalaenoptilus nuttallii*		√	√	
Tyrant flycatchers	Tyrannidae				
Say's Phoebe	*Sayornis saya*	√	√	√	
Ash-throated Flycatcher	*Myiarchus cinerascens*		√	√	
Cassin's Kingbird	*Tyrannus vociferans*		√	√	
Western Kingbird	*Tyrannus verticalis*		√	√	
Eastern Kingbird	*Tyrannus tyrannus*		√		
Scissor-tailed Flycatcher	*Tyrannus forficatus*		√	√	
Fork-tailed Flycatcher	*Tyrannus savana*			√	
Shrikes	Laniidae				
Loggerhead Shrike	*Lanius ludovicianus*		√	√	
Northern Shrike	*Lanius excubitor*	√	√		
Crows, jays	Corvidae				
Chihuahuan Raven	*Corvus cryptoleucus*		√	√	
Thrushes	Turdidae				
Eastern Bluebird	*Sialia sialis*		√	√	
Western Bluebird	*Sialia mexicana*		√	√	
Mountain Bluebird	*Sialia currucoides*		√		
Thrashers	Mimidae				
Bendire's Thrasher	*Toxostoma bendirei*			√	
Wood-Warblers	Parulidae				
Common Yellowthroat	*Geothlypis trichas*		√	√	

TABLE 2.   CONTINUED

Family		Breeding distribution			
		Arctic/alpine	Temperate	Sub-tropical/Mexico	Caribbean
Emberizids	Emberizidae				
Blue-black Grassquit	*Volatinia jacarina*			√	√
Yellow-bellied Seedeater	*Sporophila nigricollis*				√
Yellow-faced Grassquit	*Tiaris olivacea*				√
Canyon Towhee	*Pipilo fuscus*		√	√	
Rufous-winged Sparrow	*Aimophila carpalis*		√	√	
Rufous-crowned Sparrow	*Aimophila ruficeps*		√	√	
Oaxaca Sparrow**	*Aimophila notosticta*			√	
Clay-colored Sparrow	*Spizella pallida*		√		
Worthen's Sparrow**	*Spizella wortheni*			√	
Lark Sparrow	*Chondestes grammacus*		√	√	
Meadowlarks, blackbirds	Icteridae				
Red-winged Blackbird	*Agelaius phoeniceus*		√	√	√
Brewer's Blackbird	*Euphagus cyanocephalus*		√		
Shiny Cowbird	*Molothrus bonariensis*				√
Bronzed Cowbird	*Molothrus aeneus*		√	√	
Brown-headed Cowbird	*Molothrus ater*		√	√	
Finches	Fringillidae				
Gray-crowned Rosy-Finch	*Leucosticte tephrocotis*	√			
Black Rosy-Finch	*Leucosticte atrata*	√			
Brown-capped Rosy-Finch	*Leucosticte australis*	√			

Note: This list was derived from numerous sources, including Bond 1971; Johnsgard 1981; Hayman et al. 1986; Raffaele 1989; Howell and Webb 1995; AOU 1998; and J. L. Dunn, pers. comm.
* Introduced.
** Autoecology poorly known.

canti 1999a, Tubaro and Gabelli 1999). According to Wege and Long (1995), 12% of the Neotropic's threatened bird species live in grasslands and savannas. At least 34% of the grassland bird species rank as high conservation priorities, and 80% of the campos grassland birds are at risk (Stotz et al. 1996).

CONSERVATION STRATEGIES

People involved in grassland bird conservation efforts need to recognize the historical dynamics under which these unique habitats evolved. Where feasible, management should incorporate the ecological processes that have generated and maintained these distinctive ecosystems. The timing, intensity, and seasonality of grazing, fire, and other disturbances on grassland conservation areas should mimic natural processes as closely as possible. This is important for many of the plants and animals that occur in these unique habitats. In North America, for example, intensive grazing by native herbivores such as prairie dogs (*Cynomys* spp.), bison (*Bison bison*), and pronghorn (*Antilocapra americana*) was one of the major ecological forces that shaped and maintained shortgrass prairies (Vickery et al. in press). Fires, ignited both naturally and by Native Americans, were primarily responsible for maintaining tallgrass prairies in the Midwest and native grasslands in the Northeast. In Florida, lightning was the primary disturbance that helped maintain prairie habitat. Prescribed fires have generally been conducted in winter, however, whereas natural fires burn primarily in summer—and research has demonstrated that at least two species of grassland birds, Florida Grasshopper and Bachman's sparrows, generally prolong their breeding activities after summer burns (Shriver et al. 1996). In central Brazil, Parker and Willis (1997) reported that several grassland birds shift their habitats every few years in response to local fires: tallgrass species (e.g., Sharp-tailed Grass-Tyrant [*Culcivora caudacuta*] and Bearded Tachuri [*Polystictus pectoralis*]) move to older grasslands, whereas birds that prefer sparser cover (e.g., Coal-crested Finch [*Charitospiza eucosma*] and Campo Miner [*Geobates poecilopterus*]) shift to newly burned sites. Large or connected areas are needed to provide both types of habitats; small reserves protected from fire turn to scrub, whereas annually burned ranches support few species (Parker and Willis 1997).

It is especially important that small individual sites (< 500 ha) not be managed for the greatest diversity of grassland bird species. Management

TABLE 3. PRELIMINARY LIST OF OBLIGATE GRASSLAND BIRDS OF SOUTH AMERICA

Family	
Rheas	Rheidae
Lesser Rhea	*Rhea pennata*
Tinamous	Tinamidae
Red-winged Tinamou	*Rhynchotus rufescens*
Huayco Tinamou	*Rhynchotos maculicollis*
Darwin's Nothura	*Nothura darwinii*
Spotted Nothura	*Nothura maculosa*
Lesser Nothura	*Nothura minor*
Dwarf Tinamou	*Taoniscus nanus*
Waterfowl	Anatidae
Andean Goose	*Chloephaga melanoptera*
Ruddy-headed Goose	*Chloephaga rubidiceps*
Hawks	Accipitridae
Swainson's Hawk	*Buteo swainsoni*
Falcons	Falconidae
Carunculated Caracara	*Phalcoboenus carunculatus*
Mountain Caracara	*Phalcoboenus megalopterus*
White-throated Caracara	*Phalcoboenus albogularis*
Striated Caracara	*Phalcoboenus australis*
Aplomado Falcon	*Falco femoralis*
Stone curlews	Burhinidae
Double-striped Thick-knee	*Burhinus bistriatus*
Plovers, lapwings	Charadriidae
Southern Lapwing	*Vanellus chilensis*
Andean Lapwing	*Vanellus resplendens*
Rufous-chested Plover	*Charadrius modestus*
Tawny-throated Dotterel	*Eudromias ruficollis*
Diademed Sandpiper-Plover	*Phegornis mitchellii*
Seedsnipes	Thinocoridae
Rufous-bellied Seedsnipe	*Attagis gayi*
White-bellied Seedsnipe	*Attagis malouinus*
Grey-breasted Seedsnipe	*Thinocorus orbignyianus*
Shorebirds	Scolopacidae
Upland Sandpiper	*Bartramia longicauda*
Eskimo Curlew	*Numenius borealis*
Buff-breasted Sandpiper	*Tryngites subruficollis*
South American Snipe	*Gallinago paraguaiae*
Puna Snipe	*Gallinago andina*
Giant Snipe	*Gallinago undulata*
Andean Snipe	*Gallinago jamesoni*
Doves	Columbidae
Blue-eyed Ground-Dove	*Columbina cyanopis*
Black-winged Ground-Dove	*Metriopelia melanoptera*
Golden-spotted Ground-Dove	*Metriopelia aymara*
Owls	Strigidae
Burrowing Owl	*Athene cunicularia*
Short-eared Owl	*Asio flammeus*
Goatsuckers	Caprimulgidae
Least Nighthawk	*Chordeiles pusillus*
Lesser Nighthawk	*Chordeiles acutipennis*
Band-winged Nightjar	*Caprimulgus longirostris*
White-tailed Nightjar	*Caprimulgus cayennensis*
White-winged Nightjar	*Caprimulgus candicans*
Spot-tailed Nightjar	*Caprimulgus maculicaudus*

TABLE 3. CONTINUED

Family	
Hummingbirds	Trochilidae
White-tailed Goldenthroat	*Polytmus guainumbi*
Tepui Goldenthroat	*Polytmus milleri*
Ecuadorian Hillstar	*Oreotrochilus chimborazo*
Andean Hillstar	*Oreotrochilus estella*
White-sided Hillstar	*Oreotrochilus leucopleurus*
Black-breasted Hillstar	*Oreotrochilus melanogaster*
Olivaceous Thornbill	*Chalcostigma olivaceum*
Blue-mantled Thornbill	*Chalcostigma stanleyi*
Bronze-tailed Thornbill	*Chalcostigma heteropogon*
Rainbow-bearded Thornbill	*Chalcostigma herrani*
Bearded Helmetcrest	*Oxypogon guerinii*
Hooded Visorbearer	*Augastes lumachellus*
Hyacinth Visorbearer	*Augastes scutatus*
Horned Sungem	*Heliactin cornuta*
Ovenbirds	Furnariidae
Campo Miner	*Geobates poecilopterus*
Common Miner	*Geositta cunicularia*
Puna Miner	*Geositta punensis*
Dark-winged Miner	*Geositta saxicolina*
Creamy-rumped Miner	*Geositta isabellina*
Short-billed Miner	*Geositta antarctica*
Rufous-banded Miner	*Geositta rufipennis*
Slender-billed Miner	*Geositta tenuirostris*
Cipo Canastero	*Asthenes luizae*
Austral Canastero	*Asthenes anthoides*
Junin Canastero	*Asthenes virgata*
Scribble-tailed Canastero	*Asthenes maculicauda*
Straight-billed Reedhaunter	*Limnornis rectirostris*
Tapaculos	Rhinocryptidae
Varzea Tapaculo	*Scytalopus iraiensis*
Tyrant flycatchers	Tyrannidae
Sharp-tailed Grass-Tyrant	*Culicivora caudacuta*
Bearded Tachuri	*Polystictus pectoralis*
Cock-tailed Tyrant	*Alectrurus tricolor*
Fork-tailed Flycatcher	*Tyrannus savana*
Larks	Alaudidae
Horned Lark	*Eremophila alpestris*
Wrens	Troglodytidae
Sedge Wren	*Cistothorus platensis*
Merida Wren	*Cistothorus meridae*
Pipits	Motacillidae
Correndera Pipit	*Anthus correndera*
South Georgia Pipit	*Anthus antarcticus*
Short-billed Pipit	*Anthus furcatus*
Hellmayr's Pipit	*Anthus hellmayri*
Paramo Pipit	*Anthus bogotensis*
Yellowish Pipit	*Anthus lutescens*
Chaco Pipit	*Anthus chacoensis*
Ochre-breasted Pipit	*Anthus nattereri*
Emberizids	Emberizidae
Grasshopper Sparrow	*Ammodramus savannarum*
Grassland Sparrow	*Ammodramus humeralis*
Black-masked Finch	*Coryphaspiza melanotis*
Plumbeous Sierra-Finch	*Phrygilus unicolor*
Red-backed Sierra-Finch	*Phrygilus dorsalis*
White-throated Sierra-Finch	*Phrygilus erythronotos*

TABLE 3. CONTINUED

Family	
Canary-winged Finch	*Melanodera melanodera*
White-winged Diuca-Finch	*Diuca speculifera*
Short-tailed Finch	*Idiospar brachyurus*
Puna Yellow-Finch	*Sicalis lutea*
Bright-rumped Yellow-Finch	*Sicalis uropygialis*
Greater Yellow-Finch	*Sicalis auriventris*
Patagonian Yellow-Finch	*Sicalis lebruni*
Grassland Yellow-Finch	*Sicalis luteola*
Wedge-tailed Grass-Finch	*Emberizoides herbicola*
Duida Grass-Finch	*Emberizoides duidae*
Lesser Grass-Finch	*Emberizoides ypiranganus*
Great Pampa-Finch	*Embernagra platensis*
Plumbeous Seedeater	*Sporophila plumbea*
Capped Seedeater	*Sporophila bouvreuil*
Ruddy-breasted Seedeater	*Sporophila minuta*
Tawny-bellied Seedeater	*Sporophila hypoxantha*
Dark-throated Seedeater	*Sporophila ruficollis*
Marsh Seedeater	*Sporophila palustris*
Rufous-rumped Seedeater	*Sporophila hypochroma*
Chestnut Seedeater	*Sporophila cinnamonea*
Narosky's Seedeater	*Sporophila zelichi*
Black-bellied Seedeater	*Sporophila melanogaster*
Blue Finch	*Porphyrospiza caerulescens*
Cardinals and allies	Cardinalidae
Dickcissel	*Spiza americana*
Meadowlarks, blackbirds	Icteridae
Bobolink	*Dolichonyx oryzivorus*
Saffron-cowled Blackbird	*Agelaius flavus*
White-browed Blackbird	*Sturnella superciliaris*
Peruvian Meadowlark	*Sturnella bellicosa*
Red-breasted Blackbird	*Sturnella militaris*
Pampas Meadowlark	*Sturnella defilippii*
Long-tailed Meadowlark	*Sturnella loyca*
Eastern Meadowlark	*Sturnella magna*
Yellow-rumped Marshbird	*Pseudoleistes guirahuro*

Note: This list was derived primarily from the following sources: Hayman et al. 1986; Ridgely and Tudor 1989; Stotz et al. 1996; and R. S. Ridgely, pers. comm.

for enhanced alpha diversity is neither necessary nor practical and is likely to be counterproductive to regional conservation goals (Vickery et al. in press). It is important to recognize that certain sites are usually best suited to management for a particular subset of grassland birds. Sedge meadows, for example, are better suited to management for Sedge Wrens and Le Conte's Sparrows than to a full range of grassland species (Herkert et al. 1993, Sample and Mossman 1997, Vickery et al. in press).

REGIONAL CONSERVATION PLANNING

To be effective, grassland habitat conservation planning and action must be conducted within a large regional context. Although conservation action and management usually take place on a local scale at specific sites, cooperative management on a landscape or regional level makes it possible to address the complete range of habitat needs required by different species, including rare and endangered species, and to minimize the risks of stochastic catastrophic events. In Florida, extensive research on and management of the endangered Florida Grasshopper Sparrow have been site specific but have not yet incorporated landscape planning or conservation action. Despite intensive site management, populations of this endemic sparrow are declining, in part because of the absence of a broader geographic framework (Shriver and Vickery 1999).

Regional grassland habitat and bird management plans are developing in many parts of North America and are becoming established in parts of South America. These broad initiatives provide the best opportunities for grassland bird and ecosystem conservation.

Partners in Flight, an international effort to

TABLE 4.   Prelimary list of facultative grassland birds of South America

Family	
Rheas	Rheidae
Greater Rhea	*Rhea americana*
Tinamous	Tinamidae
Small-billed Tinamou	*Crypturellus parvirostris*
Ornate Tinamou	*Nothoprocta ornata*
Andean Tinamou	*Nothoprocta pentlandii*
Curve-billed Tinamou	*Nothoprocta curvirostris*
Elegant Crested-Tinamou	*Eudromia elegans*
Quebracho Crested-Tinamou	*Eudromia formosa*
Puna Tinamou	*Tinamotis pentlandii*
Patagonian Tinamou	*Tinamotis ingoufi*
Herons	Ardeidae
Whistling Heron	*Syrigma sibilatrix*
Cattle Egret	*Bubulcus ibis*
Ibis	Threskiornithidae
Plumbeous Ibis	*Theristicus caerulescens*
Buff-necked Ibis	*Theristicus caudatus*
Black-faced Ibis	*Theristicus melanopis*
Storks	Ciconiidae
Wood Stork	*Mycteria americana*
Maguari Stork	*Ciconia maguari*
Jabiru	*Jabiru mycteria*
New World vultures	Cathartidae
Black Vulture	*Coragyps atratus*
Turkey Vulture	*Cathartes aura*
Lesser Yellow-headed Vulture	*Cathartes burrovianus*
Andean Condor	*Vultur gryphus*
Waterfowl	Anatidae
Upland Goose	*Chloephaga picta*
Ashy-headed Goose	*Chloephaga poliocephala*
Hawks	Accipitridae
Pearl Kite	*Gampsonyx swainsonii*
White-tailed Kite	*Elanus leucurus*
Long-winged Harrier	*Circus buffoni*
Northern Harrier	*Circus cyaneus*
Cinereus Harrier	*Circus cinereus*
Savanna Hawk	*Buteogallus meriodionalis*
Harris's Hawk	*Parabuteo unicinctus*
Black-chested Buzzard-Eagle	*Geranoaetus melanoleucus*
Crowned Eagle	*Harpyhaliaetus coronatus*
White-tailed Hawk	*Buteo albicaudatus*
Variable Hawk	*Buteo polyosoma*
Falcons	Falconidae
Crested Caracara	*Caracara plancus*
Yellow-headed Caracara	*Milvago chimachima*
Chimango Caracara	*Milvago chimango*
Spot-winged Falconet	*Spiziapteryx circumcinctus*
Seriemas	Cariamidae
Red-legged Seriema	*Cariama cristata*
Black-legged Seriema	*Chunga burmeisteri*
Stone curlews	Burhinidae
Peruvian Thick-knee	*Burhinus supercilaris*
Seedsnipes	Thinocoridae
Least Seedsnipe	*Thinocorus rumicivorus*

TABLE 4. CONTINUED

Family	
Shorebirds	Scolopacidae
Hudsonian Godwit	*Limosa haemastica*
Baird's Sandpiper	*Calidris bairdii*
Fuegian Snipe	*Gallinago stricklandii*
Doves	Columbidae
Picazuro Pigeon	*Columba picazuro*
Spot-winged Pigeon	*Columba maculosa*
Eared Dove	*Zenaida auriculata*
Common Ground-Dove	*Columbina passerina*
Plain-breasted Ground-Dove	*Columbina minuta*
Ruddy Ground-Dove	*Columbina talpacoti*
Buckley's Ground-Dove	*Columbina buckleyi*
Picui Ground-Dove	*Columbina picui*
Bare-faced Ground-Dove	*Metriopelia ciciliae*
Moreno's Ground-Dove	*Metriopelia morenoi*
Long-tailed Ground-Dove	*Uropelia campestris*
Scaly Dove	*Scardafella squammata*
Parrots	Psittacidae
Burrowing Parakeet	*Cyanoliseus patagonus*
Monk Parakeet	*Myiopsitta monachus*
Green-rumped Parrotlet	*Forpus passerinus*
Cuckoos	Cuculidae
Striped Cuckoo	*Tapera naevia*
Smooth-billed Ani	*Crotophaga ani*
Groove-billed Ani	*Crotophaga sulcirostris*
Barn Owls	Tytonidae
Barn Owl	*Tyto alba*
Owls	Strigidae
Striped Owl	*Rhinoptynx clamator*
Goatsuckers	Caprimulgidae
Nacunda Nighthawk	*Podager nacunda*
Scrub Nightjar	*Caprimulgus anthonyi*
Scissor-tailed Nightjar	*Hydropsalis brasiliana*
Hummingbirds	Trochilidae
Fiery-throated Hummingbird	*Panterpe insignis*
Green-tailed Goldenthroat	*Polytmus theresiae*
Woodpeckers	Picidae
Andean Flicker	*Colaptes rupicola*
Campo Flicker	*Colaptes campestris*
Ovenbirds	Furnariidae
Straight-billed Earthcreeper	*Upucerthia ruficauda*
Rock Earthcreeper	*Upucerthia andaecola*
Scale-throated Earthcreeper	*Upucerthia dumetaria*
Bar-winged Cinclodes	*Cincloides fuscus*
Long-tailed Cinclodes	*Cincloides pabsti*
Dark-bellied Cinclodes	*Cincloides patagonicus*
White-winged Cinclodes	*Cincloides atacamensis*
Rufous Hornero	*Furnarius rufus*
Pale-breasted Spinetail	*Synallaxis albescens*
Lesser Canastero	*Asthenes pyrrholeuca*
Cordilleran Canastero	*Asthenes modesta*
Streak-throated Canastero	*Asthenes humilis*
Streak-backed Canastero	*Asthenes wyatti*
Puna Canastero	*Asthenes sclateri*
Many-striped Canastero	*Asthenes flammulata*
Hudson's Canastero	*Asthenes hudsoni*
Firewood-gatherer	*Anumbius annumbi*

TABLE 4. CONTINUED

Family

Tapaculos	Rhinocryptidae
Collared Crescent-chest	*Melanopareia torquata*
Tyrant flycatchers	Tyrannidae
Plain-crested Elaenia	*Elaenia cristata*
Rufous-crowned Elaenia	*Elaenia ruficeps*
Lesser Elaenia	*Elaenia chiriquensis*
Grey-backed Tachuri	*Polystictus superciliaris*
Rufous-sided Pygmy-Tyrant	*Euscarthmus rufomarginatus*
Grey Monjita	*Xolmis cinerea*
Black-crowned Monjita	*Xolmis coronata*
White-rumped Monjita	*Xolmis velata*
White Monjita	*Xolmis irupero*
Rusty-backed Monjita	*Xolmis rubetra*
Black-and-white Monjita	*Heteroxolmis dominicana*
Chocolate-vented Tyrant	*Neoxolmis rufiventris*
Black-billed Shrike-Tyrant	*Agriornis montana*
White-tailed Shrike-Tyrant	*Agriornis andicola*
Great Shrike-Tyrant	*Agriornis livida*
Grey-bellied Shrike-Tyrant	*Agriornis microptera*
Lesser Shrike-Tyrant	*Agriornis murina*
Spot-billed Ground-Tyrant	*Muscisaxicola maculirostris*
Dark-faced Ground-Tyrant	*Muscisaxicola macloviana*
Cinnamon-bellied Ground-Tyrant	*Muscisaxicola capistrata*
Rufous-naped Ground-Tyrant	*Muscisaxicola rufivertex*
Puna Ground-Tyrant	*Muscisaxicola juninensis*
White-browed Ground-Tyrant	*Muscisaxicola albilora*
Plain-capped Ground-Tyrant	*Muscisaxicola alpina*
Cinereous Ground-Tyrant	*Muscisaxicola cinerea*
White-fronted Ground-Tyrant	*Muscisaxicola albifrons*
Ochre-naped Ground-Tyrant	*Muscisaxicola flavinucha*
Black-fronted Ground-Tyrant	*Muscisaxicola frontalis*
Austral Negrito	*Lessonia rufa*
Spectacled Tyrant	*Hymenops perspicillatus*
Strange-tailed Tyrant	*Alectrurus risora*
Streamer-tailed Tyrant	*Gubernetes yetapa*
Cattle Tyrant	*Machetornis rixosus*
Crows, jays	Corvidae
White-necked Raven	*Corvus cryptoleucus*
Emberizids	Emberizidae
Rufous-collared Sparrow	*Zonotrichia capensis*
Yellow-browed Sparrow	*Ammodramus aurifrons*
Coal-crested Finch	*Charitospiza eucosma*
Many-colored Chaco-Finch	*Saltatricula multicolor*
Ash-breasted Sierra-Finch	*Phrygilus plebejus*
Carbonated Sierra-Finch	*Phrygilus carbonarius*
Yellow-bridled Finch	*Melanodera xanthogramma*
Long-tailed Reed-Finch	*Donacospiza albifrons*
Black-and-rufous Warbling-Finch	*Poospiza nigrorufa*
Stripe-tailed Yellow-Finch	*Sicalis citrina*
Pale-throated Serra-Finch	*Embernagra longicauda*
Blue-black Grassquit	*Volatinia jacarina*
Grey Seedeater	*Sporophila intermedia*
Variable Seedeater	*Sporophila corvina*
Caqueta Seedeater	*Sporophila murallae*
Wing-barred Seedeater	*Sporophila americana*
Rusty-collared Seedeater	*Sporophila collaris*
Lesson's Seedeater	*Sporophila bouvronides*
Lined Seedeater	*Sporophila lineola*
Black-and-white Seedeater	*Sporophila luctuosa*

TABLE 4. CONTINUED

Family	
Yellow-bellied Seedeater	*Sporophila nigricollis*
Double-collared Seedeater	*Sporophila caerulescens*
White-bellied Seedeater	*Sporophila leucoptera*
Chestnut-bellied Seedeater	*Sporophila castaneiventris*
Chestnut-throated Seedeater	*Sporophila telasco*
Large-billed Seed-Finch	*Oryzoborus crassirostris*
Great-billed Seed-Finch	*Oryzoborus maximiliana*
Lesser Seed-Finch	*Oryzoborus angolensis*
Band-tailed Seedeater	*Catamenia analis*
Plain-colored Seedeater	*Catamenia inornata*
Yellow-faced Grassquit	*Tiaris olivacea*
Black-faced Grassquit	*Tiaris bicolor*
Meadowlarks, blackbirds	Icteridae
Red-winged Blackbird	*Agelaius phoeniceus*
Yellow-hooded Blackbird	*Agelaius icterocephalus*
Brown-and-yellow Marshbird	*Pseudoleistes virescens*
Chopi Blackbird	*Gnorimopsar chopi*
Bay-winged Cowbird	*Molothrus badius*
Screaming Cowbird	*Molothrus rufoaxillaris*
Shiny Cowbird	*Molothrus bonariensis*
Bronzed Cowbird	*Molothrus aeneus*

Note: This list was derived primarily from the following sources: Hayman et al. 1986; Ridgely and Tudor 1989; Stotz et al. 1996; and R. S. Ridgely, pers. comm.

protect and enhance North American bird populations, is organized at state, regional, national, and international levels and provides an excellent, flexible structure for facilitating regional conservation efforts (Finch and Stangel 1992). For example, a Northeast Grassland Bird Working Group functions within the rubric of the Northeast Working Group. As a specialist group, the Northeast Grassland Bird Working Group facilitates communication, inventory, and planning across a 13-state region from Maine to Virginia. In 1997 this group was involved in a seven-state inventory of grassland birds, emphasizing regionally rare species such as Upland Sandpiper and Henslow's Sparrow (Shriver et al. 1997). Because Partners in Flight has been instrumental

TABLE 5. ESTIMATED HABITAT LOSS TO GRASSLAND ECOSYSTEMS IN THE UNITED STATES SINCE EUROPEAN SETTLEMENT

Ecosystem	Estimated loss (%)	Reference
Critically endangered ecosystems (> 98% habitat loss)[a]		
Tallgrass prairie east of Missouri River	> 99	Noss et al. 1995
Sedge meadows, Wisconsin	> 99	Reuter 1986
Black belt prairie, Alabama and Mississippi	> 99	Noss et al. 1995
Sandplain grassland, Long Island, NY	99.9	Niering 1992
Native prairie, Willamette Valley, OR	99.5	Ingersoll and Wilson 1991
Palouse prairie, Montana, Idaho, Oregon, and Washington	99.9	Noss et al. 1995
California grasslands, all types	99	Kreissman 1991
Ungrazed sagebrush steppe, Intermountain West	> 99	West 1995
Endangered ecosystems (80–98% habitat loss)		
Tallgrass prairie, all types combined	90	Madson 1990
Grassland shrubsteppe, Washington and Oregon	> 90	Noss et al. 1995
Shortgrass prairie, Montana	80–90	Chadde 1992
Shortgrass prairie, North Dakota	90	Madson 1989
Coastal heathland, s. New England and Long Island, NY	> 90	Noss et al. 1995
Sandplain grassland, New England	> 90	Noss et al. 1995
Palmetto dry prairie, Florida	81	Shriver and Vickery 1999

[a] Classification of critically endangered and endangered ecosystems adapted from Noss et al. 1995.

in bringing together multiple agencies, more than 30 collaborators and dozens of volunteers contributed to the grassland inventory, which censused nearly 1,100 sites (Shriver et al. 1997). More importantly, organizations and agencies in each of these states have become invested in the results of this regional effort. In New York, major breeding habitat for grassland birds has been included in the state's registry of important bird areas and has also received legislative protection (Wells 1998).

In the midwestern United States, a multistate plan for grassland bird conservation has developed a broad outline of the region's conservation priorities (Herkert et al. 1996). Within the region, more detailed state plans have been developed. In Wisconsin, for example, Sample and Mossman (1997) have produced a plan that describes goals and organizing principles of grassland bird management, including a detailed discussion of overall management philosophy; they also identify management priorities for both grassland birds and their habitats within this broad geographic area. The plan supplies detailed habitat management guidelines and management recommendations based on individual species' responses to specific management practices and identifies specific landscapes, sites, and properties worthy of special management attention. This type of specific targeting of conservation activities will undoubtedly result in on-the-ground management that is likely to benefit grassland birds in the target area.

In Canada, conservation of prairie grassland habitat and birds has been gaining momentum through the actions of many organizations since 1990. The scope of these partnerships and interactions has grown, culminating in the formation of provincial implementation groups for the Prairie Conservation Action Plan (PCAP) and the formation of provincial (Manitoba) and regional Partners in Flight-Canada groups. PIF-Canada sets general priorities based on trends and geographic responsibility (based on proportion of range) as set forth by Dunn 1997.

In most cases, Canadian prairie fragments in national and provincial parks, federal government bird sanctuaries, national wildlife areas (NWAs), military bases, Prairie Farm Rehabilitation Administration (PFRA) holdings, and federal and provincial crown grazing lands are secure. Examples of large blocks include Grasslands National Park, Saskatchewan (90,000 ha); Last Mountain Lake NWA, Saskatchewan (15,000 ha); and Canadian Forces Base Suffield, Alberta (270,000 ha). Large holdings include PFRA pastures (75 million ha) and Saskatchewan crown grazing lands (2.9 million ha).

Because there is presently no federal endangered species legislation in Canada, complementary provincial and federal legislation to designate species is being developed, with an emphasis on rewarding stewardship rather than punishing offenders. Efforts have centered around changing adverse government policy and working with agriculture to find "Best Management Practices" for conserving remaining native prairie and other grassland habitats. For example, the recent abolition of grain-shipping subsidies based on the number of hectares under cultivation has removed one incentive to plow native prairie.

Most farmland in Canada is privately owned, and conservation funding is limited. Identifying options that make it worthwhile for landowners to maintain native prairie or use bird-friendly cropping methods has thus proven to be the most effective and economical approach to conserving grassland habitats. Among such options are subsidy-based programs such as Agriculture Canada's Permanent Cover Program (PCP). Instituted in 1989, the PCP has converted 450,000 ha in poor soil classes to grass cover for 10 or more years. The payment to landowners covers some of the cost of seeding, and the landowner may use the land for haying or grazing so long as it is not broken. A recent study showed that many grassland obligates use PCP sites (McMaster and Davis 1998).

In Brazil, high-priority areas for biodiversity conservation in the Cerrado were identified in a 1998 workshop in which more than 200 scientists participated. The workshop was part of the Brazilian government's biome-level biodiversity program to establish biodiversity priorities in the country. Important criteria for designating sites included species richness, number of endemic species, presence of rare and/or endangered species, and sites of unique communities or key areas for migratory species. Eighty-seven priority areas were identified, 20 of which were recommended for reserve status because of their importance for birds (Silva 1998a). Priorities for conservation action for each of these areas were then determined by cross-referencing biodiversity data with data on human encroachment and land-cover changes (Cavalcanti 1999b).

In addition to creating new reserves in the Cerrado, new strategies must be adopted as soon as possible to minimize the impact of human activities on the biota of this region (Silva 1998b). The most pressing need is to provide the agricultural technology to help landowners increase productivity of lands already under cultivation. It is hoped that this will reduce the pressure on lands covered by natural vegetation. Macedo (1994) has suggested that by increasing productivity on lands already used for agriculture in the Cerrado region, it would be possible to produce 100 millions tons of food annually, or enough to feed 250 million people. The second strategy is to establish legal mechanisms that would preclude the destruction of the biological resources of the Cerrado; as an example, new agriculture projects in areas covered by natural vegetation could be banned until their impacts on fauna and flora were rigorously assessed.

HEMISPHERIC CONSERVATION PLANNING

Since most grassland birds migrate between breeding and wintering areas, it is necessary to understand the habitat requirements and conservation needs in both these areas. In South America, some grassland species breeding in Tierra del Fuego and Patagonia winter in the southern Pampas. This is the case for Upland Goose (*Chloephaga picta*), Ashy-headed Goose (*C. poliocephala*), and the endangered continental race of Ruddy-headed Goose (*C. rubidiceps*). Other grassland species, such as seedeaters and some tyrant flycatchers, breed in the Pampas but winter in northern Argentina, Paraguay, and Brazil (Ridgely and Tudor 1989, Chesser 1994).

Although some species of North American grassland birds are long-distance neotropical migrants, most species migrate relatively short distances and winter primarily in the southern United States and northern Mexico. This provides conservation opportunities for species wintering in North America and Mexico but also underscores the need for coordinated research and conservation efforts across international borders (Hagan and Johnston 1992, Wilson and Sader 1993, Vickery et al. in press).

The habitat requirements of many species wintering in Central and South America are poorly understood. Recently there have been encouraging research and educational efforts in grassland habitats in Mexico (e.g., Colorado Bird Observatory 1996, Manzano-Fischer et al. 1999) and other parts of Central and South America. For example, the Canadian Wildlife Service's newly developed Latin American Program is working to train local avian biologists and build local capacity to study and protect migratory and resident birds (Hyslop 1996). The U.S. Fish and Wildlife Service is undertaking similar collaborative efforts. Additionally, private nonprofit conservation organizations such as The Nature Conservancy and BirdLife International have also developed international bird conservation programs. There are few efforts, however, directed exclusively toward grassland bird and habitat protection. Widespread efforts by farmers in Venezuela to reduce Dickcissel crop damage (Basili and Temple 1999) and the

use of pesticides in Argentina that has killed many Swainson's Hawks (Krapovickas and de Perez 1997) clearly demonstrate the need for expanded international grassland bird research and conservation.

Changing agricultural practices in Argentina have profoundly reduced the amount of native grassland in that country, and the loss is seriously affecting populations of endemic grassland birds such as the Pampas Meadowlark (Tubaro and Gabelli 1999). This habitat change is likely to affect populations of nearctic breeders as well and may be particularly significant for long-distance migrants such as Swainson's Hawk, Eskimo Curlew, Upland Sandpiper, Buff-breasted Sandpiper (*Tryngites subruficollis*), and Bobolink, all of which winter in Argentina (Olrog 1984). Similar agricultural changes elsewhere in Central and South America will undoubtedly have consequences for both neotropical and nearctic grassland breeders.

The Western Hemisphere Shorebird Reserve Network (WHSRN), an international conservation network focused specifically on shorebirds (Bildstein et al. 1991), may provide an excellent model for international grassland bird conservation efforts. WHSRN has successfully collaborated with more than 120 other agencies, including the North American Waterfowl Management Plan and Partners in Flight, on international wetland and shorebird conservation issues and has helped protect more than 3.6 million ha of habitat in 7 countries (J. Corven, pers. comm.). For example, joint efforts by the Suriname Forest Service, Canadian Wildlife Service, and WHSRN have helped protect critical wintering habitat for Semipalmated Sandpipers (*Calidris pusilla*) in Suriname (J. Corven, pers. comm.).

Recognizing the rapid decline of many South American grassland birds, especially *Sporophila* seedeaters, Silva (1999) has suggested a system of reserves across South America that would protect a large majority of grassland endemics. Such planning, critical for the protection of endemic neotropical species, could be coupled with efforts to protect nearctic migrants such as Swainson's Hawks and Dickcissels, and thus to develop a comprehensive system for grassland bird protection throughout the Western Hemisphere. Although international efforts, initiated largely by the American Bird Conservancy, in Argentina in 1995 stopped or minimized incidental Swainson's Hawk mortality that resulted from insecticide use on agricultural fields, the absence of an established international network meant that emergency measures were required (Anonymous 1996, Krapovickas and de Perez 1997). It is hoped that an established international grassland bird network would anticipate such a major crisis and thus minimize the need for such emergency actions. We hope that publication of this volume will facilitate such a network.

SEEKING COMMON GROUND

The effective management of grassland landscapes will require the involvement of a diverse group of natural resource professionals, including range managers, game and nongame biologists, soil conservationists, agronomists, farmers, and ranchers (Vickery et al. in press). In many areas, grassland management has historically emphasized soil conservation. To increase the likelihood of successfully conserving grassland habitat, it will be important to combine the goals of avian habitat conservation with those of soil conservation and agriculture. Because the ecological and habitat requirements of many endangered grassland species in South America are poorly understood, it will be most difficult to achieve these disparate goals in South America. Although habitat loss is the main cause of grassland bird declines in South America (Bucher and Nores 1988, Cavalcanti 1988), more subtle factors such as competitive interactions, nest parasitism, social facilitation, and failure to colonize new patches are probably also involved. These factors are probably stronger when populations are small and fragmented.

The North American Waterfowl Management Plan (NAWMP), through Ducks Unlimited Canada's Prairie Care program, has established grazing systems on about 132,000 ha in the grassland portion of Canada's three prairie provinces (Alberta, Manitoba, and Saskatchewan). Provincial agricultural extension services helped producers revamp grazing systems on many additional hectares. Because these systems make grazing more economically viable, they keep the land under grass cover. Initial studies show that a greater variety of bird species, including many grassland obligates, use these sites than use continuous-grazing (i.e., season-long) sites (Dale and McKeating 1996) and that avian productivity is about the same as it was before the grazing systems were instituted (Prescott et al. 1998). The initial demonstration farms and agreements with cattle ranchers required a substantial input, but as the economic benefits became clear and neighboring cattle ranchers saw the results, the conservation management was voluntarily adopted on many more farms and ranches. NAWMP has proven to be a good partner in grassland bird conservation. The Canadian Wildlife Service initiated nongame evaluations of NAWMP in 1989 and was joined in this by provincial partners in 1993 (Dale and McKeating 1996).

GRASSLAND RESTORATION

Because loss of native grassland habitat has been so extensive and has occurred over such a broad region, habitat restoration has become increasingly important for many regions and may be critical for the persistence of some rare and endangered species. For example, a recent landscape analysis in Florida demonstrated that only 19% of the original prairie remains and that the configuration of remaining prairie is insufficient to maintain and enhance populations of the U.S. federally endangered Florida Grasshopper Sparrow (Shriver and Vickery 1999). The best option for the long-term viability of this rare taxon appears to be major habitat restoration (Shriver and Vickery 1999). Although similar landscape analyses have not been undertaken in South America, the sharp decline in Pampas Meadowlark populations in Argentina (Tubaro and Gabelli 1999) and the rapid destruction of grassland habitat in the Cerrado of central Brazil (Cavalcanti 1999a) both suggest that some form of habitat restoration may be critical for the long-term survival of endemic grassland birds in South America. At least in the Pampas, habitat restoration should be possible to achieve in a relatively short time if land is left undisturbed (Leon and Oesterheld 1982, Leon et al. 1984).

In North America, several grassland species have adapted to agricultural fields (Graber and Graber 1963, Knopf 1994) or to other artificial habitats such as airports and reclaimed surface mines (Melvin 1994, Jones and Vickery 1997). Because few native prairie or grassland remnants remain in most of midwestern and northeastern North America, effective grassland bird conservation will require the protection and enhancement of artificial grassland habitats. Reclaimed surface mines in West Virginia, Pennsylvania, Ohio, and Indiana provide important habitat for Henslow's Sparrow and other grassland birds, and airfields in northeastern North America support some of the largest New England populations of several regionally threatened species, notably Upland Sandpiper and Grasshopper Sparrow (Jones and Vickery 1997). Protection and enhancement of these non-native habitats that serve as refugia for many grassland birds will be critical. Where feasible, however, efforts to restore native habitats should be a long-term objective.

FUTURE RESEARCH

From a hemispheric perspective, the most pressing needs are additional research and related conservation in Central and South America, where loss of habitat and population declines are becoming more acute. The number of endemic species and families in the Neotropics, and the fact that this area provides habitat for wintering nearctic breeders, makes this the highest hemispheric priority for conservation research and action. As in North America, a better understanding of the ecological effects of fire and grazing on South American obligate grassland birds and their habitats should be a high priority (Collar et al. 1992).

Grassland bird conservation programs in the United States and elsewhere in the Western Hemisphere need to address both breeding and wintering ecology (Vickery et al. in press). Although the wintering ecology of most grassland birds is poorly known, there continues to be little research on the wintering habitat requirements of many grassland bird species, as the paucity of papers on wintering ecology in this book clearly demonstrates (3, versus 23 for the breeding season). It is unclear whether habitat loss and degradation on the wintering grounds are primarily responsible for the population declines reported for many species. Winter survivorship may be critically important in the long-term declines of some grassland species (Herkert and Knopf 1998, Vickery et al. in press).

Additionally, although there has been substantial research on some arctic-nesting birds, notably waterfowl (e.g., Snow Goose [*Chen caerulescens*]; Ganter et al. 1996) and shorebirds (Charadriidae and Scolopacidae; e.g., Whitfield and Brade 1991), there has been little research on other grassland species, especially passerines, that breed at high latitudes or altitudes. In particular, there is essentially no research on the winter ecology of these species on temperate grasslands, although initial efforts are underway (E. Dunn, pers. comm.). Winter habitat use, population dynamics, and survivorship of species such as Smith's Longspur and the rosy-finches (*Leucosticte* spp.) are largely unknown and merit careful study.

Unlike in North America, most species of grassland birds in Central and South America are still poorly known, and information regarding their ranges, habitat preferences, and migratory movements are based on relatively few observations and limited museum specimens. For instance, Silva (1995) found that approximately 70% of the Cerrado region has never been adequately sampled for birds. Well-sampled localities are usually natural areas near major cities or national parks with easy access. This probably reflects the situation for most of the major grassland regions in Latin America. The taxonomy for several Central and South American grassland species should be re-evaluated, as they likely comprise two or more distinct phylogenetic species, each one indicating a region where con-

servation actions need to be taken. Unfortunately, funds for basic ornithological inventory and taxonomic studies in Central and South America are scarce and, when available, are directed at studies on forests rather than grasslands or other open habitats. Any international conservation project directed at Latin American grasslands must include support for both long-term studies on threatened bird populations and basic biological inventory and taxonomic studies.

ACKNOWLEDGMENTS

We especially thank B. Dale and R. S. Ridgely for their knowledge and insights of Canadian and South American grassland birds, respectively, and for their valuable contributions to this manuscript. We also thank R. A. Askins, R. Cannings, J. L. Dunn, P. W. Dunwiddie, A. L. Jones, J. E. Pierson, J. T. Rotenberry, and W. G. Shriver for helpful comments on earlier drafts of the manuscript. Many people shared their insights regarding lists for North and South American grassland birds, and we express our deepest gratitude to them: C. Bock, S. Davis, E. Dunn, J. L. Dunn, R. Fraga, P. Handford, L. Igl, F. Knopf, M. Koenen, C. Norment, J. Pierson, F. Rabufetti, J. C. Reboreda, R. S. Ridgely, G. Shriver, and D. Stotz. We thank V. Maynard for meticulous map preparation. We are grateful to the following institutions for their support: Center for Biological Conservation, Massachusetts Audubon Society and the Switzer Foundation (Vickery); Instituto de Biología y Medicina Experimental CONICET (Tubaro); Conselo Nacional de Desenvolvimento Científico e Tecnológico (CNPq), Brazil (Silva); U.S. Geological Survey, Biological Resources Division (Peterjohn); Illinois Endangered Species Protection Board (Herkert); and Departamento de Zoologia, Universidade de Brasília, CNPq, and Conservation International, Inc. (Cavalcanti).

LITERATURE CITED

AMERICAN ORNITHOLOGISTS' UNION. 1998. Check-list of North American birds. 7th ed. American Ornithologists' Union, Washington, D.C.

ANDERSON, D. L. 1977. Las causas de la invasión de chañar en el área medanosa de pastizales e isletas de chañar. Pp. 11–13 *in* Limitación en la producción ganadera de San Luis debido a las leñosas invasoras [no editor]. Gobierno de la Provincia de San Luis. Instituto Nacional de Teconología Agropecuaria. San Luis, Argentina.

ANONYMOUS. 1996. Hawk deaths spur action. P. 14 *in* Bird Conservation (Fall Migration) [magazine of the American Bird Conservancy, Washington, D.C.].

ASKINS, R. A. 1993. Population trends in grassland, shrubland, and forest birds in eastern North America. Current Ornithology 11:1–34.

BASILI, G. D., AND S. A. TEMPLE. 1999. Winter ecology, behavior, and conservation needs of Dickcissels in Venezuela. Studies in Avian Biology 19:289–299.

BILDSTEIN, K. L., G. T. BANCROFT, P. J. DUGAN, D. H. GORDON, R. M. ERWIN, E. NOL, X. PAYNE, AND S. E. SENNER. 1991. Approaches to the conservation of coastal wetlands in the western hemisphere. Wilson Bulletin 103:218–254.

BOND, J. 1971. Birds of the West Indies. Houghton Mifflin, Boston, MA.

BUCHER, E. H., AND M. NORES. 1988. Present status of birds in steppes and savannas on northern and central Argentina. Pp. 71–79 in P. D. Goriup (editor). Ecology and conservation of grassland birds. ICBP Technical Publication no. 7. International Council for Bird Preservation, Cambridge, U.K.

BURKART, R., AND L. DEL VALLE RUIZ. 1994. Las áreas naturales protegidas del país, datos, historia y evaluación. Pp. 22–64 in El sistema de areas naturales protegidas de la Argentina [no editor]. Administración de Parques Nacionales, Buenos Aires, Argentina.

CABRERA, A. L., AND A. WILLINK. 1980. Biogeografía de América Latina. Organization of American States, Washington, D.C.

CAVALCANTI, R. B. 1988. Conservation of birds in the cerrado of central Brazil. Pp. 59–66 in P. D. Goriup (editor). Ecology and conservation of grassland birds. ICBP Technical Publication no. 7. International Council for Bird Preservation, Cambridge, U.K.

CAVALCANTI, R. B. 1999a. Bird species richness and conservation in the cerrado region of central Brazil. Studies in Avian Biology 19:244–249.

CAVALCANTI, R. B. (COORDINATOR). 1999b. Executive summary. Workshop on priority actions for the conservation of the biodiversity of the cerrado and pantanal, Brasília, Brazil. Fundação Pró Natureza, Conservation International, Fundação Biodiversitas, Universidade de Brasília, Brasília, Brazil.

CHADDE, S. 1992. Decline of natural ecosystems in Montana. Unpublished report. U.S. Forest Service, Missoula, MT.

CHESSER, R. T. 1994. Migration in South America: an overview of the austral system. Bird Conservation International 4:91–107.

COLLAR, N. J., L. P. GONZAGA, N. KRABBE, A. MADRONO NIETO, L. G. NARANJO, T. A. PARKER III, AND D. C. WEGE. 1992. Threatened birds of the Americas. Smithsonian Institution Press, Washington, D.C.

COLORADO BIRD OBSERVATORY. 1996. Annual report. Colorado Bird Observatory, Brighton, CO.

DALE, B. C., AND G. MCKEATING. 1996. Finding common ground: the nongame evaluation of the North American Waterfowl Management Plan in Canada. Pp. 258–265 in J. T. Ratti (editor). 7th international waterfowl symposium. Ducks Unlimited, Memphis, TN.

DARWIN, C. 1876. Journal of researches into the natural history and geology of the countries visited during the voyage of HMS Beagle round the world. Murray, London, U.K.

DINERSTEIN, E., D. M. OLSON, D. J. GRAHAM, A. L. WEBSTER, S. A. PRIMM, M. P. BOOKBINDER, AND G. LEBEC. 1995. A conservation assessment of the terrestrial ecoregions of Latin America and the Caribbean. World Wildlife Fund and World Bank, Washington, D.C.

DUNN, E. H. 1997. Setting priorities for conservation, research and monitoring of Canada's landbirds. Technical report no. 293, Canadian Wildlife Service, Ottawa, ON.

DUNNING, J. B. 1993. Bachman's Sparrow (Aimophila aestivalis). In A. Poole, P. Stettenhein, and F. Gill (editors). The birds of North America no. 38. Philadelphia Academy of Natural Sciences, Philadelphia, PA, and American Ornithologists' Union, Washington, D.C.

EITEN, G. 1972. The cerrado vegetation of Brazil. Botanical Review 38:201–341.

ENVIRONMENT CANADA. 1998. Terrestrial ecozones of Canada [map]. Http://www1.ec.gc.ca/~vignettes/terr.html.

FINCH, D. M., AND P. W. STANGEL (EDITORS). 1992. Status and management of neotropical migratory birds. USDA Forest Service Gen. Tech. Rep. RM-229. USDA Forest Service Rocky Mountain Forest and Range Experiment Station, Fort Collins, CO.

FJELDSÅ, J. 1988. Status of birds of steppe habitats of the Andean zone and Patagonia. Pp. 81–95 in P. D. Goriup (editor). Ecology and conservation of grassland birds. ICBP Technical Publication no. 7. International Council for Bird Preservation, Cambridge, U.K.

FRAGA, R. M., H. CASAÑAS, AND G. PUGNALI. 1998. Natural history and conservation of the endangered Saffron-cowled Blackbird Xanthopsar flavus in Argentina. Bird Conservation International 8:255–267.

GANTER, B., F. COOKE, AND P. MINEAU. 1996. Long-term vegetation changes in a Snow Goose nesting habitat. Canadian Journal of Zoology 74:965–969.

GAYTON, D. V. 1991. Grazing pressure on Saskatchewan rangelands. Rangelands 13:107–108.

GOCHFELD, M. 1979. Brood parasite and host coevolution: interactions between Shiny Cowbirds and two species of meadowlarks. American Naturalist 113:855–870.

GRABER, R. R., AND J. W. GRABER. 1963. A comparative study of bird populations in Illinois, 1906–1909 and 1956–1958. Illinois Natural History Survey Bulletin 28:383–529.

HAGAN, J. M., III, AND D. W. JOHNSTON (EDITORS). 1992. Ecology and conservation of neotropical migrant landbirds. Smithsonian Institution Press, Washington, D.C.

HAYMAN, P., J. MARCHANT, AND T. PRATER. 1986. Shorebirds: an identification guide to the waders of the world. Houghton Mifflin, Boston, MA.

HERKERT, J. R. 1991. Prairie birds of Illinois: population response to two centuries of habitat change. Illinois Natural History Survey Bulletin 34:393–399.

HERKERT, J. R. 1997. Bobolink Dolichonyx oryzivorus population decline in agricultural landscapes in the midwestern USA. Biological Conservation 80:107–112.

HERKERT, J. R. 1998. The influence of the CRP on Grasshopper Sparrow population trends in the mid-continental United States. Wildlife Society Bulletin 26:227–231.

HERKERT, J. R., AND F. L. KNOPF. 1998. Research needs for grassland bird conservation. Pp. 273–282 in J. M. Marzluff and R. Sallabanks (editors). Avian conservation: research and management. Island Press, Washington, D.C.

HERKERT, J. R., D. W. SAMPLE, AND R. E. WARNER. 1996. Management of midwestern grassland landscapes for the conservation of migratory birds. Pp. 89–116 in F. R. Thompson III (editor). Managing midwestern landscapes for the conservation of neotropical migratory birds. USDA Forest Service Gen. Tech. Rep. GTR-NC-187. USDA Forest Service North Central Forest Experimental Station, St. Paul, MN.

HERKERT, J. R., R. E. SZAFONI, V. M. KLEEN, AND J. E. SCHWEGMAN. 1993. Habitat establishment, enhancement and management for forest and grassland birds. Natural Heritage Technical Publication no. 1. Illinois Department of Conservation, Springfield, IL.

HOWELL, S. N. G., AND S. WEBB. 1995. A guide to the birds of Mexico and northern Central America. Oxford University Press, Oxford, U.K.

HYSLOP, C. 1996. From north to south: the Canadian Wildlife Service's Latin American program links two worlds. Pp. 12–13 *in* Bird Conservancy (Wintering Grounds) [magazine of the American Bird Conservancy, Washington, D.C.].

IMBODEN, C. 1988. Foreword. P. vii *in* P. D. Goriup (editor). Ecology and conservation of grassland birds. ICBP Technical Publication no. 7. International Council for Bird Preservation, Cambridge, U.K.

INGERSOLL, C. A., AND M. V. WILSON. 1991. Restoration plans of a western Oregon remnant prairie. Restoration Plans and Management Notes 9:110–111.

JOHNSGARD, P. A. 1981. The plovers, sandpipers, and snipes of the world. University of Nebraska Press, Lincoln, NE.

JONES, A. L., AND P. D. VICKERY. 1997. Distribution and population status of grassland birds in Massachusetts. Pp. 187–199 *in* P. D. Vickery and P. W. Dunwiddie (editors). Grasslands of northeastern North America: ecology and conservation of native and agricultural landscapes. Massachusetts Audubon Society, Lincoln, MA.

KANTRUD, H. A. 1981. Grazing intensity effects on the breeding avifauna of North Dakota native grasslands. Canadian Field-Naturalist 95:404–417.

KNOPF, F. L. 1988. Conservation of steppe birds in North America. Pp. 27–41 *in* P. D. Goriup (editor). Ecology and conservation of grassland birds. ICBP Technical Publication no. 7. International Council for Bird Preservation, Cambridge, U.K.

KNOPF, F. L. 1994. Avian assemblages on altered grasslands. Studies in Avian Biology 15:247–257.

KNOPF, F. L., AND J. R. RUPERT. 1999. Use of cultivated fields by breeding Mountain Plovers in Colorado. Studies in Avian Biology 19:81–86.

KRAPOVICKAS, S., AND J. A. L. DE PEREZ. 1997. Swainson's Hawk in Argentina: international crisis and cooperation. World Birdwatch 19(4):12–15.

KREISSMAN, B. 1991. California, an environmental atlas and guide. Bear Klaw Press, Davis, CA.

LAUBER, T. B. 1991. Birds and the Conservation Reserve Program: a retrospective study. M.S. thesis. University of Maine, Orono, ME.

LEON, R. J. C., AND M. OESTERHELD. 1982. Envejecimiento de pasturas en el norte de la depresión del Salado. Un enfoque sucesional. Revista de la Facultad de Agronomia 3:41–49.

LEON, R. J. C., O. M. RUSCH, AND M. OESTERHELD. 1984. Pastizales pampeanos: impacto agropecuario. Phytocoenologia 12:201–218.

MACEDO, J. 1994. Prospectives for the rational use of the Brazilian cerrados for food production. Anais da Academia Brasileira de Ciências 66:159–166.

MADSON, C. 1989. Of wings and prairie grass. Nature Conservancy 1989(3):9–13.

MADSON, C. 1990. On the Osage. Nature Conservancy 1990(3):7–15.

MANTOVANI, J. E., AND A. PEREIRA. 1998. Estimativa da integridade da cobertura vegetal do Cerrado/Pantanal através de dados TM/Landsat. Grupo temático de Geoprocessamento. Report. Workshop on biodiversity conservation priorities for the Brazilian cerrado and Pantanal, Brasília, Brazil. http://www.bdt.org.br/bdt/workcerrado/relatorios/inpe.

MANZANO-FISCHER, P., R. LIST, AND G. CEBALLOS. 1999. Grassland birds in prairie-dog towns in northwestern Chihuahua, Mexico. Studies in Avian Biology 19:263–271.

MCMASTER, D. G., AND S. K. DAVIS. 1998. Non-game evaluation of the Permanent Cover Program. Saskatchewan Wetland Conservation Corporation, Regina, SK.

MCNICHOLL, M. K. 1988. Ecological and human influences on Canadian populations of grassland birds. Pp. 1–12 *in* P. D. Goriup (editor). Ecology and conservation of grassland birds. ICBP Technical Publication no. 7. International Council for Bird Preservation, Cambridge, U.K.

MELVIN, S. M. 1994. Military bases provide habitat for rare grassland birds. Natural Heritage News 4:3 [Massachusetts Division of Fisheries and Wildlife, Boston, MA].

MENGEL, R. M. 1970. The North American central plains as an isolating agent in bird speciation. Pp. 279–340 *in* W. Dort and J. K. Jones, Jr. (editors). Pleistocene and recent environments of the central great plains. University of Kansas Press, Lawrence, KS.

NIERING, W. A. 1992. The New England forests. Restoration Plans and Management Notes 10:24–28.

NOSS, R. F., E. T. LAROE, AND J. M. SCOTT. 1995. Endangered ecosystems of the United States: a preliminary assessment of loss and degradation. Report no. 0611-R-01 (MF). U.S. Department of the Interior, National Biological Service, Washington, D.C.

O'CONNOR, R. J., M. T. JONES, R. B. BOONE, AND T. B. LAUBER. 1999. Linking continental climate, land use, and land patterns with grassland bird distribution across the conterminous United States. Studies in Avian Biology 19:45–59.

OLROG, C. C. 1984. Las aves Argentinas. Administracion de Parques Nacionales, Buenos Aires, Argentina.

PARKER, T. A., III, AND E. O. WILLIS. 1997. Notes on three tiny grassland flycatchers, with comments on the disappearance of South American fire-diversified savannas. Ornithological Monographs 48:549–555.

PETERJOHN, B. G., AND J. R. SAUER. 1999. Population status of North American grassland birds from the North American Breeding Bird Survey 1966–1996. Studies in Avian Biology 19:27–44.

PITELKA, F. A., P. Q. TOMICH, AND G. W. TREICHEL. 1955. Ecological relations of jaegers and owls as lemming predators near Barrow, Alaska. Ecological Monographs 25:85–117.

PRESCOTT, D. R. C., B. C. DALE, AND R. D. DICKSON. 1998. Effects of timing and intensity of grazing on nest success of upland-nesting birds on the University Ranch. North American Waterfowl Management Plan report 034. Land Stewardship Centre of Canada and Canadian Wildlife Service, Edmonton, AB.

PRICE, J., S. DROEGE, AND A. PRICE. 1995. The summer atlas of North American birds. Academic Press, Toronto, ON.

RAFFAELE, H. A. 1989. A guide to the birds of Puerto Rico and the Virgin Islands. Princeton University Press, Princeton, NJ.

REUTER, D. D. 1986. Sedge meadows of the upper midwest: a stewardship summary. Natural Areas Journal 6:2–34.

REYNOLDS, R. E., T. L. SHAFFER, J. R. SAUER, AND B. G. PETERJOHN. 1994. Conservation Reserve Program: benefit for grassland birds in the northern plains. Transactions of the North American Wildlife and Natural Resources Conference 59:328–336.

RIDGELY, R. S., AND G. TUDOR. 1989. The birds of South America: the oscine passerines. University of Texas Press, Austin, TX.

RISSER, P. G., E. C. BIRNEY, H. D. BLOCKER, S. W. MAY, W. J. PARTON, AND J. A. WIENS. 1981. The true prairie ecosystem. Vol. 16, United States/International Biological Program Synthesis Series. Hutchinson Ross, Stroudsburg, PA.

RODENHOUSE, N. L., L. B. BEST, R. J. O'CONNOR, AND E. K. BOLLINGER. 1995. Effects of agricultural practices and farmland structures. Pp. 269–293 in T. E. Martin and D. M. Finch (editors). Ecology and management of neotropical migratory birds. Oxford University Press, Oxford, U.K.

SAMPLE, D. W., AND M. J. MOSSMAN. 1997. Managing habitat for grassland birds: a guide for Wisconsin. Department of Natural Resources, Madison, WI.

SAMSON, F., AND F. KNOPF. 1994. Prairie conservation in North America. BioScience 44:418–421.

SHRIVER, W. G., A. L. JONES, AND P. D. VICKERY. 1997. Northeast grassland bird survey. Report to the National Fish and Wildlife Foundation, project #96-177. National Fish and Wildlife Foundation, Washington, D.C.

SHRIVER, W. G., AND P. D. VICKERY. 1999. Aerial assessment of potential Florida Grasshopper Sparrow habitat: conservation in a fragmented landscape. Florida Field Naturalist 27:1–9.

SHRIVER, W. G., P. D. VICKERY, AND S. A. HEDGES. 1996. Effects of summer burns on Florida Grasshopper Sparrow. Florida Field Naturalist 24:68–73.

SHRIVER, W. G., P. D. VICKERY, AND D. W. PERKINS. 1999. The effects of summer burns on breeding Florida Grasshopper and Bachman's sparrows. Studies in Avian Biology 19:144–148.

SILVA, J. M. C. 1995. Avian inventory of the cerrado region, South America: implications for biological conservation. Bird Conservation International 5:15–28.

SILVA, J. M. C. 1998a. Integrating biogeography and conservation: an example with birds and plants of the cerrado region. Anais da Academia Brasileira de Ciências 70:881–888.

SILVA, J. M. C. 1998b. Grupo temático das aves. Report. Workshop on biodiversity conservation priori-ties for the Brazilian cerrado and Pantanal, Brasília, Brazil. Http://www.bdt.org.br/bdt/workcerrado/rela-torios/aves.

SILVA, J. M. C. 1999. Seasonal movements and conservation of seedeaters of the genus Sporophila in South America. Studies in Avian Biology 19:272–280.

SORIANO, A. 1991. Río de la Plata grasslands. Pp. 367–407 in R. T. Coupland (editor). Ecosystems of the world. Vol. 8A. Natural grasslands, introduction and western hemisphere. Elsevier, Amsterdam, Netherlands.

STATISTICS CANADA. 1997. Indicators and detailed statistics. Government of Canada Catalogue no. 16-200-XKE. Government of Canada, Ottawa, ON.

STOTZ, D. F., J. W. FITZPATRICK, T. A. PARKER III, AND D. K. MOSKOVITS. 1996. Neotropical birds: ecology and conservation. University of Chicago Press, Chicago, IL.

TUBARO, P. L., AND F. M. GABELLI. 1999. The decline of the Pampas Meadowlark: difficulties of applying the IUCN criteria to neotropical grassland birds. Studies in Avian Bioloby 19:250–257.

VICKERY, P. D., J. R. HERKERT, F. L. KNOPF, J. RUTH, AND C. E. KELLER. In press. Grassland birds: an overview of threats and recommended management strategies. In R. E. Bonney, Jr., D. N. Pashley, and R. Cooper (editors). Strategies for bird conservation: creating the Partners in Flight planning process. Cornell Laboratory of Ornithology, Ithaca, NY.

WARNER, R. E. 1994. Agricultural land use and grassland habitat in Illinois: future shock for midwestern birds. Conservation Biology 8:147–156.

WEGE, D. C., AND A. J. LONG. 1995. Key areas for threatened birds in the neotropics. BirdLife International, Cambridge, U.K.

WELLS, J. V. 1998. Important bird areas in New York state. National Audubon Society of New York state, Albany, NY.

WEST, N. E. 1995. Strategies for maintenance and repair of biotic community diversity on rangelands. Pp. 275–289 in R. Szaro (editor). Biodiversity in managed landscapes. Oxford University Press, Oxford, U.K.

WHEELWRIGHT, N. T., AND R. A. MAUCK. 1998. Philopatry, natal dispersal, and inbreeding avoidance in an island population of Savannah Sparrows. Ecology 79:755–767.

WHEELWRIGHT, N. T., AND J. D. RISING. 1993. Savannah Sparrow (Passerculus sandwichensis). In A. Poole and F. Gill (editors). The birds of North America no. 45. Academy of Natural Sciences, Philadelphia, PA, and American Ornithologists' Union, Washington, D.C.

WHITFIELD, D. P., AND J. J. BRADE. 1991. The breeding behaviour of the Knot Calidris canutus. Ibis 133:246–255.

WILSON, A. S. 1926. Lista de aves del sur de Santa Fe. Hornero 3:349–363.

WILSON, M. H., AND S. A. SADER (EDITORS). 1993. Conservation of neotropical migratory birds in Mexico. Miscellaneous Publication no. 727. Maine Agricultural and Forest Experiment Station, Orono, ME.

Studies in Avian Biology No. 19:27–44, 1999.

POPULATION STATUS OF NORTH AMERICAN GRASSLAND BIRDS FROM THE NORTH AMERICAN BREEDING BIRD SURVEY, 1966–1996

BRUCE G. PETERJOHN AND JOHN R. SAUER

Abstract. We summarize population trends for grassland birds from 1966 to 1996 using data from the North American Breeding Bird Survey. Collectively, grassland birds showed the smallest percentage of species that increased of any Breeding Bird Survey bird group, and population declines prevailed throughout most of North America. Although 3 grassland bird species experienced significant population increases between 1966 and 1996, 13 species declined significantly and 9 exhibited nonsignificant trend estimates. We summarize the temporal and geographic patterns of the trends for grassland bird species and discuss factors that have contributed to these trends.

LA CONDICIÓN DE LA POBLACIÓN DE AVES DE PASTIZAL EN AMÉRICA DEL NORTE UTILIZANDO EL BREEDING BIRD SURVEY DE NORTEAMÉRICA, 1966–1996

Sinopsis. Resumimos las tendencias poblacionales para las aves de pastizal desde 1966 hasta 1996 utilizando datos del Breeding Bird Survey de Norteamérica. Colectivamente, las aves de pastizal tuvieron el menor porcentaje de especies que aumentaron entre todos los grupos de aves en el Breeding Bird Survey. Prevalecieron las disminuciones de poblaciones de estas aves en la mayoría de Norteamérica. Aunque 3 especies de aves de pastizal experimentaron importantes aumentos poblacionales entre 1966 y 1996, 13 especies disminuyeron significativamente y 9 manifestaron estimaciones de tendencias no significativas. Resumimos los patrones temporales y geográficos de las tendencias para especies de aves de pastizal y analizamos los elementos que han contribuido a estas tendencias.

Key Words: bird populations; Breeding Bird Survey; grassland birds.

The status and distribution of grassland birds in North America have apparently undergone dramatic changes in the past 200 yr. Settlement of the continent by Europeans had both positive and negative effects on grassland bird communities. In eastern North America, the conversion from a forested to a largely agricultural landscape enabled grassland species to increase populations and expand their distributions, primarily during the nineteenth century (Andrle and Carroll 1988, Brewer et al. 1991, Peterjohn and Rice 1991). In contrast, the native grasslands of central and western North America suffered from settlement activities, particularly where the conversion to cultivated crops or overgrazing eliminated or severely altered these habitats (Bock and Bock 1988, Knopf 1988).

Anecdotal evidence suggests that populations of most grassland birds have declined in North America during the twentieth century. Although a variety of factors have contributed to these declines, the continued degradation and destruction of native grassland habitats remain the most prominent factors across the continent (McNicholl 1988, Askins 1993, Knopf 1994). Changing agricultural land-use practices have also been detrimental, contributing to declines in species occupying non-native pastures and hayfields (Bollinger et al. 1990, Askins 1993).

In this paper, we use data from the North American Breeding Bird Survey (BBS; Robbins et al. 1986, Peterjohn and Sauer 1996) to describe the geographic and temporal patterns in trends of grassland bird populations during the breeding seasons between 1966 and 1996. We evaluate regional patterns of observed species richness and mean trends for all grassland birds, document the percentage of grassland species with increasing trends, and compare this percentage to other species groups of management and ecological interest.

METHODS

The BBS is a roadside survey of approximately 4,000 randomly located survey routes established along secondary roads in the continental United States and Canada (see Peterjohn 1994). Although route coverage varies temporally and geographically, more than 2,800 routes have been surveyed annually since 1980. Each route is 39.4 km long with 50 stops spaced at 0.8-km intervals and is surveyed once annually by a single observer during the peak of the breeding season, primarily in June. The observer records all birds heard or seen within 0.4 km of each stop during a 3-min period.

The BBS was started in 1966 in eastern North America, and by 1968 routes were established across the continental United States and southern Canada. Additional information on the history and methodology of the survey is provided by Robbins et al. 1986.

STATISTICAL ANALYSES

We used the total number of individuals of a species counted over the entire BBS route as a population index. Most of our analyses of BBS data used the time series of population indices from the routes to estimate trend (a measure of population change over a pre- scribed interval, usually presented as percent change/ year) and relative abundance (mean count). We also summarized this information for regions. Because the sites were georeferenced by route starting points, we were able to map information such as trends, relative abundance, and species richness.

Species richness maps

We calculated the number of grassland species re- corded on each BBS route in 1966–1996. We then de- veloped contour maps of species richness, using the route species totals as input to smoothing procedures (Isaaks and Srivastava 1989, Cressie 1992).

We used inverse distancing (Isaaks and Srivastava 1989) to smooth these data. In this procedure, abun- dance was estimated at a location as a distance-weight- ed average of counts from nearby sites. We used in- verse distancing to estimate abundances for uniformly spaced locations on a 21.4-km grid across the conti- nental United States and southern Canada and then used the Arc/Info Geographic Information System pro- gram to make a contour map from the estimated abun- dances (Environmental Systems Research Institute 1991). See Sauer et al. 1995 and 1997 for applications and discussions regarding mapping of survey data.

Trend estimation

We estimated trends from each route using the es- timating equation procedure in which a multiplicative trend is modeled (Link and Sauer 1994). As in earlier analyses, we incorporated observer effects in the mod- el to minimize bias associated with improved observer quality over time (Sauer et al. 1994).

Maps of regional patterns of trend were also esti- mated using contouring. To accommodate the differ- ences in quality of information among routes, however, trend estimates were weighted by estimates of vari- ances of trends and relative abundances from individ- ual routes. This weighting was similar to that used in the estimation of the regional mean trends (e.g., Geiss- ler and Sauer 1990, Link and Sauer 1994).

We estimated regional trends as a weighted mean of the route-specific trends. Weights of abundance along routes, precision of trend estimates, and areas were used to accommodate inequities in data quality and regional variation in numbers of samples (Geissler and Sauer 1990). The areas of BBS physiographic strata in states and provinces were used in the weighting (see Butcher 1990 for a map of BBS physiographic strata). Bootstrapping was used to estimate variances of trends. Regional trends were estimated for the entire survey area of the BBS (hereafter called "continen- tal"), BBS regions (Eastern, Central, and Western; Bystrak 1981), states, and provinces. Regional trends were estimated for three time periods: 1966–1996, 1966–1979, and 1980–1996. Subinterval trend esti- mates were based on smaller samples of routes and were sometimes much less precise than long-term es- timates. Hence, long-term trends may not be accurately reflected in either or both of the subinterval estimates.

Annual indices

To evaluate nonlinear patterns of population change, we used the residual method for estimating annual in- dices of abundance (Sauer and Geissler 1990). In these analyses, a composite yearly index of abundance was estimated as a mean residual from the estimated re- gional trend. Nonlinear patterns in the indices were illustrated with LOESS smooths (James et al. 1990).

Composite analysis of grassland birds

Although several authors have developed lists of grassland bird species (Udvardy 1958, Mengel 1970), no consensus exists regarding the composition of this ecological grouping. In this paper we use the 25 spe- cies included in the grassland bird group of Peterjohn and Sauer 1993. This group is generally restricted to obligate grassland species, although the raptors occupy large territories that may include mixed grassland- shrubland communities, open areas, and other habitats. The group does not include species that regularly use nongrassland habitats during some seasons of the year or in sizable portions of their ranges, however. For each BBS route, we calculated the total number of grassland bird species and mean trend for the species group. Maps were made using inverse distancing to illustrate geographic patterns in distributions and trends.

We estimated percentages of increasing species for other groupings of birds to compare with composite trends in grassland birds. These groups are defined in Peterjohn and Sauer 1993 and include groups based on breeding habitat (wetland, scrub/successional, wood- land, urban), migration form (short-distance migrant, neotropical migrant, permanent resident), nest type (cavity, open cup), and nest location (ground/low, midstory/canopy). For each group, we estimated trends for each species in the group over the surveyed area and determined the percentage of species with positive trend estimates using a procedure based on empirical- Bayes methods that incorporates the relative variances of the component trend estimates (Link and Sauer 1995). We used a z-test to evaluate the null hypothesis that the percentage of species with increasing trends did not differ from 50.

RESULTS

Grassland bird species richness in North America was greatest in the Great Plains, espe- cially in portions of North Dakota, Montana, and the adjacent prairie provinces of Canada (Fig. 1). Species richness was noticeably reduced east and west of the Great Plains, becoming most depauperate in the southeastern states. Trends for the entire group showed declines prevailing throughout most of the United States and south- ern Canada (Fig. 2). Areas with increasing pop- ulations of grassland birds were small and lo- cally distributed, although one of these areas (in northeastern Montana and northwestern North Dakota) corresponded with the northern Great Plains where species richness was greatest. Only 23% of grassland bird species—the smallest pro- portion of any BBS bird group—showed posi-

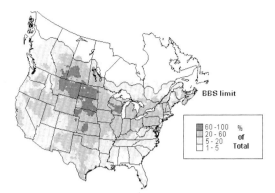

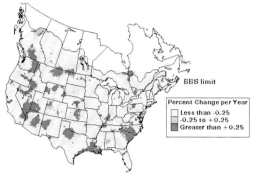

FIGURE 1. Species richness map for grassland bird group, 1966–1996, expressed as the percentage of the total group.

FIGURE 2. Population trend map for grassland bird group, 1966–1996. The map presents areas of consistent population change, grouped into categories of declining (< −0.25% change per year), indeterminate (−0.25 to +0.25% change per year), and increasing (> 0.25% change per year) trends.

tive population trend estimates during 1966–1996 (Fig. 3).

The continental trend estimates for all grassland birds (25 species) are summarized in Table 1. Although the entire grassland bird group generally declined throughout North America between 1966 and 1996, individual species showed a variety of temporal and geographic patterns in population trends. These trends are discussed in greater detail below.

SPECIES WITH INCREASING POPULATION TRENDS

BBS data indicate that only three grassland bird species experienced significant increases in their continental populations between 1966 and 1996. Few Ferruginous Hawks (*Buteo regalis*) were recorded along BBS routes prior to 1980, although their representation improved subsequently. As is true for many raptors, this species is not well sampled by the BBS methodology and was recorded in small numbers throughout its range. Population increases after 1980 were largely responsible for the increasing trends shown over the entire survey period (Table 1). These increases were evident across most of the breeding range (Fig. 4).

Upland Sandpipers (*Bartramia longicauda*) were more adequately surveyed by the BBS methodology than was the preceding species. Population increases were most evident from the Great Plains westward, whereas declines were concentrated from the Great Lakes into Minnesota and Wisconsin (Fig. 5). The remnant, locally distributed populations elsewhere in eastern North America are currently poorly monitored by the BBS. Although some regional variability exists in the temporal patterns of trends in this species, the continental increases were most consistent between 1978 and 1992 (Fig. 6).

Sedge Wrens (*Cistothorus platensis*) are op-

portunistic breeders, apparently exhibiting little site fidelity (Burns 1982). This species' erratic seasonal movements may obfuscate population-trend estimates, and they should thus be viewed with caution. The long-term trend was generally positive, reflecting increases during the 1980–1996 interval. In contrast, most trend estimates for the species were negative during the 1966–1979 interval. Increases between 1966 and 1996 were most prevalent from the Dakotas into Manitoba and portions of Minnesota, whereas declines prevailed eastward from Iowa and Wisconsin and in Saskatchewan (Fig. 7).

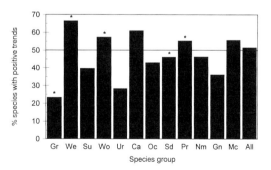

FIGURE 3. Percentages of increasing species for all BBS bird groups, 1966–1996. Gr = grassland birds, We = wetland birds, Su = shrub and successional birds, Wo = woodland birds, Ur = urban birds, Ca = cavity nesters, Oc = open-cup nesters, Sd = short-distance migrants, Pr = permanent residents, Nm = neotropical migrants, Gn = ground- and low-nesting birds, Mc = midstory- and canopy-nesting birds, All = all species. An asterisk (*) denotes a significant (P < 0.05) deviation from 50%.

TABLE 1. BBS CONTINENTAL TREND ESTIMATES FOR GRASSLAND BIRDS

Species	1966–1996				1966–1979			1980–1996		
	Trend[a]	P[b]	N[c]	RA[d]	Trend	P	N	Trend	P	N
Northern Harrier	−0.6	–	891	0.49	−1.4	–	397	−0.7	–	745
Ferruginous Hawk	5.2	***	186	0.25	2.6	–	34	7.2	**	170
Ring-necked Pheasant	−1.0	**	1,206	7.30	−0.8	–	735	−0.6	–	1,060
Sharp-tailed Grouse	0.3	–	124	0.55	−4.8	–	53	1.8	–	105
Mountain Plover	−2.7	**	33	0.31	2.0	–	9	3.7	–	29
Upland Sandpiper	1.3	***	581	2.22	3.0	**	315	−0.9	–	486
Long-billed Curlew	−1.4	–	202	1.45	1.7	–	74	−2.0	–	155
Short-eared Owl	−2.8	–	132	0.21	4.1	–	54	−0.8	–	90
Horned Lark	−1.3	***	1,805	27.02	−0.4	–	1,064	−2.0	***	1,559
Sedge Wren	2.2	**	307	1.14	−3.3	**	162	1.9	–	262
Sprague's Pipit	−4.7	***	108	1.41	−6.6	***	51	−4.5	–	94
Dickcissel	−1.6	***	783	16.29	−5.5	***	559	0.4	–	706
Cassin's Sparrow	−2.5	***	203	16.31	0.4	–	96	−0.2	–	186
Vesper Sparrow	−0.8	**	1,462	7.84	−1.9	***	816	0.1	–	1,232
Lark Bunting	−0.9	–	332	42.97	−4.0	**	154	0.2	–	288
Savannah Sparrow	−0.6	**	1,477	8.40	0.2	–	810	−0.2	–	1,336
Baird's Sparrow	−1.6	–	115	1.87	−4.7	**	52	−1.1	–	95
Grasshopper Sparrow	−3.6	***	1,404	3.97	−4.6	***	857	−2.1	***	1,193
Henslow's Sparrow	−8.8	***	149	0.15	−6.0	**	99	−10.4	***	80
Le Conte's Sparrow	1.4	–	154	0.73	−1.9	–	44	4.6	***	138
McCown's Longspur	1.1	–	59	4.57	3.5	–	27	2.7	–	44
Chestnut-collared Longspur	−0.1	–	145	9.27	1.6	–	76	1.1	–	125
Bobolink	−1.6	***	1,134	5.35	1.1	**	761	−3.8	***	1,026
Eastern Meadowlark	−2.6	***	1,921	20.29	−1.4	***	1,338	−3.0	***	1,761
Western Meadowlark	−0.6	**	1,480	44.48	−1.4	**	800	−0.3	–	1,348

Note: See American Ornithologists' Union 1983 for scientific names.
[a] Average percent change per year.
[b] ** 0.01 < P < 0.05, *** P < 0.01.
[c] Number of BBS routes on which each species has been recorded.
[d] Relative abundance; expressed as mean number of individuals per BBS route within the range of the species.

SPECIES WITH NONSIGNIFICANT POPULATION TRENDS

Nine grassland bird species had nonsignificant trend estimates, although for six of these species the trends were in a negative direction (Table 1). Sharp-tailed Grouse (*Tympanuchus phasianellus*) and Short-eared Owls (*Asio flammeus*) were poorly sampled by the BBS methodology, and estimates may not be representative of actual population trends (Table 1). Other species, including Le Conte's Sparrow (*Ammodramus leconteii*) and McCown's Longspur (*Calcarius mccownii*), have restricted ranges or are otherwise infrequently encountered along BBS routes. Their population trends were generally imprecisely estimated and should also be viewed with caution. Four other species are summarized

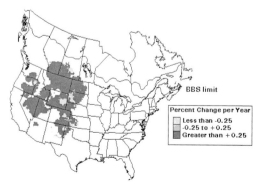

FIGURE 4. Ferruginous Hawk population trend map, 1966–1996.

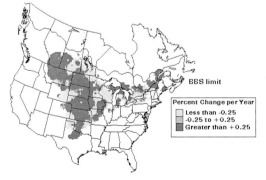

FIGURE 5. Upland Sandpiper population trend map, 1966–1996.

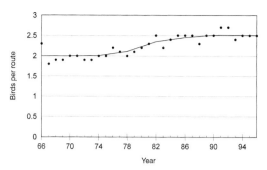

FIGURE 6. Continental indices for Upland Sandpiper, 1966–1996.

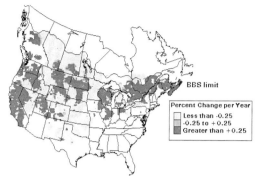

FIGURE 8. Northern Harrier population trend map, 1966–1996.

below to illustrate the temporal and geographic patterns in their trends.

Northern Harriers (*Circus cyaneus*) were widely encountered in relatively small numbers throughout their range. BBS data indicate that the most consistent declines occurred from the Great Plains westward through the intermountain states, although increases were evident in portions of the Dakotas, Montana, and Wyoming (Fig. 8). Consistent increases were also evident from Wisconsin eastward to the maritime provinces and in the states bordering the Pacific coast. This species' continental population trends remained negative from 1966 to 1996 (Table 1).

Long-billed Curlews (*Numenius americanus*) are not particularly conspicuous during the breeding season except when they vocalize at dawn (Fitzner 1978). Their relative abundance may be under-represented by the BBS methodology (Redmond et al. 1981). Also, reports of nonbreeders along BBS routes may have obscured population trends in some areas. Despite these potential limitations, BBS data suggest that Long-billed Curlews declined throughout the western Great Plains but tended to increase west

of the Rocky Mountains except in Utah (Fig. 9). No consistent temporal patterns were evident in these trends (Table 1).

Lark Buntings (*Calamospiza melanocorys*) can be nomadic during the breeding season, and these short-term movements may obscure or accentuate long-term population trends (Stewart 1975, Andrews and Righter 1992). Along BBS routes, population declines predominated throughout most of the Lark Bunting's range (Fig. 10). Increasing populations were small and localized, except in Montana. Population declines during 1966–1979 were largely responsible for the long-term trends in this species, although the estimates became more positive after 1980 (Table 1).

As a result of their limited distribution on the northern Great Plains and historic declines in some populations (Stewart 1975), Baird's Sparrows (*Ammodramus bairdii*) have received considerable attention. The BBS population trend map indicates that declines were prevalent in North Dakota and along the northern periphery of this species' range, whereas increases were evident elsewhere (Fig. 11). The trend estimates

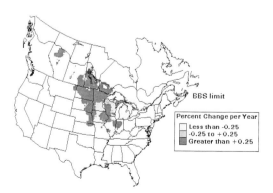

FIGURE 7. Sedge Wren population trend map, 1966–1996.

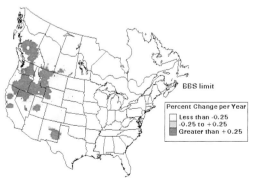

FIGURE 9. Long-billed Curlew population trend map, 1966–1996.

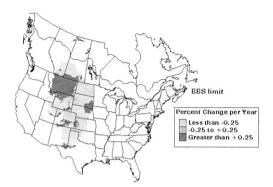

FIGURE 10.   Lark Bunting population trend map, 1966–1996.

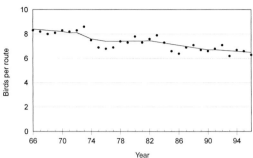

FIGURE 12.   Continental indices for Ring-necked Pheasant, 1966–1996.

were nonsignificant for the entire survey period, although a significant decline occurred during 1966–1979 (Table 1).

SPECIES WITH DECLINING POPULATION TRENDS

Most of the 13 species that experienced significant declines in their continental populations during 1966–1996 were widely distributed and well sampled by the BBS (Table 1). Mountain Plovers (*Charadrius montanus*), however, were recorded on a relatively small number of routes which precluded a detailed analysis of the species' population trends. Other species, including Sprague's Pipit (*Anthus spragueii*) and Henslow's Sparrow (*Ammodramus henslowii*), have relatively limited breeding distributions but experienced consistent significant rangewide declines between 1966 and 1996. Cassin's Sparrows (*Aimophila cassinii*) exhibit considerable annual fluctuations in abundance which produce imprecise trend estimates, but they have shown a declining tendency since the mid-1970s. Examples of other temporal and geographic patterns in population trends shown by declining species are described below.

Populations of Ring-necked Pheasants (*Phasianus colchicus*) exhibited consistent trends during 1966–1979 and 1980–1996 (Table 1). The surveywide indices declined noticeably during the mid-1970s, followed by a slight recovery and then another decline during 1982–1985 (Fig. 12). Increasing populations were most evident in the Great Plains, whereas declines were widespread from the Rocky Mountains westward and from Wisconsin and Illinois east into New England (Fig. 13).

BBS data indicate that Horned Lark (*Eremophila alpestris*) populations experienced widespread declines between 1966 and 1996 (Table 1, Fig. 14). Declining trends were prevalent in most regions of the continent, although local increases were evident from the western Great Lakes across the northern Great Plains and into the intermountain western states.

The status and distribution of the Dickcissel (*Spiza americana*) have always been confounded by the species' irregular population movements (Emlen and Wiens 1965, Ewert and Cantino 1967). These movements normally produce influxes near the northern periphery of the breeding range that are inversely correlated with

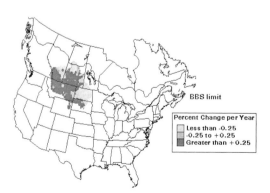

FIGURE 11.   Baird's Sparrow population trend map, 1966–1996.

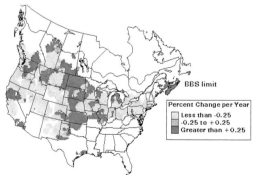

FIGURE 13.   Ring-necked Pheasant population trend map, 1966–1996.

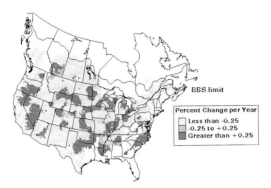

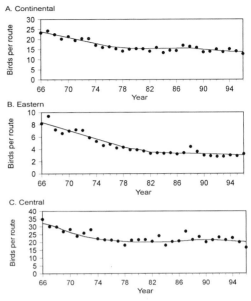

FIGURE 14. Horned Lark population trend map, 1966–1996.

FIGURE 16. BBS annual indices for Dickcissel populations, 1966–1996: A = continental, B = Eastern BBS region, C = Central BBS region.

habitat suitability in the southern portion of the range (Fretwell 1986). Perhaps as a result of these irregular movements, the geographic patterns in the long-term trends of Dickcissels are not uniform (Fig. 15). Declines were most prevalent across the northern half of the range and in central Texas. Increases predominated from northern Texas through Oklahoma into Kansas and from Arkansas and Louisiana east into Alabama and Tennessee. The continental annual indices exhibited a distinct decline from 1966 through the late 1970s, followed by variable but fairly stable counts (Fig. 16A). Declines during the first 10 yr of the BBS were evident in the Eastern and Central BBS regions, but populations in both regions were reasonably stable between 1980 and 1996 (Figs. 16B and C).

Vesper Sparrow (*Pooecetes gramineus*) populations showed consistent declines from Minnesota, Wisconsin, and Indiana eastward and from Montana and South Dakota south to northern New Mexico, northern Arizona, and Nevada (Fig. 17). Increasing populations predominated from Illinois across Iowa to Kansas and northward into North Dakota. The continental indices

varied, but declines were most evident before the mid-1970s (Fig. 18). This temporal pattern reflected similar trends in the Central and Western BBS regions; populations in the Eastern BBS region declined throughout the survey period (Fig. 17).

Savannah Sparrows (*Passerculus sandwichensis*) have expanded their breeding range during the twentieth century, most noticeably in the midwestern states where their breeding distribution has spread southward from the upper Great Lakes (Monroe et al. 1988, Peterjohn and Rice 1991). Despite this range expansion, populations declined from Ontario, Minnesota, and Iowa eastward between 1966 and 1996 (Fig. 19).

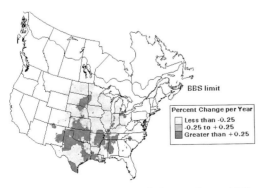

FIGURE 15. Dickcissel population trend map, 1966–1996.

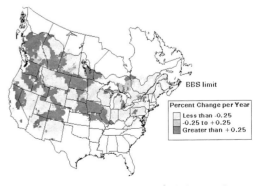

FIGURE 17. Vesper Sparrow population trend map, 1966–1996.

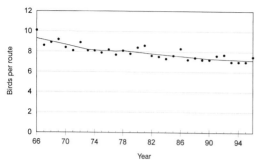

FIGURE 18.   Continental indices for Vesper Sparrow, 1966–1996.

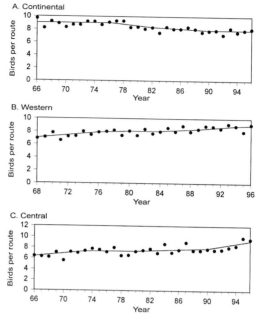

FIGURE 20.   BBS annual indices for Savannah Sparrow populations, 1966–1996: A = continental, B = Western BBS region, C = Central BBS region.

A mosaic of increases and decreases was evident elsewhere, with increases most prevalent in the Rocky Mountains and northern Great Plains. Regional trends exhibited increases in the Western BBS region and more variation, including a fairly distinct decline during the late 1970s, in the Central BBS region (Figs. 20A and B). The continental indices also showed the most marked declines in the late 1970s (Fig. 20C).

Grasshopper Sparrows (*Ammodramus savannarum*) showed some of the most consistent declines of any grassland bird. The declines prevailed throughout most of the Grasshopper Sparrow's range (Fig. 21), although some local increases were evident in the western states and elsewhere. These trends were fairly consistent from 1966 to 1996, with a slight moderation in the rate of decline in recent years.

BBS data indicate that Bobolinks (*Dolichonyx oryzivorus*) have generally declined throughout their breeding range (Fig. 22). Areas with increasing populations were small and locally distributed, most notably from North Dakota to western Ontario and in Pennsylvania. The continental indices were fairly stable through the late 1970s, followed by a consistent decline

(Fig. 23). The general population declines in 1980–1996 contrasted sharply with the population estimates for 1966–1979, when the continental population significantly increased (Table 1).

Eastern Meadowlarks (*Sturnella magna*) also exhibited consistent declines on the BBS. Declining populations prevailed throughout most of the range except in the southwestern states (Fig. 24). The long-term trends were almost entirely negative, and most declines were significant. These declining trends prevailed during the 1966–1979 and 1980–1996 intervals (Table 1).

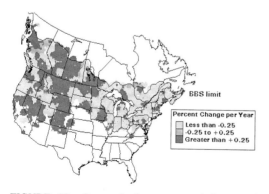

FIGURE 19.   Savannah Sparrow population trend map, 1966–1996.

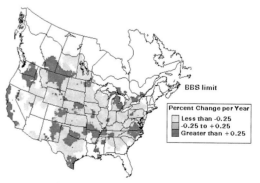

FIGURE 21.   Grasshopper Sparrow population trend map, 1966–1996.

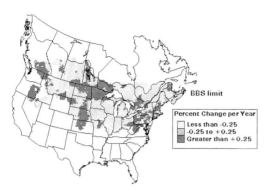

FIGURE 22. Bobolink population trend map, 1966–1996.

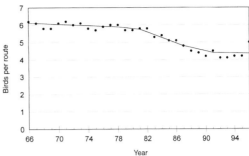

FIGURE 23. Continental indices for Bobolink, 1966–1996.

Robbins et al. (1986) reported declines in Eastern Meadowlark populations associated with the severe winters of 1976–1978. These declines were most apparent in the Midwest, especially in Illinois, Indiana, Michigan, and Kentucky (Figs. 25A–D). Populations in Indiana recovered in 3 yr, but no substantial recovery was evident in the other states.

Western Meadowlarks (*S. neglecta*) have undergone a range expansion in the twentieth century, spreading eastward into the Great Lakes region (Lanyon 1956, DeVos 1964). This expansion largely occurred before the start of the BBS, and Western Meadowlark populations generally declined between 1966 and 1996 (Table 1). These declines were evident throughout most of the Western Meadowlark's range, although increases occurred from southern California across the southwestern states to Texas and locally northward along the Rocky Mountains and Great Plains (Fig. 26).

DISCUSSION

Although BBS data indicate the trends of grassland bird populations, they do not identify the factors responsible for these trends. Some factors, such as habitat alteration, degradation, and destruction, may be common to many grassland birds, whereas other factors may influence only certain species or may operate in only portions of a species' range. The factors believed to be responsible for the reported population trends are discussed below, although for many species the causes of their population trends have not been conclusively identified.

SPECIES WITH INCREASING POPULATION TRENDS

Ferruginous Hawk populations have experienced significant declines and range contractions in the past 100 yr, but these trends were most evident before 1960 (Houston and Bechard 1984, Schmutz 1984, Houston and Schmutz

1999). The conversion of native grasslands to agricultural fields was largely responsible for these trends (Schmutz 1984). Contributing factors included persecution, reductions in prey populations, fewer fires, and shortages of suitable nest sites (Houston and Bechard 1984).

Ferruginous Hawk population trends after 1960 have been less certain. Since most tillable lands had already been converted into agricultural fields, additional declines in response to habitat loss have been relatively small (Houston and Bechard 1984). The declines apparently have been reversed in portions of the species' range, where Ferruginous Hawks may have increased during the late 1980s (Harlow and Bloom 1989). These increases were reflected in the positive BBS trend estimates for 1980–1996 (Table 1). Short-term population increases in Ferruginous Hawks are not unexpected, as the birds are known to be fairly nomadic and local influxes have been documented in response to prey availability (Gilmer and Stewart 1983). Additional data from the BBS and other sources are needed to determine if the increases since 1980 reflect short-term fluctuations or a long-term reversal of historic declines.

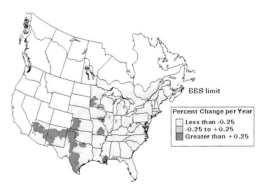

FIGURE 24. Eastern Meadowlark population trend map, 1966–1996.

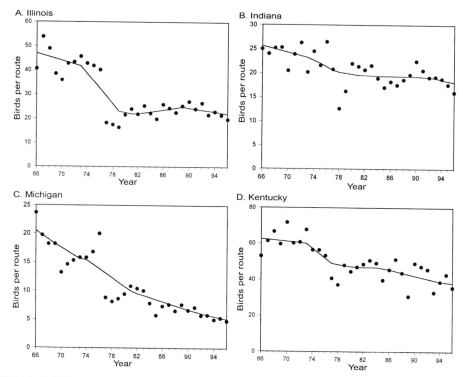

FIGURE 25.   BBS annual indices for Eastern Meadowlark populations, 1966–1996: A = Illinois, B = Indiana, C = Michigan, D = Kentucky.

Upland Sandpiper populations suffered significant declines in the late nineteenth and early twentieth centuries as a result of market hunting and habitat destruction (Bent 1929). Their numbers recovered, however, when hunting ceased. More recent declines have been evident in the eastern portion of the species' range since the 1940s, and only small isolated populations remain in most of this region (Peterjohn and Rice 1991, Carter 1992). BBS trend estimates were

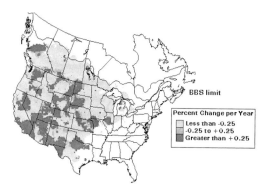

FIGURE 26.   Western Meadowlark population trend map, 1966–1996.

consistent with this pattern; there were declines in the Eastern BBS region, but relatively few Upland Sandpipers were recorded on those BBS routes, and the eastern regional trend estimates thus had little influence on the continental trend estimates.

Increases in the Great Plains were largely responsible for the positive continental trend estimates for Upland Sandpipers. Factors that contributed to these positive trends merit additional study since the increases occurred in areas where most other grassland birds declined. Breeding Upland Sandpipers occupy much larger home ranges than other grassland birds (Mitchell 1967), so nesting pairs may be less affected by unfavorable agricultural practices in individual fields. These sandpipers also prefer to nest where the grass cover is of mixed short and medium heights (Kirsch and Higgins 1976, Ailes 1980). Hence, they tolerate moderate levels of grazing, especially in habitats where the grass cover may otherwise be too tall. This ability to tolerate some disturbance may have allowed populations to increase in recent decades. Overgrazing, standing water, burning, and mowing, however, can still make breeding habitats unsuitable for this species (Mitchell 1967).

Factors on the Upland Sandpiper's South American winter range may also have influenced BBS population trends. Unfortunately, this species' winter ecology is poorly understood (White 1988). Although pesticide use and unfavorable agricultural practices remain threats, deforestation and the subsequent creation of grasslands are probably beneficial for Upland Sandpipers. Some range extensions have been reported in deforested areas of South America (White 1988).

The erratic intraseasonal movements of Sedge Wrens may not have greatly influenced the BBS trend estimates since these movements are most evident in late summer after breeding surveys have been completed (Meanley 1952, Schwilling 1982). Bedell (1996), for example, documented Sedge Wrens on some Nebraska BBS routes in August, even though the species had never been recorded during the June surveys. Although lack of site fidelity during the breeding season may contribute to considerable annual fluctuations in abundance of this species (Burns 1982), the BBS data may reasonably reflect population trends in June. How these June population trends relate to the entire Sedge Wren population, however, cannot be determined until the birds' seasonal movements are better understood.

Despite fluctuations, some marked declines have been apparent in Sedge Wren populations in the twentieth century, especially in the northeastern states and near the eastern Great Lakes (Brewer et al. 1991, Peterjohn and Rice 1991, Gibbs and Melvin 1992). These trends have continued in recent decades, with declines along BBS routes most consistent in the eastern half of the species' range. Habitat loss appears to have been the most important factor contributing to these declines, although burning and overgrazing may have been important in some areas (Gibbs and Melvin 1992).

In contrast, Sedge Wren population increases on the Great Plains during 1980–1996 were largely responsible for generally positive continental trend estimates in 1980–1996 and 1966–1996 (Table 1). These increases were most evident in the 1990s. Since Sedge Wrens frequently occupy grasslands created by the Conservation Reserve Program (CRP; Johnson and Schwartz 1993), increased habitat availability may have contributed to these increases. Also, increased annual precipitation has improved wetland conditions in this portion of the Great Plains (U.S. Fish and Wildlife Service 1997), expanding the extent of damp grassland habitats favored by nesting Sedge Wrens.

SPECIES WITH NONSIGNIFICANT POPULATION TRENDS

For those species that are poorly sampled by the BBS, trend estimates may not represent the true status of their breeding populations. Any discussion of factors responsible for these reported trends would be speculative. Only those species adequately surveyed by the BBS are discussed below.

The BBS trends for Northern Harrier populations were similar to those reported by Martin (1989), Serrentino and England (1989), and Sweet (1991). Martin (1989) indicated that several factors combine to prevent clear interpretation of population trends for this species. Its specialized predation on voles (*Microtus* spp.) produces extensive nomadic movements which, in concert with a fluctuating prey base, obscure distinguishing between actual trends and normal fluctuations. Precipitation extremes also influence population levels since droughts or floods can affect habitat suitability and prey populations. Severe winter weather and its effects on prey populations can also influence short-term fluctuations in Northern Harrier populations (Hamerstrom 1986). In the BBS data, these marked short-term fluctuations were apparent only in the annual indices for states and provinces and in physiographic strata. Where long-term declines were documented, as in portions of the northeastern and midwestern United States, habitat destruction and intensified agricultural use of remaining grasslands are believed to have been largely responsible (Serrentino and England 1989, Sweet 1991). Reforestation has also eliminated many suitable grasslands in the Northeast (Serrentino and England 1989).

Breeding Long-billed Curlews are associated with shortgrass steppe communities on the western Great Plains and with grasslands in the Great Basin. They prefer habitats that have been heavily grazed where the vegetation is less than 10 cm high and the soils are moist (Knopf 1988). Populations were decimated by uncontrolled hunting in the nineteenth and early twentieth centuries, causing a noticeable contraction of the breeding range (Page and Gill 1994). The conversion of native grasslands to agricultural fields has not permitted a sustained population recovery (Page and Gill 1994), and the breeding range has experienced some local contractions since 1960 (McCallum et al. 1977, Renaud 1980). Since Long-billed Curlews prefer grazed habitats, major threats to their breeding populations are the continued conversion of grasslands into cultivated fields and the loss of wetlands, which may eliminate the moist soils preferred for feeding (Knopf 1988, Page and Gill 1994). These factors may be responsible for the general population declines of Long-billed Curlews along BBS routes on the western Great Plains between 1966 and 1996. However, loss of coastal foraging habitats during the winter, exposure to toxic chemicals, and increased predation may also have contributed to the declines of some populations (Page and Gill 1994). Factors that may have contributed to the apparent increase in populations along BBS routes in the Great Basin have not been identified.

Breeding Lark Buntings are conspicuous occupants of short- and mixed-grass communities of the Great Plains. Their nomadic movements are poorly understood, but fluctuations in precipitation levels and the influence of these fluctuations on habitat conditions and food availability are believed to be primarily responsible for these movements (Stewart 1975, Andrews and Righter 1992). Large influxes of Lark Buntings may appear for a single year or for several years in any portion of the species' range, only to disappear quickly when conditions change (Shane 1996). Regional populations may show cyclical fluctuations, and Shane (1996) has theorized that a single population cycle may require several decades to complete. Until this species' population fluctuations are better understood, the biological significance of BBS trend estimates for Lark Burnings remains in question.

Despite these fluctuations, the generally negative trends for Lark Bunting populations between 1966 and 1996 were associated with the destruction and degradation of their preferred grassland habitats (Andrews and Righter 1992). These buntings are also nomadic during the winter months (Shane and Seltman 1995), and changing habitat conditions in their winter range may have contributed to population trends. Since 1990, however, Lark Buntings have benefited from habitats created by the CRP on the Great Plains (Johnson and Igl 1995). These new habitats have allowed some populations to expand and may have contributed to the more positive population trend estimates since 1980.

Baird's Sparrows have not been extensively studied, and the factors affecting their population trends are poorly understood. They frequent mixed-grass communities or, in more arid regions, the taller grasslands bordering wetlands, lakes, or other water sources. They prefer relatively undisturbed grasslands and avoid intensively grazed areas (Stewart 1975). Habitat destruction and degradation during the breeding season have been associated with population declines in the past (Stewart 1975). Habitats created by the CRP may have benefited this species in the 1990s (Johnson and Igl 1995). Factors influencing grassland habitats on the winter range in the southwestern United States and Mexico may also influence population trends of Baird's Sparrows; their winter distribution is poorly understood (Phillips et al. 1964), however, and

their habitat preferences and ecological requirements are largely unknown.

SPECIES WITH DECLINING POPULATION TRENDS

Many of the factors important in the declines of grassland bird populations are common to most species. These factors are discussed first, followed by a summary of the species-specific factors that have contributed to declining trends.

Habitat destruction

The destruction of grassland habitats has been implicated in the declines of all grassland birds. The loss of native grasslands in North America has been dramatic, especially in the eastern half of the continent (Vickery 1996). Most of these grasslands disappeared before the twentieth century, but the conversion of shortgrass communities into agricultural habitats has continued (Knopf 1988). The conversion of non-native pastures and hayfields into other agricultural habitats has also been prevalent during the past 50 yr (Herkert 1994).

Until recently, few new grasslands had been created to compensate for habitats converted into agricultural fields or urban development or lost through forest regeneration. Reclamation of strip mines in portions of the northern Appalachian Mountain region created extensive grasslands in areas that were formerly forested, producing local increases in some grassland birds (Whitmore and Hall 1978). Reproductive success may be low in these habitats, however, so they may actually serve as population "sinks" for some species (Wray et al. 1982).

Beginning in the 1980s, the CRP was initiated to reduce agricultural overproduction. Millions of hectares of cropland were converted to grasslands or other perennial cover, with the greatest enrollment of area in the central United States (Young and Osborn 1990). Although the CRP lands represent a very small proportion of all agricultural lands in North America, creation of these habitats has benefited grasslands birds and even reversed the long-term declines of some regional populations (Johnson and Schwartz 1993, Johnson and Igl 1995). This reversal of some population trends in association with the creation of CRP lands demonstrates the importance of habitat availability in influencing population trends in grassland birds.

Habitat fragmentation

Although the effect of habitat fragmentation on woodland bird communities has been the subject of many studies, little information is available on its effects on grassland birds. Herkert (1994) examined area relationships of grassland birds in Illinois and noted that both area and vegetative structure significantly influenced the composition of grassland bird communities. Five species were area sensitive in Illinois, and only Dickcissels were unaffected by this factor. In Maine, Vickery et al. (1994) found similar results, suggesting that large area requirements for grassland birds may be an important factor influencing habitat use and that fragmentation of remaining grassland habitats may play a significant role in the population trends of some species.

Habitat degradation

Grazing has been implicated in the declines of some local grassland bird populations, but its impact on regional populations is difficult to assess. Some species, such as Grasshopper Sparrow, may benefit from light to moderate grazing in portions of their range but be adversely affected in other areas (Vickery 1996). Other species may be fairly sensitive to grazing across their range and may serve as indicators of overall habitat quality (Bock and Webb 1984, Baker and Guthry 1990). Species that prefer shortgrass habitats, such as Long-billed Curlew and Horned Lark, may benefit from intensive grazing under some circumstances (Knopf 1988).

Agricultural practices, particularly those associated with hay cropping, have also been detrimental to many grassland birds. Hayfields are being cropped more frequently and at earlier dates (Rodenhouse et al. 1993), which under many circumstances prohibits grassland birds from successfully raising young during the breeding season (Warner and Etter 1989, Bollinger et al. 1990). Since hayfields provide most of the remaining grassland habitats in eastern North America (Herkert 1994), this agricultural practice may have serious adverse effects on the regional populations of grassland birds.

Grazing, fire, and agricultural practices also influence the successional stages of grassland communities. Habitats that have not been disturbed for 5–10 yr are favored by a few species such as Upland Sandpiper, Grasshopper and Henslow's sparrows, and Eastern Meadowlark (Bollinger 1995), which are less numerous in or completely absent from younger grasslands. Hence, regular disturbance to grasslands may favor generalist species such as Savannah Sparrow but may contribute to the declines of species favoring more mature grasslands (Bollinger 1995).

Mortality from toxic chemicals

Direct mortality of grassland birds from poisoning by toxic chemicals such as Carbofuran and Fenthion has been reported in a few cases (Stone 1979, Deweese et al. 1983). The geographic extent of this problem is poorly understood, however. Species that spend considerable time in agricultural fields, such as Ring-necked Pheasant and Horned Lark, may be most susceptible to the toxic effects of these chemicals.

Nest parasitism

Brown-headed Cowbirds (*Molothrus ater*) are known to parasitize the nests of most grassland-nesting passerines (Friedmann 1963). Rates of nest parasitism are generally believed to be low, but there is much interspecific variability in parasitism rates within sites (Hill 1976) as well as intraspecific variability across a species' range (Vickery 1996). Nest parasitism has been shown to have a negative impact on the recruitment of Dickcissels (Zimmerman 1983) and may have a similar effect on other species.

Adverse winter weather

Unusually severe winter weather is known to significantly reduce populations of some bird species (Robbins et al. 1986, Sauer and Droege 1990, Sauer et al. 1996). These reductions are normally short-term, with populations returning to normal within several years following the return to normal weather patterns. These weather conditions are most likely to affect species breeding in the northern United States, although during exceptionally harsh winters, such as occurred during 1975–1977, harsh conditions can extend south to the Gulf Coast states. Among grassland birds, species that winter in the northern United States, such as Ring-necked Pheasant and Eastern Meadowlark, appear to be most susceptible to these conditions.

Species-specific factors

Habitat destruction, fragmentation, and degradation are common causes of declines of all grassland species, but additional factors may have contributed to the population trends evident between 1966 and 1996.

Factors responsible for declines in Ring-necked Pheasant populations included intensified agricultural land-use practices (resulting in reduced habitat availability), increased use of pesticides, and adverse weather conditions (Dahlgren 1988). Adverse weather normally produced short-term population fluctuations, as exemplified by declines during the mid-1970s in portions of the range, whereas the other factors were largely responsible for long-term declines.

The loss of agricultural fields to reforestation and development contributed to Horned Lark population declines in eastern North America (Laughlin and Kibbe 1985, Buckelew and Hall 1994). Factors responsible for this species' decline elsewhere are poorly understood. Since Horned Larks are frequently associated with agricultural fields throughout their range, their extensive decline may indicate that some agricultural practices have contributed to these negative trends. For example, mortality of Horned Larks has been reported after exposure to certain pesticides (Beason 1995). In contrast, population increases in the intermountain region of the western United States corresponded with the conversion of sagebrush (*Artemisia*) habitats to grasslands (Knick and Rotenberry 1999).

Several factors contributed to trends in Dickcissel populations. This species is well adapted to residing in agricultural landscapes, inhabiting hayfields, pastures, weedy fallow fields, and weedy margins of ditches and roadsides. Conversion of these habitats to cultivated fields and more frequent mowing of hayfields, however, contributed to declines in some areas (Fretwell 1986). Brood parasitism by Brown-headed Cowbirds had a negative effect on Dickcissel recruitment (Zimmerman 1983), as did increased nest predation in certain habitats (Zimmerman 1984). Factors on the Dickcissel's tropical winter range are also believed to be important; the birds are viewed as pests in grain fields, and control operations at winter roosts have caused extensive mortality (Fretwell 1986, Basili and Temple 1999).

Several factors contributed to declines in Vesper Sparrow populations in eastern North America. Loss of grassland habitat to reforestation and urbanization was a major factor, although "clean farming" practices such as the removal of hedgerows and more frequent mowing of hayfields also contributed to declines (Laughlin and Kibbe 1985, Brauning 1992). The Vesper Sparrow is one of the first species to occupy reclaimed strip mines, however, and it has expanded its range in heavily forested portions of West Virginia and surrounding states since 1960 (Whitmore and Hall 1978).

The factors responsible for the trends in Savannah Sparrow populations are poorly understood (Wheelwright and Rising 1993). In the eastern United States, reforestation, conversion of grasslands to cultivated crops, and more frequent mowing of hayfields contributed to declines (Laughlin and Kibbe 1985, Peterjohn and Rice 1991). Factors associated with population trends in western North America, where areas of increase and decline were interspersed, were not identified.

Habitat destruction, fragmentation, and degradation have been the primary factors responsible for declines in Grasshopper Sparrow populations since 1966 (Vickery 1996). Because this species prefers relatively large grassland tracts (Herkert 1994, Vickery et al. 1994, Bollinger 1995), it may be particularly susceptible

to changes in habitat availability. Additionally, early mowing of hayfields can result in abandonment of breeding territories and can contribute to local annual fluctuations in abundance (Smith 1963).

In addition to habitat destruction, the factor most frequently cited for declines in Bobolink populations is more frequent mowing of hayfields (Bollinger et al. 1990). Many hayfields are cut in late May and at regular intervals throughout the summer, which does not provide Bobolinks with an opportunity to successfully raise a brood between mowing operations. Also, habitat preferences and other aspects of the species' winter biology are poorly understood, so factors on its South American winter range may also have contributed to population declines.

Eastern Meadowlarks tend to winter farther north than most other grassland birds, which may explain their greater susceptibility to periodic severe winter weather, as shown in the BBS annual indices. Their population declines, however, have generally been attributed to habitat destruction, more frequent mowing of hayfields, and similar factors affecting the populations of most grassland birds (Peterjohn and Rice 1991, Brauning 1992). Breeding meadowlarks are very sensitive to disturbance around the nest, either by people or livestock. Certain agricultural practices, such as spring tillage (which can reduce nest success and increase adult mortality), are also detrimental to breeding populations (Lanyon 1995).

Factors responsible for declines in Western Meadowlark populations are believed to be similar to those described for Eastern Meadowlarks (Lanyon 1994). Extensive droughts in the 1930s may have contributed to this species' eastward range expansion into the Great Lakes area, but causes for this expansion and subsequent decline have never been fully explained (Lanyon 1956).

CONCLUSIONS AND CONSERVATION IMPLICATIONS

BBS data indicate negative population trends for most grassland bird species between 1966 and 1996. The declines were fairly consistent throughout the survey period and, for many species, prevailed across most of the breeding range. A few exceptions existed, with Ferruginous Hawks, Upland Sandpipers, and Sedge Wrens exhibiting significant increases. The general declines in grassland birds shown by the BBS, however, reflected similar trends reported in the decades prior to the 1960s.

Although BBS data can be used to identify temporal and geographic patterns in population trends, the data do not identify the causes of these patterns. Other sources of information must be used to establish the factors responsible for these trends. The common factors of habitat destruction, fragmentation, and degradation influence population trends of most grassland bird species. Agricultural practices such as earlier and more frequent mowing of hayfields may also contribute to population declines in some species, whereas other factors may be important for individual species or in specific geographic areas. These factors affect each species differently and produced the variety of geographic and temporal patterns in population trends evident in the BBS estimates.

Despite the prevalence of negative trend estimates, the situation is not entirely bleak for grassland birds. The CRP has shown that deterioration of grassland habitats can be reversed over the short term, even on fairly large geographic scales. Efforts to mitigate some of the other adverse factors discussed above can only help grassland birds. Grassland birds have evolved in relatively harsh and constantly changing habitats, requiring considerable adaptability in order to survive in this environment. With some assistance from humans, this adaptability may allow many of these species to recover if habitat availability and conditions improve.

The reversal of population declines resulting from the habitats created by the CRP is just the first step toward an overall improvement in the status of grassland birds. The conservation of these species must receive greater priority, particularly in the Great Plains where grassland bird communities are richest. Additional research is needed to better understand how these species respond to the factors that affect their population trends. This understanding may be crucial for the development of successful efforts to produce a long-term reversal of the general decline in grassland bird populations.

ACKNOWLEDGEMENTS

We thank the thousands of observers who have surveyed BBS routes. Our analyses would have been impossible without the data they collected. We are grateful to K. Boone and K. Pardieck for preparing the figures. Earlier drafts of this manuscript benefited from comments by D. Dawson, K. Pardieck, C. Robbins, S. Knick, P. D. Vickery, and an anonymous reviewer.

LITERATURE CITED

AILES, I. W. 1980. Breeding biology and habitat use of the Upland Sandpiper in central Wisconsin. Passenger Pigeon 42:53–63.

AMERICAN ORNITHOLOGISTS' UNION. 1983. Check-list of North American birds. 6th ed. American Ornithologists' Union, Washington, D.C.

ANDREWS, R., AND R. RIGHTER. 1992. Colorado birds. Denver Museum of Natural History, Denver, CO.

ANDRLE, R. F., AND J. R. CARROLL (EDITORS). 1988. The atlas of breeding birds in New York state. Cornell University Press, Ithaca, NY.

ASKINS, R. A. 1993. Population trends in grassland, shrubland, and forest birds in eastern North America. Current Ornithology 11:1–34.

BAKER, D. L., AND F. S. GUTHRY. 1990. Effects of continuous grazing on habitat and density of ground-foraging birds in south Texas. Journal of Range Management 43:2–5.

BASILI, G. D., AND S. A. TEMPLE. 1999. Winter ecology, behavior, and conservation needs of Dickcissels in Venezuela. Studies in Avian Biology 19:289–299.

BEASON, R. C. 1995. Horned Lark (*Eremophila alpestris*). *In* A. Poole and F. Gill (editors). The birds of North America, no. 195. Academy of Natural Sciences, Philadelphia, PA, and American Ornithologists' Union, Washington, D.C.

BEDELL, P. A. 1996. Evidence of dual breeding ranges for the Sedge Wren in the central Great Plains. Wilson Bulletin 108:115–122.

BENT, A. C. 1929. Life histories of North American shore birds. U.S. National Museum Bulletin 146:55–69.

BOCK, C. E., AND J. H. BOCK. 1988. Grassland birds in southeastern Arizona: impacts of fire, grazing and alien vegetation. Pp. 43–58 *in* P. D. Goriup (editor). Ecology and conservation of grassland birds. ICBP Technical Publication no. 7. International Council for Bird Preservation, Cambridge, U.K.

BOCK, C. E., AND B. WEBB. 1984. Birds as grazing indicator species in southeastern Arizona. Journal of Wildlife Management 48:1045–1049.

BOLLINGER, E. K. 1995. Successional changes and habitat selection in hayfield bird communities. Auk 112:720–730.

BOLLINGER, E. K., P. B. BOLLINGER, AND T. A. GAVIN. 1990. Effects of hay-cropping on eastern populations of the Bobolink. Wildlife Society Bulletin 18:142–150.

BRAUNING, D. W. (EDITOR). 1992. Atlas of breeding birds in Pennsylvania. University of Pittsburgh Press, Pittsburgh, PA.

BREWER, R., G. A. MCPEEK, AND R. J. ADAMS, JR. (EDITORS). 1991. The atlas of breeding birds of Michigan. Michigan State University Press, East Lansing, MI.

BUCKELEW, A. R., JR., AND G. A. HALL. 1994. The West Virginia breeding bird atlas. University of Pittsburgh Press, Pittsburgh, PA.

BURNS, J. T. 1982. Nests, territories and reproduction of Sedge Wrens (*Cistothorus platensis*). Wilson Bulletin 94:338–349.

BUTCHER, G. S. 1990. Audubon Christmas Bird Counts. Pp. 5–13 *in* J. R. Sauer and S. Droege (editors). Survey designs and statistical methods for the estimation of avian population trends. U.S. Fish and Wildlife Service Biological Report 90(1).

BYSTRAK, D. 1981. The North American Breeding Bird Survey. Studies in Avian Biology 6:34–41.

CARTER, J. W. 1992. Upland Sandpiper. Pp. 235–252 *in* K. J. Schneider and D. M. Pence (editors). Migratory nongame birds of management concern in the northeast. U.S. Fish and Wildlife Service, Newton Corner, MA.

CRESSIE, N. 1992. Statistics for spatial data. John Wiley and Sons, New York, NY.

DAHLGREN, R. B. 1988. Distribution and abundance of the Ring-necked Pheasant in North America. Pp. 29–43 in D. L. Hallett, W. R. Edwards, and G. V. Burger (editors). Pheasants: symptoms of wildlife problems on agricultural lands. Wildlife Society, Bloomington, IN.

DEVOS, A. 1964. Range changes of birds in the Great Lakes region. American Midland Naturalist 71:489–502.

DEWEESE, L. R., L. C. MCEWEN, L. A. SETTIMI, AND R. D. DEBLINGER. 1983. Effects on birds of Fenthion aerial application for mosquito control. Journal of Economic Entomology 76:906–911.

EMLEN, J. T., AND J. A. WIENS. 1965. The Dickcissel invasion of 1964 in southern Wisconsin. Passenger Pigeon 27:51–59.

ENVIRONMENTAL SYSTEMS RESEARCH INSTITUTE. 1991. Surface modeling with TIN. Environmental Systems Research Institute, Redlands, CA.

EWERT, D. N., AND P. D. CANTINO. 1967. Summer observations of Dickcissels and Western Meadowlarks in the Lansing area. Jack-Pine Warbler 45:128–130.

FITZNER, J. N. 1978. The ecology and behavior of the Long-billed Curlew (Numenius americanus) in southeastern Washington. Ph.D. dissertation. Washington State University, Pullman, WA.

FRETWELL, S. D. 1986. Distribution and abundance of the Dickcissel. Current Ornithology 4:211–242.

FRIEDMANN, H. 1963. Host relations of the parasitic cowbirds. U.S. National Museum Bulletin 233.

GEISSLER, P. H., AND J. R. SAUER. 1990. Topics in route-regression analysis. Pp. 54–57 in J. R. Sauer and S. Droege (editors). Survey designs and statistical methods for the estimation of avian population trends. U.S. Fish and Wildlife Service Biological Report 90(1).

GIBBS, J. P., AND S. M. MELVIN. 1992. Sedge Wren. Pp. 191–209 in K. J. Schneider and D. M. Pence (editors). Migratory nongame birds of management concern in the northeast. U.S. Fish and Wildlife Service, Newton Corner, MA.

GILMER, D. S., AND R. E. STEWART. 1983. Ferruginous Hawk populations and habitat use in North Dakota. Journal of Wildlife Management 47:146–157.

HAMERSTROM, F. 1986. Harrier, hawk of the marsh: the hawk that is ruled by a mouse. Smithsonian Institution Press, Washington, D.C.

HARLOW, D. L., AND P. H. BLOOM. 1989. Buteos and the Golden Eagle. Pp. 102–110 in B. G. Pendleton (editor). Proceedings of the western raptor management symposium and workshop. National Wildlife Federation Scientific Technical Series no. 12.

HERKERT, J. R. 1994. The effects of habitat fragmentation on midwestern bird communities. Ecological Applications 4:461–471.

HILL, R. A. 1976. Host parasite relationships of the Brown-headed Cowbird in a prairie habitat of west central Kansas. Wilson Bulletin 88:555–565.

HOUSTON, C. S., AND M. J. BECHARD. 1984. Decline of the Ferruginous Hawk in Saskatchewan. American Birds 36:166–170.

HOUSTON, C. S., AND J. K. SCHMUTZ. 1999. Changes in bird populations on Canadian grasslands. Studies in Avian Biology 19:87–94.

ISAAKS, E. H., AND R. M. SRIVASTAVA. 1989. An introduction to applied geostatistics. Oxford University Press, New York, NY.

JAMES, F. C., C. E. MCCULLOCH, AND L. E. WOLFE. 1990. Methodological issues in the estimation of trends in bird populations with an example: the Pine Warbler. Pp. 84–97 in J. R. Sauer and S. Droege (editors). Survey designs and statistical methods for the estimation of avian population trends. U.S. Fish and Wildlife Service Biological Report 90(1).

JOHNSON, D. H., AND L. D. IGL. 1995. Contributions of the Conservation Reserve Program to populations of breeding birds in North Dakota. Wilson Bulletin 107:709–718.

JOHNSON, D. H., AND M. D. SCHWARTZ. 1993. The Conservation Reserve Program and grassland birds. Conservation Biology 7:934–937.

KIRSCH, L. M., AND K. F. HIGGINS. 1976. Upland Sandpiper nesting and management in North Dakota. Wildlife Society Bulletin 4:16–20.

KNICK, S. T., AND J. T. ROTENBERRY. 1999. Spatial distribution of breeding passerine bird habitats in a shrubsteppe region of southwestern Idaho. Studies in Avian Biology 19:104–111.

KNOPF, F. L. 1988. Conservation of steppe birds in North America. Pp. 27–41 in P. D. Goriup (editor). Ecology and conservation of grassland birds. ICBP Technical Publication no. 7. International Council for Bird Preservation, Cambridge, U.K.

KNOPF, F. L. 1994. Avian assemblages on altered grasslands. Studies in Avian Biology 15:247–257.

LANYON, W. E. 1956. Ecological aspects of sympatric distribution of meadowlarks in the north-central states. Ecology 37:98–108.

LANYON, W. E. 1994. Western Meadowlark (Sturnella neglecta). In A. Poole and F. Gill (editors). The birds of North America, no. 104. Academy of Natural Sciences, Philadelphia, PA, and American Ornithologists' Union, Washington, D.C.

LANYON, W. E. 1995. Eastern Meadowlark (Sturnella magna). In A. Poole and F. Gill (editors). The birds of North America, no. 160. Academy of Natural Sciences, Philadelphia, PA, and American Ornithologists' Union, Washington, D.C.

LAUGHLIN, S. B., AND D. P. KIBBE (EDITORS). 1985. The atlas of breeding birds of Vermont. University Press of New England, Hanover, NH.

LINK, W. A., AND J. R. SAUER. 1994. Estimating equations estimates of trend. Bird Populations 2:23–32.

LINK, W. A., AND J. R. SAUER. 1995. Estimation of empirical mixing distributions in summary analyses. Biometrics 51:810–821.

MARTIN, J. W. 1989. Harriers and kites. Pp. 92–101 in B. G. Pendleton (editor). Proceedings of the western raptor management symposium and workshop. National Wildlife Federation Scientific Technical Series no. 12, Washington, D.C.

MARTIN, S. G., AND T. A. GAVIN. 1995. Bobolink (Dolichonyx oryzivorous). In A. Poole and F. Gill (editors). The birds of North America, no. 176. Academy of Natural Sciences, Philadelphia, Pa., and American Ornithologists' Union, Washington, D.C.

MCCALLUM, D. A., W. D. GRAUL, AND R. ZACCAGNINI.

1977. The status of the Long-billed Curlew in Colorado. Auk 94:599–601.

McNicholl, M. K. 1988. Ecological and human influences on Canadian populations of grassland birds. Pp. 1–25 *in* P. D. Goriup (editor). Ecology and conservation of grassland birds. ICBP Technical Publication no. 7. International Council for Bird Preservation, Cambridge, U.K.

Meanley, B. 1952. Notes on the ecology of the Short-billed Marsh Wren in the lower Arkansas rice fields. Wilson Bulletin 64:22–25.

Mengel, R. M. 1970. The North American central plains as an isolating agent in bird speciation. Pp. 280–340 *in* W. Dort and J. K. Jones (editors). Pleistocene and recent environments of the central Great Plains. University of Kansas Press, Lawrence, KS.

Mitchell, G. J. 1967. The Upland Plover and its status in relation to environmental conditions and situations, past and present. Blue Jay 25:58–63.

Monroe, B. L., Jr., A. L. Stamm, and B. L. Palmer-Ball, Jr. 1988. Annotated checklist of the birds of Kentucky. Kentucky Ornithological Society, Louisville, KY.

Page, G. W., and R. E. Gill, Jr. 1994. Shorebirds in western North America: late 1800s to late 1900s. Studies in Avian Biology 15:147–160.

Peterjohn, B. G. 1994. The North American Breeding Bird Survey. Birding 26:386–398.

Peterjohn, B. G., and D. L. Rice. 1991. The Ohio breeding bird atlas. Ohio Department of Natural Resources, Columbus, OH.

Peterjohn, B. G., and J. R. Sauer. 1993. North American Breeding Bird Survey annual summary 1990–1991. Bird Populations 1:52–67.

Peterjohn, B. G., and J. R. Sauer. 1996. The 1994 and 1995 summary of the North American Breeding Bird Survey. Bird Populations 3:48–66.

Phillips, A., J. Marshall, and G. Monson. 1964. The birds of Arizona. University of Arizona Press, Tucson, AZ.

Redmond, R. L., T. K. Bicek, and D. A. Jenni. 1981. An evaluation of breeding season census techniques for Long-billed Curlews (*Numenius americanus*). Studies in Avian Biology 6:197–201.

Renaud, W. E. 1980. The Long-billed Curlew in Saskatchewan: status and distribution. Blue Jay 38:221–237.

Robbins, C. S., D. Bystrak, and P. H. Geissler. 1986. The Breeding Bird Survey: its first fifteen years 1965–1979. U.S. Fish and Wildlife Service Research Publication no. 157.

Rodenhouse, N. L., L. B. Best, R. J. O'Connor, and E. K. Bollinger. 1993. Effects of temperate agriculture on neotropic migrant landbirds. Pp. 280–295 *in* D. M. Finch and P. W. Stangel (editors). Status and management of neotropical migratory birds. USDA Forest Service Gen. Tech. Rep. RM-229. USDA Forest Service Rocky Mountain Forest Station, Fort Collins, CO.

Sauer, J. R., and S. Droege. 1990. Recent population trends of the Eastern Bluebird. Wilson Bulletin 102:239–252.

Sauer, J. R., and P. H. Geissler. 1990. Annual indices from route regression analyses. Pp. 58–62 *in* J. R. Sauer and S. Droege (editors). Survey designs and statistical methods for the estimation of avian population trends. U.S. Fish and Wildlife Service Biological Report 90(1).

Sauer, J. R., J. E. Hines, G. Gough, I. Thomas, and B. G. Peterjohn. 1997. The North American Breeding Bird Survey results and analysis. Ver. 96.3: www.mbr-pwrc.usgs.gov/bbs/bbs.html. U.S. Geological Survey, Patuxent Wildlife Research Center, Laurel, MD.

Sauer, J. R., G. W. Pendleton, and S. Orsillo. 1995. Mapping of bird distributions from point count surveys. Pp. 151–160 *in* C. J. Ralph, J. R. Sauer, and S. Droege (editors). Monitoring bird populations by point counts. USDA Forest Service Gen. Tech. Rep. PSW-GTR-149. USDA Forest Service Pacific Southwest Research Station, Albany, CA.

Sauer, J. R., G. W. Pendleton, and B. G. Peterjohn. 1996. Evaluating causes of population change in North American insectivorous songbirds. Conservation Biology 10:465–478.

Sauer, J. R., B. G. Peterjohn, and W. A. Link. 1994. Observer differences in the North American Breeding Bird Survey. Auk 111:50–62.

Schmutz, J. K. 1984. Ferruginous and Swainson's hawk abundance and distribution in relation to land use in southeastern Alberta. Journal of Wildlife Management 48:1180–1187.

Schwilling, M. D. 1982. Sedge Wrens nesting into September. Kansas Ornithological Society Bulletin 33:22–23.

Serrentino, P., and M. England. 1989. Northern Harrier. Pp. 37–46 *in* B. G. Pendleton (editor). Proceedings of the northeast raptor management symposium and workshop. National Wildlife Federation Scientific Technical Series no. 13, Washington, D.C.

Shane, T. G. 1996. The Lark Bunting: in peril or making progress? Colorado Field Ornithologists' Journal 30:162–168.

Shane, T. G., and S. S. Seltman. 1995. The historical development of wintering Lark Bunting populations north of the thirty-seventh parallel in Colorado and Kansas. Kansas Ornithological Society Bulletin 46:36–39.

Smith, R. L. 1963. Some ecological notes on the Grasshopper Sparrow. Wilson Bulletin 75:159–165.

Stewart, R. E. 1975. Breeding birds of North Dakota. Harrison Smith, Lund Press, Minneapolis, MN.

Stone, W. B. 1979. Poisoning of wild birds by organophosphate and carbamate pesticides. New York Fish and Game Journal 26:37–47.

Sweet, M. J. 1991. Kites and Northern Harrier. Pp. 32–41 *in* B. G. Pendleton and D. L. Krahe (editors). Proceedings of the midwest raptor management symposium and workshop. National Wildlife Federation Scientific Technical Series no. 15, Washington, D.C.

Udvardy, M. D. F. 1958. Ecological and distributional analysis of North American birds. Condor 60:50–66.

U.S. Fish and Wildlife Service. 1997. Waterfowl: status and fall flight forecast, 1997. U.S. Fish and Wildlife Service, Office of Migratory Bird Management, Laurel, MD.

Vickery, P. D. 1996. Grasshopper Sparrow (*Ammodramus savannarum*). *In* A. Poole and F. Gill (editors). The birds of North America, no. 239. Academy of Natural Sciences, Philadelphia, PA, and American Ornithologists' Union, Washington, D.C.

VICKERY, P. D., M. L. HUNTER, JR., AND S. M. MELVIN. 1994. Effects of habitat area on the distribution of grassland birds in Maine. Conservation Biology 8: 1087–1097.

WARNER, R. E., AND S. L. ETTER. 1989. Hay cutting and the survival of pheasants: a long-term perspective. Journal of Wildlife Management 53:455–461.

WHEELWRIGHT, N. T., AND J. D. RISING. 1993. Savannah Sparrow (*Passerculus sandwichensis*). *In* A. Poole and F. Gill (editors). The birds of North America, no. 45. Academy of Natural Sciences, Philadelphia, PA, and American Ornithologists' Union, Washington, D.C.

WHITE, R. P. 1988. Wintering grounds and migration patterns of the Upland Sandpiper. American Birds 42:1247–1253.

WHITMORE, R. C., AND G. A. HALL. 1978. The response of passerine species to a new resource: reclaimed strip mines in West Virginia. American Birds 32:6–9.

WRAY, T., II, K. A. STRAIT, AND R. C. WHITMORE. 1982. Reproductive success of grassland sparrows on a reclaimed surface mine in West Virginia. Auk 99:157–164.

YOUNG, E. C., AND C. T. OSBORN. 1990. Costs and benefits of the Conservation Reserve Program. Journal of Soil and Water Conservation 45:370–373.

ZIMMERMAN, J. L. 1983. Cowbird parasitism of Dickcissels in different habitats and at different nest densities. Wilson Bulletin 95:7–22.

ZIMMERMAN, J. L. 1984. Nest predation and its relationship to habitat and nest density in Dickcissels. Condor 86:68–72.

Studies in Avian Biology No. 19:45–59, 1999.

LINKING CONTINENTAL CLIMATE, LAND USE, AND LAND PATTERNS WITH GRASSLAND BIRD DISTRIBUTION ACROSS THE CONTERMINOUS UNITED STATES

RAYMOND J. O'CONNOR, MALCOLM T. JONES, RANDALL B. BOONE, AND T. BRUCE LAUBER

Abstract. Associations of the abundance and temporal incidence of 17 grassland bird species with climate, weather, farm crops, and landscape metrics were determined for the conterminous United States using hierarchical models. We developed statistical models using two versions of classification and regression tree analysis in which the variation of each species' response variable (both as number of individuals [1973–1989] and as temporal incidence [1981–1990] per Breeding Bird Survey route) was recursively partitioned into statistically distinct chains of environmental determinants or associations. The predictive power of these models was bimodal, yielding high R^2 values (above 38 percent) for one group of 12 species and low values (below 20 percent) for a second group of 5 (generally scarce or restricted-range) species. The fit of the models was strongly correlated with the size of each species' range. Climate variables—long-term annual precipitation, January temperature, and July temperature—appeared in many of the species models, often with strong effects (large R^2 values). January weather (annual deviation from long-term mean temperature) was also a consistent, though weaker, correlate. Sorghum (*Sorghum vulgare*) was the only strong crop correlate of most species abundances, but grain corn (*Zea mays*) and enrollment in the Conservation Reserve Program were consistent smaller contributors to most models. Wheat (*Triticum aestivum*) and durum wheat (*T. durum*) were other noteworthy variables, occurring in about half of the species models. The presence of soybeans (*Glycine max*) was a local modifier of abundance for almost all species. Considering only the leading variables for individual species, precipitation occurred in five species, grain corn in three, and durum wheat and sunflower (*Helianthus* sp.) in two each. The Conservation Reserve Program variable pre-empted grain corn for two species in the two years Conservation Reserve Program data were available. Other leading variables each appeared in only one species. A parallel analysis using remotely sensed land-use data to assess the relative roles of land-cover proportions and habitat patch attributes showed that grassland species were more strongly influenced by habitat patch variables, but less strongly influenced by land-cover proportions, than were nongrassland species. Grassland species' sensitivity to habitat patch variables appeared to be greater in wooded and cropland habitats than in habitats dominated by grass.

EL ENLACE ENTRE EL CLIMA CONTINENTAL, EL USO DE TERRENO Y LOS PATRONES DE TERRENO CON LA DISTRIBUCIÓN DE AVES DE PASTIZAL A TRÁVES DE LOS ESTADOS UNIDOS CONTÉRMINOS

Sinopsis. Se determinaron asociaciones de abundancia e incidencia temporal de 17 especies de aves de pastizal con el clima, el tiempo, las cosechas y las mediciones de paisaje para los Estados Unidos contérminos utilizando modelos jerárquicos. Elaboramos modelos estadísticos aplicando dos versiones diferentes de análisis de árboles de regresión y clasificación. En ellos, la variación de la variable respuesta de cada especie (tanto el número de individuos [1973–1989] como la incidencia temporal [1981–1990] por ruta del Breeding Bird Survey) se divide recursivamente en cadenas de determinantes ambientales o asociaciones que difieren estadísticamente. La capacidad de predicción de estos modelos fue bimodal, lo que produjo altos valores R^2 (más de un 38 por ciento) para un grupo de 12 especies y bajos valores (menos de un 20 por ciento) para un segundo grupo de 5 especies (generalmente escasas o con una extensión restringida). La conformidad de los modelos se correlacionó estrechamente con el tamaño de la extensión de cada especie. Las variables de clima—precipitación anual a largo plazo, temperatura en enero y temperatura en julio—aparecieron en muchos de los modelos de especie, a menudo con grandes efectos (altos valores de R^2). El tiempo en enero (la desviación anual de la temperatura promedio a largo plazo) fue también un correlativo congruente, aunque de menor importancia. El sorgo (*Sorghum vulgare*) fue el único correlativo de cosecha marcado para la abundancia de la mayoría de las especies, pero el maíz (*Zea mays*) y la inscripción en el Programa de Reservas de Conservación fueron factores menores siempre presentes que contribuyeron en la mayoría de los modelos. El trigo (*Triticum aestivum*) y el *Triticum durum* fueron otras variables que cabe mencionar, que aparecieron en aproximadamente la mitad de los modelos de especie. La presencia de soya (*Glycine max*) fue un modificador local de abundancia para casi todas las especies. Tomando en cuenta solamente las variables principales para las especies individuales, hubo precipitación en cinco especies, maíz en tres, y *Triticum durum* y girasol (*Helianthus* sp.) en dos cada uno. La variable del Programa de Reservas de Conservación reemplazó la variable de maíz para dos especies durante los dos años en que había datos disponibles del Programa de Reservas de Conservación. Otras variables principales aparecieron en sólo una especie cada una. Un análisis paralelo utilizando datos de usos del territorio obtenidos por detección remota para evaluar los papeles relativos de las proporciones de cobertura de terreno y las características de rodales de hábitat demostró que las especies de pastizal fueron influidas en mayor grado por las variables de rodales de hábitat, pero que fueron influidas en menor grado por las proporciones de cobertura de terreno, que las especies que no eran de pastizal. La sensibilidad de especies de pastizal a las variables de rodales de hábitat pareció ser más grande en hábitats de árboles y de cosechas que en hábitats dominados por la hierba.

Key Words: agriculture; area sensitivity; climate; grassland birds; landscape ecology; regression trees.

Grassland birds have generally declined in the United States because of intensification of agriculture in the Midwest (Askins 1993) and reforestation and increased urbanization in the East (Witham and Hunter 1992, Litvaitis 1993). These declines have been particularly severe where the prairie has been fragmented and disturbed by farming, as in Illinois (Warner 1994). Farmland intensification has been aided by the development of new mechanical and chemical means of treating cropland and by economic support systems promoting their use (O'Connor and Shrubb 1986). In the United States these trends have been reflected in intensified corn (*Zea mays*) and soybean (*Glycine max*) production and in reductions in small-grain and forage crops, livestock, and pasture. Additionally, most hayfields are now intensively cultivated alfalfa (*Medicago sativa*) monocultures rather than mixed-species grasslands. The shift from perennial grassland to annually cultivated cropland is thought to be a major factor in the decline of several formerly common grassland bird species (Johnson and Schwartz 1993).

Much of the information available on the habitat requirements of grassland birds originates in site-intensive studies and focuses on microhabitat features. More spatially extensive studies, such as those by Johnson and Schwartz (1993), have used a regional set of sites and mesoscale habitat variables to characterize the correlates of favorable and unfavorable sites, and With (1994) has taken an explicitly landscape approach in studying the requirements of McCown's Longspur (*Calcarius mccownii*). Another approach is that of Whitmore (1981), who compared his results with those of Wiens (1973) to demonstrate that the habitat requirements of Grasshopper Sparrows (*Ammodramus savannarum*) are similar in different parts of the country.

Much less is known about the correlates of these species' distributions over large spatial extents; the assumption is that the effects of microhabitat or mesoscale correlates determine the larger distribution (Brown 1984). Distributions, and particularly continental distributions, are more likely to be controlled by hierarchies of controlling or constraining factors (Krebs 1985). Before effective conservation programs for grassland species can be developed, we need to identify controlling factors at spatial scales other

than that of the microscale of the local habitat patch (Wiens 1981). In this paper we take a macroecological approach (Brown 1995) to assess the pattern of environmental correlates for 17 species of grassland birds in the conterminous United States (Table 1). We used a class of statistical models known as classification and regression tree (CART) analysis that can handle hierarchical effects (see Rodenhouse et al. 1993).

METHODS

BIRD DATA

The bird data we analyzed were from the Breeding Bird Survey (BBS) for the conterminous United States. The BBS is based on 40-km roadside surveys, each containing 50 stops at 0.8-km intervals. Approximately 2,000 BBS routes are distributed randomly in the conterminous United States in 1-degree blocks of latitude and longitude by state. The number of routes per 1-degree block of latitude and longitude varies among states but is held constant in a state (Bystrak 1981). We used only "type one" routes (routes passing all quality-assurance checks) for the period 1973 through 1990. We used the total count (i.e., number of individuals) for each species and the incidence (i.e., proportion of years observed) for each species on each route. For crop analyses, we assigned each route to the county in which its starting coordinates lay, and in a spatial tessellation of a remotely sensed land-use analysis we assigned each route to the corresponding hexagon (see below). A variety of spatial autocorrelation analyses

TABLE 1.   TOTAL VARIANCE ACCOUNTED FOR BY THE DECISION-TREE MODELS FOR INDIVIDUAL SPECIES

Species	% variance
Western Meadowlark	76.1
Dickcissel	71.8
Horned Lark	64.8
Eastern Meadowlark	64.6
Ring-necked Pheasant	62.5
Bobolink	62.3
Savannah Sparrow	59.6
Vesper Sparrow	59.0
Grasshopper Sparrow	52.1
Lark Bunting	51.6
Upland Sandpiper	41.3
Chestnut-collared Longspur	38.9
Baird's Sparrow	15.3
Gray Partridge	11.7
Long-billed Curlew	11.1
Henslow's Sparrow	3.7
McCown's Longspur	3.3

indicated that these assignments retained adequate spatial resolution for the purposes of our study. Data for 17 species were extracted for analysis on the basis of adequate data in our time period (Table 1).

Range estimates were derived from maps of breeding densities prepared by the Patuxent Wildlife Research Center from BBS data (Sauer et al. 1997). Images of each species' range were converted to raster coverages using a Geographic Information System. The proportion of North America sampled by the BBS that was occupied by the species was used as the range estimate for each species. Although this approach may underestimate the total range of some species, by excluding the southern- and northernmost extents, it is spatially consistent with the abundance data for each species, and in our analyses an underestimate of range for a widespread species would be a conservative error.

AGRICULTURE DATA

Agriculture data for each county came from the periodic Censuses of Agriculture (U.S. Department of Commerce, Bureau of the Census) and the annual National Agricultural Statistics Service (NASS) estimates (U.S. Department of Agriculture). We used the Censuses of Agriculture for 1974, 1978, 1982, and 1987 that contained summary statistics for thousands of agriculture variables for each county in the United States. Censuses of Agriculture include acreages of common crops (e.g., corn, cotton [*Gossypium* sp.], and hay) as well as of uncommon crops (e.g., mint [*Mentha* spp.] for oil, hops [*Humulus lupulus*], and kale [*Brassica oleracea*]). The NASS compiles annual estimates of agriculture for each county in the conterminous United States. Counties are grouped into crop-reporting districts by state and according to climate, cropping practices, and other variables (U.S. Department of Agriculture 1987). The NASS agricultural statistics include annual estimates of common crops, with total acreage planted, seeded, and harvested. Estimates of crops sown and harvested from 1972 to 1989 were included in our database. Thus, the NASS agricultural statistics provide data for years without direct Census of Agriculture information. Data on the county acreage of land enrolled in the Conservation Reserve Program (CRP), a federal program initiated in 1986 which retires cropland from production, were obtained from the Natural Resources Conservation Service and were included as an additional cropping variable.

WEATHER AND CLIMATE DATA

The primary weather and climate data used in the crop analyses were the Climatic Division Data from World WeatherDisc, a commercial product from WeatherDisc Associates, Inc. (Seattle, Washington). The WeatherDisc data we used covered the period 1961 through 1988; data from mid-1988 through 1990 came from the National Climatic Data Center. We used mean January and July temperatures and mean annual precipitation as parsimonious representatives of bird-relevant weather. We computed 30-yr averages for 1961–1990 to index long-term weather (i.e., climatic conditions) and computed the deviations of the annual values from these means as measures of short-term weather conditions. Thus, we had six climate or weather variables for each spatial unit in our analyses.

REMOTELY SENSED DATA

For a subsidiary analysis, we used data from O'Connor et al.'s (1996) regression tree analysis of bird distribution in relation to remotely sensed data. O'Connor et al. (1996) used data from the Loveland et al. (1991) land-cover prototype, supplemented with an urban layer from the Digital Chart of the World (Danko 1992). This chart classifies each 1-km^2 pixel in the United States in 1990 in one of 159 (160 with the urban class) land-cover classes, doing so on the basis of the seasonal Advanced Very High Resolution Radiometry (AVHRR) profile for that point. O'Connor et al. (1996) adopted the U.S. Environmental Protection Agency's (EPA) Environmental Monitoring and Assessment Program hexagonal grid (Overton et al. 1990, White et al. 1992) as a spatial framework for this analysis. Each hexagon is approximately 635 km^2, with a point-to-point (center-to-center) spacing of approximately 27 km. All environmental correlates were determined as values typifying each hexagon, using only the 1,198 hexagons with BBS data satisfying our data quality criteria. Although this hexagon-based sampling averages the environmental data over a fixed area, the point-to-point spacing of 27 km across hexagons is acceptable given the length of each BBS route (40 km).

O'Connor et al.'s (1996) approach captured spatial variation in landscape structure that might reflect habitat fragmentation and other land-use "stressors," doing so by calculating various metrics of spatial pattern developed under the rubric of "landscape ecology" (Turner and Gardner 1990). In this context, stressors were regarded as any measures, or metrics, reflecting negative impacts on species richness. Various landscape metrics were calculated from the landscape pattern delineated with AVHRR imagery. The distribution of pixels in each hexagon was analyzed by treating contiguous pixels as "patches" for which metrics such as dominance, contagion, fractal dimensions, connectivity, and patch and edge characteristics could be calculated (O'Neill et al. 1988). Three metrics were determined for each land-cover class in each hexagon: the average size of patches of that class, the size of the largest patch of that class, and the largest value of the patch perimeter calculated for all patches of that class. Where a land-cover class was absent from the hexagon, the corresponding metric was set to zero. In addition, the average patch size in each hexagon, irrespective of land-cover class, was computed. Four climatic variables were available from the analyses: long-term averages of January mean temperature, July mean temperature, and annual precipitation and an index of seasonality, which was computed as the within-pixel change between the January and July temperature values (for further details see O'Connor et al. 1996).

ANALYTICAL APPROACH

We programmed a Fortran version of the decision-tree algorithm of Sonquist et al. (1973; Knowledge Seeker, version 2.0) to assess the association of our independent variable, the count of species on a BBS route, with a set of independent variables spanning climate and cropping information. Counts of zero were fairly frequent, and consequently bird counts were first normalized by use of the random normal scores transformation (Bradley 1968). The decision-tree algorithm sorted the bird counts in the region on each independent variable in turn and determined the best threshold along this gradient that maximized the difference between the dependent variable values in the two subsets. For example, in evaluating wheat (*Triticum aestivum*) as a splitting variable, the BBS routes were ordered from those in the area with the lowest wheat acreage to those in the area with the highest wheat acreage. The data set was split at the median wheat value into a low-wheat group and a high-wheat group, and the normalized bird counts in the two groups were tested for significant difference ($P < 0.01$) by means of a t-test. The remaining explanatory variables were then analyzed and similarly tested. If more than one variable resulted in a significant difference between species counts in high and low groups, the variable explaining the greatest percentage of the variance in the set of routes was chosen and the routes were split into two subsamples at the threshold for that variable. The splitting process was repeated for each of the two groups, leading to the identification of four subsamples. The process was again repeated until no division of a group across any of the available variables resulted in a significant difference in average bird counts between subsamples. The final output was represented as a decision tree with a series of end-nodes whose values for species abundance were set by the chain of environmental conditions along the path back to the root node. This method identified the extent and pattern of correlation between dependent and independent variables, and in particular allowed for the occurrence of constraints and of contingent effects (Breiman et al. 1984).

We summarized the output of the algorithm by computing the proportion of variance accounted for by a given model and by dividing this variance among the individual explanatory variables present in the final model (Clark and Pregibon 1992). To incorporate sampling variance in our estimates, we used a bootstrapping approach (Efron 1982) to select repeated random samples of the data set for analysis and reported the median percentage of variance in the data set explained by each variable over all bootstrap replicates. Preliminary analysis suggested that 60-plus bootstrap replicates were needed to stabilize the variance of these medians. Our final analyses were based on 100 bootstrap replicates.

We analyzed data for each odd-numbered year from 1973 through 1989. Differences in results between years arose for two reasons: because some variables were mutually correlated and varied from year to year, or because the true association of a species with a variable changed substantially from year to year because of changes in cropping practices, weather, or other variables.

Because of the computational complexity of the method, not every explanatory variable was considered in the tree construction for every species. An abbreviated screening analysis, based on 10 bootstrap samples of the data set, was performed first for each species for 1973, 1979, 1985, and 1989. This analysis was used to determine which variables were likely to be statistically significant in the final analysis. A full analysis, based on 100 bootstrap samples, was then performed on data from every other year using variables that had been identified in the initial screening analysis. The final results considered 30 variables that could potentially explain the BBS counts in each year examined (Table 2). Twenty-two variables measured land use (percent of county land planted in a crop and CRP acreage); three measured climate (30-yr averages of annual precipitation and January and July temperatures); three measured weather (deviation from 30-yr averages of annual precipitation and January and July temperatures); and two were geographic variables (latitude and longitude). Measurements of most explanatory variables were available from 1973 through 1989, but occasionally a variable had to be omitted for a year in which its value was unreported.

We also examined the environmental correlates, derived from the remotely sensed data, of temporal incidence for each grassland species using the regression tree modules of the S-plus statistical package (MathSoft Inc., Seattle, Washington). We used cross-validation techniques to optimize the fit of each regression tree (Clark and Pregibon 1992), an approach preferable to the bootstrap sampling we used in the crop analyses (Breiman et al. 1984). For these analyses incorporating landscape metrics, we report the percent mean deviance explained as a measure of the goodness-of-fit equivalent to an R^2 value (S. Urquhart, pers. comm.).

RESULTS

GOODNESS-OF-FIT OF MODELS

The percentage of variance explained by each species model ranged from 76.1% for Western Meadowlark (*Sturnella neglecta*) to 3.3% for McCown's Longspur (Table 1). The models fell into two groups: 12 species whose models accounted for 38% or more of the variance in abundance and 5 species whose models accounted for less than 20% of the variance (Table 1).

We were interested in determining whether the range in the variance explained by each of these 17 models might be a scale phenomenon (Table 1). Given the spatially extensive nature of variables such as climate and common crop acreages, a wide-ranging species might be expected to adapt to one or more of these variables, whereas a restricted-range species might simply incorporate the variation in these same variables across its range as a constant (Allen and Starr 1982). If this were the case, one would expect model fit to be correlated with range size across species. We tested this hypothesis by computing the Spearman rank correlation of model fit (as percent variance explained) with the proportion of the North American BBS area occupied by the species and found a strong correlation to support this explanation (Spearman rho = 0.733, $P < 0.002$).

PREDICTOR VARIABLES

The variables that appeared in most species models were mean annual precipitation (15 spe-

TABLE 2. NUMBER OF SPECIES SHOWING CORRELATION WITH INDIVIDUAL VARIABLES AND SUMMARY STATISTICS FOR CORRESPONDING SPECIES VARIANCES FOR EACH VARIABLE

Variable (+/− effect)	Number of species	Species effect (% variance explained)					Median rank
		Mean	SD	Minimum	Maximum	Years	
Mean annual precip. (−)	15	7.2	11.52	0.05	36.4	9	3.0
CRP (+)	10	6.1	6.05	0.80	19.6	2	4.5
January climate (−)	13	4.2	10.04	0.05	37.4	9	10.0
Sorghum (+)	12	4.0	8.23	0.05	29.9	9	7.0
Latitude (+)	13	3.9	7.06	0.05	26.0	9	7.0
July climate (m)	12	3.8	4.30	0.05	16.2	9	6.0
Longitude (+)	13	3.8	3.32	0.05	11.1	9	5.0
Durum wheat (+)	7	3.5	8.77	0.05	23.4	6	3.0
Grain corn (+)	11	2.9	2.90	0.05	8.4	9	5.0
Wheat (+)	8	2.9	3.56	0.05	9.4	4	4.5
Oats (+)	10	2.5	3.20	0.70	10.5	9	15.0
January weather (m)	11	1.7	1.32	0.05	5.4	9	5.0
All hay (+)	7	1.5	1.27	0.05	3.8	4	6.0
Soybeans (+)	13	1.5	1.61	0.05	5.1	9	10.0
Winter wheat (+)	12	1.4	1.29	0.05	4.0	9	9.0
Spring wheat (+)	8	1.4	3.06	0.05	8.9	5.5	6.0
Alfalfa (+)	7	1.3	0.56	0.70	2.3	4	11.0
Sunflowers (+)	5	1.2	1.29	0.05	3.2	5	14.0
Barley (m)	10	1.2	0.67	0.05	2.5	9	13.0
Other hay (m)	6	1.2	0.31	0.80	1.7	4	15.5
Deviation precip. (+)	10	1.0	0.42	0.05	1.7	9	10.5
July weather (+)	9	1.0	0.55	0.05	2.0	9	12.0
Tobacco (m)	1	0.9	0.90	0.90	0.9	9	23.0
Corn silage (+)	8	0.8	0.53	0.05	1.4	9	11.5
Cotton (−)	3	0.7	0.56	0.20	1.3	9	22.0
Beans (+)	1	0.6	0.60	0.60	0.6	8	17.0
Peanuts (−)	2	0.6	0.07	0.60	0.7	8.5	20.0
Potatoes (+)	4	0.5	0.32	0.05	0.8	4	17.5
Sugar beets (+)	3	0.3	0.49	0.05	0.9	2	9.0
Flaxseed (+)	5	0.2	0.42	0.05	1.0	2	10.0

Note: "Years" is the median of the number of years for which the variable was a correlate of the individual species (maximum 9 odd-numbered years, 1973–1989). Median rank was computed by ranking all variables in each species model as 1, 2, etc., by size and taking the median for each variable across species. Signs in parentheses indicate the dominant direction of the effect of the variable; "m" indicates mixed effects. "Climate" refers to 30-yr mean temperatures; "weather" refers to deviations about these means.

cies, accounting on average for 7.2% of the variance), mean January temperature (13 species, average effect 4.2%), latitude and longitude (13 species each, with average effects of 3.9 and 3.8%, respectively), soybeans (13 species, average effect 1.5%), and sorghum (*Sorghum vulgare*; 12 species, average effect 4.0%; Table 2). Note that these are highly summarized estimators. The effects of each variable considered were estimated in each of the nine annual models (alternate years from 1973 through 1989) computed for each species; the median of these annual effects for the variable was tabulated as a summary statistic for the species; and the species-specific medians were averaged across those species with non-zero medians as a summary statistic of the influence of that variable. In calculating these averages, species with no correlation with the variable were omitted rather than treated as zeros. We omitted these species because the magnitude of effect is of most in-

terest for species correlated with that variable, whereas the proportion of species associated with the variable could be summarized separately. For individual species, both the median effects and the effects in individual years were often much higher (see below). It is important to remember that these effects are statistical correlates and may be directly responsible for the response or may have an indirect effect, the latter occurring in the case of variables that may be highly correlated with an unmeasured variable (in sensu "surrogacy" of Breiman et al. 1984).

The number of species correlated with a variable and the average size of the correlation effect were themselves broadly correlated, but there were a few exceptions (Table 2). Soybeans (13 species), winter wheat (*Triticum* sp.; 12 species), and perhaps barley (*Hordeum vulgare*; 10 species) all appeared in more of the species models than was typical for their mean effects

(Table 2). This was also true for the three weather variables—deviations from long-term mean January and July temperatures and from long-term annual precipitation—but this was likely due to correlated responses by all the species to regional weather in individual years. Conversely, some variables had atypically few species correlates (Table 2), most notably the level of CRP enrollment in the county, a variable with strong effects on certain species (Lauber 1991, Johnson and Schwartz 1993). CRP data were available in our analyses only for 1987 and 1989, and the low representation of the CRP enrollment variable surely reflects that fact. Durum wheat (*T. durum*; 7 species, average effect 3.5%), wheat (8 species, average effect 2.9%), and all hay (7 species, average effect 1.5%), however, were under-represented variables that lacked such obvious analysis bias by way of explanation. Some variables, such as tobacco (*Nicotiana tabacum*), beans (Leguminosae), and peanuts (*Arachis hypogea*), were only weakly correlated with just one or two species (Table 2).

As a measure of the consistency of these associations between species and crop or environmental variables, we tallied the number of years in which the correlation was significantly nonzero for each species (maximum of 9 odd-numbered years, 1973–1989). In most cases, strongly correlated variables had the most consistent results, occurring in all years for all species (acknowledging that the CRP variable could appear in at most 2 yr for each species). The exceptions were durum wheat, wheat, and all hay, all of which appeared only in four of the year-specific models and in fewer species models than might have been expected.

Conversely, some variables (e.g., cotton [*Gossypium*] and corn silage) had weak effects but appeared consistently in the annual species models (Table 2). The remaining cases with lower numbers of years with effects were all variables with weak overall effects and with eight or fewer species correlates. Most crops were positively associated with the abundance of the species with which they were correlated (Table 2); only peanuts and cotton, both minor influences, were consistently negative. January climate and mean annual precipitation had negative correlations with most species, but July climate had different effects with different species. Weather effects were likewise variable; warm summers and wet years favored most species, but January weather was more varied in its effects.

As previously noted, the distribution of the variance explained by all models was bimodal. It was possible that the importance of some variables in well-fitting models was diluted by weak associations of those same variables with species with poor-fitting models. We therefore addressed the question of whether certain variables might not be consistently the most important variable (largest variance explained) across many species, irrespective of the size of the variance explained by the variable. We ranked the variables in each species model based on the size of the contribution to explained variance to obtain the median ranks across all species (Table 2). This ranking revealed a consistent pattern: certain variables (e.g., mean annual precipitation and extent of durum wheat cultivation) were generally the strongest predictors in individual grassland bird species models; CRP, cultivation of wheat or grain corn, annual January temperature, and longitude were usually the five strongest predictor variables for individual species. Spring wheat (*Triticum* sp.), hay, and sorghum production, July climate, and latitude were also fairly high ranking variables. Other variables, notably beans, potatoes (*Solanum tuberosum*), peanuts, cotton, and tobacco, were typically low-ranking predictors for most species (Table 2). Most crop correlates were again positive and most weather and climate correlates negative (Table 2).

Examination of the major correlates (i.e., variables accounting for > 5% of the median variance explained) for each species showed clear patterns when summarized across species. Agriculture and climate variables had substantial effects in the breeding distribution of all 17 species, whereas geographic and weather variables had substantial effects in only 11 and 6 species, respectively (Table 3). Similar patterns were observed after grouping all predictor variables into three categories (agricultural, climatic, and geographic [latitude/longitude]) and ranking them by total variance explained for each species (Table 4). Agriculture variables were dominant for eight species (Gray Partridge [*Perdix perdix*], Ring-necked Pheasant [*Phasianus colchicus*], Upland Sandpiper [*Bartramia longicauda*], Grasshopper Sparrow, Baird's Sparrow [*Ammodramus bairdii*], Henslow's Sparrow [*A. henslowii*], Chestnut-collared Longspur [*Calcarius ornatus*], and Dickcissel [*Spiza americana*]); climate variables for six species (Long-billed Curlew [*Numenius americanus*], Horned Lark [*Eremophila alpestris*], Lark Bunting [*Calamospiza melanocorys*], McCown's Longspur, Bobolink [*Dolichonyx oryzivorous*], and Western Meadowlark); and geographic variables for only one species (Savannah Sparrow [*Ammodramus savannarum*]). Two species (Vesper Sparrow [*Pooecetes gramineus*] and Eastern Meadowlark [*Sturnella magna*]) had models in which agriculture and climatic variables accounted for sim-

TABLE 3. VARIABLES ACCOUNTING FOR AT LEAST 5% OF THE MEDIAN VARIANCE EXPLAINED FOR EACH SPECIES

Species	Predictor variables
Gray Partridge	sunflower (+), CRP (+), durum wheat (+), January climate (−), all hay
Ring-necked Pheasant	CRP (+), grain corn (+), wheat (+), latitude (+), mean annual precipitation
Upland Sandpiper	sunflower (+), durum wheat (+), mean annual precipitation, sorghum, flaxseed, January weather, CRP, longitude
Long-billed Curlew	mean annual precipitation (−), January climate (−), longitude (+), winter wheat (+), soybeans, spring wheat
Horned Lark	mean annual precipitation (−), CRP (+), wheat, soybeans, grain corn, winter wheat
Vesper Sparrow	spring wheat (+), January climate (−), latitude (+), mean annual precipitation, oats
Lark Bunting	mean annual precipitation (−), longitude (m), July climate, January climate, spring wheat, January weather
Savannah Sparrow	latitude (+), oats (+), January climate, sorghum, July climate
Grasshopper Sparrow	CRP (+), grain corn (+), wheat, all hay, January weather, cotton, July weather, sorghum, mean annual precipitation
Baird's Sparrow	durum wheat (+), latitude (+), mean annual precipitation (−), soybeans, wheat
Henslow's Sparrow	grain corn (+), July climate (−), potatoes (+)
McCown's Longspur	mean annual precipitation (−), corn silage (−)
Chestnut-collared Longspur	durum wheat (+), longitude (+), mean annual precipitation (−), spring wheat, flaxseed, soybeans
Dickcissel	sorghum (+), longitude (+), July climate, January weather, soybeans, all hay
Bobolink	January climate (−), longitude (−), oats
Eastern Meadowlark	July climate (+), January weather (m), grain corn, longitude, latitude, all hay, sorghum, mean annual precipitation
Western Meadowlark	mean annual precipitation (−), CRP (+), January weather (m)

Note: Variables accounting for at least 10% of the median variance show direction of effect in parentheses; effects are positive (+), negative (−), or mixed (m). Data on the Conservation Reserve Program (CRP) were available only for 1987 and 1989. "Climate" refers to 30-yr mean temperatures; "weather" refers to deviations about these means.

TABLE 4. RELATIVE IMPORTANCE OF VARIABLE GROUPINGS (AGRICULTURE, CLIMATE, AND GEOGRAPHIC) FOR EACH SPECIES

Species	\[Rank\] 1	N	2	N	3	N
Dickcissel	Agriculture (42.2%)	10	Climate (18.8%)	6	LatLong (10.8%)	2
Ring-necked Pheasant	Agriculture (40.3%)	15	Climate (13.4%)	5	LatLong (8.9%)	2
Vesper Sparrow	Agriculture (26.3%)	12	Climate (22.8%)	6	LatLong (9.9%)	2
Grasshopper Sparrow	Agriculture (33.1%)	16	Climate (14.7%)	6	LatLong (4.0%)	2
Upland Sandpiper	Agriculture (27.0%)	12	Climate (11.4%)	6	LatLong (2.9%)	2
Chestnut-collared Longspur	Agriculture (28.4%)	7	LatLong (6.9%)	1	Climate (3.7%)	1
Baird's Sparrow	Agriculture (11.9%)	3	LatLong (1.9%)	1	Climate (1.5%)	1
Gray Partridge	Agriculture (9.8%)	9	Climate (1.8%)	1	LatLong (0.14%)	1
Henslow's Sparrow	Agriculture (2.2%)	2	Climate (1.5%)	1	—	—
Western Meadowlark	Climate (50.3%)	6	Agriculture (17.6%)	9	LatLong (8.2%)	2
Horned Lark	Climate (35.9%)	6	Agriculture (24.9%)	12	LatLong (4.1%)	2
Eastern Meadowlark	Climate (29.9%)	7	Agriculture (27.1%)	17	LatLong (7.6%)	2
Bobolink	Climate (42.4%)	5	Agriculture (11.2%)	8	LatLong (8.6%)	2
Lark Bunting	Climate (29.1%)	5	LatLong (13.5%)	1	Agriculture (8.8%)	7
Long-billed Curlew	Climate (6.0%)	2	Agriculture (2.9%)	5	LatLong (2.1%)	2
McCown's Longspur	Climate (2.9%)	1	Agriculture (0.4%)	1	—	—
Savannah Sparrow	LatLong (26.7%)	2	Agriculture (19.3%)	9	Climate (13.7%)	6

Note: Total variance explained for each category, in parentheses, was calculated by summing across each category's variables. The number of variables that contributed to each category is given as N.

TABLE 5.   RELATIVE IMPORTANCE OF LAND-COVER AND PATCH VARIABLES IN DIFFERENT HABITATS

	Anderson land covers	Frequency of correlations (negative)			
Class	Type	Land-cover variables	Patch variables	Total variables	% patch variables
4	grass-dominated	7(1)	6(1)	13	46
1	cropland and pasture	4	8(1)	12	67
3	woodland/cropland	3	7(2)	10	70
9	mixed (decid./conif.) forest	3	4(2)	7	57
6	mixed grass/shrub rangeland	2(1)	2	4	50
7	deciduous forest	3	1	4	25
5	shrub-dominated rangeland	1	0	1	0
8	coniferous forest	0	1	1	100
14	urban	1	0	1	0
2	grassland/cropland	1	0	1	0
Totals		25(2)	29(6)	54	54

ilar amounts of the explained variation (Table 4). Of these three categories, geographic variables typically (11 of 17 species) accounted for the least amount of explained variation (Table 4).

Among climate variables, it is interesting to note the lower median ranking of January weather (annual deviation from long-term mean temperature) than of January climate (mean temperature) values (median rank of 5 versus 10; Table 2). This was the result of a markedly bimodal distribution of ranks for January climate. For six species (Gray Partridge, Long-billed Curlew, Vesper Sparrow, Lark Bunting, Savannah Sparrow, and Bobolink), January climate was among the top four most significant variables (Table 3). For another group of seven species (Ring-necked Pheasant, Upland Sandpiper, Horned Lark, Grasshopper Sparrow, Dickcissel, and Eastern and Western meadowlarks), January climate appeared only at rank 10 or higher, indicating that the variable had only a peripheral or local effect in the decision trees involved. For all 13 of these species except Gray Partridge and Long-billed Curlew, however, January weather also appeared in the species models, as a subsidiary modifier to climate effects for four of the species above (Vesper Sparrow, Lark Bunting, Savannah Sparrow, and Bobolink) and as a variable dominant to climate for the last seven species. For species wintering in Central and South America, these correlations must be due to indirect effects.

When considering other weather and climate variables, annual precipitation had the strongest effects. For Horned Lark, Lark Bunting, and Western Meadowlark, long-term annual precipitation was far more important ($R^2 = 29.3$, 15.0, and 32.0%, respectively) than January climate. July climate had a large effect only for Eastern Meadowlark ($R^2 = 14.3\%$), though Horned Lark, Lark Bunting, and Western Meadowlark

all had high-ranking contributions (range 4–6%). Annual variation in July temperature had its strongest link with Grasshopper Sparrow (but only at $R^2 = 3.2\%$), and variation in annual precipitation was weakly linked (approximately 2%) with Upland Sandpiper, Dickcissel, and Eastern and Western meadowlarks.

An analysis of satellite-derived land-use and land-pattern variables yielded regression tree models of the incidence of each species over a set of 1,198 BBS routes in the conterminous United States (Table 5). Incidence is the proportion of surveys on each BBS route in which a species was recorded between 1981 and 1990. For most species, incidence and abundance were well correlated (Wright 1991). The independent variables considered were climatic data, proportions of each land-cover class (of 160 classes) around each route, and various pattern metrics of patch size and edge characteristics of the landscape around each route. The data set is described in more detail in O'Connor et al. 1996. The frequency of occurrence of land-use and land-pattern variables that occurred in the regression tree models is summarized across all 17 species (Table 5). To avoid excessive detail, the summary collapses the 160 land-cover classes used in the analyses to the 14 classes of an Anderson et al. (1976) Level II classification. Thus, the incidence of seven species was correlated with the extent of one of the grass-dominated habitats that comprise the Anderson land-cover Class 4 (Table 5). Of these correlates, only one was negative. Similarly, six species models contained a statistical dependence on one of the patch attributes of habitat in land-cover Class 4, with five species more abundant and one less abundant in areas with larger patches of this cover type (Table 5).

Some evidence suggests that habitat patch features may be significant in certain land clas-

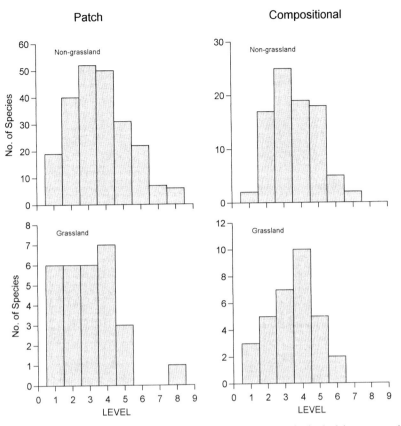

FIGURE 1. Frequency distributions of the level (e.g., level 1 is the root node) in decision-tree models at which patch variables and proportion of land-class (i.e., compositional) variables act. Grassland bird species show a significant skew to the left for patch variables and a significant skew to the right for compositional variables.

ses (Table 5). Overall, patch variables occurred more frequently in the models (53.7%) than did land-cover variables (Table 5). However, these patch correlates were more frequently influential in the Anderson Level II land classes not dominated by grass or rangeland, and particularly so in those classes with five or more correlations in total (Classes 1, 3, and 9). As expected, Class 4 (grass dominated) had the most correlations for grassland species; in this and the two rangeland classes, patch variables provided about half the predictors of species incidence (8 of 18 correlates). Patch variables were in the minority (1 of 4, or 25%) in Class 7 (deciduous forest). Among the four classes with most correlations, 46% of the correlations were patch related in Class 4, but 66% (19 of 29) were patch related in Classes 1, 3, and 9. The sample sizes were too small to obtain significant results even with the marked imbalance between land classes.

We analyzed the significance of patch variables for grassland species further, by comparing the relative influence of patch and land-proportion (compositional) variables in models for grassland and for all other species in the BBS (R. J. O'Connor, unpubl. data). We considered only those species with models involving either of these variable types. We plotted the frequency with which patch variables had their effect at the root level (level 1) of their trees, at the next level down (level 2), and so on (Fig. 1). Variables acting nearer the root of a regression tree have a more widespread, and usually stronger, influence than do variables acting deeper in the tree. A comparison of patch variables for nongrassland and grassland species showed a significant skew to the left for grassland species (Wilcoxon test, $P = 0.012$; Fig. 1). Similarly, a comparison of the location of action of associations involving the proportion of land class present in the hexagon showed the reverse: grassland species had compositional variables acting farther away from the tree root than did other species (Wilcoxon test, $P = 0.028$; Fig. 1). These results confirm the idea that patch variables were more critical, and compositional variables less critical, in the distribution of grassland species than of other species.

DISCUSSION

Grassland bird distributions at the spatially extensive scale of our analyses were markedly influenced first by crop distribution, second by climate, and third by habitat patch size and shape (Tables 2 and 4).

CROP CORRELATES

Areas of extensive cultivation of sorghum, wheat, and grain corn were generally favorable to grassland bird species. Correlations with these crops were among the largest contributors of variance explained in many species models and, for at least some species, explained much of the variance. Several other crops, either more regional in distribution or only locally grown, were likewise positively associated with the abundance of grassland species but contributed less to the overall variance explained and had low ranking in the individual regression trees. This last feature can be summarized as reflecting local modification of predictions, with these variables having only local effects in regions where abundance was set by constraints imposed by other crop or climate variables.

Our results suggest that farmers' choices about cropping practices have implications for grassland species at several levels. First, it is clear that high enrollment in the CRP has major benefits for grassland birds. Despite our having only 2 yr of CRP data, many species were more abundant in CRP areas than in non-CRP areas, and several species, notably Gray Partridge and Ring-necked Pheasant, showed strong positive associations with CRP enrollment, which were consistent with previous analysis of BBS data with respect to the CRP (Lauber 1991). Lauber found that many species showed spatial associations of density with CRP enrollment but that many of these correlations were apparent even prior to the advent of the CRP. However, he was able to show that for several species, including Ring-necked Pheasant and Western Meadowlark, densities increased differentially in these areas with the advent of the CRP. A possible explanation for high densities in what later proved to be areas of high CRP enrollment may well be that these have long been areas of high soil erosion; enrollment by farmers in earlier "set-aside" programs to reduce erosion could have favored grassland species by the cessation of tillage operations inimical to the birds' success (Lauber 1991). Lauber's analyses of temporal trends are supported by the results of detailed studies of use of CRP fields in particular regions. Johnson and Schwartz (1993) found that several prairie species with restricted ranges (particularly Lark Bunting, Grasshopper and Baird's sparrows, Dickcissel, and Bobolink) were less abundant on annually tilled cropland than on CRP lands and that many of these species had previously been declining in the central United States. The only grassland species they found to be less abundant on CRP than on non-CRP lands were Vesper Sparrow and Chestnut-collared Longspur, both of which prefer sparse vegetation.

A second conclusion to be drawn from our findings in relation to cropping is that the spatially extensive cultivation of certain crops, notably sorghum, grain corn, and wheat, may create agricultural environments conducive to breeding for grassland birds. We do not claim that these crops are necessarily favorable through cause and effect; instead, they may share with grassland birds environmental requirements we did not directly measure (e.g., topography, soil type). Alternatively, the cultivation practices and associated land-management patterns may create conditions favorable to these birds. Long-billed Curlews apparently do well in wheat fields in Oklahoma that are subjected only to spraying (Shackford 1994), and Horned Larks have long been known to thrive in cultivated fields (Graber and Graber 1963). The benefits of particular crops need not accrue solely to breeding birds; certain crops modify the effects of snow cover in winter, permitting foraging to continue in fields where other vegetation would trap the snow in an impenetrable mass (Larsen et al. 1994). For some grassland birds, small grains may approximate a natural grassland, as shown by Warner (1994) for Ring-necked Pheasants; only Horned Larks, however, appear capable of persisting in a monoculture of cereal crops (Owens and Myres 1973). It is also possible that cultivation maintains ephemeral conditions that some species prefer. Grasshopper Sparrows favor open grasslands providing openings and gaps through which the birds can move while foraging (Whitmore 1981), and open-planted crops may provide an adequate substitute. Chestnut-collared Longspurs, however, though needing open vegetation in which to forage, will not nest in cultivated fields (Owens and Myres 1973).

The third point to be drawn from our crop analyses is that some crops—among them soybeans, oats (*Avena*), alfalfa, sunflowers (*Helianthus* spp.), and barley—appeared only as local modifiers of species distributions already largely constrained by other factors. Some of these may be chance correlations; sunflowers, for example, are grown mainly in the Dakotas, and their correlations with species with ranges centered in this region may be due to confounding effects. Barley and soybeans, however, consistently displayed the same correlations from year to year (Table 2), so they may have a more ecological basis. Some of these small correlations probably reflect use of the crop as an adequate substitute for native habitat; thus the correlation of durum wheat with Baird's Sparrow (Table 3) may result from the species using this crop as a source of vegetative cover in what is otherwise an agricultural waste (Owens and Myres 1973).

INFLUENCE OF CLIMATE

The pattern of influence of climate variables in our analysis is of considerable interest given Root's (1988a) demonstration of the power of climatic limits to constrain winter bird distribution. We found that in most grassland bird species there were significant associations between climate and weather variables and local breeding abundance. Breeding-season analyses of climate influences on bird populations are more likely to be mediated indirectly (e.g., by climate influence on productivity; Rotenberry et al. 1995). Currie (1991) hypothesized that the latitudinal gradient in breeding-species richness was set largely by the corresponding productivity gradient. In contrast, wintering-distribution limits appear to be very close to those set by a model of physiological limits to maximum daily metabolic rates for resident species (Root 1988a). Among the seven species for which a climate variable was the largest correlate of breeding distribution, only that for the Bobolink involved winter climate (Table 3). Because Bobolinks winter in South America, however, winter temperatures in the United States cannot be directly related to their abundance; whatever effects winter temperatures have on Bobolinks must therefore be indirect. Price (1995) reached the same conclusion from his model of the climate envelope of the Bobolink.

Our other major climate effects largely differ from those reported by Price (1995). Our results implied that Eastern Meadowlarks were more abundant in hot summer areas (Table 3), but Price (1995) found a complex pattern of responses to temperature for this species, with quadratic functions of mixed sign describing dependencies on temperatures in summer and in the wettest month of the year. Where we found negative effects of annual precipitation for Horned Lark, Lark Bunting, and Western Meadowlark, Price (1995) reported generally negative effects only for Lark Bunting. For Horned Lark he found positive effects of precipitation in spring and in the coldest month, and for Western

Meadowlark his largest terms were positive contributions from precipitation in winter and in the hottest and driest month but with negative terms for other seasonal components of precipitation. Thus, the overall effect of precipitation on Western Meadowlarks depends on the distribution of seasonality of that precipitation. It is also worth noting here how different methods yield different answers to what is apparently the same general question of climate correlates. Price (1995) derived a single climate envelope for the entire range of each species, producing rules applicable over the entire range but expressed in strongly seasonal aspects of climate. Our study modeled regional abundance in terms of less seasonal climate variables using CART. Walker (1990) has previously shown how the climate envelope and CART approaches yield complementary perspectives on the environmental correlates of species distribution and has pioneered their integration into a common model.

Root's (1988a, b) work focused on the correlation of wintering limits with midwinter climate conditions. She has elsewhere identified the lack of knowledge about breeding limits as a critical gap in our understanding of environmental constraints on birds (Root 1993). We found that, for several species, breeding densities were also correlated with midwinter climates, with fewer breeding pairs where winters are cold (Table 2); however, winter climate was a major predictor only for the Bobolink, a neotropical migrant (Table 3). Whereas climatic constraint by January temperatures was clearly widespread across species (Table 2), year-to-year variation in January temperatures also appeared regularly and at some strength in species models. The bimodal distribution of ranks for January climate, in combination with consistent effects for January weather, revealed the existence of one group of species with breeding distributions sensitive to midwinter climate conditions (Gray Partridge, Long-billed Curlew, Vesper Sparrow, Lark Bunting, Savannah Sparrow, and Bobolink) and a second group (Ring-necked Pheasant, Upland Sandpiper, Horned Lark, Grasshopper Sparrow, Dickcissel, and Eastern and Western meadowlarks) more sensitive to year-to-year variation in conditions. Dickcissels have long been known to be sensitive to annual variations in winter conditions, largely because poor winters may constrain the rate of progression of the spring migration northward (Fretwell 1986). Our findings suggest that other grassland bird species may share a similar sensitivity. For resident species such as Gray Partridge and Ring-necked Pheasant, however, winter conditions can have direct effects; heavy precipitation as snow covers the ground, and food resources for overwintering become limiting (Riley 1995).

Our results suggest that summer temperature limits are not as important for grassland birds as studies suggest they are for other groups of birds (Blake et al. 1992, O'Connor 1992). Similarly, Price (1995) found only 7 of 23 species to be correlated either with summer temperatures or with temperatures in the hottest month, generally with negative effects evident. The link with drought identified by Blake et al. (1992) is congruent with the importance of precipitation associations found here. July temperatures typically may be associated with drought, such that our analyses attribute variations in density to variations in precipitation rather than to temperature. Drought effects appear to be rather short-lived in grassland birds, with most species recovering within 1 yr (George et al. 1992). It is tempting to suggest that the absence of summer temperature links is because grassland birds redistribute themselves each year in line with the prevailing distribution of weather-controlled resources, as argued previously of Dickcissels by Fretwell (1986). If this were the case, one might expect a pattern of strong correlations with the weather variables considered here instead of the lack of correlations we found (Table 2). Therefore, we consider whether breeding distributions might not instead be constrained in a climate envelope by the distribution of habitat.

INFLUENCE OF PATCH VARIABLES

Our analyses lend considerable support to earlier research that suggested that grassland birds are particularly sensitive to habitat fragmentation. Area sensitivity is well established. Samson (1980) and Johnson and Temple (1986) concluded that small fragments of grasslands cannot support species that need interior habitats, and Vickery et al. (1994) and Herkert (1994) have shown through site-specific studies that grassland birds are more likely to occur on large patches of grassland habitat than on small ones. Vickery et al. (1994) demonstrated area sensitivity for Upland Sandpipers, Vesper, Savannah, and Grasshopper sparrows, Bobolinks, and Eastern Meadowlarks. Our results expand these studies in two significant ways. First, we found that grassland bird species as a class are more influenced by habitat patch variables, and less influenced by land-use proportions in an area, than are other bird species (Fig. 1). Patch variables are present significantly higher in the regression tree models for grassland species than for other species, thus ensuring that they affect proportionately more of the survey area and that they constrain distributions more than does landscape

composition. Thus, grassland species are differentially susceptible to habitat fragmentation.

Second, we raise the possibility that patch variables are more influential in habitats less dominated by grass (Table 5). A differential toward stronger association of incidence and patch variables in nongrassland habitats implies that patch configuration or size issues have become more important in the cropland and wooded areas that have replaced native prairies. To our knowledge, no one has previously suggested that species might be more acutely selective in less favored habitats than in preferred habitats, though it is a logical outcome of more general phenomena such as the habitat hierarchies of Brown (1969) and Fretwell and Lucas (1969). One might expect that birds using secondary habitats would be more selective as to which parts of these habitats they use if they are unable to settle in their preferred habitats. In their study in Maine, Vickery et al. (1994) noted that the grassland species they studied may have favored grassland-barrens rather than hayfields and pastures simply because grassland-barrens were the principal source of large expanses of grassland habitat.

If grassland habitats are generally becoming scarcer in North America, and particularly in agricultural areas (Askins 1993, Warner 1994), birds are likely to use near-equivalent patches of cropland and other nonnatural habitat (Litvaitis 1993, Vickery et al. 1994) but to require larger areas of such before settling there. Thus, With (1994) suggests that the natural habitat of McCown's Longspur in native short-grass prairies has now become a mosaic of pastures variably grazed by cattle and fragmented by agricultural activities and human development, and that the species may treat heavily grazed pastures as near approximations of the original habitat. In cropland-pasture, one would expect larger patches to be favored over smaller ones. Similarly, Warner (1994) found that the diversity of grassland species was highest on those study sites closest to grassland. Warner also demonstrated that Ring-necked Pheasant nests hatched more successfully the greater the amount of grassland (whether strip cover, forage crops, or small grains) surrounding the nest. These studies indicate how the increased influence of patch variables in secondary habitats might arise, under the assumption that these habitats are being used by populations displaced from preferred grassland habitats.

A more alarmist interpretation is also possible: some of the scarcer grassland species may display greater apparent selectivity simply because there are now so few individuals remaining that they fill only the better components of the available habitats (O'Connor 1981, Vickery et al. 1994). Whatever the processes underlying the pattern, our findings endorse the need to preserve remaining large plots of grassland habitats and to consolidate smaller patches in management efforts. The role of the CRP may be critical in this regard.

A CAUTIONARY NOTE

An important reservation about the findings here, not only for crop variables but for climate and habitat patch analyses, is that the CART models we used, despite their sophistication, return only estimates of correlations. Therefore, our conclusions are subject to the normal caveats of correlation analysis, in particular that correlation does not ensure causation. Some conclusions are likely to be stronger than first apparent with a correlation analysis. Our emphasis on patch variables and on CRP effects are each based on analyses with very different biases than in the site-specific studies of Vickery et al. (1994) and Herkert (1994) for area sensitivity and of Johnson and Schwartz (1993) for the CRP. Hence, our arrival at a similar assessment of the importance of these variables for grassland bird species lends strength to all the studies; different sources of bias are unlikely to yield similar conclusions in the absence of a real ecological effect. The broad spatial extent of our analyses and their replication across multiple years provide a robust overview of the correlates of grassland bird distribution that has hitherto been unavailable. Our results highlight particular patterns of correlation as deserving of further attention and raise some important new questions about constraints on the distribution of grassland bird species.

ACKNOWLEDGMENTS

We thank C. Hunsaker, S. Timmons, and B. Jackson (Oak Ridge National Laboratory) for providing landscape metrics and G. Nielsen (U.S. EPA, Corvallis, Oregon) for data from the Historical Climate Network climate databank. We thank D. White for help in using the climate data. We thank S. Moulton for secretarial support. R. J. O'Connor was supported by a National Research Council Senior Research Fellowship at the U.S. EPA, Corvallis, Oregon, while on sabbatical leave from the University of Maine 1993–1994. We acknowledge the following financial support for this work: U.S. EPA Cooperative Agreements CR 818843-01-0 and CR 823806-01-0 (RJOC, MTJ) and U.S. Department of Agriculture Forest Service Cooperative Agreement PNW 93-0462 (RJOC and MTJ). Additional financial support came from a consortium of agrochemical corporations: American Cyanamid, CIBA-Geigy, E. I. Dupont de Nemours and Company, FMC Corporation, Mobay, and Rhône-Poulenc.

LITERATURE CITED

ALLEN, T. F. H, AND T. B. STARR. 1982. Hierarchy: perspectives for ecological complexity. University of Chicago Press, Chicago, IL.

ANDERSON, J. R., E. E. HARDY, J. T. ROACH, AND R. E. WITMER. 1976. A land use and land cover classification system for use with remote sensor data. U.S. Geological Survey Professional Paper 964.

ASKINS, R. A. 1993. Population trends in grassland, shrubland, and forest birds in eastern North America. Current Ornithology 11:1–34.

BLAKE, J. G., G. J. NIEMI, AND J. M. HANOWSKI. 1992. Drought and annual variation in bird populations. Pp. 419–430 *in* J. M. Hagan III and D. W. Johnston (editors). Ecology and conservation of neotropical migrant landbirds. Smithsonian Institution Press, Washington, D.C.

BRADLEY, J. V. 1968. Distribution-free statistical tests. Prentice-Hall, Englewood Cliffs, NJ.

BREIMAN, L., J. H. FRIEDMAN, R. A. OLSHEN, AND C. J. STONE. 1984. Classification and regression trees. Wadsworth, Belmont, CA.

BROWN, J. H. 1984. On the relationship between abundance and distribution of species. American Naturalist 124:255–279.

BROWN, J. H. 1995. Macroecology. University of Chicago Press, Chicago, IL.

BROWN, J. L. 1969. The buffer effect and productivity in tit populations. American Naturalist 103:347–354.

BYSTRAK, D. 1981. The North American Breeding Bird Survey. Studies in Avian Biology 6:34–41.

CLARK, L. A., AND D. PREGIBON. 1992. Tree-based models. Pp. 377–419 *in* J. M. Chambers and T. J. Hastie (editors). Statistical models in S. Wadsworth & Brooks/Cole Advanced Books & Software, Pacific Grove, CA.

CURRIE, D. J. 1991. Energy and large-scale patterns of animal and plant species richness. American Naturalist 137:27–49.

DANKO, D. M. 1992. The digital chart of the world. GeoInfo Systems 2:29–36.

EFRON, B. 1982. The jackknife, the bootstrap and other resampling plans. Society for Industrial and Applied Mathematics, Philadelphia, PA.

FRETWELL, S. D. 1986. Distribution and abundance of the Dickcissel. Current Ornithology 4:211–242.

FRETWELL, S. D., AND H. L. LUCAS. 1969. On territorial behaviour and other factors influencing habitat distribution in birds. I. Theoretical development. Acta Biotheoretica 19:16–36.

GEORGE, T. L., A. C. FOWLER, R. L. KNIGHT, AND L. C. McEWEN. 1992. Impacts of a severe drought on grassland birds in western North Dakota. Ecological Applications 2:275–284.

GRABER, R. R., AND J. W. GRABER. 1963. A comparative study of bird populations in Illinois, 1906–1909 and 1956–1958. Illinois Natural History Survey Bulletin 28:383–528.

HERKERT, J. R. 1994. The effects of habitat fragmentation on midwestern grassland bird communities. Ecological Applications 4:461–471.

JOHNSON, D. G., AND M. D. SCHWARTZ. 1993. The Conservation Reserve Program and grassland birds. Conservation Biology 7:934–937.

JOHNSON, R. G., AND S. A. TEMPLE. 1986. Assessing

habitat quality for bird nesting in fragmented tallgrass prairies. Pp. 245–249 in J. Verner, M. L. Morrison, and C. J. Ralph (editors). Wildlife 2000: modeling habitat relationships of terrestrial vertebrates. University of Wisconsin Press, Madison, WI.

KREBS, C. J. 1985. Ecology: the experimental analysis of distribution and abundance. 3d ed. Harper and Row, New York, NY.

LARSEN, D. T., P. L. CROOKSTON, AND L. D. FLAKE. 1994. Factors associated with Ring-necked Pheasant use of winter food plots. Wildlife Society Bulletin 22:620–626.

LAUBER, T. B. 1991. Birds and the Conservation Reserve Program: a retrospective study. M.S. thesis. University of Maine, Orono, ME.

LITVAITIS, J. A. 1993. Response of early successional vertebrates to historic changes in land use. Conservation Biology 7:866–873.

LOVELAND, T. R., J. W. MERCHANT, D. J. OHLEN, AND J. F. BROWN. 1991. Development of a land-cover characteristics database for the conterminous U.S. Photogrammetric Engineering and Remote Sensing 57:1453–1463.

O'CONNOR, R. J. 1981. Habitat correlates of bird distribution in British census plots. Studies in Avian Biology 6:533–537.

O'CONNOR, R. J. 1992. Population variation in relation to migrancy status in some North American birds. Pp. 64–74 in J. M. Hagan III and D. W. Johnston (editors). Ecology and conservation of neotropical migrant landbirds. Smithsonian Institution Press, Washington, D.C.

O'CONNOR, R. J., M. T. JONES, D. WHITE, C. HUNSAKER, T. LOVELAND, B. JONES, AND E. PRESTON. 1996. Spatial partitioning of the environmental correlates of avian biodiversity in the lower United States. Biodiversity Letters 3:97–110.

O'CONNOR, R. J., AND M. SHRUBB. 1986. Farming and birds. Cambridge University Press, Cambridge, U.K.

O'NEILL, R. V., J. R. KRUMMEL, R. H. GARDNER, G. SUGIHARA, B. JACKSON, D. L. DEANGELIS, B. T. MILNE, M. G. TURNER, B. ZYGMUNT, S. W. CHRISTENSEN, V. H. DALE, AND R. L. GRAHAM. 1988. Indices of landscape pattern. Landscape Ecology 1: 153–162.

OVERTON, W. S., D. WHITE, AND D. L. STEVENS. 1990. Design report for EMAP: environmental monitoring and assessment program, EPA/600/3-91/053. U.S. Environmental Protection Agency, Office of Research and Development, Washington, D.C.

OWENS, R. A., AND M. T. MYRES. 1973. Effects of agriculture upon populations of native passerine birds of an Alberta fescue grassland. Canadian Journal of Zoology 51:697–713.

PRICE, J. T. 1995. Potential impacts of global climate change on the summer distributions of some North American grassland birds. Ph.D. thesis. Wayne State University, Detroit, MI.

RILEY, T. Z. 1995. Association of the Conservation Reserve Program with Ring-necked Pheasant survey counts in Iowa. Wildlife Society Bulletin 23:386–390.

RODENHOUSE, N. L., L. B. BEST, R. J. O'CONNOR, AND E. K. BOLLINGER. 1993. Effects of temperate agriculture on neotropical migrant landbirds. Pp. 280–

295 in D. M. Finch and P. W. Stangel (editors). Status and management of neotropical migratory birds. USDA Forest Service Gen. Tech. Rep. RM-229. USDA Forest Service Rocky Mountain Forestry and Range Experimental Station, Fort Collins, CO.

ROOT, T. L. 1988a. Energy constraints on avian distributions and abundances. Ecology 69:330–339.

ROOT, T. L. 1988b. Atlas of wintering North American birds: an analysis of Christmas Bird Count data. University of Chicago Press, Chicago, IL.

ROOT, T. L. 1993. Effects of global climate change on North American birds and their communities. Pp. 280–292 in P. M. Kareiva, J. G. Kingsolver, and R. B. Huey (editors). Biotic interactions and global change. Sinauer Associates, Sunderland, MA.

ROTENBERRY, J. T., R. J. COOPER, J. M. WUNDERLE, AND K. G. SMITH. 1995. When and where are populations limited? The roles of insect outbreaks, fire, and other natural perturbations. Pp. 55–84 in T. E. Martin and D. M. Finch (editors). Ecology and management of neotropical migratory birds: a synthesis and review of critical issues. Oxford University Press, Oxford, U.K.

SAMSON, F. B. 1980. Island biogeography and the conservation of prairie birds. Proceedings of the North American Prairie Conference 7:293–305.

SAUER, J. R., J. E. HINES, G. GOUGH, I. THOMAS, AND B. G. PETERJOHN. 1997. The North American Breeding Bird Survey results and analysis. Ver. 96.4: www.mbr.nbs.gov/bbs/bbs.html. Patuxent Wildlife Research Center, Laurel, MD.

SHACKFORD, J. S. 1994. Nesting of Long-billed Curlews on cultivated fields. Bulletin of the Oklahoma Ornithological Society 27:17–20.

SONQUIST, J. A., E. L. BAKER, AND J. N. MORGAN. 1973. Searching for structure. Survey Research Center, University of Michigan, Ann Arbor, MI.

TURNER, M. G., AND R. H. GARDNER. 1990. Quantitative methods in landscape ecology: the analysis and interpretation of landscape heterogeneity. Springer Verlag, New York, NY.

U.S. DEPARTMENT OF AGRICULTURE. 1987. Agricultural statistics. U.S. Government Printing Office, Washington, D.C.

VICKERY, P. D., M. L. HUNTER, JR., AND S. M. MELVIN. 1994. Effects of habitat area on the distribution of grassland birds in Maine. Conservation Biology 8: 1087–1097.

WALKER, P. A. 1990. Modeling wildlife distributions using a geographic information system: kangaroos in relation to climate. Journal of Biogeography 17: 279–289.

WARNER, R. E. 1994. Agricultural land use and grassland habitat in Illinois: future shock for midwestern birds? Conservation Biology 8:147–156.

WHITE, D., J. KIMMERLING, AND W. S. OVERTON. 1992. Cartographic and geometric components of a global design for environmental monitoring. Cartography and Geographic Information Systems 19:5–22.

WHITMORE, R. C. 1981. Structural characteristics of Grasshopper Sparrow habitat. Journal of Wildlife Management 45:811–814.

WIENS, J. A. 1973. Interterritorial habitat variation in Grasshopper and Savannah sparrows. Ecology 54: 877–884.

WIENS, J. A. 1981. Scale problems in avian censusing. Studies in Avian Biology 6:513–521.

WITH, K. A. 1994. The hazards of nesting near shrubs for a grassland bird, the McCown's Longspur. Condor 96:1009–1019.

WITHAM, J. W., AND M. L. HUNTER. 1992. Population trends of neotropical migrant landbirds in northern coastal New England. Pp. 85–95 *in* J. M. Hagan III and D. W. Johnston (editors). Ecology and conservation of neotropical migrant landbirds. Smithsonian Institution Press, Washington, D.C.

WRIGHT, D. H. 1991. Correlations between incidence and abundance are expected by chance. Journal of Biogeography 18:463–466.

Studies in Avian Biology No. 19:60–71, 1999.

HISTORY OF GRASSLAND BIRDS
IN EASTERN NORTH AMERICA

ROBERT A. ASKINS

Abstract. Until recently the severe decline in the populations of many species of grassland birds in eastern North America has aroused relatively little concern or conservation action. This response appears to be rooted in the perception that grassland birds invaded the East Coast from western grasslands after European settlers cleared the forest. Detailed historical accounts and analysis of pollen deposits, however, show that open grasslands existed on the East Coast of North America at the time of European settlement. Extensive grasslands resulted from burning and agricultural clearing by Native Americans. Natural disturbances, such as wildfire and beaver (*Castor canadensis*) activity, produced grasslands even before Native Americans cleared the forest. The presence of specialized grassland birds in Pleistocene deposits and in the earliest ornithological collections from eastern North America, and the existence of distinctive eastern populations of the Greater Prairie-Chicken (*Tympanuchus cupido*), Henslow's Sparrow (*Ammodramus henslowii*), and Savannah Sparrow (*Passerculus sandwichensis*), indicate that grassland birds are an ancient component of biological diversity on the heavily forested East Coast of North America.

LA HISTORIA DE LAS AVES DE PASTIZAL EN EL ESTE DE NORTEAMÉRICA

Sinopsis. Hasta hace poco tiempo, la declinación severa de las poblaciones de muchas especies de aves de pastizal en el este de América del Norte ha causado poco interés o acción de conservación. Esta respuesta se basa en la percepción de que las aves de pastizal invadieron la costa este de América del Norte de los pastizales occidentales después de la tala del bosque por los colonos europeos. Sin embargo, relatos históricos detallados y análisis de depósitos de polen indican que pastizales abiertos existían en época en la costa este de América del Norte en la época de la colonización europea. Quemas y desbrozos agrícolas de los indígenas norteamericanos se tradujeron en pastizales extensivos. Disturbios naturales, como los hechos por incendios y castores (*Castor canadensis*), produjeron pastizales antes de que los indígenas talaran el bosque. La presencia de aves de pastizal especialistas en los depósitos pleistocenos y en las colecciones ornitológicas más antiguas del este de América del Norte, y la existencia de poblaciones orientales distintivas de *Tympanuchus cupido*, el Gorrión de Henslow (*Ammodramus henslowii*), y el Gorrión Sabanero (*Passerculus sandwichensis*), indican que las aves de pastizal forman una parte antigua de la diversidad biológica en la arbolada costa este de América del Norte.

Key Words: beaver; bird populations; disturbance; eastern grasslands; grassland birds.

Many grassland bird species were common or even abundant along the East Coast through most of the nineteenth century, but their numbers diminished noticeably between the late nineteenth and mid-twentieth centuries. Griscom (1949) described the Upland Sandpiper (*Bartramia longicauda*), Bobolink (*Dolichonyx oryzivorus*), Eastern Meadowlark (*Sturnella magna*), and Grasshopper Sparrow (*Ammodramus savannarum*) as formerly common but declining in Massachusetts. Forbush (1925:449) mourned the virtual disappearance of the Upland Sandpiper from New England: "our children's children may never see an Upland Plover in the sky or hear its rich notes on the summer air. Its cries are among the most pleasing and remarkable sounds of rural life."

Although the decline of grassland birds was obvious to any careful observer, it is only in recent decades that we have been able to calculate the precise rate and extent of these population changes. The best evidence for this comes from the Breeding Bird Survey, a system of roadside routes scattered throughout the United States and southern Canada where birds are counted each year (Peterjohn 1994). The results for all of the survey routes east of the Mississippi River indicate that since 1966, when the surveys began, the abundance of 14 of the 19 species of grassland and savanna birds in eastern North America has declined significantly (Table 1). Some have shown rapid population changes. Between 1966 and 1994, for example, Grasshopper Sparrows decreased at a rate of 6% per year, whereas the annual rates of decline were 3% for Vesper Sparrows (*Pooecetes gramineus*), 9% for Henslow's Sparrows (*Ammodramus henslowii*), and 3% for Eastern Meadowlarks. In contrast, only 2 of 40 species of forest-dwelling migratory birds—a group that has received considerable attention from conservationists—decreased at a rate of more than 2% per year during approximately the same period (Askins 1993).

Another indication that grassland birds in the eastern United States are in trouble comes from state lists of endangered and threatened species

TABLE 1. POPULATION TRENDS OF GRASSLAND AND SAVANNA SPECIALISTS IN NORTH AMERICA EAST OF THE MISSISSIPPI RIVER BETWEEN 1966 AND 1994

Species	% change per year	Statistical significance[a]	Number of routes
Grassland species[b]			
Northern Harrier (*Circus cyaneus*)	+2.1	*	227
Ring-necked Pheasant (*Phasianus colchicus*)	−2.2	−	522
Northern Bobwhite (*Colinus virginianus*)	−3.3	***	880
Upland Sandpiper (*Bartramia longicauda*)	+1.2	−	201
Horned Lark (*Eremophila alpestris*)	0.0	−	642
Dickcissel (*Spiza americana*)	−4.3	***	269
Vesper Sparrow (*Pooecetes gramineus*)	−3.3	***	650
Lark Sparrow (*Chondestes grammacus*)	−6.9	*	39
Savannah Sparrow (*Passerculus sandwichensis*)	−1.7	***	727
Grasshopper Sparrow (*Ammodramus savannarum*)	−5.9	***	730
Henslow's Sparrow (*A. henslowii*)	−9.3	***	137
Bobolink (*Dolichonyx oryzivorus*)	−1.4	***	745
Eastern Meadowlark (*Sturnella magna*)	−3.4	***	1,330
Western Meadowlark (*S. neglecta*)	−7.2	***	174
Savanna species[c]			
Common Ground-Dove (*Columbina passerina*)	−3.4	***	127
Red-headed Woodpecker (*Melanerpes erythrocephalus*)	−2.1	***	667
Eastern Bluebird (*Sialia sialis*)	+2.2	***	1,185
Loggerhead Shrike (*Lanius ludovicianus*)	−4.3	***	379
American Goldfinch (*Carduelis tristis*)	−1.1	***	1,349

Note: Data are from the Breeding Bird Survey database, U.S. Fish and Wildlife Service (Sauer et al. 1995). Habitat classifications are based on DeGraaf and Rudis 1986, DeGraaf et al. 1991, and Askins 1993.
[a] * P < 0.05, *** P < 0.001.
[b] Species dependent on open habitats dominated by grass and forbs, with little woody vegetation.
[c] Species found primarily in open grassland with scattered trees or shrubs.

(Vickery 1992). Of the 40 species listed as endangered, threatened, or of special concern in three or more northeastern states, 13 are grassland or savanna specialists and only 3 are forest specialists. For example, Upland Sandpiper, Northern Harrier (*Circus cyaneus*), Loggerhead Shrike (*Lanius ludovicianus*), and Grasshopper, Henslow's, and Vesper sparrows are listed in all or most of the New England states (Vickery 1992). The populations of many of these species have declined in other parts of the eastern United States, both in heavily forested areas along the East Coast and in the more agricultural Midwest (Herkert 1991, Bollinger and Gavin 1992).

What Mayfield (1988) called the "quiet decline" of grassland birds has attracted surprisingly little attention or concern from most government wildlife agencies and conservation organizations. This response is rooted in the widely held view that before Europeans cleared the land, unbroken forest stretched from the Atlantic to the Great Plains, leading to the general impression that grassland species invaded the eastern states from western savannas and prairies after the clearing of the forest for agriculture. For example, Whitcomb (1987) argued that this invasion of the eastern "neosavanna" created by agriculture has been a "failed experiment for

many of these species," which are now declining. The implication is that this is a return to ecosystems more similar to those before European settlement and therefore should not be a cause for concern. According to Whitcomb, these species could survive only with active management to preserve grassland "in a region where [grassland] is inappropriate as an equilibrium community" (Whitcomb 1987:165).

Many historians and botanists have depicted the landscape of the ancient East Coast of North America as carpeted with forest, a forest so continuous that a squirrel could travel from the Atlantic Ocean to the Mississippi River without touching the ground (Day 1953). Clearly forests in eastern North America were extensive, and in some areas they were essentially unbroken (Siccama 1971, Lorimer 1977, Bormann and Likens 1979, Runkle 1990, Seischab and Orwig 1991). Since the early 1900s, however, some botanists have argued that the forest was not always continuous; in coastal areas and even in some inland areas, it was interrupted by scrubland, barrens, glades, and even, in places, prairielike grasslands (Day 1953). If this is true, then grassland birds would have had a place in the landscape before European settlement.

WERE THERE GRASSLANDS ON THE EAST COAST BEFORE EUROPEAN SETTLEMENT?

When Conrad (1935) visited Long Island's Hempstead Plains in the 1930s, much of the area was little bluestem (*Schizachyrium scoparius*) prairie, a yellow-green grassland dotted with the small, bright green hemispheres of wild indigo (*Baptista tinctoria*). In May the prairie was blue with the blossoms of birdfoot violets (*Viola pedata*). As Conrad pointed out, this grassland on the New York coast was remarkably similar to the tallgrass prairies of Iowa and Nebraska. Moreover, the Hempstead Plains had a rich community of grassland birds: Upland Sandpipers, Bobolinks, and Vesper and Grasshopper sparrows were all common there in the 1920s (Bull 1974).

European travelers described the Hempstead Plains as treeless in the 1600s (Harper 1911), so this grassland was not a product of European agriculture. The Hempstead Plains were characterized by thin soil resting on a porous foundation of quartz and granite pebbles (Conrad 1935, Cain et al. 1937), features that, in combination with periodic fires, appeared to favor the growth of grasses and herbs rather than trees and shrubs.

The Plains once covered more than 20,000 ha, and for many years the area was used primarily for grazing sheep and racing horses (Svenson 1936, Stalter and Lamont 1987). Large areas of grassland remained in the 1930s, but after World War II these open areas were subdivided for housing or plowed for truck farms. Today only a few acres of this prairie survive: an 8-ha parcel belonging to Nassau County Community College and managed by The Nature Conservancy, and a 19-ha parcel managed as a nature preserve by Nassau County (Antenen et al. 1994). The smaller preserve has been maintained with controlled burning.

Although the Hempstead Plains may have been one of the largest and most distinctive grasslands on the East Coast, it was not the only one. Another grassland, the Montauk Downs, covered approximately 2,400 ha of eastern Long Island (Taylor 1923), and several large grasslands, called "glades," characterized a plateau in the Allegheny Mountains of western Pennsylvania (Whitney 1994). Also, in the 1600s a savanna where occasional large oaks (*Quercus*) broke an expanse of tall, wiry grass (probably bluestem) stretched for 24 km along the Quinnipiac River north of New Haven, Connecticut (Olmsted 1937). After decades of overgrazing, this area became the almost desertlike North Haven Sand Plains, and subsequently most of the

area was developed. Blueberry barrens, which are open expanses covered with lowbush blueberry (*Vaccinium angustifolium*) shrubs and grasses, still cover large areas in eastern Maine, where they are maintained by burning for blueberry production. Some of the largest East Coast populations of Upland Sandpipers, Vesper Sparrows, and other species of grassland birds breed on these barrens (Vickery et al. 1994).

Many of these grasslands may have resulted from the activities of Native Americans before European settlement. Early explorers and colonists frequently encountered open landscapes created by firewood harvesting, agricultural clearing, and burning to enhance hunting. For example, Giovanni da Verrazano described the area around Narragansett Bay (Rhode Island) in 1524 as open plains, without forests or trees, for many leagues inland (Day 1953). Samuel de Champlain and John Smith reported extensive areas of cleared land along the New England coast before Europeans colonized the area (Whitney 1994). Moreover, an early settler in Salem, Massachusetts, described "open plains, in some places five hundred acres. . .not much troublesome for to cleere for the plough to goe in" (Day 1953:331). These clearings were not restricted to coastal areas; accounts of early settlers indicate that river valleys had been cleared by Native Americans for farming and hunting (Patterson and Sassaman 1988).

Early assessments that Native American agriculture had relatively little effect on the landscape were based on population estimates after European settlement, but population densities were much higher before contact with Europeans triggered massive epidemics that killed a large proportion of the people in most tribes (Crosby 1972, Cronon 1983, Denevan 1992, Whitney 1994). As Kulikoff (1986:29) wrote regarding the Chesapeake Bay area, "though English settlers did not find a wilderness, they did create one"; extensive agricultural clearings reverted to forest as Native American populations declined. Pilgrims traveling through the area near Warren, Massachusetts, in 1621 "saw the remains of so many once occupied villages and such extensive formerly cultivated fields that they concluded thousands of people must have lived there before the plague" (Russell 1980:24). Maps, drawings, and written accounts of the landscape around Native American settlements in the southeastern United States before European settlement provide evidence of extensive clearings created by farming and of "parklands" maintained by controlled burning (Hammett 1992). In New York and southern New England, relatively high population densities combined with slash-and-burn agriculture (Whitney 1994) would have resulted in extensive areas of cleared land in the form of both active and abandoned fields. This would have produced a "mosaic of forests and fields in varying stages of succession" (Patterson and Sassaman 1988: 115). Another view is that Eastern tribes used large permanent agricultural fields from which tree stumps had been removed rather than temporary fields cut out of the forest for slash-and-burn agriculture (Doolittle 1992). This permanent farmland would have had to be rested occasionally, however, producing "weed-covered" fallow fields of the sort seen by Champlain near the site of Boston in 1605 (Doolittle 1992). Regardless of whether Native Americans used slash-and-burn or permanent-field agriculture, their activities would have produced open habitats (abandoned or fallow fields) that could have been used by grassland birds.

There also is good evidence that the Native Americans of the East Coast burned large areas to create open woodlands and grassland for hunting. For example, Roger Williams wrote in the 1640s that Native Americans in New England "burnt up all the underwoods in the Countrey, once or twice a yeare and therefore as Noble men in England possessed great Parkes . . . onely for their game" (Williams 1963:47). In 1818, B. Trumbull reported that the Native Americans of Connecticut "so often burned the country, to take deer and other wild game, that in many of the plain dry parts of it, there was but little small timber. Where the lands were thus burned there grew bent grass, or as some called it, thatch, two, three and four feet high" (Olmsted 1937:266). Native Americans in New York not only burned the woods each autumn to create a more open understory but also burned plains and meadows to improve hunting (Whitney 1994).

Although fires were probably infrequent in most forests that were remote from Native American settlements (Russell 1983), fire and other disturbances near settlements provided extensive habitat for early successional species, including potential habitat for grassland birds. An analysis of charcoal deposits in the sediments of 11 lakes in New England demonstrated that before European settlement, fires were frequent in densely populated coastal areas but infrequent in inland and northern areas (Patterson and Sassaman 1988). Moreover, Winne's (1988) analysis of pollen and charcoal in lake sediments showed that the area around Pineo Pond in eastern Maine has been characterized by frequent, moderate fires and scrubby, fire-adapted vegetation for at least 900 yr. Today this area is dominated by blueberry barrens that are maintained by con-

trolled burning. These support a diversity of breeding grassland birds (Vickery et al. 1994).

The extent of forest clearing by Native Americans in the northeastern United States probably paled in comparison with the extensive agricultural fields created by the Moundbuilders, who lived along the Mississippi River and its tributaries in much of what is now the southeastern and midwestern United States. Moundbuilding cultures existed in the lower Mississippi River Valley as early as 1500 B.C. The early Moundbuilding cultures probably depended on a mixture of hunting, gathering of nuts, fishing, and small-scale farming based on native plants such as sunflower (*Helianthus*) and marsh elder (*Iva frutescens*; Shaffer 1992). Later, during the Mississippian Period, which lasted from A.D. 700 until the early 1700s, large-scale agriculture supported a dense population living in closely spaced villages. Corn (*Zea mays*) and beans (Leguminosae) from Mexico replaced indigenous crops, and large areas were cleared for farming (Shaffer 1992). The largest population center was Cahokia, located on the Mississippi River near its confluence with the Missouri River (Shaffer 1992). This center covered 800 ha, with 160 ha enclosed in a wooden palisade. The site was dotted with as many as 120 earthen mounds, the largest of which rose to 30 m and covered more than 6 ha. The mounds supported wooden buildings, and the area below the mounds was densely packed with rectangular thatched-roof houses where an estimated 15,000–38,000 people lived. Cahokia and the many villages and towns around it were supported by farming the American Bottom, a 324-km^2 strip of rich alluvial soil in the floodplain along the eastern bank of the Mississippi River. In A.D. 1000 there were 50 villages and 8 other large or medium-sized centers within 40 km of Cahokia.

There are no historical accounts of Cahokia because it was abandoned after A.D. 1200 (Shaffer 1992). Early Spanish visitors visited similar sites that were still occupied in the 1500s, however. A chronicler of Hernando de Soto's expedition (1539–1542) described a Moundbuilder town along the Mississippi River as being "in an open field, that for a quarter of a league over was all inhabited; and at the distance of from half a league to a league off were many other large towns, in which was a good quantity of maize, beans, walnuts [*Juglans*], and dried *Ameixas* [persimmons]" (Bourne 1904:149).

The Moundbuilding centers were abandoned long before Europeans settled the southeastern United States or Mississippi River Valley. This culture may have been destroyed by Old World diseases that swept inland from European outposts on the Florida and Gulf Coasts (Crosby

1986). Before the collapse of this agricultural society, however, there were extensive areas of open fields in many parts of the Southeast, especially the lower Mississippi River Valley.

GRASSLANDS BEFORE NATIVE AMERICAN AGRICULTURE

The patterns of Native American land use observed in the 1600s began to emerge about 2,000 yr ago (Smith 1989, 1995). Many species of grassland birds may have colonized cultivated areas after the initiation of Native American, rather than European, agriculture, and their current decline represents a return to conditions before humans began to substantially modify the vegetation of eastern North America.

Undoubtedly, many apparently "natural" open grasslands of eastern North America were the product of human activities. For example, historical accounts and analysis of the pollen record indicate that the extensive heathlands and sandplain grasslands on Nantucket Island, Massachusetts, resulted from the clearing of oak forest and grazing of sheep after Europeans settled that island (Dunwiddie 1989).

Some of the open habitats on the East Coast may predate disturbance by Native Americans or Europeans, however. Smaller shrubby and grassy openings in the eastern forest result from dam-building by beavers (*Castor canadensis*). After beavers exhaust the food supply around a pond, they move to another area. When the abandoned pond drains, the pond bed often becomes a "beaver meadow," a patch of shrubby vegetation or grassland. This meadow eventually is overgrown with young forest, and after 10–30 yr beavers may recolonize the site and initiate another cycle (Remillard et al. 1987).

Although beaver meadows are largely restricted to flood plains, their total area was probably extensive before beavers were extirpated in most parts of eastern North America (Naiman et al. 1988). In Ontario's Algonquin Provincial Park, where beavers are protected, there is a high density of beaver ponds and meadows (Coles and Orme 1983). After beavers became reestablished at Quabbin Reservoir in Massachusetts in 1952, the population grew rapidly until the density reached 0.8 colony per kilometer of stream (Howard and Larson 1985). The impact of a dense beaver population can be considerable. In the Adirondack Mountains of New York, beaver dams created patches of disturbance that covered an average area of 7 ha, with a maximum area of 12 ha (Remillard et al. 1987). Bela Hubbard, who surveyed land in Michigan before European settlement, reported that one-fifth of the area within 19 km of what is now Detroit was covered with "marshy tracts or prairies which had

their origin in the work of the beaver" (Whitney 1994:304). Coles and Orme (1983:99) argued that ancient forests in England must have been "moth-holed with clearings wherever beaver were present." These "grassy meadows of relict pools" were also an important feature of the pre-settlement landscape of eastern North America. Although beaver meadows are generally too small to accommodate many species of specialized grassland birds, some other species (e.g., Eastern Meadowlark and Savannah Sparrow) occur in patches of grassland of similar size (5–10 ha; Herkert 1994, Vickery et al. 1994).

Many regions of the East were subject to disturbances that created large openings in the forest (Runkle 1990). Grassland, savanna, and grassy scrub were probably created by large fires, particularly fires that burned following hurricanes or tornadoes that periodically leveled forests. These catastrophic disturbances were probably most frequent in low-lying sandy areas on the coastal plain. In many regions farther inland, fires, windstorms, and other disturbances were infrequent, and consequently the forest canopy was almost continuous, with few large openings (Lorimer 1977). For example, the northern hardwood forest of western New York and of the White Mountains of New Hampshire probably formed an almost unbroken canopy (Bormann and Likens 1979, Seischab and Orwig 1991). Large grassy openings may have occurred in some of the river valleys in the interior, however. John Winthrop (Hosmer 1959:85) described how one of the first European expeditions to the White Mountains passed through "many thousands of acres of rich meadow" as it paddled birch-bark canoes up the Saco River in what is now Maine.

A LONGER VIEW: PLEISTOCENE STEPPE AND SAVANNA

When continental glaciers covered much of Canada and the northern United States, the regions immediately south of the glaciers were dominated by a spruce (*Picea*) parkland, a grassy savanna with scattered spruce trees (Webb 1988). Samples of pollen from lake sediments deposited 18,000–12,000 yr ago show that this savanna stretched westward from the Atlantic Coast to the Great Plains. Most species of deciduous trees, and presumably the closed forests where these species grow today, were restricted to the extreme southeastern United States (Webb 1988). Thus, in eastern North America there was a gradient from savanna in the north to dense forest in the south.

Vegetation zones shifted and changed as the glaciers retreated northward beginning about 12,000 yr ago. Spruce parkland largely disappeared, and a new gradient, from eastern forest to western prairie, gradually formed (Webb 1988). Before this transition occurred, however, the spruce parkland was occupied by a diversity of large open-country mammals; caribou (*Rangifer tarandus*), mastodons (*Mammut americanum*), and long-nosed peccaries (*Mylohyus nasutus*) are frequently found in fossil deposits from the time of the spruce parkland (Kurtén and Anderson 1980).

One of the best samples of spruce parkland animals comes from a site called New Paris No. 4 in Pennsylvania (Guilday et al. 1964). Approximately 11,000 yr ago, a deep sinkhole acted like a pitfall trap, collecting the skeletons of more than 2,700 animals that fell into the crevice and died. The mixture of small mammals and skeletal remains of Sharp-tailed Grouse (*Tympanuchus phasianellus*) at this site suggests that there was extensive grassland habitat in this region.

A better picture of the birdlife of the postglacial period comes from another site, the caves of Natural Chimneys in Virginia, where skeletons were deposited at about the same time as at the New Paris No. 4 site. The skeletons at Natural Chimneys were deposited in owl pellets, so both small mammals and birds were well represented (Guilday 1962). Although remains of these animals may have accumulated over a long period while the vegetation was changing, they provide a glimpse of the bird community of the spruce parkland. The bones of Sharp-tailed Grouse, Northern Bobwhite (*Colinus virginianus*), Upland Sandpiper, Red-headed Woodpecker (*Melanerpes erythrocephalus*), Black-billed Magpie (*Pica pica*), and Brown-headed Cowbird (*Molothrus ater*), along with other grassland vertebrates such as thirteen-lined ground squirrel (*Spermophilus tridecemlineatus*), point to a landscape with large amounts of open savanna or grassland. The remains of woodland species such as Red-bellied Woodpecker (*Melanerpes carolinus*), Eastern Wood-Pewee (*Contopus virens*), and Red-breasted Nuthatch (*Sitta canadensis*) in the same deposits suggest either that woodland and savanna were found in the area at the same time or that woodland invaded and replaced the savanna while the bones accumulated at Natural Chimneys. In either case, it is clear that grassland birds occurred in eastern North America before the spruce parkland receded and disappeared.

A site farther south, at Duck River, Tennessee, revealed that in the late Pleistocene typical coniferous forest species (Northern Hawk-Owl [*Surnia ulula*], Boreal Owl [*Aegolius funereus*], Northern Saw-whet Owl [*A. acadicus*], Gray Jay [*Perisoreus canadensis*], and Pine Grosbeak [*Pinicola enucleator*]) lived alongside grassland species such as Sharp-tailed Grouse, Greater Prairie-Chicken (*Tympanuchus cupido*), Horned Lark (*Eremophila alpestris*), meadowlark (*Sturnella* sp.), pocket gopher (*Geomys* spp.), and thirteen-lined ground squirrel (Parmalee and Klippel 1982).

A key question is whether grassland birds could have survived the northward spread of closed-canopy forest over eastern North America after the continental glaciers melted. This is an issue not only for the current warm interglacial period but also for previous interglacial periods. In all previous interglacial periods and at the beginning of the current postglacial period, large browsers such as mastodons and giant ground sloths (*Megalonyx jeffersonii* and other species) may have created and maintained openings in the forest in much the same way as African elephants (*Loxodonta africana*) maintain open savannas in East Africa today (Dublin et al. 1990). European ecologists have recognized that giant herbivores, particularly the extinct relatives of elephants, probably opened the forest, creating glades, parklike woods, or even savannas in areas that would otherwise be dominated by dense forest (Andersson and Appelquist 1990, Puchkov 1992). Such openings would have supported a variety of animal and plant species that depend on grassy habitats. Through most of the past 1 million yr, as forests retreated and advanced in response to the shrinking and growing of glacial ice sheets, woodland habitats may have been modified and opened by giant herbivores. Only in the present interglacial did mastodons, ground sloths, and other giants disappear from North America, perhaps as a result of the invasion of the continent by people who had already developed efficient tools and strategies for hunting large animals (Martin and Klein 1984). Human activities such as burning and agricultural clearing subsequently may have substituted for giant herbivores in creating a mosaic of forest and openings (Andersson and Appelquist 1990), permitting open-country species to persist in eastern woodlands.

THE ORIGIN OF EASTERN GRASSLAND BIRDS

The common impression that many species of grassland birds spread eastward from the prairies of the Midwest to the newly cleared farmland of the East Coast is substantiated by several well-documented examples of range expansion. For example, the prairie subspecies of Horned Lark (*Eremophila alpestris praticola*) spread eastward from Illinois and Wisconsin, reaching Michigan and Ontario in the 1870s, New York in the 1880s, New England by 1891, and Pennsylvania and Maryland by 1910 (Forbush 1927, Thomas 1951, Hurley and Franks 1976). The Dickcissel (*Spiza americana*) spread eastward from the tallgrass prairies in the early 1800s, but its range contracted after 1850, and it eventually disappeared as a regular breeding bird along the East Coast (Hurley and Franks 1976). Western Meadowlarks (*Sturnella neglecta*) expanded east into Wisconsin and Michigan after 1900 (Lanyon 1956), and Lark Sparrows (*Chondestes grammacus*) spread eastward from the prairies into agricultural areas in the Ohio Valley, West Virginia, and western Maryland (Brooks 1938).

Although these eastward range expansions were well documented, there is no similar evidence for invasion of the East by the species that are most abundant and widespread in eastern grasslands. Upland Sandpipers, Grasshopper Sparrows, Bobolinks, Eastern Meadowlarks, and other common grassland birds were reported by the earliest ornithologists who systematically documented the distribution of birds on the eastern coast of North America. Alexander Wilson's *American Ornithology* (originally published between 1808 and 1814; Brewer 1839) and John James Audubon's *Ornithological Biography* (Audubon 1831–1849) were published more than 100 yr after most of the eastern seaboard had been cleared, so it is possible that grassland birds colonized the meadows and pastures created by Europeans long before their occurrence was initially documented. Some seventeenth-century European observers, such as John Josselyn (Lindholt 1988) and William Wood (Vaughan 1977), described gamebirds and the more conspicuous songbirds, but only a few species are recognizable because descriptions are sketchy and the names of British birds were frequently used for North American species. Mark Catesby's *Natural History of Carolina, Florida, and the Bahama Islands,* completed in 1747, includes descriptions and paintings of many species of eastern birds, including two species of grassland songbirds, Eastern Meadowlark and Bobolink (Feduccia 1985). It is not surprising, however, that there are relatively few descriptions of grassland songbirds from this period. Many grassland birds are small, inconspicuous, and dull colored, so they could have been overlooked by early observers.

Significantly, the East Coast populations of three species of grassland birds were distinctive enough from western populations to be considered separate subspecies. This suggests that these populations have existed in isolation in the East for many thousands of years, perhaps since unbroken grasslands reached from the Great Plains to the Atlantic during the last glacial period. The eastern Henslow's Sparrow (*Ammo-*

dramus henslowii susurrans) has a breeding range restricted to central New York and southern New England south to Virginia, eastern West Virginia, and North Carolina (Smith 1968). It is darker than the western subspecies, with a deeper bill and more buff on the underparts and more yellow in the wing (Smith 1968).

The "Ipswich" Sparrow (*Passerculus sandwichensis princeps*), a subspecies of the Savannah Sparrow, is also restricted to the East Coast (Wheelwright and Rising 1993). This population is so distinctive that it was considered a separate species until 1973. After reclassifying it as a subspecies of Savannah Sparrow, the American Ornithologists' Union (1957) recommended that it be designated by its vernacular name in quotes ("Ipswich" Sparrow). Vernacular names are only officially recognized for particularly distinctive subspecies (Stobo and McLaren 1975).

The "Ipswich" Sparrow was not described until 1868, when C. J. Maynard collected one in the coastal dunes at Ipswich, Massachusetts (Elliott 1968). Its breeding range on Sable Island, a 32-km-long island about 135 km off the coast of Nova Scotia, was not discovered until 1884.

"Ipswich" Sparrows spend both summers and winters in extremely open habitats. During the breeding season they are virtually restricted to low shrubby vegetation and stands of marram grass (*Ammophila breviligulata*) on Sable Island (Stobo and McLaren 1975). In winter they occur primarily in a narrow zone of dunes near Atlantic beaches from Nova Scotia to Florida, with the highest densities on relatively undeveloped barrier islands and sandy peninsulas between New Jersey and Virginia (Stobo and McLaren 1971).

The "Ipswich" Sparrow is adapted to living in the dunes and sandy scrub adjacent to the ocean. It is paler gray than other Savannah Sparrow subspecies, so it tends to be well camouflaged in the light-colored dune and beach areas where it lives (Stobo and McLaren 1975). Also, it averages 9% larger than other eastern subspecies of Savannah Sparrow, which might be an adaptation to feeding on the exceptionally large seeds of dune grasses such as marram grass and sea oats (*Uniola paniculata*; Stobo and McLaren 1975). Finally, unlike other Savannah Sparrow subspecies, the "Ipswich" Sparrow has a short tail, making it more similar to Grasshopper Sparrow, Seaside Sparrow (*Ammodramus maritimus*), and other sparrows that live in open habitats with few tall shrubs or trees. These specific adaptations indicate that grassy habitats must have existed along the outer beaches of the East Coast for a long time.

The now-extinct Heath Hen (*Tympanuchus cupido cupido*) was the eastern subspecies of the

Greater Prairie-Chicken. During the early years of European settlement, the Heath Hen was common or even abundant in open grasslands and scrublands on Long Island and around Boston, and it ranged along the coast from southern Maine as far south as Virginia (Gross 1932). Because it was an important game species, it was described by many early settlers. In the 1600s, William Wood, Thomas Morton, and other observers wrote that the Heath Hen was common in eastern Massachusetts (Forbush 1927, Gross 1932, Vaughan 1977). Heath Hens inhabited sandy scrub-oak plains, pine (*Pinus*) barrens, blueberry barrens, and other open habitats (Forbush 1927, Johnsgard 1983). In the nineteenth century they were common in the open grassland of the Hempstead Plains on Long Island (Bull 1974).

The abundance of Heath Hens at the time of European settlement, and the recognition of the Heath Hen and eastern populations of two other species of grassland birds as distinct subspecies, suggest that grassland birds inhabited the East Coast long before Europeans arrived or even before Native Americans started clearing the land for farming. This is consistent with the evidence on grassland plants. Several plant species are restricted to eastern grasslands (Mehrhoff 1997; P. Dunwiddie, pers. comm.), suggesting that they evolved in isolation from the grasslands of the Great Plains. Bushy rockrose (*Helianthemum dumosum*) is found from Massachusetts to Long Island; sandplain agalinis (*Agalinis acuta*) from Massachusetts to Maryland; and sickle-leaved golden aster (*Pityopsis* [*Chrysopsis*] *falcata*) from Massachusetts to New Jersey (Gleason and Cronquist 1991). In addition, a subspecies of northern blazing star (*Liatris scariosa* var. *novae-angliae*) is found only in eastern grasslands.

Because of the paucity of historical records of small birds in the 1600s and 1700s, it is likely that only carefully dated skeletal remains could provide definitive evidence of the occurrence of most species of grassland birds before European settlement. There is strong evidence, however, that extensive grasslands and savannas occurred in eastern North America at the time of European settlement. We also know that some grassland species were found in the spruce parkland of postglacial times, about 11,000 yr ago, and that distinctive eastern subspecies evolved in three grassland species. Therefore, it is reasonable to conclude that many open-country species are native to the region, not recent invaders from the western prairies. During the eighteenth and nineteenth centuries these species probably became much more abundant than they had been before Europeans cleared the land, but subsequently they may have declined far below the level of abundance characteristic of the presettlement landscape. Many of these species are now in danger of regional extinction, and they deserve the same attention from conservationists as birds associated with eastern forests, marshes, and lakes.

CONSERVATION OF GRASSLAND BIRDS

Many of the original grasslands, such as beaver meadows and recently burned areas, were ephemeral. Other areas may have been disturbed frequently enough to create stable grasslands; the Hempstead Plains in New York and some of the barrens in eastern Maine are obvious candidates. Temporary grasslands are created much less frequently today because beavers are less abundant and fires are controlled, and most of the areas that may have been stable grasslands have been developed for agriculture or housing. The blueberry barrens of eastern Maine are an exception; these open habitats have been maintained in a seminatural state by controlled burning to sustain commercial blueberry production (Vickery et al. 1994).

With the exception of Maine's blueberry barrens and a few other areas remaining as seminatural open habitat for centuries, present-day habitats used by grassland birds along the East Coast are highly artificial. Populations of grassland species have diminished primarily because much of the farmland in the Northeast and parts of the Southeast has been abandoned and has reverted to forest, and because the remaining farmland is now managed more intensively for agricultural production (Hart 1968, Askins 1993). For example, hayfields have become less suitable as nesting habitat for Eastern Meadowlarks, Bobolinks, and some other grassland species because they are mowed earlier in the summer, before the end of the nesting season, and because they are rotated more frequently (Bollinger and Gavin 1992). In southern New England, most of the remaining populations of Grasshopper Sparrows and Upland Sandpipers are found in extensive mowed areas at airports and military airfields (Veit and Petersen 1993, Bevier 1994, Melvin 1994). The farmland once used by these species has either disappeared or become unsuitable for nesting.

Regional populations of grassland birds can be maintained with proper management of artificial grasslands such as fallow farmland and the mowed areas near airport runways. The Conservation Reserve Program (CRP), which pays farmers to take land out of production in order to manage it for conservation of soil and wildlife (Dunn et al. 1993), could potentially benefit grassland birds in the East as it already has in some western prairie regions (Johnson and

Schwartz 1993, Johnson and Igl 1995). However, most of the CRP land is concentrated in the northcentral United States (Rodenhouse et al. 1995), and abandoned farmlands in the East quickly become wooded, so a better approach might be to compensate farmers who use less intensive farming methods to create traditional hay meadows and other types of farmland that once sustained grassland birds. This approach has been successful in preserving open-country species in the Netherlands (Beintema 1988).

Relatively simple changes in airport management (e.g., removing woody vegetation and changing mowing schedules to avoid the nesting season) have sustained or improved habitat for grassland birds at Westover Air Reserve Base in Massachusetts (Melvin 1994), Bradley International Airport in Connecticut (Crossman 1989), and Floyd Bennett Field, a former naval air base on Long Island, New York (Lent and Litwin 1989). Habitat management at Westover resulted in substantial increases in the abundance of Grasshopper Sparrows and Upland Sandpipers between 1987 and 1994 (Melvin 1994).

Even when grassland birds are absent from an area, it should be possible to create habitat that will attract them. Probably because eastern grassland birds have always depended on patches of ephemeral habitat, they have a remarkable ability to find and colonize remote sites, even sites far from other bird populations of the same species. When a field in Lincoln, Massachusetts, was managed to maintain tall grass for nesting Bobolinks, in 1995 it attracted a breeding pair of Henslow's Sparrow, a species that has almost disappeared from Massachusetts, with no known breeding records in the preceding 20 yr (Ells 1995). Similarly, when abandoned strip mines in heavily forested areas of West Virginia were restored and seeded with grass, they were colonized by Horned Larks, Eastern Meadowlarks, and Savannah, Vesper, and Grasshopper sparrows (Whitmore and Hall 1978). These new grasslands were extremely isolated from other grasslands supporting grassland birds, but they still attracted breeding populations of several species.

Expending scarce resources to maintain meadows, fallow fields, and airfields may seem unwise to many conservationists who are accustomed to protecting forests and wilderness areas. Yet many species of birds, insects, plants, and other organisms depend on these grassland habitats. Artificial habitats are critical for many of these species because people have destroyed most of the native grassland habitat, including most of the midwestern tallgrass prairies where these species may have once been most abundant (Bollinger et al. 1990). People have not only destroyed natural grasslands directly, but they also have interrupted or suppressed many of the natural processes of disturbance, such as fires and beaver activity, that once created the early successional habitats that grassland species need. In the near term, artificial grasslands represent our best hope for maintaining grassland species. These species are an important, and probably ancient, component of biological diversity along the East Coast of North America.

ACKNOWLEDGMENTS

I have gained insights about the questions addressed in this paper in discussions with P. D. Vickery, W. A. Niering, G. D. Dreyer, and R. M. DeGraaf. P. D. Vickery, J. R. Herkert, and an anonymous reviewer made helpful suggestions for improving the manuscript. My research was supported by funds from the USDA Forest Service, Northeastern Forest Experiment Station. An earlier version of this paper was published in the book *Grasslands of Northeastern North America: Ecology and Conservation of Native and Agricultural Landscapes* (P. D. Vickery and P. W. Dunwiddie [editors]. 1997. Massachusetts Audubon Society, Lincoln, MA). This paper is also being revised for a chapter in a book by the author that will be published by Yale University Press.

LITERATURE CITED

AMERICAN ORNITHOLOGISTS' UNION. 1957. Check-list of North American birds. 5th ed. American Ornithologists' Union, Washington, D.C.

ANDERSSON, L., AND T. APPELQUIST. 1990. The influence of the Pleistocene megafauna on the nemoral and the boreonemoral ecosystem: a hypothesis with implications for nature conservation strategy. Svensk Botanisk Tidskrift 84:355–368.

ANTENEN, S., M. JORDAN, K. MOTIVANS, J. B. WASHA, AND R. ZAREMBA. 1994. Hempstead Plains fire management plan, Nassau County, Long Island, New York. Report to Long Island Chapter of The Nature Conservancy, Cold Spring Harbor, NY.

ASKINS, R. A. 1993. Population trends in grassland, shrubland, and forest birds in eastern North America. Pp. 1–34 in D. M. Power (editor). Current ornithology, vol. 11. Plenum Publishing, New York, NY.

AUDUBON, J. J. 1831–1849. Ornithological biography, or an account of the birds of the United States of America. Vol. 1, J. Dodson, Philadelphia, PA; vols. 2–5, A. and C. Black, Edinburgh, Scotland.

BEINTEMA, A. J. 1988. Conservation of grassland bird communities in the Netherlands. Pp. 105–111 in P. D. Goriup (editor). Ecology and conservation of grassland birds. ICBP Technical Publication no. 7. International Council for Bird Preservation, Cambridge, U.K.

BEVIER, L. R. (EDITOR). 1994. The atlas of breeding birds of Connecticut. State Geological and Natural History Survey of Connecticut Bulletin 113.

BOLLINGER, E. K., P. B. BOLLINGER, AND T. A. GAVIN. 1990. Effects of hay-cropping on eastern populations of the Bobolink. Wildlife Society Bulletin 18: 142–150.

BOLLINGER, E. K., AND T. A. GAVIN. 1992. Eastern Bobolink populations: ecology and conservation in an agricultural landscape. Pp. 497–506 in J. M. Hagan III and D. W. Johnston (editors). Ecology and conservation of neotropical migrant landbirds. Smithsonian Institution Press, Washington, D.C.

BORMANN, F. H., AND G. E. LIKENS. 1979. Catastrophic disturbance and the steady state in northern hardwood forests. American Scientist 67:660–669.

BOURNE, E. G. 1904. Narratives of the career of Hernando de Soto. Vol. 1. A. S. Barnes and Co., New York, NY.

BREWER, T. M. 1839. Wilson's American ornithology. Charles L. Cornish, New York, NY.

BROOKS, M. 1938. The eastern Lark Sparrow in the upper Ohio valley. Cardinal 4:181–200.

BULL, J. 1974. Birds of New York state. Doubleday, Garden City, NY.

CAIN, S. A., M. NELSON, AND W. McLEAN. 1937. Andropogonetum Hempsteadi: a Long Island grassland vegetation type. American Midland Naturalist 18:334–350.

COLES, J. M., AND B. J. ORME. 1983. Homo sapiens or Castor fiber? Antiquity 57:95–102.

CONRAD, H. S. 1935. The plant associations of central Long Island: a study in descriptive plant sociology. American Midland Naturalist 16:433–516.

CRONON, W. 1983. Changes in the land: Indians, colonists, and the ecology of New England. Hill and Wang, New York, NY.

CROSBY, A. W., JR. 1972. The Columbian exchange: biological and cultural consequences of 1492. Greenwood Press, Westport, CT.

CROSBY, A. W., JR. 1986. Ecological imperialism: the biological expansion of Europe, 900–1900. Cambridge University Press, New York, NY.

CROSSMAN, T. I. 1989. Habitat use of Grasshopper and Savannah sparrows at Bradley International Airport and management recommendations. M.S. thesis. University of Connecticut, Storrs, CT.

DAY, G. M. 1953. The Indian as an ecological factor in the northeastern forest. Ecology 34:329–346.

DEGRAAF, R. M., AND D. D. RUDIS. 1986. New England wildlife: habitat, natural history, and distribution. USDA Forest Service Gen. Tech. Rep. NE-108. USDA Forest Service, Northeastern Forest Experiment Station, Broomall, PA.

DEGRAAF, R. M., V. E. SCOTT, R. H. HAMRE, L. ERNST, AND S. H. ANDERSON. 1991. Forest and rangeland birds of the United States: natural history and habitat use. Agricultural handbook 688, USDA Forest Service, Washington, D.C.

DENEVAN, W. M. 1992. The pristine myth: the landscape of the Americas in 1492. Annals of the Association of American Geographers 82:369–385.

DOOLITTLE, W. E. 1992. Agriculture in North America on the eve of contact: a reassessment. Annals of the Association of American Geographers 82:386–401.

DUBLIN, H. T., A. R. E. SINCLAIR, AND J. McGLADE. 1990. Elephants and fire as causes of multiple stable states in the Serengeti-Mara woodlands. Journal of Animal Ecology 59:1147–1164.

DUNN, C. P., F. STEARNS, G. R. GUNTENSPERGEN, AND D. M. SHARPE. 1993. Ecological benefits of the Conservation Reserve Program. Conservation Biology 7:132–139.

DUNWIDDIE, P. W. 1989. Forest and heath: the shaping of vegetation on Nantucket Island. Journal of Forest History 33:126–133.

ELLIOTT, J. J. 1968. Passerculus princeps (Maynard). Ipswich Sparrow. Pp. 657–675 in A. C. Bent (editor). Life histories of North American grosbeaks, buntings, towhees, finches, sparrows, and allies. U.S. National Museum Bulletin 237, pt. 2.

ELLS, S. F. 1995. Breeding Henslow's Sparrows in Lincoln, Massachusetts, 1994. Bird Observer 23:113–115.

FEDUCCIA, A. 1985. Catesby's birds of colonial America. University of North Carolina Press, Chapel Hill, NC.

FORBUSH, E. H. 1925. Birds of Massachusetts and other New England states. Pt. 1. Massachusetts Department of Agriculture, Boston, MA.

FORBUSH, E. H. 1927. Birds of Massachusetts and other New England states. Pt. 2. Massachusetts Department of Agriculture, Boston, MA.

GLEASON, H. A., AND A. CRONQUIST. 1991. Manual of vascular plants of northeastern United States and adjacent Canada. 2d ed. New York Botanical Garden, New York, NY.

GRISCOM, L. 1949. The birds of Concord. Harvard University Press, Cambridge, MA.

GROSS, A. O. 1932. Heath Hen. Pp. 264–280 in A. C. Bent (editor). Life histories of North American gallinaceous birds. U.S. National Museum Bulletin 162.

GUILDAY, J. E. 1962. The Pleistocene local fauna of the Natural Chimneys, Augusta County, Virginia. Annals of the Carnegie Museum 36:87–122.

GUILDAY, J. E., P. S. MARTIN, AND A. D. McGRADY. 1964. New Paris No. 4: a Pleistocene cave deposit on Bedford County, Pennsylvania. Bulletin of the National Speleological Society 26:121–194.

HAMMETT, J. E. 1992. The shapes of adaptation: historical ecology of anthropogenic landscapes in the southeastern United States. Landscape Ecology 7:121–135.

HARPER, R. M. 1911. The Hempstead Plains: a natural prairie on Long Island. Bulletin of the American Geographic Society 43:351–360.

HART, J. F. 1968. Loss and abandonment of cleared land in the eastern United States. Annals of the Association of American Geographers 58:417–440.

HERKERT, J. R. 1991. Prairie birds of Illinois: population response to two centuries of habitat change. Illinois Natural History Survey Bulletin 34:393–399.

HERKERT, J. R. 1994. The effect of habitat fragmentation on midwestern grassland bird communities. Ecological Applications 4:461–471.

HOSMER, J. K. 1959. Winthrop's journal, "History of New England", 1630–1649. Barnes and Noble, New York, NY.

HOWARD, R. J., AND J. S. LARSON. 1985. A stream habitat classification system for beaver. Journal of Wildlife Management 49:19–25.

HURLEY, R. J., AND E. C. FRANKS. 1976. Changes in the breeding ranges of two grassland birds. Auk 93:108–115.

JOHNSGARD, P. A. 1983. The grouse of the world. University of Nebraska Press, Lincoln, NE.

JOHNSON, D. H., AND L. D. IGL. 1995. Contributions of the Conservation Reserve Program to populations of breeding birds in North Dakota. Wilson Bulletin 107:709–718.

JOHNSON, D. H., AND M. D. SCHWARTZ. 1993. The Conservation Reserve Program and grassland birds. Conservation Biology 7:934–937.

KULIKOFF, A. 1986. Tobacco and slaves: the development of southern cultures in the Chesapeake, 1680–1800. University of North Carolina Press, Chapel Hill, NC.

KURTÉN, B., AND E. ANDERSON. 1980. Pleistocene mammals of North America. Columbia University Press, New York, NY.

LANYON, W. E. 1956. Ecological aspects of the sympatric distribution of meadowlarks in the north-central states. Ecology 37:98–108.

LENT, R. A., AND T. S. LITWIN. 1989. Bird-habitat relationships as a guide to ecologically-based management at Floyd Bennett Field, Gateway National Recreation Area. Part 1. Baseline study. Seatuck Research Program, Cornell Laboratory of Ornithology, Islip, NY.

LINDHOLT, P. J. 1988. John Josselyn, colonial traveler: a critical edition of account of two voyages to New-England. University Press of New England, Hanover, NH.

LORIMER, C. G. 1977. The presettlement forest and natural disturbance cycle of northeastern Maine. Ecology 58:139–148.

MARTIN, P. S., AND R. G. KLEIN (EDITORS). 1984. Quaternary extinctions: a prehistoric revolution. University of Arizona Press, Tucson, AZ.

MAYFIELD, H. F. 1988. Changes in bird life at the western end of Lake Erie. Part 1. American Birds 42:393–398.

MEHRHOFF, L. J. 1997. Thoughts on the biogeography of grassland plants in New England. Pp. 15–23 in P. D. Vickery and P. W. Dunwiddie (editors). Grasslands of northeastern North America: ecology and conservation of native and agricultural landscapes. Massachusetts Audubon Society, Lincoln, MA.

MELVIN, S. 1994. Military bases provide habitat for rare grassland birds. Massachusetts Division of Fisheries and Wildlife Natural Heritage News 4:3.

NAIMAN, R. J., J. M. MELILLO, AND J. E. HOBBIE. 1988. Ecosystem alteration of boreal forest streams by beaver (Castor canadensis). Ecology 67:1254–1269.

OLMSTED, C. E. 1937. Vegetation of certain sand plains of Connecticut. Botanical Gazette 99:209–300.

PARMALEE, P. W., AND W. E. KLIPPEL. 1982. Evidence of a boreal avifauna in middle Tennessee during the late Pleistocene. Auk 99:365–368.

PATTERSON, W. A., III, AND K. E. SASSAMAN. 1988. Indian fires in the prehistory of New England. Pp. 107–135 in G. P. Nichols (editor). Holocene human ecology in northeastern North America. Plenum Publishing, New York, NY.

PETERJOHN, B. 1994. The North American Breeding Bird Survey. Birding 26:386–398.

PUCHKOV, P. V. 1992. Uncompensated Wuermian extinctions. Part 2. Transformation of the environment by giant herbivores. Vestnik Zoologii 0(1):58–66.

REMILLARD, M. M., G. K. GRUENDLING, AND D. J. BOGUCKI. 1987. Disturbance by beaver (Castor canaden-

sis Kuhl) and increased landscape heterogeneity. Pp. 103–122 in M. G. Turner (editor). Landscape heterogeneity and disturbance. Springer-Verlag, New York, NY.

RODENHOUSE, N. L., L. B. BEST, R. J. O'CONNOR, AND E. K. BOLLINGER. 1995. Effects of agricultural practices and farmland structures. Pp. 269–293 in T. E. Martin and D. M. Finch (editors). Ecology and management of neotropical migratory birds: a synthesis and review of critical issues. Oxford University Press, New York, NY.

RUNKLE, J. R. 1990. Gap dynamics in an Ohio Acer-Fagus forest and speculations on the geography of disturbance. Canadian Journal of Forest Research 20:632–641.

RUSSELL, E. W. B. 1983. Indian-set fires in the forests of the northeastern United States. Ecology 64:78–88.

RUSSELL, H. S. 1980. Indian New England before the Mayflower. University Press of New England, Hanover, NH.

SAUER, J. R., B. G. PETERJOHN, S. SCHWARTZ, AND J. E. HINES. 1995. The grassland bird home page. Ver. 95.1: www.mbr.nbs.gov/bbs/grass/grass.htm. U.S. Geological Survey, Patuxent Wildlife Research Center, Laurel, MD.

SEISCHAB, F. K., AND D. ORWIG. 1991. Catastrophic disturbances in the presettlement forests of western New York. Bulletin of the Torrey Botanical Club 114:330–335.

SHAFFER, L. N. 1992. Native Americans before 1492: the moundbuilding centers of the eastern woodlands. M. E. Sharpe, Armonk, NY.

SICCAMA, T. G. 1971. Presettlement and present forest vegetation in northern Vermont with special reference to Chittenden County. American Midland Naturalist 85:153–172.

SMITH, B. D. 1989. Origins of agriculture in eastern North America. Science 246:1566–1571.

SMITH, B. D. 1995. The origins of agriculture in the Americas. Evolutionary Anthropology 3:174–184.

SMITH, W. P. 1968. Eastern Henslow's Sparrow. Pp. 776–778 in A. C. Bent (editor). Life histories of North American grosbeaks, buntings, towhees, finches, sparrows, and allies. U.S. National Museum Bulletin 237, pt. 2.

STALTER, R., AND E. E. LAMONT. 1987. Vegetation of the Hempstead Plains, Mitchell Field, Long Island, New York. Bulletin of the Torrey Botanical Club 114:330–335.

STOBO, W. T., AND I. A. MCLAREN. 1971. Late winter distribution of the Ipswich Sparrow. American Birds 25:941–944.

STOBO, W. T., AND I. A. MCLAREN. 1975. The Ipswich Sparrow. Nova Scotian Institute of Science, Halifax, NS.

SVENSON, H. K. 1936. The early vegetation of Long Island. Brooklyn Botanic Garden Journal 25:207–227.

TAYLOR, N. 1923. The vegetation of Long Island, part 1. The vegetation of Montauk: a study of grassland and forest. Brooklyn Botanic Garden Memoirs vol. 2.

THOMAS, E. S. 1951. Distribution of Ohio animals. Ohio Journal of Science 51:153–167.

VAUGHAN, A. T. 1977. New England's prospect (by

William Wood). University of Massachusetts Press, Amherst, MA.

VEIT, R. R., AND W. R. PETERSEN. 1993. Birds of Massachusetts. Massachusetts Audubon Society, Lincoln, MA.

VICKERY, P. D. 1992. A regional analysis of endangered, threatened, and special concern birds in the northeastern United States. Transactions of the Northeast Section of the Wildlife Society 48:1–10.

VICKERY, P. D., M. L. HUNTER, JR., AND S. M. MELVIN. 1994. Effects of habitat area on the distribution of grassland birds in Maine. Conservation Biology 8: 1087–1097.

WEBB, T., III. 1988. Eastern North America. Pp. 385–414 *in* B. Huntley and T. Webb III (editors). Vegetation history. Kluwer Academic Publishers, Hingham, MA.

WHEELWRIGHT, N. T., AND J. D. RISING. 1993. Savannah Sparrow (*Passerculus sandwichensis*). *In* A. Poole and F. Gill (editors). The birds of North America, no. 45. Academy of Natural Sciences, Philadel-

phia, PA, and American Ornithologists' Union, Washington, D.C.

WHITCOMB, R. F. 1987. North American forests and grassland: biotic conservation. Pp. 163–176 *in* D. A. Saunders, G. W. Arnold, A. A. Burbidge, and A. J. M. Hopkins (editors). Nature conservation: the role of remnants of native vegetation. Surrey Beatty & Sons, Chipping Norton, New South Wales, Australia.

WHITMORE, R. C., AND G. A. HALL. 1978. The response of passerine species to a new resource: reclaimed surface mines in West Virginia. American Birds 32: 6–9.

WHITNEY, G. G. 1994. From coastal wilderness to fruited plain. Cambridge University Press, New York, NY.

WILLIAMS, R. 1963. The complete writings of Roger Williams. Vol. 2. Russell and Russell, New York, NY.

WINNE, J. C. 1988. History of vegetation and fire on the Pineo Ridge blueberry barrens in Washington County, Maine. M.S. thesis. University of Maine, Orono, ME.

Studies in Avian Biology No. 19:72–80, 1999.

GRASSLAND BIRD CONSERVATION IN NORTHEASTERN NORTH AMERICA

Jeffrey V. Wells and Kenneth V. Rosenberg

Abstract. As a first step in the development of a conservation plan for grassland birds in the northeastern United States, we prioritized species based on the percent of estimated total breeding population in states and provinces throughout North America. As expected, most species had only a small percent of their total breeding population in the Northeast. We estimated that 82 percent of all Savannah Sparrows (*Passerculus sandwichensis*), 47 percent of Vesper Sparrows (*Pooecetes gramineus*), and 37 percent of Bobolinks (*Dolichonyx oryzivorous*) breed in Canada. An estimated 60 percent of North American Grasshopper Sparrows (*Ammodramus savannarum*) breed in Kansas, Nebraska, North Dakota, and South Dakota. The grassland species we consider to be most at risk, Henslow's Sparrow (*A. henslowii*), has a relatively restricted breeding range with most of the population (more than 50 percent) in Ohio, Michigan, and Wisconsin but with a substantial percent (more than 20 percent) in the Northeast as well. This highlights the responsibility of different regions to the global, long-term persistence of species. A species-level analysis, however, does not consider regional genetic variability that may include taxonomic recognition below the species level. We considered this factor by repeating the above process for each subspecies of eastern grassland bird. We found that 100 percent of Eastern Henslow's Sparrows (*A. h. susurrans*) breed in the northeastern United States. Similarly, the Northeast supports 12 percent of the breeding Eastern Grasshopper Sparrows (*A. s. pratensis*) but only 4 percent of the total breeding population (all subspecies combined). This perspective counters the suggestion that the northeastern United States is unimportant for grassland birds. A regional grassland bird conservation plan should include (1) standardized inventory and monitoring, particularly for Henslow's Sparrow; (2) identification of key nesting sites supporting high diversity and abundance of grassland birds and development of plans for management or acquisition of these sites where appropriate; (3) completion of a preliminary population viability analysis for the least abundant species to assess the relative importance of different sites; and (4) development of guidelines for how private landowners and public land managers can manage grasslands to benefit grassland birds.

CONSERVACIÓN DE AVES DE PASTIZAL EN EL NORESTE DE AMÉRICA DEL NORTE

Sinopsis. Como primer paso en el desarrollo de un plan de conservación para aves de pastizal en el noreste de los Estados Unidos, pusimos en orden de las especies a partir de su porcentaje de la tasa total de la población reproductiva en estados y provincias en toda América del Norte. Como esperamos, la mayoría de las especies tenía sólo un pequeño porcentaje del total de su población reproductiva en el noreste. Estimamos en un 82 por ciento los Gorriones Sabaneros (*Passerculus sandwichensis*), en un 47 por ciento los Gorriones Coliblancos (*Pooecetes gramineus*) y en un 37 por ciento los Tordos Arroceros (*Dolichonyx oryzivorous*) que se reproducen en Canadá. Un número aproximado al 60 por ciento de los Gorriones Chapulines (*Ammodramus savannarum*) de América del Norte se reproducen en Kansas, Nebraska, Dakota del Norte y Dakota del Sur. La especie de pastizal que consideramos con más riesgo, el Gorrión de Henslow (*A. henslowii*), tiene una extensión reproductiva relativamente reducida, con la mayoría de la población (más de un 50 por ciento) en Ohio, Michigan y Wisconsin, pero también con una presencia importante (más de un 20 por ciento) en el noreste. Esto subraya la responsabilidad de varias regiones ante la sobrevivencia mundial de especies a largo plazo. Sin embargo, un análisis a nivel de especie no considera la variación genética regional que puede incluir un reconocimiento taxonómico menor al de especie. Consideramos este elemento al repetir el proceso anterior para cada subespecie de ave de pastizal del este. Descubrimos que 100 por ciento de los Gorriones de Henslow del Este (*A. h. susurrans*) se reproducen en el noreste de los Estados Unidos. De igual manera el noreste mantiene un 12 por ciento de los Gorriones Chapulines del Noreste (*A. s. pratensis*) en reproducción, pero tiene sólo un 4 por ciento de la población reproductiva total (todas las subespecies combinadas). Esta perspectiva contradice la idea sugerida de que el noreste de los Estados Unidos no es importante para las aves de pastizal. Un plan de conservación regional para aves de pastizal debe incluir (1) inventario y medición uniformes, especialmente para los Gorriones de Henslow; (2) identificación de lugares de reproducción que mantienen mucha diversidad y abundancia de aves de pastizal, y desarrollo de planes para la administración o adquisición de estos lugares donde sea apropiado; (3) realización de un análisis preliminar de la viabilidad de la población para las especies menos abundantes, con el fin de determinar la importancia relativa de varios lugares; y (4) desarrollo de sugerencias para dueños particulares y administradores de terrenos públicos en relación al manejo de pastizales para beneficiar a las aves de pastizal.

Key Words: bird conservation; conservation priorities; grassland birds; Henslow's Sparrow; northeastern United States; subspecies.

Assessing regional species and habitat priorities is critical to the conservation planning process and is central to the North American songbird management plan under development through the Partners In Flight coalition (Finch and Stangel 1993). Bird species may be prioritized for conservation consideration based on several global and regional criteria (Hunter et al. 1993, Carter et al. in press) or on the proportion of their total breeding population supported in a particular region (Rosenberg and Wells 1995, in press). This latter approach, which provides a global perspective on the relative responsibility of each region to the overall conservation of each species, has been applied to all neotropical migratory landbirds breeding in the northeastern United States (Rosenberg and Wells 1995, in press). That analysis highlighted a potential conflict between long-term planning for species with high proportions of their total breeding population in the region and local concern for species showing significant population declines. Bird species of grasslands and other early-successional habitats are at the center of this dichotomy.

In the northeastern United States, grassland and shrubland birds have been identified as the habitat-community groups showing the most widespread and persistent declines in abundance (Witham and Hunter 1992, Askins 1993). Initially, however, these declines were treated as a matter of little importance because of a perception that there had been little grassland and shrubland habitat in the Northeast prior to European colonization. More recently, careful reviews of the available evidence have shown that open grassland and shrubland habitats composed a significant proportion of the pre–European arrival landscape (Marks 1983, Askins 1993). One of the most compelling pieces of evidence for the existence—and rapid destruction—of such habitats is the evolution of a distinct taxonomic form of the Greater Prairie Chicken (*Tympanuchus cupido*) in the eastern United States: the Heath Hen (*T. c. cupido*), which became extinct on Martha's Vineyard, Massachusetts, in 1932 (AOU 1957).

Concern for the conservation of declining grassland birds has resulted in legal designation of one or more species on virtually every northeastern state's threatened and endangered species list (Vickery 1992). For example, Upland Sandpiper (*Bartramia longicauda*) and Grasshopper Sparrow (*Ammodramus savannarum*) are listed by at least seven states, and Vesper Sparrow (*Pooecetes gramineus*) and Henslow's Sparrow (*Ammodramus henslowii*) are listed by at least five states. In addition, Henslow's Sparrow was recently assessed as a potential candidate for listing by the U.S. Fish and Wildlife Service (USFWS; Pruitt 1996).

In this paper we assess the conservation status of grassland bird species in the northeastern United States from a continental perspective. We first consider the importance of the Northeast to the total breeding population of each species; we then compare population trends in the Northeast with those in other regions of the United States and Canada. Finally, because of the potential distinctiveness of eastern populations of certain grassland birds, we discuss how consideration of subspecies affects our current view of grassland bird conservation in the Northeast.

METHODS

We considered the following eight species of eastern grassland birds: Upland Sandpiper, Horned Lark (*Eremophila alpestris*), Savannah Sparrow (*Passerculus sandwichensis*), Grasshopper Sparrow, Henslow's Sparrow, Vesper Sparrow, Bobolink (*Dolichonyx oryzivorus*), and Eastern Meadowlark (*Sturnella magna*). As a measure of potential genetic diversity, we considered the subspecies described in the 1957 American Ornithologists' Union's check-list (AOU 1957), which was the most recent reference that systematically reviewed subspecies in all North American species north of Mexico.

We estimated the proportion of the total population of each species breeding in each U.S. state and Canadian province using the following procedure. First, using ranges described in Peterson 1980 and 1990, we estimated the proportion of each state occupied and then multiplied that proportion by the area of each state. We then multiplied the range area occupied in each state and province by the relative abundance calculated for that area based on USFWS Breeding Bird Survey (BBS) data from 1966 to 1994 (Sauer et al. 1996). These state and province values were then summed to get an index of the total breeding population size. Note that this index represents a species' total breeding range size as well as the species' relative abundance across its breeding range; it is not, however, an accurate estimate of the total number of individuals in the species' breeding population.

For each species we then divided the value for each state or province by the total population size index to get the estimated percent of the total population breeding in each state and province. These percentages were then summed to give an estimate of the percent of the total population breeding in the Northeast (here defined as USFWS Region-5 [Maine, Vermont, New Hampshire, Massachusetts, Connecticut, Rhode Island, New York, New Jersey, Pennsylvania, Maryland, Delaware, Virginia, and West Virginia]), other USFWS regions, and Canada (Table 1). For species with subspecies described in the American Ornithologists' Union's 1957 check-list, we also determined what proportion of the relevant subspecies breed in the Northeast. Finally, to assess geographic patterns in population trends, we compared percent of population in USFWS regions and Canada against the 1966–1994 BBS trend (Sauer et al. 1996).

TABLE 1. PERCENT OF TOTAL BREEDING POPULATION OF EIGHT GRASSLAND BIRD SPECIES IN THE NORTHEASTERN UNITED STATES (USFWS REGION-5), OTHER USFWS REGIONS, AND CANADA

Species	Region					
	NE	SE	MW	GP	SW	CAN
Upland Sandpiper	0.3[a]	0.0	5.6	85.0	0.0	9.1
Horned Lark	0.1	0.1	6.0	47.5	13.7	19.4
Savannah Sparrow	1.6	0.0	9.1	5.1	0.0	81.7
Grasshopper Sparrow	3.6	2.2	19.8	70.0	4.1	0.2
Henslow's Sparrow	21.3	0.0[b]	78.6	0.0	0.0[c]	0.0
Vesper Sparrow	0.6	0.0	15.1	31.7	0.0	46.6
Bobolink	13.7	0.0	32.6	17.0	0.0	36.5
Eastern Meadowlark	5.4	31.9	23.3	3.6	35.1	0.6

Note: NE = Northeast (Connecticut, Delaware, Maine, Maryland, Massachusetts, New Hampshire, New Jersey, New York, Pennsylvania, Rhode Island, Vermont, Virginia, West Virginia); SE = Southeast (Alabama, Arkansas, Florida, Georgia, Kentucky, Louisiana, Mississippi, North Carolina, South Carolina, Tennessee); MW = Midwest (Illinois, Indiana, Iowa, Michigan, Minnesota, Missouri, Ohio, Wisconsin); GP = Great Plains (Colorado, Kansas, Montana, Nebraska, North Dakota, South Dakota, Utah, Wyoming); SW = Southwest (Arizona, New Mexico, Oklahoma, Texas); CAN = Canada.
[a] Estimate may be low because BBS abundance was not calculated for most northeastern states.
[b] Small, recently discovered population in North Carolina.
[c] Large, recently discovered population in Oklahoma.

RESULTS AND CONSERVATION IMPLICATIONS

Of the eight species considered at the species level, Henslow's Sparrow had the highest percent of its breeding population in the Northeast, with 21.3%, followed by Bobolink with 13.7% and Eastern Meadowlark with 5.4% (Table 1). None of the other species had more than 5% of their estimated population in the region. Most species had a high percent of their total breeding population in a single region. For example, 85% of Upland Sandpipers and 70% of Grasshopper Sparrows were estimated to breed in the Great Plains region (USFWS Region-6). Similarly, the Midwest (USFWS Region-3) supported an estimated 78.6% of the world's breeding Henslow's Sparrows. Canada had 81.7% of breeding Savannah Sparrows and 46.6% of breeding Vesper Sparrows (Table 1).

When we considered subspecies, the importance of the Northeast to certain grassland birds was highlighted (Table 2). For example, although the Northeast held 1.6% of all breeding Savannah Sparrows, it supported 55% of the eastern subspecies, *P. s. savanna*. Similarly, the Northeast held 3.6% of breeding Grasshopper Sparrows but 11.5% of the eastern subspecies, *A. s. pratensis*. The most dramatic example was Henslow's Sparrow, for which the Northeast supported 21.3% of the entire breeding population but 100% of the remaining populations of the described eastern subspecies, *A. h. susurrans.*

All eight grassland species under consideration, except Upland Sandpiper, showed a significant negative trend based on continental BBS data (Sauer et al. 1996). Henslow's Sparrow, with the lowest population size index, also had the greatest negative trend (Fig. 1).

If the percent of total breeding population in each region is compared with the trends for those regions, a geographic pattern of the conservation status of each species emerges (Fig. 2). These patterns show where conservation efforts will have the greatest overall influence on each species and help put the conservation status of grassland birds in the Northeast in a larger perspective. We summarize these patterns in the following species accounts.

TABLE 2. PERCENT OF TOTAL BREEDING POPULATION OF NINE GRASSLAND BIRD SPECIES IN THE NORTHEASTERN UNITED STATES, CONSIDERING GEOGRAPHICALLY VARIABLE SUBSPECIES

Species	Eastern subspecies	All subspecies
Heath Hen	100.0 (*T. c. cupido*)	?
Upland Sandpiper	no subspecies	0.3
Horned Lark	2.1 (*E. a. praticola*)	0.1
Savannah Sparrow	55.2 (*P. s. savanna*)	1.6
Grasshopper Sparrow	11.5 (*A. s. pratensis*)	3.6
Henslow's Sparrow	100.0 (*A. h. susurrans*)	21.3
Vesper Sparrow	3.1 (*P. g. gramineus*)	0.6
Bobolink	no subspecies	13.7
Eastern Meadowlark	12.9 (*S. m. magna*)	5.4

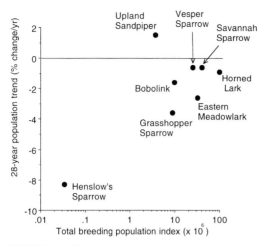

FIGURE 1. Total breeding population index versus 28-year population trend in eight species of northeastern grassland birds.

FIGURE 3. Schematic showing general areas of highest abundance for eight species of northeastern grassland birds.

UPLAND SANDPIPER

The largest breeding populations of Upland Sandpipers occur in the Great Plains states of South Dakota (34%), North Dakota (19%), Nebraska (15%), and Kansas (11%; Fig. 3). In the Great Plains, the species shows an increasing population trend, indicating that the overall population is doing well where the species is most abundant (Fig. 2). The northeastern United States supports a small percentage of the total

breeding population of this species, and no subspecies have been described. The long-term population trend for the region appears to be stable, although there is clear evidence for declines in Upland Sandpipers in portions of the Northeast (Andrle and Carroll 1988, Brauning 1992, Foss 1994). Conservation of Upland Sandpipers in the Northeast will have little impact on the global population status, but as this species is an indicator of intact and diverse grassland commu-

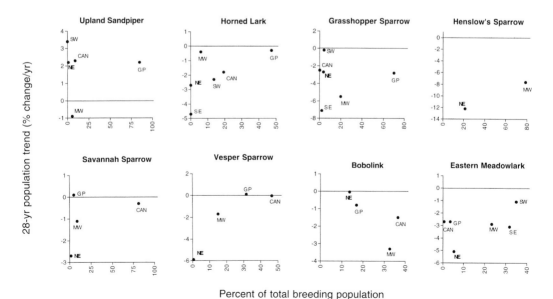

FIGURE 2. Percent of total breeding population for U.S. Fish and Wildlife Service (USFWS) regions and Canada (see Table 1 for abbreviations) versus 28-year population trend for eight species of northeastern grassland birds.

nities, local conservation efforts undoubtedly will continue.

HORNED LARK

The largest percentage of the total Horned Lark breeding population occurs in the western Great Plains states and provinces, including Montana (13%), Saskatchewan (12%), Colorado (10%), and North Dakota (7%; Fig. 3). Percentages for this species are probably exaggerated somewhat because far-northern populations in Canada and Alaska are not censused by the BBS and therefore are not included in our analyses. The northeastern United States currently supports less than 1% of the total breeding population of this species and only 2% of the eastern subspecies, *E. a. praticola.* Horned Lark populations are stable in areas where they are most abundant but are decreasing over much of the remainder of the breeding range (Fig. 2). Particularly large declines are seen in northeastern states such as New York (−5.7%) and Pennsylvania (−9.7%) as well as at the southern limit of the eastern breeding range in Kentucky (−9.1%) and Tennessee (−7.9%). By itself the Horned Lark may not be considered a high priority species in the region, as conservation efforts will have minimal impact on the species as a whole. To conserve the rich genetic diversity evident in this highly variable species, however, a continentwide strategy for stabilizing populations is desirable.

SAVANNAH SPARROW

The largest proportion of all Savannah Sparrows breed in the Canadian provinces from Alberta to Quebec (Fig. 3). The northeastern United States supports less than 2% of the total breeding population of this species but 55% of the eastern subspecies, *P. s. savanna.* Savannah Sparrows are increasing in the western Canadian provinces but decreasing in the eastern provinces (except Newfoundland), resulting in a stable trend overall in Canada (Fig. 2). Steepest declines are occurring in the Northeast, including most of the range of the eastern subspecies. Because the northeastern United States supports a large percentage of the population of this declining subspecies, its status should be elevated to that of moderate conservation concern in the Northeast. Fortunately, both the global population and local densities of Savannah Sparrows are very high, and the species is more generalized in its habitat selection than are most other grassland species in the region (Wheelwright and Rising 1993).

GRASSHOPPER SPARROW

Grasshopper Sparrow breeding populations are largest in the Great Plains states of Kansas (19%), South Dakota (17%), North Dakota (13%), and Nebraska (12%; Fig. 3). The northeastern United States supports only 3.6% of the total breeding population of this species but 11.5% of the eastern subspecies, *A. s. pratensis.* Population declines are evident throughout the range of this species, except in the Southwest (Fig. 2). Declines are particularly steep in some northeastern states, especially New York (−10.2%), New Jersey (−10.2%), and West Virginia (−12.5%), but an increasing population trend in the Piedmont of Virginia (+4.9%) caused the regionwide population decline to be less steep. Because Grasshopper Sparrows are in need of a continentwide conservation strategy, we think efforts to stabilize or enhance local populations in the Northeast are justified.

HENSLOW'S SPARROW

Henslow's Sparrow has the smallest total breeding range of any of the species we considered, with virtually the entire global population concentrated in the Midwest and Northeast (Fig. 3). Henslow's Sparrow also shows the steepest declines of any grassland bird, both in the Northeast and throughout its range (Fig. 2). Percentages for these regions may be exaggerated because this species is too rare to be detected on BBS routes in certain states, and these are therefore not included in our trend analysis. For example, fairly large numbers have been found breeding in northeastern Oklahoma since the early 1990s, though the species has only occasionally been registered on BBS routes in that state (Pruitt 1996).

We consider this species to rank first in conservation priority among grassland birds in the Northeast, and efforts to stabilize or enhance regional populations should be made in coordination with an overall strategy to protect this species.

VESPER SPARROW

The Vesper Sparrow's breeding distribution overlaps broadly with that of the Horned Lark (Fig. 3), with the largest percentage of the Vesper Sparrow's total breeding population in Alberta (18%), Montana (16%), and Saskatchewan (15%). Populations in these areas, and in the remainder of the species' western range, are stable or increasing (Fig. 2). In contrast, small populations in the northeastern states are declining precipitously. These populations represent 3% of the eastern subspecies, *P. g. gramineus,* which is declining throughout its range. As with Horned Lark and other widespread species, conservation efforts in the Northeast will have little impact on the total breeding population of Vesper Sparrows; however, concern for the eastern subspecies, if warranted, could elevate this species' conservation status in the region.

BOBOLINK

Unlike most of the other species considered here, the Bobolink is fairly evenly distributed over a broad area; no single state or province supports more than about 10% of the total breeding population. The largest numbers occur in a belt from North Dakota and Minnesota east to southern Quebec (Fig. 3). Unlike populations of the other species we considered, Bobolink populations have been stable in most northeastern states (Fig. 2); the largest declines have occurred in the Midwest (especially Indiana [−8.7%] and Illinois [−10.7%]) and in Quebec (−4.1%). The Northeast has a relatively large percent of the total breeding population (13.7%); only Henslow's Sparrow has more of its total breeding population in this region (21.3%). The lack of declining populations and lack of geographic variation evident in this species, however, suggest that the Bobolink is only a moderate conservation priority in the region.

EASTERN MEADOWLARK

The largest breeding populations of Eastern Meadowlarks occur in the southern Great Plains states, from Missouri to Texas (Fig. 3). Populations in these states show a weak negative population trend (Fig. 2). Throughout the remainder of the species' range, declines are much steeper, with declines of more than 8% per year in some northeastern states. All states with significant declining trends are in the range of the eastern subspecies, *S. m. magna*. Conservation status of the Eastern Meadowlark in the Northeast is similar to that of the Grasshopper Sparrow, in that although regional efforts will have little impact on the global population, they may be coordinated with a rangewide strategy to conserve the species. Similarly, recognition that the eastern subspecies is particularly vulnerable elevates its conservation priority in the region.

DISCUSSION

Our analyses confirm that the northeastern United States does not support a large proportion of the total breeding population of most grassland species. Henslow's Sparrow is the only species for which a substantial proportion of the total breeding population is restricted to the Northeast. Clearly, Henslow's Sparrow is the highest priority grassland species in the region based on this criterion, and any regional conservation plan should focus on stabilizing or en-

hancing populations of this species. Indeed, Henslow's Sparrow ranked first in regional concern, even when compared with all nongrassland birds (Rosenberg and Wells 1995, in press). Therefore, in a regional grassland bird initiative, states such as Pennsylvania and New York, with high proportions of the total breeding population, are most responsible for plans to protect and manage Henslow's Sparrows. Recent status assessments of this species recommended that comprehensive inventory and monitoring programs be undertaken throughout the breeding range, especially since the ability to monitor Henslow's Sparrows through BBS data will become increasingly problematic as the species declines (Smith 1992, Pruitt 1996).

Should other grassland species be given low priority for conservation in the Northeast? Even though conservation actions in this region will have little effect on the long-term continental persistence of these species, several factors argue for continued concern for regional populations. First, most of the declining grassland species are found in habitats that support unique assemblages of plants, invertebrates, and other nonavian vertebrates. For example, northern blazing star (*Liatris scariosa* var. *novae-angliae*) is a rare grassland perennial found only in the northeastern United States; it occurs in habitats that also support grassland birds (Vickery 1996).

Additionally, for several geographically variable species, eastern populations represent described subspecies, and in nearly every case the eastern subspecies are exhibiting the most precipitous declines. Even for widespread species such as Savannah Sparrow and Eastern Meadowlark, significant genetic diversity may be represented in the Northeast and is therefore worthy of protection.

Changes in species-level taxonomy, reflecting modern knowledge of genetic variation, continue to have profound effects on conservation priorities. A recent example is the elevation of Bicknell's Thrush (*Catharus bicknelli*) to full species (Ouellet 1993, AOU 1995), changing its status in the Northeast from a marginal population of the widespread Gray-cheeked Thrush (*C. minimus*) to being among the highest priority landbird species in the region (Rosenberg and Wells 1995, in press). Similarly, the recognition of Salt-marsh Sharp-tailed Sparrow (*Ammodramus caudacutus*) as a separate species (AOU 1995) has made it one of the Northeast's highest priorities in terms of importance of the region to the global population of the species. Importantly, these examples serve to focus attention on the restricted habitats of these "new" species, in these cases stunted mountaintop forests and coastal salt marshes, respectively. Although modern studies of geographic variation are lacking for most North American bird species (Zink and Remsen 1986), we feel that assessing conservation priorities based on even a dated assessment of morphological distinctiveness (i.e., the 1957 American Ornithologists' Union's check-list) is preferable to ignoring potential regional genetic diversity in northeastern grassland species.

BIOGEOGRAPHIC PERSPECTIVE ON GRASSLAND BIRD CONSERVATION

Our analyses have identified areas of North America where the largest breeding populations of each grassland species are concentrated (Fig. 3). Each of these areas has a high responsibility for the overall conservation of a particular species or suite of species, and conservation efforts outside these areas should be coordinated with efforts in the core of each species' range. Interestingly, species that are similar in overall breeding distribution also tend to be similar in their local distribution and habitat affinities in the Northeast. For example, Vesper Sparrows and Horned Larks, which both reach their highest abundance in the western Great Plains, have similar breeding distributions in the northeastern United States based on atlas-block occurrence (Rosenberg and Wells 1995). Both species also tend to occupy dry, sparsely vegetated sites. These distributions are different, however, from those of Bobolinks and Savannah Sparrows, which are also similar to each other in continental and regional breeding distribution as well as in habitat preference. A third example is that of Upland Sandpipers and Grasshopper Sparrows, whose highest abundances are concentrated in the prairie states from North Dakota to Kansas. These two species require larger habitat areas than other species in the Northeast (Vickery et al. 1994), and they tend to share a similar distribution throughout the region.

None of these grassland-species clusters, however, was strongly tied to any geographic portions of the region, such as particular physiographic areas (Rosenberg and Wells 1995). This means there is no clearly defined physiographic region in the Northeast where management plans could be developed for grassland birds as a whole. Instead, what is required is a larger, regionwide initiative that would set different goals for different species in each area.

DEVELOPING A CONSERVATION PLAN FOR THE NORTHEAST

The first step in developing a management plan for grassland species in the Northeast is to carry out a comprehensive inventory so we know where the species of interest occur and how many occur at each site. Fortunately, in New England many of the sites where grassland birds occur have been identified and surveyed (Jones and Vickery 1995), and monitoring efforts are well underway. Inventories are also being undertaken in other northeastern states, including New York and Pennsylvania, through the National Audubon Society Important Bird Areas programs in coordination with the Northeastern Grassland Bird Working Group of Partners In Flight.

Estimates of many other demographic parameters for each population (fecundity, mortality, mean population growth rates, etc.) are also needed to understand the factors affecting abundance trends and to model extinction probabilities (Boyce 1992, Burgman et al. 1993). There are, however, first approximations of these parameters available from other studies (Wells 1995) that allow at least preliminary consideration of the importance of different sites to the extinction risks of grassland species. In Maine, a population viability analysis (PVA) that was carried out for Grasshopper Sparrows yielded useful management recommendations (Wells 1995). Carrying out a preliminary PVA for the New England grassland bird species of concern would help identify those sites of highest importance for the long-term persistence of grassland species in the Northeast. These sites could then be targeted for action, whether it be acquisition, easements, management agreements, or other options.

Another logical step in developing a regional plan for grassland birds would be to identify sites that support multiple grassland species and to see how many of these sites are protected. This is the basic concept of GAP analysis as applied to a limited bird community (Scott and Csuti 1991). For example, consider the number of sites in New England (excluding Vermont) where all of the following species breed: Upland Sandpiper, Vesper Sparrow, and Grasshopper Sparrow. There are perhaps six sites where all three species are known to breed (P. Vickery, pers. comm.). Only one of these is a protected wildlife preserve (Kennebunk Plains Wildlife Management Area, Maine). Four of the other sites are military or municipal airports, and one is a privately owned parcel. The airports could be managed quite easily and effectively for grassland birds with little added expense or modification of airport management plans, as has been shown at Westover Air Force Base in Massachusetts (Melvin 1994, Jones and Vickery 1995). Clearly, however, the long-term persistence of any grassland species in New England will require preservation and management at more than these six sites.

For Henslow's Sparrow, which we have identified as one of the species of most immediate concern in the Northeast, conservation plans are not fully developed. The first priority for developing a plan is to find out where the birds occur and how many are at each site. Therefore, a regional cooperative effort, largely involving New York and Pennsylvania, must be undertaken to identify and survey sites for Henslow's Sparrow. The majority of the most important sites have been identified through the site inventory programs of the National Audubon Society Important Bird Areas programs in New York and Pennsylvania. These sites, and others throughout New England, are being inventoried and monitored using a standardized methodology coordinated through the Northeastern Grassland Bird Working Group of Partners In Flight.

One aspect of the conservation of all species of grassland birds in the Northeast is the importance of military installations and of commercial and municipal airports. Many of the largest concentrations of grassland birds occur at these sites throughout the region. In New England, cooperative management between airport or site managers and wildlife managers has been successful in increasing grassland bird populations (Melvin 1994). The importance of these sites should be assessed for the entire region, and coordination of management efforts among sites (particularly those in the same organizations, i.e., naval bases, air-force bases, etc.) should be encouraged.

Finally, we note that the long-term persistence of grassland bird species in the Northeast is unlikely if these species are restricted to a few isolated, publicly managed sites. Private landowners and public land managers must be provided with guidelines for management practices that are beneficial to grassland birds, and they must be encouraged to implement them.

ACKNOWLEDGMENTS

This paper is partly based on a report submitted to USFWS Region-5; we are grateful to D. Pence and the USFWS for funding this project. For providing BBS data and advice, we thank B. Peterjohn and J. Sauer. We benefited from discussions with members of the Northeast Grassland Bird Working Group, in particular P. D. Vickery and D. Brauning, who also provided helpful comments on the manuscript.

LITERATURE CITED

AMERICAN ORNITHOLOGISTS' UNION. 1957. Check-list of North American birds. 5th ed. American Ornithologists' Union, Washington, D.C.

AMERICAN ORNITHOLOGISTS' UNION. 1995. Fortieth supplement to the American Ornithologists' Union check-list of North American birds. Auk 112:819–830.

ANDRLE, R. F., AND J. R. CARROLL. 1988. The atlas of breeding birds in New York state. Cornell University Press, Ithaca, NY.

ASKINS, R. A. 1993. Population trends in grassland, shrubland, and forest birds in eastern North America. Current Ornithology 11:1–34.

BOYCE, M. S. 1992. Population viability analysis. Annual Review of Ecology and Systematics 23:481–506.

BRAUNING, D. W. 1992. Atlas of breeding birds in Pennsylvania. University of Pittsburgh Press, Pittsburgh, PA.

BURGMAN, M. A., S. FERSON, AND H. R. AKÇAKAYA. 1993. Risk assessment in conservation biology. Chapman & Hall, New York, NY.

CARTER, M. F., W. C. HUNTER, D. N. PASHLEY, J. M. BRADLEY, J. PRICE, AND G. S. BUTCHER. In press. Setting landbird conservation priorities for states and physiographic regions within the United States. *In* R. E. Bonney, Jr., D. N. Pashley, and R. Cooper (editors). Strategies for bird conservation: creating the Partners in Flight planning process. Cornell Laboratory of Ornithology, Ithaca, NY.

FINCH, D. M., AND P. W. STANGEL (EDITORS). 1993. Status and management of neotropical migratory birds. USDA Forest Service Gen. Tech. Rep. RM-229. USDA Forest Service, Fort Collins, CO.

FOSS, C. R. 1994. Atlas of breeding birds in New Hampshire. Audubon Society of New Hampshire, Concord, NH.

HUNTER, W. C., M. F. CARTER, D. N. PASHLEY, AND K. BARKER. 1993. The Partners In Flight prioritization scheme. Pp. 109–119 *in* D. M. Finch and P. W. Stangel (editors). Status and management of neotropical migratory birds. USDA Forest Service Gen. Tech. Rep. RM-229. USDA Forest Service, Fort Collins, CO.

JONES, A. L., AND P. D. VICKERY. 1995. Distribution and population status of grassland birds in Massachusetts. Bird Observer 23:89–96.

MARKS, P. L. 1983. On the origin of the field plants of the northeastern United States. American Naturalist 122:210–228.

MELVIN, S. M. 1994. Military bases provide habitat for rare grassland birds. Natural Heritage News, Massachusetts Division of Fisheries and Wildlife 4:3.

OUELLET, H. 1993. Bicknell's Thrush: taxonomic status and distribution. Wilson Bulletin 105:545–572.

PETERSON, R. T. 1980. A field guide to the birds. Houghton Mifflin, Boston, MA.

PETERSON, R. T. 1990. A field guide to western birds. Houghton Mifflin, Boston, MA.

PRUITT, L. 1996. Henslow's Sparrow status assessment. U.S. Fish and Wildlife Service, Bloomington Ecological Services Field Office, Bloomington, IN.

ROSENBERG, K. V., AND J. V. WELLS. 1995. Final report: importance of geographic areas to neotropical migrant birds in the northeast. U.S. Fish and Wildlife Service, Region 5, Hadley, MA.

ROSENBERG, K. V., AND J. V. WELLS. In press. Global perspectives on neotropical migrant bird conservation in the northeast U.S. *In* R. E. Bonney, Jr., D. N. Pashley, and R. Cooper (editors). Strategies for bird conservation: creating the Partners in Flight planning process. Cornell Laboratory of Ornithology, Ithaca, NY.

SAUER, J. R., B. G. PETERJOHN, S. SCHWARTZ, AND J. E. HINES. 1996. The North American Breeding Bird Survey home page. Ver. 95.1: www.mbr.nbs.gov/bbs/bbs.html. U.S. Geological Survey, Patuxent Wildlife Research Center, Laurel, MD.

SCOTT, J. M., AND B. CSUTI. 1991. GAP analysis: blueprint for proactive conservation. FOCUS on Renewable Natural Resources 17:1–2.

SMITH, C. R. 1992. Henslow's Sparrow, *Ammodramus henslowii*. Pp. 315–330 *in* K. J. Schneider and D. M. Pence (editors). Migratory nongame birds of management concern in the northeast. U.S. Fish and Wildlife Service, Newton, MA.

VICKERY, P. D. 1992. A regional analysis of endangered, threatened, and special-concern birds in the northeastern United States. Transactions of the Northeast Section of the Wildlife Society 48:1–10.

VICKERY, P. D. 1996. Effects of prescribed fire on the reproductive ecology of northern blazing star (*Liatris scariosa* var. *novae-angliae*). Report to Maine Natural Areas Program, Department of Conservation, Augusta, ME.

VICKERY, P. D., M. L. HUNTER, JR., AND S. M. MELVIN. 1994. Effects of habitat area on the distribution of grassland birds in Maine. Conservation Biology 8: 1087–1097.

WELLS, J. V. 1995. Investigations into the distribution and abundance of species. Ph.D. dissertation. Cornell University, Ithaca, NY.

WHEELWRIGHT, N. T., AND J. D. RISING. 1993. Savannah Sparrow (*Passerculus sandwichensis*). *In* A. Poole and F. Gill (editors). The birds of North America, no. 45. Academy of Natural Sciences, Philadelphia, PA, and American Ornithologists' Union, Washington, D.C.

WITHAM, J. W., AND M. L. HUNTER, JR. 1992. Population trends of neotropical migrant landbirds in northern coastal New England. Pp. 85–95 *in* J. M. Hagan III and D. W. Johnston (editors). Ecology and conservation of neotropical migrant landbirds. Smithsonian Institution Press, Washington, D.C.

ZINK, R. M., AND J. V. REMSEN. 1986. Evolutionary processes and patterns of geographic variation in birds. Current Ornithology 4:1–69.

Studies in Avian Biology No. 19:81–86, 1999.

USE OF CULTIVATED FIELDS BY BREEDING MOUNTAIN PLOVERS IN COLORADO

FRITZ L. KNOPF AND JEFFERY R. RUPERT

Abstract. Populations of breeding Mountain Plovers (*Charadrius montanus*) in North America declined an average of 3.7 percent per year from 1966 through 1993, resulting in a 63 percent total decline during that period. This decline led to listing the species as a Candidate Species under the federal Endangered Species Act. Mountain Plovers have been observed nesting on cultivated fields, but nest loss may be high on these sites. During the 1994 breeding season we surveyed Mountain Plover use of contiguous cultivated and native-prairie sites in Weld County, Colorado. Birds used both sites equally in April. The cultivated field was planted in early May, which probably destroyed nests and resulted in plovers reinitiating courtship and renesting. No resurgence of courtship was observed on native prairie during the same period. Observations of Mountain Plovers with radio transmitters during the 1994 breeding seasons revealed that some of the birds that lost nests or chicks on native prairie moved to the recently cultivated field to forage. Two of three Mountain Plovers that hatched eggs within 2 kilometers of the cultivated field moved chicks onto that field until the chicks fledged. We conclude that cultivated fields provide acceptable, and locally valuable, feeding habitat for Mountain Plovers. Because Mountain Plovers have also been reported to nest on plowed ground from Nebraska to Oklahoma, however, and because 31.9 percent of native habitats in the southwestern Great Plains have been cultivated, we also conclude that mechanical working of fields during the nest and early chick phases may contribute to the 3.7 percent annual rate of decline of this species. Four management options are suggested to improve Mountain Plover recruitment on and near cultivated lands.

EL USO DE CAMPOS CULTIVADOS EN COLORADO POR PARTE DE LOS CHORLITOS LLANEROS EN REPRODUCCIÓN

Sinopsis. Las poblaciones en reproducción de Chorlitos Llaneros (*Charadrius montanus*) en América del Norte disminuyeron en un promedio de 3,7 por ciento por año desde 1966 hasta fines de 1993, lo que se tradujo en una disminución total de un 63 por ciento durante aquel período. Esta disminución produjo la clasificación de la especie como Especie Candidata estipulada en la ley federal Endangered Species Act. Se han observado Chorlitos Llaneros haciendo sus nidos en campos cultivados, pero la pérdida de nidos puede ser alta en estos sitios. Durante la estación de reproducción en 1994 censamos el uso por parte del Chorlito Llanero de dos clases de sitios llaneros contiguos, cultivados y nativos, en el Condado de Weld, Colorado. En abril las aves usaron ambos sitios con la misma frecuencia. Se sembró el campo cultivado a principios de mayo, lo cual probablemente destruyó los nidos e indujo a los chorlitos a reiniciar el cortejo y a hacer los nidos nuevamente. No se observó ningún resurgimiento de cortejo en la llanura nativa durante el mismo período. Las observaciones de Chorlitos Llaneros con radiotransmisores durante las estaciones de reproducción de 1994 revelaron que algunas de las aves que perdieron sus nidos o sus pollos en la llanura nativa se mudaron al campo recién cultivado para forrajear. Dos de tres Chorlitos Llaneros que criaron pollos dentro de 2 kilómetros del campo cultivado trasladaron sus pollos allí hasta que volaron. Concluimos que los campos cultivados proveen un hábitat alimenticio aceptable y localmente valioso para los Chorlitos Llaneros. Sin embargo, dado que la información da cuenta de que los Chorlitos Llaneros hacen sus nidos en terreno arado desde Nebraska a Oklahoma, y como un 31,9 por ciento de los hábitats nativos en el suroeste de la Gran Llanura han sido cultivados, concluimos asimismo que la labranza mecánica de los campos durante las fases del nido y de los pollos nuevos puede explicar en gran medida la tasa anual de disminución de 3,7 por ciento en esta especie. Se sugieren cuatro opciones para mejorar el restablecimiento del Chorlito Llanero en terrenos cultivados y cerca de los mismos.

Key Words: *Charadrius montanus*; Colorado; Mountain Plover.

The Great Plains grasslands are the most endangered ecosystem in North America (Samson and Knopf 1994). As a group, grassland birds have shown the most universal and most severe declines of all native bird species, including neotropical migrants (Knopf 1994). Breeding populations of Mountain Plovers (*Charadrius montanus*) declined 63 percent from 1966 to 1993, despite what appeared to be normal rates of productivity in native habitats (Miller and Knopf 1993) and high adult survival (Knopf and Rupert 1995). Because of this decline, the U.S. Fish and Wildlife Service has listed the species as a Candidate Species for Threatened or Endangered status under the federal Endangered Species Act.

Mountain Plovers nest across the western Great Plains and eastern Colorado Plateau region, with a core breeding area in Weld County, Colorado (Graul and Webster 1976). The species nests in areas of shortgrass prairie historically grazed by native herbivores and currently managed as rangeland for domestic herbivores or as dryland (non-irrigated) farms.

The breeding biology of Mountain Plovers is best known from studies at the Pawnee National Grassland in northcentral Colorado. Nests are usually located in areas of native shortgrass prairie dominated by blue grama (*Bouteloua gracilis*) and buffalo grass (*Buchloë dactyloides*; Graul 1975) with the area around nests being 30% or more bare ground (Knopf and Miller 1994). Chicks leave the nest shortly after hatching and often move more than 1 km from the nest site (Knopf and Rupert 1996). Chicks raised on these grasslands generally use disturbed sites (e.g., areas that have suffered locally severe overgrazing, roadsides), especially where some forbs have invaded (Graul 1975).

Breeding Mountain Plovers forage, and occasionally nest, on cultivated fields near native shortgrass-prairie landscapes. Since the early 1990s, nesting on such fields has been relatively common in areas along the eastern boundary of the shortgrass-prairie region, from Texas to Wyoming (Shackford 1991; J. Shackford, pers. comm.). During our ongoing studies of Mountain Plovers in Colorado, we conducted a periodic survey of plover use of a cultivated field contiguous to native-prairie habitat on the Pawnee National Grassland. In this paper we document relative use of native versus cultivated sites; describe habitats used for nesting and brood-rearing on native prairie; and document movements of birds that indicate that this species readily uses cultivated fields during the nesting and brood-rearing periods of the reproductive cycle.

METHODS

We studied Mountain Plovers on the Pawnee National Grassland, a 780-km^2 shortgrass prairie in Weld County, Colorado, during the 1992–1994 breeding seasons. Graul (1973) summarized the physiography, vegetation, and climate of this region.

In 1993 many cultivated fields within 2 km of our study area were left fallow during the April–July breeding season. In 1994 one field contiguous to the study area was left fallow. We implemented a 20-point survey of Mountain Plovers along the fenceline separating the native prairie and cultivated field, with survey points 0.15 km apart. In 1994 we conducted 19 replications, from 20 April through 13 June. All surveys were conducted at sunrise. From each survey point we counted the number of adult Mountain Plovers we saw and/or heard on each side of the survey

line. We were confident that the birds were equally visible on both sides of the survey line. Trends in the use of the two sites were compared using univariate repeated-measures analyses of variance and paired t-tests.

In 1994 we captured 26 adult birds at nests on the Pawnee National Grassland and fitted them with radio transmitters before their eggs hatched. Birds were captured with a leg snare or swing-door box trap (Knopf and Rupert 1996). We relocated each adult almost daily from the time its chicks hatched until the adult left the study area. Because the landowner denied us access to the adjacent cultivated field, we did not conduct any nest searches there, nor did we capture and fit adults with transmitters on that land.

We determined the relative coverage of grass versus bare ground around nests and brood-rearing sites (at distances of 10, 25, and 50 m in each of the cardinal directions) for 11 adult Mountain Plovers that fledged chicks in 1993 or 1994 on the Pawnee National Grassland. Twelve 0.5-m^2 plots were photographed at each nest and brood-rearing site after Knopf and Miller 1994, except that in our study we took photographs in all four cardinal directions. A clear dot-grid was placed over each photograph to determine the percentages of area in grass or bare ground. We also recorded frequencies of cow manure piles and prickly pear cactus (*Opuntia* spp.).

RESULTS

POPULATION SURVEYS

Mountain Plovers were easily detected from distances up to 150 m away. Individuals occasionally could be seen from two adjacent survey points, in which case they were recorded only for the first point. Plovers moved freely back and forth between the cultivated field and native prairie. We frequently watched individual birds walk from one side of the fenceline to the other during a survey. Repeated-measures analysis of variance revealed no difference in the number of Mountain Plovers detected on native and cultivated sites throughout the survey season (20 April–13 June; F = 1.35, df = 16, P = 0.16).

The number of Mountain Plovers using native-prairie ($\bar{X}$ = 12.5 ± 4.24) and cultivated ($\bar{X}$ = 12.5 ± 4.12) sites (t < 0.01, P > 0.99) and the pattern of use (F = 0.79, df = 6, P = 0.58) were similar in the first 7 of the 19 surveys we conducted (Fig. 1). The number of birds peaked on the third survey but then declined markedly through the seventh survey. Between 3 and 6 May the cultivated field was chemically treated for weeds and planted. In the eighth survey, Mountain Plover detections on native prairie remained low, whereas detections on the cultivated field peaked sharply (Fig. 1). Birds at this time were seen only foraging on native prairie but were seen mostly advertising territories and courting on the cultivated field (see Knopf 1996b for review of behaviors).

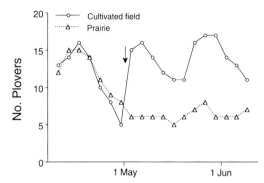

FIGURE 1. Number of adult Mountain Plovers detected on paired plots at a native-prairie and cultivated-field interface in Weld County, Colorado, in 1994. Plotted values are 3-point running means; statistics presented in text were calculated on raw data. The arrow indicates the date when the cultivated field was planted.

In the remaining 11 surveys, numbers of Mountain Plovers detected on native prairie remained relatively constant (Fig. 1). Numbers on the cultivated field peaked for a third time in the fifteenth survey, 36 d into the survey period (May 25); no courtship behaviors were seen at this time. The number of plovers detected was greater ($t = 5.47$, df = 6, $P = 0.002$) on cultivated ($\bar{X} = 13.9 \pm 4.30$) than on native-prairie ($\bar{X} = 6.1 \pm 1.95$) sites in the last seven surveys, when all courtship behavior had ended on the cultivated field.

MOVEMENTS TO CULTIVATED FIELDS

After losing a nest or chicks, adult Mountain Plovers sometimes stayed in the study vicinity. After losing chicks to predators in mid-July 1994, 2 of 17 adults with transmitters moved to forage on recently cultivated fields. These individuals remained on the cultivated fields 3–5 d as part of a loose flock that varied from 35 to 55 individuals.

We often saw Mountain Plovers with small chicks on cultivated fields near our study site. In 1994 we monitored the movements of three adults with transmitters that had nested on the Pawnee National Grassland within 2 km of a

cultivated field. Two of those adults moved their chicks to a cultivated field within 2 d of hatching, and these families stayed on the field until the chicks fledged.

BROOD HABITATS ON NATIVE-PRAIRIE GRASSLANDS

In the Pawnee National Grassland, habitats used for brood-rearing contained more bare ground and less grass cover than did habitats surrounding nests (Table 1). Occurrences of forbs ($F = 1.80$, $P = 0.18$), prickly pear ($F = 0.01$, $P = 0.94$), and cow manure ($F = 0.14$, $P = 0.71$) were similar between nest and brood-rearing habitats.

Many Mountain Plovers nesting in the Pawnee National Grassland moved broods to the vicinity of cattle-watering tanks, which were generally devoid of vegetation for more than 20 m around the tank. To determine if birds were simply attracted to bare ground or if the presence of cattle enhanced the attractiveness of a site, we surveyed for Mountain Plovers at 56 stock tanks and compared plover presence to cattle use. Mountain Plovers occurred at 11 of 28 stock tanks with cattle but were absent at the 28 stock tanks where cattle were absent ($\chi^2 = 29.29$, df = 3, $P > 0.0001$). This survey indicated that Mountain Plovers are strongly attracted either to cattle or, as with cultivated fields, to recent site disturbance.

DISCUSSION

USE OF CULTIVATED FIELDS

The first peak in Mountain Plover numbers was similar between the cultivated field and native prairie. Detectability of birds began to drop in both areas as individuals began incubating eggs. Birds were confirmed nesting at this time, and six nests were found on the native-prairie side of the survey line. The cultivated field was private land, and although we were not granted permission to survey for nests, we used reproductive behaviors to track breeding phenology and were confident that birds were also nesting on the cultivated field.

A second peak in Mountain Plover numbers on the cultivated field occurred immediately af-

TABLE 1. MEAN ($\pm$ SE) PERCENT COVER OF GRASS VERSUS BARE GROUND IN MOUNTAIN PLOVER NEST HABITAT AND BROOD-REARING HABITAT, WELD COUNTY, COLORADO, 1993–1994

Plot	Grass			Bare ground		
	$\bar{X}$	Z/F	P	$\bar{X}$	Z/F	P
Nest habitat	87 ± 1.6	2.4	0.001	9 ± 1.0	2.6	0.002
Brood habitat	84 ± 1.4			15 ± 1.3		

Note: Comparisons are for 11 adults that successfully raised chicks to fledging. All data are from native-prairie habitats only.

ter the field was sprayed for weeds and then planted to millet (*Setaria*). The machinery working the field probably destroyed most nests, as adults immediately began courting again. Numbers of birds detected again dropped rapidly, as clutches presumably were completed and birds began incubating.

Mountain Plover numbers on the cultivated field peaked a third time in late May, but no courtship behaviors were observed at this time. Instead, this third peak was associated with the hatching of the original nests on the Pawnee National Grassland and the movement of broods to the cultivated field to forage. One adult with a transmitter moved from the grassland to the cultivated field and remained there until its two chicks fledged.

Numbers of Mountain Plovers using the cultivated field began to decline steadily in early June (Fig. 1). This decline was likely a response to the rapidly growing millet crop which made the site less acceptable as plover habitat. Mountain Plovers require very short vegetation, which facilitates predator detection (Graul 1975). At this time, plovers with broods moved back to the Pawnee National Grassland. The fate of most nests on the cultivated field was uncertain; however, a single nest we observed daily was abandoned when the millet reached a height of about 20 cm.

Adult Mountain Plovers nesting in Pawnee National Grassland that lost all their eggs or chicks to predation sometimes moved to cultivated fields to forage, where loose flocks of 50–100 birds were common. These flocks also included some adults that had moved their chicks to the cultivated fields (Knopf and Rupert 1996). Generally, however, flocks stayed at a specific field only for a few days after it had been cultivated or planted and then moved again; this pattern is seen regularly among wintering flocks of Mountain Plovers in California (Knopf and Rupert 1995). In our study, adults with chicks either stayed on the same cultivated field until the chicks could fly or moved back to native prairie when the cropland vegetation became too tall.

MOUNTAIN PLOVERS AS BARE-GROUND ASSOCIATES

Mountain Plovers have evolved, as have other shortgrass-prairie birds, in an intensively grazed ecosystem dominated by bison (*Bison bison*), prairie dogs (*Cynomys* spp.), and pronghorn (*Antilocapra americana*; Knopf 1996a). In taller, mixed-grass prairies, Mountain Plovers are associated primarily with the intensive grazing found in prairie-dog towns (Knowles et al. 1982, Olson-Edge and Edge 1987). On the Pawnee

National Grassland, Mountain Plovers select both nest and brood-rearing sites that have more bare ground than do surrounding areas. We do not think, however, that Mountain Plovers choose to nest specifically in areas of approximately 30% bare ground or to raise chicks in areas of approximately 15% bare ground. Rather, these percentages represent the average maximum bare ground currently available to birds on the Pawnee National Grassland.

Mountain Plovers regularly use cultivated fields on migration and in winter, as well as in the breeding season (Grinnell and Miller 1944, Laymon et al. 1986, Knopf and Rupert 1995). Knopf and Miller (1994) first concluded that Mountain Plovers are associated with bare ground, based on data collected at the nest site. Prior to that time, this species had been described as a prairie associate of blue grama and buffalo grass landscapes. During three breeding seasons (1992–1994) in Colorado, however, we found no nests in buffalo grass (N = 147). This grass reproduces asexually by sending out stolons and has a tendency to mat, thus precluding a bare-ground component for situating nests.

Breeding Mountain Plovers in Colorado use cultivated lands where range-management practices strive to protect soils and provide relatively uniform landscapes of grass cover. Most grazing prescriptions on public lands use some variation of the allotment approach to regulate stocking densities and herbage removal, thus favoring homogenous grass cover across broad landscapes (Knopf 1996c). Standardized grazing of allotments precludes areas of excessive grass/soil disturbances characteristic of native ungulate and rodent herbivores—disturbances to which Mountain Plovers have evolved. Using allotments contrasts with grazing by bison; this native grazer preferentially forages on black-tailed prairie dog (*Cynomys ludovicianus*) towns (Krueger 1986), thus maximizing grazing pressure at some sites while leaving others only lightly grazed. These intensively grazed sites provide specific habitats used by other grassland birds (Knopf 1996a).

MANAGING FOR MOUNTAIN PLOVERS ON OR NEAR PLOWED GROUND

Mountain Plovers in Colorado appear to be equally attracted to cultivated fields and grazed native prairie. Most cultivated fields, however, are usually planted to a late-season crop or are recultivated every 4–6 wk to control weeds. These activities certainly destroy some nests and chicks, which use crypsis to avoid detection (Sordahl 1991). Mountain Plovers have been documented nesting on plowed fields in Texas, Oklahoma, Kansas, Colorado, Nebraska, New

TABLE 2. RELATIVE EXTENT OF CROPLAND VERSUS NATIVE RANGELAND IN THE PRIMARY BREEDING RANGE OF MOUNTAIN PLOVERS IN THE SHORTGRASS-PRAIRIE REGION OF THE SOUTHWESTERN GREAT PLAINS

	Cropland (ha)	Rangeland (ha)	Cropland (%)
Colorado	2,760,763	6,225,134	30.7
Kansas	329,387	93,150	78.0
Nebraska	112,351	59,454	65.4
New Mexico	344,291	631,695	35.3
Oklahoma	128,223	262,845	32.8
Texas	514,310	823,527	38.4
Wyoming	167,873	1,215,203	12.1
Totals	4,357,198	9,311,008	31.9

Note: Data are from the Natural Resource Inventory, U.S. Department of Agriculture, 1994.

Mexico, and Wyoming (J. Shackford, pers. comm.). Because more than 30% of native habitats used by Mountain Plovers have been converted to cropland in this region (Table 2), we hypothesize that reduced productivity as a result of tillage may explain part of the 3.7% annual rate of decline of this species continentally from 1966 to 1993. It seems likely that cultivated fields represent regional reproductive "sinks" for nesting Mountain Plovers (Pulliam 1988).

In view of the fact that agricultural practices may play a large role in the decline of Mountain Plovers, we offer four management options to reduce nest and chick losses on cultivated fields.

1. Encourage farmers to prepare and plant fields used by Mountain Plovers in a short window of time in May and June. Fields are currently prepared weeks or even months in advance of planting.

2. If weed control is necessary during the period 1 May–15 July, encourage chemical rather than physical treatments on fields used by Mountain Plovers.

3. Mandate seeding of native grasses only and allow grazing of lands registered in the Conservation Reserve Program (CRP). Current practices often result in tame (introduced) cool-season grasses being planted on the western plains and preclude grazing in an ecosystem that evolved with intensive grazing pressure. Grazing on CRP lands will increase the amount of habitat suitable for grassland species and will also provide additional economic incentives to enroll in the CRP.

4. Management of publicly owned (or private) grazing allotments adjacent to cultivated fields could be changed to make them more attractive to Mountain Plovers during the period when the birds select nest sites. Highly intensive, long-term grazing of contiguous native grasslands should enhance nesting habitat. In ad-

dition, Mountain Plovers tend to select grasslands that are occupied by cattle or other herbivores. Cattle generally are not moved onto the Pawnee National Grassland until late May, depending on growth of the warm-season grasses. Moving cattle onto pastures in early May should further enhance the attractiveness of native-prairie sites over cultivated lands. Mountain Plovers are also attracted to recently burned grasslands (Knopf and Rupert 1995). Winter or early spring burning could be used to make native rangelands more attractive than cultivated lands for breeding Mountain Plovers.

ACKNOWLEDGMENTS

We thank the U.S. Forest Service for financial assistance and personnel at the Rocky Mountain National Forest, Arapaho-Roosevelt National Forest, and Pawnee National Grassland for technical assistance. Natural Resource Inventory data (U.S. Department of Agriculture) were provided courtesy of A. Allen and T. Osborn. We are especially grateful to L. Mullen for his interest and administrative support. F. C. Knopf provided assistance in the field. E. K. Bollinger, J. R. Herkert, and P. D. Vickery reviewed the manuscript.

LITERATURE CITED

GRAUL, W. D. 1973. Adaptive aspects of the Mountain Plover social system. Living Bird 12:69–94.

GRAUL, W. D. 1975. Breeding biology of the Mountain Plover. Wilson Bulletin 87:6–31.

GRAUL, W. D., AND L. E. WEBSTER. 1976. Breeding status of the Mountain Plover. Condor 78:265–267.

GRINNELL, J., AND A. H. MILLER. 1944. The distribution of the birds of California. Pacific Coast Avifauna 27.

KNOPF, F. L. 1994. Avian assemblages on altered grasslands. Studies in Avian Biology 15:247–257.

KNOPF, F. L. 1996a. Prairie legacies—birds. Pp. 135–148 *in* F. B. Samson and F. L. Knopf (editors). Prairie conservation: preserving North America's most endangered ecosystem. Island Press, Covelo, CA.

KNOPF, F. L. 1996b. Mountain Plover (*Charadrius montanus*). *In* A. Poole and F. Gill (editors). The birds of North America, no. 211. Academy of Natural Sciences, Philadelphia, PA, and American Ornithologists' Union, Washington, D.C.

KNOPF, F. L. 1996c. Grazing nongame bird habitats. Pp. 51–58 *in* P. R. Krausmann (editor). Rangeland wildlife. Society for Range Management, Denver, CO.

KNOPF, F. L., AND B. J. MILLER. 1994. *Charadrius montanus*—montane, grassland, or bare-ground plover? Auk 11:504–506.

KNOPF, F. L., AND J. R. RUPERT. 1995. Habits and habitats of Mountain Plovers in winter. Condor 97:743–751.

KNOPF, F. L., AND J. R. RUPERT. 1996. Reproduction and movements of Mountain Plovers breeding in Colorado. Wilson Bulletin 108:28–35.

KNOWLES, C. J., C. J. STONER, AND S. P. GIEB. 1982. Selective use of black-tailed prairie dog towns by Mountain Plovers. Condor 84:71–74.

KRUEGER, K. 1986. Feeding relationships among bison,

pronghorn, and prairie dogs: an experimental analysis. Ecology 67:760–770.

LAYMON, P., J. MARCHANT, AND T. PRATER. 1986. Shorebirds. Houghton Mifflin, Boston, MA.

MILLER, B. J., AND F. L. KNOPF. 1993. Growth and survival of Mountain Plovers. Journal of Field Ornithology 64:500–506 and 65:193.

OLSON-EDGE, S. L., AND W. D. EDGE. 1987. Density and distribution of the Mountain Plover on the Charles M. Russell National Wildlife Refuge. Prairie Naturalist 19:233–238.

PULLIAM, H. R. 1988. Sources, sinks, and population regulation. American Naturalist 132:652–661.

SAMSON, F. B., AND F. L. KNOPF. 1994. Prairie conservation in North America. BioScience 44:418–421.

SHACKFORD, J. S. 1991. Breeding ecology of the Mountain Plover in Oklahoma. Bulletin of the Oklahoma Ornithological Society 24:9–13.

SORDAHL, T. 1991. Antipredator behavior of Mountain Plover chicks. Prairie Naturalist 23:109–115.

Studies in Avian Biology No. 19:87–94, 1999.

CHANGES IN BIRD POPULATIONS ON CANADIAN GRASSLANDS

C. Stuart Houston and Josef K. Schmutz

Abstract. Before the Canadian prairies were settled in the 1880s, the grassland birds of that region were catalogued in the 1820s, 1850s, and 1870s by John Richardson, Thomas Blakiston, and Elliott Coues, respectively. Ernest Thompson Seton recorded changes in southern Manitoba during the first 10 years of settlement. Tree plantings on the open plains made nest sites available for several species, but human encroachment was harmful to other, especially larger, species. Breeding Bird Surveys on the Canadian prairies between 1966 and 1994 documented steep declines of Sprague's Pipit (*Anthus spragueii*; 7.3 percent per year) and Loggerhead Shrike (*Lanius ludovicianus*; 5.6 percent per year) and less severe (but still more than 2.0 percent per year) declines of Northern Harrier (*Circus cyaneus*), Killdeer (*Charadrius vociferus*), Burrowing Owl (*Athene cunicularia*), Short-eared Owl (*Asio flammeus*), and Western Meadowlark (*Sturnella neglecta*). Swainson's Hawk (*Buteo swainsoni*) and Ferruginous Hawk (*B. regalis*) have shown significantly reduced productivity, coincident with sharp declines in their main prey, Richardson's ground squirrel (*Spermophilus richardsonii*). Both hawk species are now showing evidence of population declines as well. Introduced trees in deserted farmsteads are dying from neglect, drought, herbicides, and bulldozers, offering fewer nesting sites and less protective cover. Until recently, the Canadian government has encouraged plowing native prairie and substituting grain crops or crested wheatgrass (*Agropyron cristatum*) in its place. Marked increases in red fox (*Vulpes fulva*) numbers (which may have contributed to decreased numbers of Richardson's ground squirrels) and increased use of pesticides, fertilizers, and other chemicals have coincided with bird declines. Declines in numbers of small grassland birds and in numbers and productivity of three grassland raptors seem disproportionate to these factors and may be more severe than in the western United States.

CAMBIOS EN LAS POBLACIONES DE AVES EN LOS PRADOS DE CANADÁ

Sinopsis. Antes de la colonización de los prados canadienses en los años de la década de 1880, las aves de pastizal de esa región habían sido catalogadas en las décadas de 1820, 1850 y 1870 por John Richardson, Thomas Blakiston y Elliott Coues, respectivamente. Ernest Thompson Seton anotó cambios en el sur de Manitoba durante los primeros 10 años de colonización. La siembra de árboles en las llanuras descampadas proporcionó sitios de nidos para algunas especies, pero la invasión humana fue perjudicial para otras especies, especialmente las más grandes. Los Breeding Bird Surveys en las llanuras canadienses entre 1966 y 1994 documentaron disminuciones precipitadas de la Bisbita de Sprague (*Anthus spragueii*; 7,3 por ciento por año) y de Lanio Americano (*Lanius ludovicianus*; 5,6 por ciento por año) y disminuciones menos severas (pero de todos modos de más de un 2,0 por ciento por año) del Gavilán Rastrero (*Circus cyaneus*), del Chorlito Tildío (*Charadrius vociferus*), del Búho Llanero (*Athene cunicularia*), del Búho Orejicorto (*Asio flammeus*) y del Pradero Occidental (*Sturnella neglecta*). El Aguililla de Swainson (*Buteo swainsoni*) y el Aguililla Real (*B. regalis*) han experimentado una importante reducción en la productividad, coincidente con una drástica disminución de su presa principal, la ardilla terrestre de Richardson (*Spermophilus richardsonii*). Asimismo, ambas especies de halcón ahora muestran indicios de disminuciones poblacionales. Los árboles introducidos en cortijos abandonados están muriendo por el descuido, por la sequía, por los herbicidas y por los bulldozers, y ofrecen menos sitios de nidos y menos cobertura protectora. Hasta hace poco, el gobierno canadiense ha favorecido el arado de la pradera nativa y, en su lugar, ha dado preferencia a la sustitución de cosechas de granos o de *Agropyron cristatum*. Aumentos marcados de los números de los zorros rojos (*Vulpes fulva*) (que pueden haber contribuido a los números redicidos de ardillas terrestres de Richardson) y el aumento del uso de pesticidas, de abonos y de otras sustancias químicas han coincidido con las disminuciones de las aves. Las disminuciones de los números de aves pequeñas de pastizal y de los números y la productividad de tres aves rapaces de pastizal parecen desproporcionadas para estos factores y pueden ser más severas que en el oeste de los Estados Unidos.

Key Words: agriculture; Alberta; Canadian prairies; grassland birds; Manitoba; presettlement; Saskatchewan.

There is widespread concern about the decline in grassland birds throughout the Canadian prairies, a profoundly altered habitat. "Between plowing and overgrazing, it is perhaps the most extensively altered biome on the planet" (Gayton 1990:25). With historical information that extends back to the 1820s (Richardson and Swainson 1832, Blakiston 1861–1863, Coues 1878), no locality in North America can surpass the presettlement inventory available for Saskatchewan. In this paper we summarize for selected species 177 yr of observations in southern Saskatchewan, describe population trends for selected species since 1966, and suggest possible

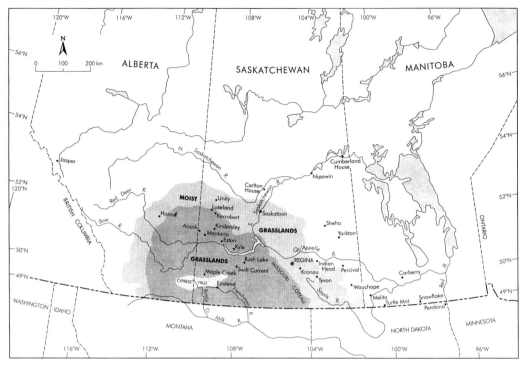

FIGURE 1. Map of Canadian prairie grasslands and of cities and villages mentioned in text. Dark shading represents open grassland, lighter shading represents moist grassland with some aspen copses. (Map by K. Bigelow, Department of Geography, University of Saskatchewan, Saskatoon, SK.)

links between species declines and widespread ecosystem change. We stress some of the major changes in bird populations resulting from the extirpation of bison (*Bison bison*), the conversion of native grassland to agricultural fields, the cessation of regular prairie fires, the regrowth of quaking aspen (*Populus tremuloides*) from dormant roots (Maini 1960), the planting of trees in shelterbelts, and the declines in trees associated with deserted farmsteads, herbicides, bulldozers, and drought.

Some bird species, among them Mourning Dove (*Zenaida macroura*), Western Kingbird (*Tyrannus verticalis*), Black-billed Magpie (*Pica pica*), American Crow (*Corvus brachyrhynchos*), Tree Swallow (*Tachycineta bicolor*), Barn Swallow (*Hirundo rustica*), and Mountain Bluebird (*Sialia currucoides*), adapted to human settlement and the tree planting that followed it and increased in numbers (Houston 1977a, b, 1979, 1986; Houston and Houston 1988, 1997). Populations of most other species in the mixed prairie ecosystem of the prairie ecozone (Padbury and Acton 1994) remained relatively stable until about 1970, although satisfactory monitoring of numbers by Breeding Bird Surveys (BBSs) has been available only since 1966. In the early

1970s, about the same time as agriculture became more technological with higher chemical inputs (Goldsborough 1993), declines in populations and productivity of several grassland species became evident (Downes and Collins 1996). For Burrowing Owls (*Athene cunicularia*; Houston et al. 1996) and Loggerhead Shrikes (*Lanius ludovicianus*; Peterjohn and Sauer 1995), evidence of decline has been universal and consistent across the Canadian prairies.

HISTORICAL PERSPECTIVE

THE NINETEENTH CENTURY

In the 1820s, bison and recurrent fires maintained open grassland north to Carlton House, Saskatchewan (52°52′ N, 106°32′ W; Fig. 1) on the North Saskatchewan River (Houston 1977a). This was the site of intensive natural-history cataloguing by two Scotsmen, surgeon-naturalist Dr. John Richardson and naturalist Thomas Drummond (Richardson 1823, 1829, 1836; Sabine 1823; Richardson and Swainson 1832; Kirby 1837; Hooker 1840). On his first visit to Carlton House, in May 1820, Richardson noted that the interface between mixed forest and grassland had exceptional diversity (Houston and Street 1959).

Three decades later, from October 1857 until June 1858, the birdlife at Carlton House was assessed by English surveyor Thomas Wright Blakiston (Blakiston 1861–1863, Houston and Street 1959). Blakiston found the American Crow so uncommon he could not collect a specimen of it, whereas the Common Raven (*Corvus corax*) was numerous and nested commonly on open grasslands. In 1873 and 1874, further studies prior to the advent of farming were carried out along the Manitoba-United States boundary by American surgeon-naturalist Elliott Coues (1878), who reported that Tree Swallows were rare and that Barn Swallows nested sparingly on cliff faces, separate from the more common Cliff Swallows (*Hirundo pyrrhonota*). Red-winged Blackbird (*Agelaius phoeniceus*) was the least common blackbird, and the American Crow was still uncommon. Upland Sandpipers (*Bartramia longicauda*) were numerous, and both Whooping Cranes (*Grus americana*) and Sandhill Cranes (*G. canadensis*) were sparingly but quite evenly distributed. Coues commented that between Pembina Mountain (present-day Snowflake) and Turtle Mountain, Manitoba (Fig. 1), Baird's Sparrow (*Ammodramus bairdii*) was the "most abundant and characteristic species...in some places outnumbering all the other birds together" (Coues 1873:695–696). Coues also noted that in the same area Chestnut-collared Longspurs (*Calcarius ornatus*) occurred "in profusion" (Coues 1878:579). West of where the Missouri Coteau crosses the 49th parallel, near the present boundary between North Dakota and Montana, shortgrass prairie predominated and McCown's Longspurs (*C. mccownii*) became abundant as Chestnut-collared Longspurs declined. When Walter Raine, a lithographer by trade and an oologist by avocation, visited new ranching territory at Rush Lake, Saskatchewan (Fig. 1), in 1891, McCown's Longspur was the most common small bird on the elevated prairies (Raine 1892, Houston 1981). In 1873 and 1874, Chestnut-collared Longspurs and Sprague's Pipits (*Anthus spragueii*) were also abundant (Coues 1873); at the eastern crossing of the Souris River loop, Sprague's Pipits were "so numerous that the air seemed full of them" (Coues 1878:560).

By 1882, naturalist and well-known author Ernest E. Thompson (later known as Ernest Thompson Seton) had made careful observations in southwestern Manitoba and adjacent Saskatchewan (Thompson 1890); settlers were still thinly scattered but the Passenger Pigeon (*Ectopistes migratorius*) had all but vanished. Ten years later, Seton noted the influx of Mourning Doves, the westward advance of the Greater Prairie-Chicken (*Tympanuchus cupido*) and

Eastern Bluebird (*Sialia sialis*) with settlement, and the virtual disappearance of Upland Sandpipers and Sprague's Pipit as native prairie was plowed for agriculture (Houston 1980). Seton also noted declines in Chestnut-collared Longspurs and Swainson's Hawks (*Buteo swainsoni*) and increases in Western Meadowlarks (*Sturnella neglecta*) and Horned Larks (*Eremophila alpestris*) during the first 10 yr of settlement (Houston 1980).

Because they provided food, large birds were often hunted by farmers. Canada Geese (*Branta canadensis*) soon became less common. Greater Sandhill Cranes (*Grus canadensis tabida*) and Whooping Cranes were also shot for food. Some large birds, however, did not disappear until the end of the nineteenth century. At Rush Lake in 1891, Turkey Vultures (*Cathartes aura*), present since the days of the bison, were still common on the open prairie, as were a few Common Ravens (Raine 1892).

THE TWENTIETH CENTURY

In Saskatchewan, Black-billed Magpies (*Pica pica*) retreated from the plains in the late 1800s and by the early twentieth century were restricted to the Cypress Hills in southwestern Saskatchewan (Houston 1977a; Fig. 1). From 1904 through 1910, magpies disappeared even from nearby Maple Creek and Eastend (Fig. 1), but in the 1920s they increased and spread out. They reappeared in small numbers to the north and east at Unity and Sheho in 1926, Percival in 1929, and Nipawin in 1930, and they were common at Wauchope in 1939 and Yorkton in 1951 (Fig. 1). They became city residents in Saskatoon (Fig. 1) beginning in the late 1960s and have increased throughout the province since then (Houston 1977a). Between 1885 and 1903, Mourning Doves spread out from the Qu'Appelle River valley onto the newly settled plains near Indian Head (Houston 1986; Fig. 1).

Spreading northeastward from river valleys onto the plains as domestic trees reached about 6 m in height, the Western Kingbird has served as a useful indicator species for tree growth. For example, at the Harley Ranson farm at Tyvan, Saskatchewan (Fig. 1), where trees were planted in 1903, Western Kingbirds first nested in 1924; at the Stewart Houston farm 8 km to the west, where trees were planted in 1917, the kingbirds took up residence in 1937 (Houston 1979). Red-tailed Hawks (*Buteo jamaicensis*), once quite uncommon even in migration, extended their range southward onto former prairie areas as aspen (*Populus* spp.) copses, locally known as "bluffs," grew up from dormant roots once prairie fires came under control about 1910 (Houston and Bechard 1983).

Grasslands and trees

Native grasslands were quickly plowed following settlement. By 1911 there were 95,013 farms in Saskatchewan comprising an area of 113,843 km^2, of which 48,076 km^2 (42%) were plowed (Archibold and Wilson 1980). The number of farms peaked at 142,391 in 1936 and dropped to 60,840 by 1991, yet total farm area increased to 268,738 km^2 in 1991, a year when 134,624 km^2 (50%) were in crops, 57,143 km^2 (21%) in summerfallow, 10,759 km^2 (4%) in tame pasture, and 66,198 km^2 (25%) were undesignated (Saskatchewan Agriculture and Food 1994). As a result of these changes, remaining grasslands have became smaller, more fragmented, and of poorer quality. Between 1976 and 1986, 8% of grassland was lost in Alberta, 8% in Manitoba, and 6% in Saskatchewan (Wellicome and Haug 1995). By 1978, nearly 18% (69,243 of 385,832 ha) of the Prairie Farm Rehabilitation Administration (PFRA) pastures in the mixed grassland ecoregion had been seeded (Agriculture and Agri-Food Canada 1996).

A 1972 study of 16 townships in Saskatchewan, together representing more than 1% of Saskatchewan grassland, showed 269 occupied farmsteads and 244 abandoned farmsteads, 80% of the latter still with tree cover (Smith 1973).

Insecticides, herbicides, and fertilizer

Chemicals were used sparingly by Canadian farmers prior to 1947. Use of 2,4-D, one of the phenoxy herbicides, began at this time, and by 1966 high volumes of it were in use (Goldsborough 1993). Other herbicides appeared in 1965 and were being used in high volumes by 1980.

Peregrine Falcons (*Falco peregrinus*) were rare and local breeders along the Frenchman River valley and Battle Creek in the grasslands of extreme southwestern Saskatchewan until at least 1917 (Bechard 1981, 1982) but persisted until the 1950s in Alberta valleys such as that of the Red Deer River (e.g., Taverner 1919; Fig. 1). In 1975, following widespread use of DDT, a survey of historical Peregrine Falcon breeding sites in southern Alberta showed that none were occupied (Fyfe et al. 1976).

With extensive use of dieldrin in the late 1950s and early 1960s, Merlins (*Falco columbarius*) declined moderately in Alberta and almost disappeared from the grassland near Kindersley, Saskatchewan, for 10 yr (Hodson 1976, Houston and Schmidt 1981); by 1995, Merlin numbers had returned to preinsecticide levels in Saskatchewan (Houston and Hodson 1997).

Mammalian predators

Red foxes (*Vulpes fulva*) were extremely rare in southern Saskatchewan until 1965 at Luseland and 1966 at Kyle (Fig. 1); they quickly became common in the 1970s (Jordheim 1995, Finley 1996). Coyotes (*Canis latrans*) have increased in the same area since the late 1980s (Finley 1996). It is likely that increasing populations of foxes on the Canadian prairies have had a detrimental effect on populations of grassland birds. In North Dakota, Sovada et al. (1995) found that duck nesting success averaged 32% where coyotes were the principal canid but fell to 17% where foxes were the principal canid.

Breeding Bird Surveys

BBSs began in Manitoba, Saskatchewan, and Alberta in 1966. Since that time, populations of many grassland species in the southern portions of the Canadian prairie provinces have shown significant negative trends. For example, BBS data for grassland portions of Alberta, Saskatchewan, and southwestern Manitoba indicate significant ($P < 0.05$) population declines between 1966 and 1994 for Sprague's Pipit (-7.3% per annum), Loggerhead Shrike (-5.2%), Killdeer (*Charadrius vociferus*; -3.3%), Short-eared Owl (*Asio flammeus*; -2.9%), Western Meadowlark (-2.1%), and Burrowing Owl (-2.0%) (Downes and Collins 1996). Grassland species that have shown nonsignificant ($P > 0.05$) population declines during the same period include Lark Bunting (*Calamospiza melanocorys*; -11.2% per annum), McCown's Longspur (-9.0%), Lark Sparrow (*Chondestes grammacus*; -3.2%), Chestnut-collared Longspur (-2.2%), and Horned Lark (-1.1%) (Downes and Collins 1996). All of these species, with the exception of the shrike, are ground-nesters that are likely to be extremely vulnerable to predation. Knopf (1994:25), referring to both the United States and Canada, noted that "grassland birds have shown steeper, more consistent and more geographically widespread declines than any other behavioral or ecological guild of North American species."

Burrowing Owls

Burrowing Owls, which in the 1830s extended north at least to Carlton House, Saskatchewan (Houston and Street 1959), have declined steadily in range and abundance in the three prairie provinces since the late 1970s (Houston et al. 1996). The harmful effects of the insecticide Carbofuran on this species were first demonstrated in 1986 (James and Fox 1987), but the decline has continued even after restrictions on using this chemical within 250 m of owl colonies were implemented. This decline is due in part to habitat loss and fragmentation and to increases in predator populations (Wellicome and Haug 1995). On the plains near Regina, Sas-

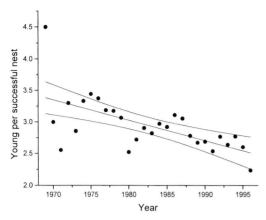

FIGURE 2.   Productivity (young per successful nest produced to banding age) of Ferruginous Hawks in Saskatchewan, 1969–1996. Curved lines represent the 95% confidence interval about the linear regression (r = −0.63, P < 0.001)

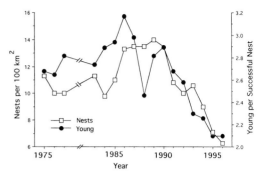

FIGURE 3.   Population (nests per 100 km²) and productivity (young per successful nest) of Ferruginous Hawks near Hanna, Alberta, 1975–1996.

katchewan, the Burrowing Owl population declined steadily from 76 pairs in 1987 to 29 pairs in 1992 and 9 pairs in 1994 (Warnock and James 1997). During this period, the percentage of successful pairs dropped from 72 to 45%, and the number of young produced per nest attempt dropped from 3.1 to 1.8 (James et al. 1997). In large PFRA pastures in the Kindersley, Saskatchewan, region (Fig. 1), Burrowing Owls were last seen breeding at Antelope Park in 1980, Heart's Hill in 1985, Mantario in 1986, Newcombe in 1990, Eagle Lake in 1993, Kindersley-Elna in 1993, and Progress in 1994. A single pair persisted at Mariposa in 1996. At Kindersley-Elna Pasture (63.5 km²) there were 18 pairs of Burrowing Owls in 1991, 9 pairs in 1992, 2 pairs in 1993, and none thereafter (Houston et al. 1996). The Committee on the Status of Endangered Wildlife in Canada elevated the Burrowing Owl's status from threatened to endangered in 1995 (Wellicome and Haug 1995).

Swainson's and Ferruginous hawks

In Saskatchewan, Swainson's Hawk productivity averaged 2.09 young per successful nest from 1964 through 1987 (N = 985 successful nests; S. Houston, unpubl. data). Productivity then declined sharply, averaging 1.63 young per successful nest from 1988 through 1994 and dropping as low as 1.27 young per successful nest in 1993 (N = 602 successful nests; Houston and Schmutz 1995).

Near Hanna, Alberta (Fig. 1), Swainson's Hawk productivity fell from a long-time mean of 2.03 to 1.14 young per successful nest in 1993 (N = 1,170; Houston and Schmutz 1995),

rose to 1.69 in 1994, and then dropped to 1.22 in 1995 and 1.40 in 1996 (J. Schmutz, unpubl. data). We know of no mechanism by which short-acting pesticide (monocrotophos) poisoning on this species' wintering grounds in Argentina (Goldstein et al. 1996) should have detrimental effects on brood size 6 mo later.

Ferruginous Hawks have disappeared from nearly half of their presettlement territory in Saskatchewan (Houston and Bechard 1984), and their productivity has declined. Between 1969 and 1987, the number of young fledged per successful nest averaged 3.01 (N = 369 successful nests; S. Houston, unpubl. data). Since 1988 this number has remained below 2.82 and has averaged 2.63 (N = 488 successful nests; S. Houston, unpubl. data). Overall productivity has declined in recent years (r = 0.63, P < 0.001; S. Houston, unpubl. data; Fig. 2). The species has declined even more severely in Alberta. The number of nests in the Hanna study area dropped from a peak of 14 per 100 km² in 1989 to 7 and 6 per 100 km² in 1995 and 1996, respectively, and productivity declined from 3.2 young per successful nest in 1986 to 2.1 in 1995 and 1996 (J. Schmutz, unpubl. data; Fig. 3).

The nesting period of the Ferruginous Hawk coincides with the peak abundance of young Richardson's ground squirrels (*Spermophilus richardsonii*), which are the main prey of Ferruginous Hawks in Saskatchewan and Alberta (Schmutz et al. 1980). The decline in productivity of both Ferruginous and Swainson's hawks is probably the result of the sharp decline in this rodent since 1987. This decrease began at Kindersley, Saskatchewan, and extended west to Mantario, Saskatchewan, and then Hanna, Alberta (Houston and Schmutz 1995; S. Houston and J. Schmutz, unpubl. data). One possible explanation for the steep decline in ground squirrels is the substantial increase in the red fox population.

Nest sites for both Ferruginous and Swainson's hawks have also been lost. South of the aspen parkland belt, the remaining planted trees, largely in shelterbelts of deserted farms, are dying from neglect, drought, and herbicide sprays and are razed by bulldozers as farmers try to increase the amount of land they have in production.

DISCUSSION

The declines of small grassland birds in Canada since the mid-1960s and the earlier decline of the Upland Sandpiper more than a century ago can be explained, at least in part, by an ever-diminishing and ever-more-fragmented amount of native grassland. This pertains particularly to Sprague's Pipit and Chestnut-collared Longspur, species that prefer native grassland over seeded pasture, hayland, and cropland (S. K. Davis, unpubl. data). The decline in Sprague's Pipit may have been hastened by overgrazing (Dale 1984, Sutter 1996), but Horned Larks and Chestnut-collared Longspurs, which usually respond favorably to grazing (Owens and Myres 1973), have also declined (Dale 1984). In Saskatchewan, numbers of Baird's Sparrows correlated positively with grass/sedge (*Carex*) cover and negatively with bare ground cover (Sutter et al. 1995). Clay-colored Sparrows (*Spizella pallida*) were also detected more often in native pasture than in any seeded pasture with crested wheatgrass (*Agropyron cristatum*; Davis and Duncan 1999). Fragmentation of prairie can also have adverse effects, including an increase in Brown-headed Cowbird (*Molothrus ater*) parasitism (Davis and Sealy in press).

The Canadian government has provided monetary incentives that have encouraged grain rather than cattle production and hence has encouraged the breaking of marginal lands (Fulton et al. 1989; Anderson et al. 1991; Riemer 1993, 1995). The "Crow's Nest Pass Rate," for example, which was in effect from 1897 until 1995, subsidized grain but not cattle shipments to ports, and the grain quota system, abandoned only in 1996, allowed sales based on cultivated acreage—the more land a farmer plowed, the more grain he was allowed to sell. The government has paid farmers when grain (but not cattle) prices fell below a 5-yr average and has subsidized crop insurance to underwrite the risk of growing grain. These are but a few examples of the government policies that have favored grain production over cattle production in the twentieth century. Additionally, the development of larger farm machinery and of mechanical rock-pickers has allowed hilly and rocky pastures to be broken, large sloughs to be drained, and shelterbelts and streamside vegetation to be removed

(Anderson et al. 1991). Increasing farm debt, which averaged \$89,000 per farm by 1985, has added financial pressures to this mix (Anderson et al. 1991). Although major government assistance programs were discontinued in 1995 and 1996, which should reduce pressure to convert pastures into cropland, such changes are so recent that beneficial effects will probably not be apparent or measurable for at least a few years.

Concern is not restricted to small grassland birds and three raptor species. Waterfowl nest success in the prairie pothole region has declined at a significant annual rate of about 0.5%, even on islands without mammalian predators and in study areas where large predators have been removed or excluded by fencing (Beauchamp et al. 1996). Increased predation by mammals, especially red foxes, striped skunks (*Mephitis mephitis*; Pasitschniak-Arts and Messier 1995), and Franklin's ground squirrels (Sargeant et al. 1987), has contributed to duck declines, with as yet undetermined effects on ground-nesting passerines.

The loss of prairie alone cannot explain the severity of the Burrowing Owl decline in the Canadian prairies and northwestern North Dakota (R. K. Murphy, pers. comm.), which contrasts with slowly declining numbers in southwestern North Dakota and increasing numbers in southwestern Idaho from the 1970s through the 1990s (K. Steenhof, pers. comm.). Carbofuran may have contributed to Burrowing Owl declines at one stage, but its use is now prohibited within 250 m of a Burrowing Owl nest. The declines in productivity among Swainson's and Ferruginous hawks, which have continued for 9 yr in Saskatchewan and Alberta, appear to differ from anything described in the United States. The causes of these declines, though probably associated with acute declines in prey species, are still not well understood.

Unprecedented industrialization of farming has occurred, partially overlapping with the declines in grassland birds described here. Such associations, while intriguing, may be partially coincidental, but further scrutiny is indicated. We do not know the cause of the recent but widespread declines in productivity, largely or entirely restricted to Canada, among three grassland raptor species. Careful study of these species must continue as we search for answers.

ACKNOWLEDGMENTS

M. Fulton, Saskatchewan Institute of Pedology, provided valuable insight and commentary; G. Riemer, B. Bristol, and G. Wrubleski provided unpublished data about the PFRA and other government projects; and K. Bigelow, University of Saskatchewan, and D. S. Houston assisted with graphics. J. Harris, D. Francis, and D. Zazelenchuk found many Swainson's and Ferruginous hawk nests in Saskatchewan, and D. G. Miller and M. A. Gerard were among the many people who helped with the Saskatchewan banding operation. P. D. Vickery, B. Dale, and two anonymous reviewers provided helpful criticism.

LITERATURE CITED

AGRICULTURE AND AGRI-FOOD CANADA. 1996. Sensitivity analysis of economic impacts of proposed endangered species legislation and community pasture grazing. Internal report, Land Management and Diversification Service, Prairie Farm Rehabilitation Administration, Regina, SK.

ANDERSON, D. W., C. J. ROPPEL, AND R. M. GRAY. 1991. Sustainability in Canadian agriculture. Science Council of Canada, Ottawa, ON.

ARCHIBOLD, O. W., AND M. B. WILSON. 1980. The natural vegetation of Saskatchewan prior to agricultural settlement. Canadian Journal of Botany 58:2031–2042.

BEAUCHAMP, W. D., T. D. NUDDS, AND R. G. CLARK. 1996. Duck nest success declines with and without predator management. Journal of Wildlife Management 60:258–264.

BECHARD, M. J. 1981. Historic nest records of the Peregrine Falcon in southern Saskatchewan and southern Manitoba. Blue Jay 39:182–183.

BECHARD, M. J. 1982. Further evidence for a historic population of Peregrine Falcons in southern Saskatchewan. Blue Jay 40:125.

BLAKISTON, T. 1861–1863. On birds collected and observed in the interior of British North America. Ibis 3:314–320; 4:3–10; 5:39–87; 5:121–155.

COUES, E. 1873. Notes on two little-known birds of the United States. American Naturalist 7:695–697.

COUES, E. 1878. Field-notes on birds observed in Dakota and Montana along the forty-ninth parallel during the seasons of 1873 and 1874. Bulletin of the U.S. Geological and Geographical Survey of the Territories 4(3):545–661.

DALE, B. C. 1984. Birds of grazed and ungrazed grasslands in Saskatchewan. Blue Jay 42:102–104.

DAVIS, S. K., AND D. C. DUNCAN. 1999. Grassland songbird abundance in native and crested wheatgrass pastures of southern Saskatchewan. Studies in Avian Biology 19:211–218.

DAVIS, S. K., AND S. G. SEALY. In press. Cowbird parasitism and nest predation in fragmented grasslands of southwestern Manitoba. *In* J. N. Smith, T. L. Cook, S. I. Rothstein, S. G. Sealy, and S. K. Robinson (editors). Ecology and management of cowbirds. University of Texas Press, Austin, TX.

DOWNES, C., AND B. T. COLLINS. 1996. The Canadian Breeding Bird Survey, 1966–1994. Canadian Wildlife Service Progress Notes no. 210.

FINLEY, K. 1996. The red fox invasion and other changes in wildlife populations in west-central Saskatchewan since the 1960s. Blue Jay 54:206–210.

FULTON, M., K. ROSAASEN, AND A. SCHMITZ. 1989. Canadian agricultural policy and prairie agriculture. Economic Council of Canada, Ottawa, ON.

FYFE, R. W., S. A. TEMPLE, AND T. J. CADE. 1976. The 1975 North American Peregrine Falcon survey. Canadian Field-Naturalist 90:228–273.

GAYTON, D. 1990. The wheatgrass mechanism: science and imagination in the western Canadian landscape. Fifth House, Saskatoon, SK.

GOLDSBOROUGH, L. G. 1993. Studies on the impact of agricultural and forestry herbicides on non-target aquatic plant communities. Pp. 49–57 *in* G. L. Holroyd, H. L. Dickson, M. Regnier, and H. C. Smith (editors). Prairie conservation and endangered species workshop, Brandon, 1992. Provincial Museum of Alberta Occasional Papers no. 19.

GOLDSTEIN, M. L., B. WOODBRIDGE, M. E. ZACCAGNINI, AND S. B. CANEVELLI. 1996. An assessment of mortality of Swainson's Hawks on wintering grounds in Argentina. Journal of Raptor Research 30:106–107.

HODSON, K. A. 1976. The ecology of Richardson's Merlins on the Canadian prairies. M. S. thesis. University of British Columbia, Vancouver, BC.

HOOKER, W. J. 1840. Flora boreali-americana. William G. Bohn, London, U.K.

HOUSTON, C. S. 1977a. Changing patterns of corvidae on the prairies. Blue Jay 35:149–155.

HOUSTON, C. S. 1977b. The prairie bluebird trail. Nature Canada 6(2):3–9.

HOUSTON, C. S. 1979. The spread of the Western Kingbird across the prairies. Blue Jay 37:149–157.

HOUSTON, C. S. 1980. Introduction. Pp. 5–15 *in* Ernest Thompson Seton in Manitoba [no editor]. Manitoba Naturalists' Society, Winnipeg, MB.

HOUSTON, C. S. 1981. An assessment of Walter Raine and his Saskatchewan records. Blue Jay 39:168–181.

HOUSTON, C. S. 1986. Mourning Dove numbers explode on the Canadian prairies. American Birds 40:52–54.

HOUSTON, C. S., AND M. J. BECHARD. 1983. Trees and the Red-tailed Hawk in southern Saskatchewan. Blue Jay 41:99–109.

HOUSTON, C. S., AND M. J. BECHARD. 1984. Decline of the Ferruginous Hawk in Saskatchewan. American Birds 38:166–170.

HOUSTON, C. S., D. G. HJERTAAS, R. L. SCOTT, AND P. C. JAMES. 1996. Experience with Burrowing Owl nest-boxes in Saskatchewan, with comment on decreasing range. Blue Jay 54:136–140.

HOUSTON, C. S., AND K. A. HODSON. 1997. Resurgence of breeding Merlins, *Falco columbarius richardsonii*, in Saskatchewan grasslands. Canadian Field-Naturalist 111:243–248.

HOUSTON, C. S., AND M. I. HOUSTON. 1988. Tree Swallow banding near Saskatoon, Saskatchewan. North American Bird-Bander 12:103–108.

HOUSTON, C. S., AND M. I. HOUSTON. 1997. Saskatchewan bird species which increased with settlement. Blue Jay 55(2):90–96.

HOUSTON, C. S., AND A. SCHMIDT. 1981. History of Richardson's Merlin in Saskatchewan. Blue Jay 39:30–37.

HOUSTON, C. S., AND J. K. SCHMUTZ. 1995. Declining reproduction among Swainson's Hawks in prairie Canada. Journal of Raptor Research 29:198–201.

HOUSTON, C. S., AND M. G. STREET. 1959. The birds of the Saskatchewan River. Saskatchewan Natural History Society, Regina, SK.

JAMES, P. C., T. J. ETHIER, AND M. K. TOUTLOFF. 1997. Parameters of a declining Burrowing Owl population in Saskatchewan. Raptor Research Report 9:34–37.

JAMES, P. C., AND G. A. FOX. 1987. Effects of some insecticides on productivity of Burrowing Owls. Blue Jay 45:65–71.

JORDHEIM, S. 1995. Foxes in south-central Saskatchewan. Blue Jay 43:232–233.

KIRBY, W. 1837. Fauna boreali-americana. Vol. 4. The insects. Josiah Fletcher, Norwich, U.K.

KNOPF, F. 1994. Avian assemblages on altered grasslands. Studies in Avian Biology 15:247–257.

MAINI, J. S. 1960. Invasion of grassland by *Populus tremuloides* in the northern Great Plains. Ph.D. dissertation. University of Saskatchewan, Saskatoon, SK.

OWENS, R. A., AND M. T. MYRES. 1973. Effects of agriculture upon populations of native passerine birds of an Alberta fescue grassland. Canadian Journal of Zoology 51:697–713.

PADBURY, G. A., AND D. F. ACTON. 1994. Ecoregions of Saskatchewan. Central Survey and Mapping Agency, Regina, SK.

PASITSCHNIAK-ARTS, M., AND F. MESSIER. 1995. Predator identification at simulated waterfowl nests using inconspicuous hair catchers and wax-filled eggs. Canadian Journal of Zoology 73:984–990.

PETERJOHN, B. G., AND J. R. SAUER. 1995. Population trends of the Loggerhead Shrike from the North American Breeding Bird Survey. Proceedings of the Western Foundation of Vertebrate Zoology 6:117–121.

RAINE, W. 1892. Bird nesting in north-west Canada. Hunter Rose, Toronto, ON.

RICHARDSON, J. 1823. Botanical appendix. Pp. 729–768 *in* J. Franklin. Narrative of a journey to the shores of the Polar Sea in the years 1819, 20, 21, and 22. John Murray, London, U.K.

RICHARDSON, J. 1829. Fauna boreali-americana. Vol. 1. The mammals. John Murray, London, U.K.

RICHARDSON, J. 1836. Fauna boreali-americana. Vol. 3. The fish. Richard Bentley, London, U.K.

RICHARDSON, J., AND W. SWAINSON. 1832. Fauna boreali-americana. Vol. 2. The birds. John Murray, London, U.K.

RIEMER, G. 1993. Agricultural policy impacts on land use decision making and options for reform. Pp. 123–132 *in* P. Rakowski and R. Massey (editors). Proceedings of the first national Wildlife Habitat workshop. Wildlife Habitat Canada, Ottawa, ON.

RIEMER, G. 1995. The effects of GATT on Canadian environmental and farm policy. Pp. 129–135 *in* R.

Gray, T. Becker, and A. Schmitz (editors). World agriculture in a post-GATT environment: new rules, new strategies. University Extension Press, University of Saskatchewan, Saskatoon, SK.

SABINE, J. 1823. Zoological appendix. Pp. 647–703 *in* J. Franklin. Narrative of a journey to the shores of the Polar Sea in the years 1819, 20, 21, and 22. John Murray, London, U.K.

SARGEANT, A. B., M. A. SOVADA, AND R. J. GREENWOOD. 1987. Responses of three prairie ground squirrel species, *Spermophilus franklinii, S. richardsonii,* and *S. tridecemlineatus,* to duck eggs. Canadian Field-Naturalist 101:95–97.

SASKATCHEWAN AGRICULTURE AND FOOD. 1994. Agricultural statistics 1993. Saskatchewan Agriculture and Food, Regina, SK.

SCHMUTZ, J. K., S. M. SCHMUTZ, AND D. A. BOAG. 1980. Coexistence of three species of hawks (*Buteo* spp.) in the prairie-parkland ecotone. Canadian Journal of Zoology 58:1075–1089.

SMITH, A. R. 1973. The value of abandoned farmsteads as a wildlife resource. Department of Natural Resources, Saskatoon, SK.

SOVADA, M. A., A. B. SARGEANT, AND J. W. GRIER. 1995. Differential effects of coyotes and red foxes on duck nest success. Journal of Wildlife Management 59:1–9.

SUTTER, G. C. 1996. Habitat selection and prairie drought in relation to grassland bird community structure and the nesting ecology of Sprague's Pipit, *Anthus spragueii*. Ph.D. dissertation. University of Regina, Regina, SK.

SUTTER, G. C., T. TROUPE, AND M. FORBES. 1995. Abundance of Baird's Sparrows, *Ammodramus bairdii,* in native prairie and introduced vegetation. Ecoscience 2:344–348.

TAVERNER, P. A. 1919. The birds of the Red Deer River, Alberta. Auk 36:1–21, 248–265.

THOMPSON, E. E. 1890. The birds of Manitoba. Proceedings of the U.S. National Museum 13:457–643.

WARNOCK, R. G., AND P. C. JAMES. 1997. Habitat fragmentation and Burrowing Owls (*Speotyto cunicularia*) in Saskatchewan. Pp. 477–486 *in* J. R. Duncan, D. H. Johnson, and T. H. Nicholls (editors). Biology and conservation of owls of the northern hemisphere. USDA Forest Service Gen. Tech Rep. NC-190. USDA Forest Service North Central Experiment Station, St. Paul, MN.

WELLICOME, T. L., AND E. A. HAUG. 1995. Second update on status report on the Burrowing Owl, *Speotyta cunicularia*. Committee on the Status of Endangered Species in Canada, Ottawa, ON.

Studies in Avian Biology No. 19:95–103, 1999.

MULTISCALE HABITAT ASSOCIATIONS OF THE SAGE SPARROW: IMPLICATIONS FOR CONSERVATION BIOLOGY

JOHN T. ROTENBERRY AND STEVEN T. KNICK

Abstract. General patterns of habitat association of common shrubsteppe passerine birds, as indicated by correlations of population abundance with plot-level habitat variables, are well known. We demonstrated that for Sage Sparrows (*Amphispiza belli*) these population correlations were consistent with the behavior of individual birds as they selected patches of shrubs on which to forage. Furthermore, individuals appeared to track local-scale variation in habitat variables that changed annually. Despite these linkages, the ability of plot-level correlations to predict abundances across sites or years was weak. We also examined landscape-level correlates of species distributions. For Sage Sparrows, presence and persistence at a sampling point were related to landscape attributes such as shrubland fragment size and configuration. We concluded that failure of plot-level correlations to predict changes in abundance at broader scales stemmed both from failure to include landscape-level attributes and from failure to consider an intrinsic decoupling of population density from local habitat details. We discuss the implications of these results for conservation studies.

ASOCIACIONES DE HÁBITAT MULTIESCALA DEL GORRIÓN DE ARTEMISIA: IMPLICACIONES PARA LA BIOLOGÍA CONSERVACIONISTA

Sinopsis. Son bien conocidos los esquemas generales de asociación de hábitat de aves paseriformes comunes en las estepas arbustivas. Estos fueron indicados a través de las correlaciones de abundancia de población con variables de hábitat a nivel de parcela. Demostramos que para los Gorriones de Artemisia (*Amphispiza belli*), estas correlaciones de población fueron concordantes con el comportamiento de aves individuales cuando escogían parcelas de arbustos donde forrajear. Además, las aves individuales parecían adoptar cambios anuales en las variables de hábitat a nivel local. A pesar de estas conexiones, la habilidad de predecir abundancias entre sitios o años usando correlaciones a nivel de parcela fue leve. Examinamos también los correlativos de distribución de especies a nivel de paisaje. Para los Gorriones de Artemisia, se relacionaron su presencia y persistencia en un sitio de muestreo a características de paisaje tales como tamaño y configuración del fragmento de matorral. Inferimos que la deficiencia de las correlaciones a nivel de parcela para predecir los cambios en abundancia en escalas amplias, radicaba en la falta de inclusión de atributos a nivel de paisaje y en no considerar una separación intrínseca entre la densidad de población y los detalles del hábitat local. Analizamos las implicaciones de estos resultados para los estudios conservacionistas.

Key Words: *Amphispiza belli*; *Artemisia tridentata*; bird-habitat relationships; Great Basin; individual behavior; landscape; sagebrush; Sage Sparrow; shrubsteppe.

Research into the relationships between the abundance of vertebrates and certain features of their habitat, both physical and biotic, has been a cornerstone of modern ecology (Rotenberry 1981). Once such relationships are established, they can be applied both to theoretical and practical questions. Many theoretical models that seek to explain adaptive variation in animal behavior include as one of their essential elements the relationship between the number of individuals in a habitat and various aspects of environmental "quality," quality presumably relating to the fitness of the individual within that habitat. Such information is of increasing importance to wildlife managers concerned with preserving adequate numbers of individuals or species in an environment increasingly disrupted and fragmented by humans. Indeed, the conservation value of identifying animal-habitat relationships cannot be underestimated. In the case of songbirds, their populations are usually managed by manipulating features of their habitat rather than

by directly manipulating numbers. If we can identify habitat attributes that directly or indirectly influence bird-population numbers—through the provision of food, shelter, nest sites, or protection from predators—then we can attempt to alter these attributes to achieve a desired conservation goal.

The use of information about bird-habitat relationships rests on certain assumptions, however, and it is an empirical examination of those assumptions that we examine here. This review is not exhaustive but instead relies heavily on our own research on Great Basin shrubsteppe birds, conducted over a span of almost 20 yr.

Because of the hierarchical nature of the processes involved (e.g., Allen and Starr 1982), we discuss three levels of investigation in our research. Presumably, the process of habitat selection that results in associations between a species and its habitat is an evolutionarily derived mechanism that ensures that individuals seek out and remain in the particular habitats to which they are adapted. Thus, we expect successful individuals to reflect a phenotype that has been molded by and remains suitable for the habitat in which we find them. Expression of this phenotype may be morphological or behavioral or, more likely, both. We further expect that the patterns of habitat selection by individuals are reflected in habitat occupancy by populations. It is this emergent property of individual behavior that we assume is responsible for producing correlations between bird densities and habitat variables, and it provides the rationalization for interpreting these bird-habitat correlations in an adaptationist framework.

It is also clear that the associations between a species and habitat variables recorded on any particular plot of ground can be influenced by the nature of the surrounding landscape (O'Neill et al. 1988). In most cases, these landscape-level effects are manifest through processes related to habitat fragmentation and its effects on population dynamics (e.g., Rolstad 1991, Porneluzi et al. 1993). Increasingly, however, it is recognized that it is often the structure of an entire landscape mosaic that may be important to birds, not just the size and shape of individual fragments (e.g., Bolger et al. 1991, 1996; Pearson 1993; Knick and Rotenberry 1995). Thus, it is reasonable to expect an interaction between local- and landscape-level attributes in determining observed bird-habitat relationships.

A second major assumption is that the ecological associations we observe are stable and consistent through time and space—that patterns detected at one time and place can be generalized to other times and places. It is often assumed that natural selection for some sort of optimal habitat response is strong and continuous, and thus that populations are generally at or near equilibrium with respect to the resources with which any set of habitat variables is associated (e.g., Cody 1981, 1985).

We know that environments vary through time, however, and this can be especially true in arid regions. For example, one can easily document substantial fluctuation in the physical environment in the form of annual variation in precipitation. In arid lands these fluctuations can in turn drive enormous annual changes in primary and secondary productivity, and the difference between a dry and a wet year can be substantial (Noy-Meir 1973, Rotenberry and Wiens 1980, Cody 1981, Fuentes and Campusano 1985). This annual variation can influence the reproductive success of bird species in these ecosystems (Rotenberry and Wiens 1989, 1991). Likewise, abundance of bird species may also fluctuate substantially, both from year to year as well as from site to site within years (Wiens and Roten-

berry 1981a, Knick and Rotenberry 1995). Of primary interest is whether these changes in bird abundance are associated with changes in habitat. In other words, are population numbers coupled to environmental variation, and do fluctuations in animal numbers represent a "tracking" of changes in habitat?

Clearly, this is an important question for both scientists and conservationists to consider: are individuals and populations consistent and predictable in their habitat associations through time and space? Do populations track environmental variation in a consistent fashion at the spatial and temporal scales over which habitat relationships are traditionally determined? There may be a variety of reasons why species abundances might not be associated with changes in habitat or its associated resources (see below). If so, population densities may become "decoupled" from habitat parameters that might otherwise influence changes in local population sizes. If this is the case, what are the implications for populations, and how do we go about studying them? Our studies of birds in shrubsteppe habitats of the northern Great Basin can shed some light on these issues.

STUDY AREA AND SPECIES

Our research was conducted in arid shrubsteppe habitat of western North America, primarily in the northern Great Basin and Snake River Plains. This shrubsteppe is dominated by sagebrush (*Artemisia* [primarily big sagebrush (*A. tridentata*)]), saltbush (*Atriplex*), rabbitbrush (*Chrysothamnus* [particularly gray rabbitbrush (*C. nauseosus*) and green rabbitbrush (*C. viscidiflora*)]), and greasewood (*Sarcobatus*) among the shrubs and by bluegrass (*Poa*), wheatgrass (*Agropyron*), fescue (*Vulpia* [= *Festuca*]), and brome (*Bromus*) among the grasses.

In this paper we restrict our analyses to habitat relationships of the Sage Sparrow (Emberizidae: *Amphispiza belli nevadensis*), a common and widespread inhabitant of shrubsteppe. In the Great Basin this species is found mainly in association with sagebrush. Individuals weigh about 20 g and, where present, densities range from about 15 to 180 individuals per square kilometer (Wiens and Rotenberry 1981a). This subspecies is migratory, wintering in arid shrublands from central Nevada through northern Mexico (Martin and Carlson 1998).

PLOT-LEVEL ASSOCIATIONS

The most common method of establishing bird-habitat correlations is to census a series of representative plots or transects, usually ranging in area from 5 to 50 ha (Wiens and Rotenberry 1981b, Rotenberry 1982). A variety of habitat variables, both physical and biotic, are scored on the same plots or transects. Habitat relationships then are estimated using correlations between species abundance and environmental variables, frequently employing a variety of bivariate and/ or multivariate approaches (Wiens and Rotenberry 1981b).

As an example, we surveyed 14 "original" sites scattered throughout the northern Great Basin of southeastern Oregon and northern Nevada and selected to represent an array of common shrubsteppe habitats (Wiens and Rotenberry 1981a). At each site we censused birds and measured habitat features for 3 successive years. Birds were surveyed along 600-m Emlen-type transects (Emlen 1977). Percent coverage of each shrub species was determined from 10 100-m transects arrayed perpendicular to the bird transects and then reduced to independent axes using principal components analysis. We derived relationships of Sage Sparrows to habitat variables using both bivariate and multiple correlations. Although we also measured a variety of other habitat attributes, we discuss below only those variables associated with shrub coverage because they yielded the strongest patterns with widespread shrubsteppe bird species (Wiens and Rotenberry 1981a).

Sage Sparrow abundance was highly correlated with sagebrush coverage ($r = 0.61$, df $= 40$, $P < 0.001$; Wiens and Rotenberry 1981a). Additionally, substantial variation in the distribution of Sage Sparrows was statistically explained by a multiple regression of abundance on shrub-species components ($R^2 = 0.70$, $N = 42$, $P < 0.001$; Rotenberry 1986). The pattern of significance of regression coefficients again implicated sagebrush as the dominant covariate. A similar association was shown by Dobler (1994) using a different approach. Examining 55 10-ha transects scattered throughout southeastern Washington, Dobler noted that transects with Sage Sparrows had significantly higher coverage of sagebrush than those without. Taken together, these observations, based on plot-level analyses, lead to the conclusion that Sage Sparrow population levels in shrubsteppe habitat are strongly associated with sagebrush coverage.

INDIVIDUAL-LEVEL ASSOCIATIONS

The strength of population-level patterns in Sage Sparrows led us to investigate the behavior of individual birds, to see if individuals acted in a manner consistent with those patterns (Wiens 1985, Rotenberry and Wiens 1998). We assumed that population-level correlations reflected the aggregate response of individuals to habitat variation. We observed individual birds in a study area and quantified their behavior throughout a range of habitat variations, which we also quantified. We changed methods of measuring habitat variables to reflect the fact that we changed the scale of our focus from 600-m transects to the

TABLE 1.   PATCH SELECTION BY SAGE SPARROWS

Patch component	Selection
I: size	large***
II: % sage vs. % green rabbitbrush	sage***
III: shape	compact, densely foliated***
IV: % sage vs. % gray rabbitbrush	sage**

Note: Patch components are independent axes of variation in patch attributes determined from principal components analysis of 900 randomly selected patches. Selection denotes direction and significance of difference between randomly selected and bird-selected ($N = 181$) patches. See Rotenberry and Wiens 1998 for details. ** $P < 0.01$, *** $P < 0.001$.

few square meters in the vicinity of an individual bird. Here we emphasized the attributes of individual or small clusters of shrubs ("patches"), most of which were less than 2 m in canopy diameter. As before, we concentrated on both floristic and physiognomic variables. We then asked if birds used these patches in a nonrandom fashion.

For each of 3 yr, we randomly selected 300 patches in an 800- × 300-m sampling area to characterize the structure and composition of patches available to foraging birds. A patch was defined as a more or less contiguous association of living and/or standing dead shrub material, distinctly set off from neighboring patches and usually consisting of one or a few closely imbricated shrubs. We measured variables relating to the size, shape, and shrub-species composition of each patch. During mornings, we followed individual Sage Sparrows and marked the patches in which they foraged. During afternoons, we returned to the plot and measured the same physical and compositional attributes of bird-selected patches that we had measured on randomly selected patches.

We summarized independent patterns of covariation of attributes of randomly selected patches using principal components analysis. We scored bird-selected patches on those components and then compared those average scores to the random ones using one-way analysis of variance (ANOVA) and multiple analysis of variance (MANOVA).

Sage Sparrows did indeed use habitat nonrandomly (Table 1; Rotenberry and Wiens 1998), and the pattern of patch use by individuals was generally consistent with the population patterns noted before: individuals used sagebrush much more often than either green or gray rabbitbrush, were associated with larger shrubs, and were seen much more frequently in compact and densely, rather than sparsely, foliated shrubs. Furthermore, because we conducted this study over a 3-yr period during which precipitation (and hence patch attributes) varied considerably, we documented that patterns of use by birds changed in concert with variation in the patch variables we measured. For Sage Sparrows, the average scores on patch components not only varied significantly among years (MANOVA: F = 11.11; df = 4, 1076; P < 0.001), but these scores were also significantly correlated with changes in random patch components (r = 0.93, df = 6, P < 0.001). In other words, not only did individual birds use features of the habitat nonrandomly, they also tracked changes in those features from one year to the next.

PROJECTING BIRD-HABITAT RELATIONSHIPS THROUGH SPACE AND TIME

Results from the individually based studies, when combined with the strong patterns of correlations noted at the plot level, led us to expect that we would see variation in avian population numbers that closely matched temporal and spatial variation in habitat parameters. We expected that populations would be consistent in their expression of the detailed habitat associations described by the various correlations and that we could take those correlations, combine them with values of habitat variables at any given site or time, and accurately predict bird numbers.

To assess temporal consistency, we continued to census birds and measure habitat variables on a representative subset of five of our original sample sites for 4 yr or longer (Rotenberry 1986). We then ran the new habitat measurements through the previously derived multiple regression model (see above; Rotenberry 1986) to generate predicted bird abundances. We compared predicted with observed abundances; if the correlation was high, we inferred consistency in the expression of the details of habitat relationships through time.

For Sage Sparrows, the correlation between predicted and observed abundances was essentially nonexistent (r = −0.07, df = 18, P > 0.75; Rotenberry 1986). What was previously the best-fitting model (Sage Sparrow abundance and shrub-species principal components), with an R^2 of 70%, now explained less than 1% of the variation in Sage Sparrow abundances. This poor fit was not the result of some peculiarity of the sites selected for continued sampling, as a cross-validation correlation between predicted and observed abundances during the initial sampling period was 0.80 (df = 13).

To assess the degree of spatial consistency in habitat association, we selected four additional shrubsteppe sites that were sampled during the original time period but were not included in the

original analysis. Two of these were located in the same general area as the original sites, and two were located in similar habitat but about 500 km north in southeastern Washington (Rotenberry 1986). As before, we applied the original multiple regression model to the habitat measurements for the new sites to generate expected bird abundances which could then be compared to observed abundances. Because the sample size was small, however, correlation coefficients were too weak to detect a good relationship; instead, we used a t-test (each value predicted from the regression analysis had an associated standard error). If observed abundances were close to predicted abundances, a t-test would not be significant; if the t-test was significant, there would be a serious discrepancy between observed and predicted abundances.

Results from these tests were inconsistent. The model predicted accurately for Sage Sparrows at both of the distant sites (i.e., the probability that the observed abundance at a site was sampled from the population estimated by the multiple regression was > 0.05) but failed at both of the near sites (the same probability was < 0.05; Rotenberry 1986).

Finally, we wanted to know what happens when we intentionally modify the environment in a quasi-experimental design: do Sage Sparrows respond in ways that are consistent with their previous habitat responses and thus are predictable from the original correlations? We were afforded an excellent opportunity to address this question by assessing the effects of a large-scale habitat manipulation "experiment" conducted by the Oregon State Land Board. One of our original plots (Guano Valley) was included in an approximately 75-km² area that was sprayed with a broad-spectrum herbicide in an attempt to eradicate sagebrush. The area was subsequently chained and reseeded with non-native grasses (mainly crested wheatgrass [*Agropyron desertorum*]) to make it more suitable for cattle-grazing. The herbicide treatment came at the end of our initial 3-yr monitoring period, so we continued to visit the site to survey habitat and birds for an additional 3 yr postspray (Wiens and Rotenberry 1985). The treatment had an immediate effect: sagebrush coverage was much reduced and there was a substantial change in the structure of the habitat (Wiens and Rotenberry 1985). Even after 4 yr the site had not recovered; sagebrush coverage remained low, whereas green rabbitbrush and grasses had increased considerably, filling in much of the previously bare areas between shrubs.

How well did Sage Sparrows respond to this manipulation given their previous habitat relationships? Not well at all, at least in terms of

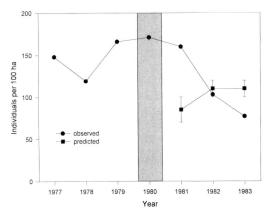

FIGURE 1. Observed abundance of Sage Sparrows before and after major habitat modification (herbicide, chaining, reseeding) at Guano Valley, Oregon. Predicted values (± 1 SE) from multiple regression of Sage Sparrow abundance on shrub-species components ($R^2 = 0.70$, N = 42, $P < 0.001$; Rotenberry 1986). Hatched area denotes year in which treatment was applied.

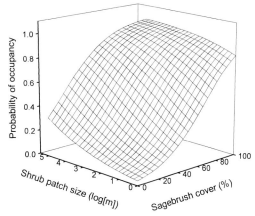

FIGURE 2. Relationship between probability of occupancy and sagebrush cover and shrub patch size for Sage Sparrows. The surface was developed by varying patch size and sagebrush cover and setting spatial similarity and shadscale coverage to systemwide values, using a logistic regression of sparrow presence/absence on local and landscape habitat variables (Knick and Rotenberry 1995).

consistency with predictions from the previously derived multiple regression model (Fig. 1). Despite the fact that the observed value for 1982 fell within the 95% confidence limits of the predicted abundance, there was a poor fit between the two, and trends between predicted and observed abundances were in opposite directions.

We conclude, therefore, that although we can develop models of relatively high statistical significance that account for a high proportion of variation in Sage Sparrow abundance, the habitat associations they describe are insufficient to project Sage Sparrow abundance accurately through time or space, either as a result of natural changes or of environmental modification.

INTERACTION BETWEEN LOCAL- AND LANDSCAPE-LEVEL ATTRIBUTES

More recently we have examined the relationship between landscape-level attributes and their potential influence on shrubsteppe bird abundances, particularly how variation in the landscape context of sampling points may appear to alter patterns of association between bird abundance and local-level habitat variables (Knick and Rotenberry 1995). These studies are based on 183 sample points scattered over approximately 200,000 ha in the Snake River Birds of Prey National Conservation Area in southwestern Idaho. In addition to counting birds (5-min unlimited-radius point counts), at each point (plus 213 additional random points) we measured local vegetation characteristics (percent cover of individual shrub species and some

grass/shrub cover types) on transects scattered throughout a 4-ha area. We determined landscape characteristics for a 1-km radius around each sampling point from a detailed habitat classification map derived from satellite imagery (Knick et al. 1997). Variables obtained from this large-scale (>300 ha) analysis included average size of shrubland or grassland patches, proportion of landscape in shrubland or grassland, and spatial similarity (related to fractal dimension; Palmer 1988). We used logistic regression of Sage Sparrow presence/absence to develop a habitat-selection model based on both local and landscape variables (e.g., Manly et al. 1993).

The probability of the presence of Sage Sparrows at a sampling point increased with increasing spatial similarity of sites (i.e., decreased habitat heterogeneity over the landscape scale), increasing shrubland patch size, and increasing local coverage of sagebrush and shadscale (*Atriplex confertifolia*; Fig. 2). Standardized estimates of regression coefficients implied that landscape features were more important in predicting presence than was coverage of individual shrub species, and that sagebrush was more important than shadscale (Knick and Rotenberry 1995). Furthermore, it was clear that landscape features interacted with local habitat variables to alter the expression of probability of occurrence. For example, the form of the relationship between percent cover of sagebrush and probability of occupancy by Sage Sparrows, although always positive (hence consistent with both plot-

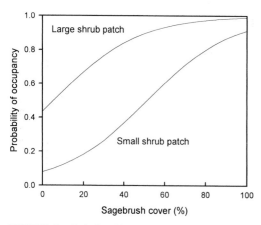

FIGURE 3. Relationship between probability of occupancy by Sage Sparrows and local sagebrush cover for large (10^5 m²) and small (10^2 m²) average shrub patch sizes in a landscape. These curves are slices through the surface in Fig. 2.

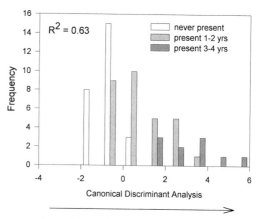

increasing sagebrush, shadscale, shrub patch size
decreasing disturbance (Russian thistle)

FIGURE 4. Histogram of canonical scores for sites where Sage Sparrows were observed in 0, 1–2, or 3–4 yr at 66 sites surveyed in 3 consecutive years. Interpretation of canonical discriminant axis is based on correlations of original variables with canonical scores.

and individual-level results), changed shape as a function of shrub patch size (Fig. 3). Thus, differences in the structure of landscapes in which local plots are embedded may produce differences in apparent bird-habitat relationships derived from those local plots.

As we sampled a subset of 66 point counts for 4 consecutive years, we were also able to assess habitat correlates of temporal persistence. We classified points into three categories based on Sage Sparrow occurrence rates: unoccupied (never present), marginal (present 1–2 yr), or occupied (present 3–4 yr). We then contrasted sites with different occupancy rates using canonical discriminant analysis applied to the set of local and landscape habitat variables.

There were significant differences among habitat attributes associated with temporal persistence (MANOVA: F = 4.97; df = 2, 63; P < 0.001), and the first canonical axis (the only one statistically significant at P < 0.05) explained 63% of the variation in occupancy rates (Fig. 4). Persistence increased with increasing local cover of sagebrush and shadscale, increasing proportion of the landscape in shrubland and the minimum size of shrubland patches, and decreasing local cover of Russian thistle (*Salsola iberica* [= *kali*]), a species associated with severe habitat disturbance. As before, landscape variables were as important as local variables in determining habitat associations.

SUMMARY AND CONCLUSIONS

Although the behavior of individual Sage Sparrows was generally consistent with bird-habitat associations derived from plot-based cor-

relations of population abundances, those population-level relationships did not match habitat variation projected through space or time, or via habitat manipulation. From these observations and subsequent analyses, we draw two general conclusions.

First, although there appears to be a basic component to habitat association in Sage Sparrows (i.e., they are rarely found in areas in the Great Basin lacking sagebrush), once this coarse habitat preference is expressed, fluctuations in density become largely decoupled from the details of habitat variation, both among sites and years. Thus, although there exist individual behavioral responses that are generally appropriate to environmental variation, these do not translate readily into strong patterns linking variations in population density with variation in habitat. Such linkages may be eroded because this species is migratory; it breeds in the Great Basin, where we study it, but winters in the southwestern United States and northern Mexico, up to 2,000 km farther south (Martin and Carlson 1998). We and others (e.g., Pulliam and Parker 1979, Rotenberry and Wiens 1980, Wiens and Rotenberry 1981b, Dunning and Brown 1982, Dunning 1986) have proposed that sizes of shrubsteppe passerine populations are most likely regulated during winter. We assume that most mortality for postfledging and adult shrubsteppe birds occurs during migration and in winter, as is the case for many migrant passerines (e.g., Sherry and Holmes 1995). Thus, a breeding territory may become empty (and hence influence estimates of population density) not because of its intrinsic character but because its previous owner perished 1,500 km to the south. If breeding-bird densities are not near saturation, as seems to be the case in our system (Rotenberry and Wiens 1980, Wiens and Rotenberry 1981a, Wiens 1985), then otherwise suitable territories may remain unfilled for several years. The superposition of strong site tenacity for returning breeders, even in the face of substantial habitat alteration (Wiens and Rotenberry 1985, Wiens et al. 1986), further exacerbates this decoupling.

Our second conclusion is that landscape-level features are as important as local-level features in determining patterns of local occupancy and abundance, as well as temporal persistence, of Sage Sparrows and other shrubland species (Knick and Rotenberry 1995, 1999). Perhaps more importantly, differences in the structure of landscapes in which local study plots are embedded may produce differences in apparent bird-habitat relationships derived from local plots. This may account not only for the inability to project plot-level relationships through time and space (because relevant habitat [landscape] variables have been omitted in deriving those relationships) but also for discrepancies in relationships observed between different studies (e.g., Wiens and Rotenberry 1981a, Petersen and Best 1987) or in the same study over a large geographical area (e.g., Collins 1983).

The foregoing observations carry important implications for how we study bird populations in a conservation context. Many birds breeding in temperate North America are migratory and thus manifest many of the same traits as Sage Sparrows. Because most bird species in North America migrate, studies of these species concern "open" ecological systems. Conditions far beyond the local plot's boundaries influence these birds on their breeding grounds. Instead of finding breeding populations in equilibrium at carrying capacity, we might expect to find a pattern of habitat occupancy not well explained in terms of local biotic conditions. The conservation and management implications are clear: attempts to frame management policies based on assessing the effects of various treatments (e.g., herbicide application in our case), or any other scheme that alters habitat structure and composition, will require much more than a single before-and-after survey to determine those effects. Because systems such as shrubsteppe may be variable even when unaltered, it will take more than a single survey to determine the "normal" state of such systems prior to treatment (Wiens 1981). Clearly, natural-resource management programs will require a long-term perspective. Constraints imposed by the immediate need for

management decisions prompted by political considerations may favor short-term studies or experiments as being better than none at all. In any system characterized by any of the attributes we have discussed, however, short-term studies may yield incomplete and even misleading results. Thus, we strongly support the caveat brought forth by Petersen and Best (1999): inadequate study design and duration can lead to inaccurate conclusions and misdirected conservation efforts.

Although our principal argument is for the necessity of considering landscape-level influences on habitat associations, we do not mean to imply that research focused on individual breeding birds should be secondary. Although individually based patterns of habitat associations may be too variable to predict bird abundances effectively, they are nonetheless key to understanding how organisms are adapted and how they interrelate with other species. On the breeding ground we can still study foraging behavior, mate selection, predator avoidance, reproductive success, and a host of other features that contribute to the fitness of individuals and populations. Although populations of these individuals may not be in equilibrium with respect to habitat and its resources, this does not mean natural selection has stopped shaping other adaptations of these species. Perhaps most importantly, it is at the local level that we are most likely to determine the biological mechanisms that produce landscape-level associations (e.g., nest predation, nest parasitization; Johnson and Temple 1990).

FUTURE DIRECTIONS

The analyses presented above suggest three major avenues for future research. The first is to test the ability of the large-scale logistic regression and discriminant models to predict occurrences of Sage Sparrows through time and space. Although we are optimistic that the present models accurately capture the appropriate level at which habitat associations are most likely to be repeatable (Rotenberry 1986), we were previously optimistic about the abilities of the plot-level relationships to be projected as well. Our second goal is to document more carefully the apparent geographical variation in local habitat associations. We propose to do this by examining a variety of data sets containing vegetation and bird-abundance data collected by several different investigators throughout the Intermountain West. Finally, we are undertaking a study to examine potential mechanisms acting at the level of the individual that ultimately may be responsible for both plot- and landscape-level patterns in abundance. Our initial focus is on reproductive success as a function of local and landscape habitat features. We believe that by combining these three lines of investigation, we may approach a better understanding of the relationships among individual behavior, habitat selection, and population dynamics in Sage Sparrows.

ACKNOWLEDGMENTS

Our most recent studies have been funded by the Challenge Cost Share Program of the U.S. Bureau of Land Management in cooperation with the University of California at Riverside and by the U.S. Fish and Wildlife Service and U.S. National Biological Service (now Biological Resources Division, U.S. Geological Survey). We developed the vegetation map and Geographic Information System coverages under the Global Climate Change programs of the U.S. Bureau of Land Management and U.S. National Biological Service. Administrative support was provided by S. G. Coloff, M. R. Fuller, M. N. Kochert, and S. Sather-Blair.

We thank J. B. Dunning, P. D. Vickery, and an anonymous reviewer for their insightful comments. JTR thanks J. A. Wiens for introducing him to shrubsteppe birds and for collaborating in the collection and analysis of much of the data presented here.

LITERATURE CITED

ALLEN, T. H. F., AND T. B. STARR. 1982. Hierarchy: perspectives for ecological complexity. University of Chicago Press, Chicago, IL.

BOLGER, D. T., A. C. ALBERTS, AND M. E. SOULÉ. 1991. Occurrence patterns of bird species in habitat fragments: sampling, extinction, and nested species subsets. American Naturalist 37:155–166.

BOLGER, D. T., T. A. SCOTT, AND J. T. ROTENBERRY. 1996. Breeding bird abundance in an urbanizing landscape in coastal southern California. Conservation Biology 11(2):1–16.

CODY, M. L. 1981. Habitat selection in birds: the roles of vegetation structure, competition, and productivity. BioScience 31:107–113.

CODY, M. L. (EDITOR). 1985. Habitat selection in birds. Academic Press, New York, NY.

COLLINS, S. L. 1983. Geographical variation in habitat structure of the Black-throated Green Warbler (Dendroica virens). Auk 100:382–389.

DOBLER, F. C. 1994. Washington State shrubsteppe ecosystem studies with emphasis on the relationship between nongame birds and shrub and grass cover densities. Pp. 149–161 in S. B. Monsen and S. G. Kitchen (compilers). Proceedings: ecology and management of annual rangelands. USDA Forest Service Gen. Tech. Rep. INT-GTR 313. USDA Forest Service Intermountain Research Station, Ogden, UT.

DUNNING, J. B. 1986. Shrub-steppe bird assemblages revisited: implications for community theory. American Naturalist 128:82–98.

DUNNING, J. B., AND J. H. BROWN. 1982. Summer rainfall and winter sparrow densities: a test of the food limitation hypothesis. Auk 99:123–129.

EMLEN, J. T. 1977. Estimating breeding season bird densities from transect counts. Auk 94:455–468.

FUENTES, E. R., AND C. CAMPUSANO. 1985. Pest outbreaks and rainfall in the semi-arid region of Chile. Journal of Arid Environments 8:67–72.

JOHNSON, R. G., AND S. A. TEMPLE. 1990. Nest predation and brood parasitism of tallgrass prairie birds. Journal of Wildlife Management 54:106–111.

KNICK, S. T., AND J. T. ROTENBERRY. 1995. Landscape characteristics of fragmented shrubsteppe habitats and breeding passerine birds. Conservation Biology 9:1059–1071.

KNICK, S. T., AND J. T. ROTENBERRY. 1999. Spatial distribution of breeding passerine bird habitats in a shrubsteppe region of southwestern Idaho. Studies in Avian Biology 19:104–111.

KNICK, S. T., J. T. ROTENBERRY, AND T. J. ZARRIELLO. 1997. Supervised classification of Landsat thematic mapper imagery in a semi-arid rangeland by nonparametric discriminant analysis. Photogrammetric Engineering and Remote Sensing 63:79–86.

MANLY, B., L. B. MCDONALD, AND D. THOMAS. 1993. Resource selection by animals. Chapman and Hall, London, U.K.

MARTIN, J. W., AND B. A. CARLSON. 1998. Sage Sparrow (Amphispiza belli). In A. Poole and F. Gill (editors). The birds of North America, no. 326. Academy of Natural Sciences, Philadelphia, PA, and American Ornithologists' Union, Washington, D.C.

NOY-MEIR, I. 1973. Desert ecosystems: environment and producers. Annual Review of Ecology and Systematics 4:25–51.

O'NEILL, R. V., B. T. MILNE, M. G. TURNER, AND R. H. GARDNER. 1988. Resource utilization scales and landscape patterns. Landscape Ecology 2:63–69.

PALMER, M. W. 1988. Fractal geometry: a tool for describing spatial patterns of plant communities. Vegetatio 75:91–102.

PEARSON, S. M. 1993. The spatial extent and relative influence of landscape-level factors on wintering bird populations. Landscape Ecology 8:3–18.

PETERSEN, K. L., AND L. B. BEST. 1987. Effects of prescribed burning on nongame birds in a sagebrush community. Wildlife Society Bulletin 15:317–325.

PETERSEN, K. L., AND L. B. BEST. 1999. Design and duration of perturbation experiments: implications for data interpretation. Studies in Avian Biology 19:230–236.

PORNELUZI, P., J. C. BEDNARZ, L. J. GOODRICH, N. ZAWADA, AND J. HOOVER. 1993. Reproductive performance of territorial Ovenbirds occupying forest fragments and contiguous forest in Pennsylvania. Conservation Biology 7:618–622.

PULLIAM, H. R., AND T. A. PARKER III. 1979. Population regulation of sparrows. Fortschrift für Zoologie 25:137–147.

ROLSTAD, J. 1991. Consequences of forest fragmentation for the dynamics of bird populations: conceptual issues and the evidence. Biological Journal of the Linnean Society 42:149–163.

ROTENBERRY, J. T. 1981. Why measure bird habitat? Pp. 29–32 in D. Capen (editor). The use of multivariate statistics in studies of wildlife habitat. USDA Forest Service Gen. Tech. Rep. RM-87. USDA Forest Service Rocky Mountain Research Station, Ft. Collins, CO.

ROTENBERRY, J. T. 1982. Censusing birds in shrubsteppe

habitat. Pp. 307–309 *in* D. E. Davis (editor). Handbook of census methods for terrestrial vertebrates. CRC Press, Boca Raton, FL.

ROTENBERRY, J. T. 1986. Habitat relationships of shrubsteppe birds: even "good" models cannot predict the future. Pp. 217–221 *in* J. Verner, M. L. Morrison, and C. J. Ralph (editors). Wildlife 2000: modeling habitat relationships of terrestrial vertebrates. University of Wisconsin Press, Madison, WI.

ROTENBERRY, J. T., AND J. A. WIENS. 1980. Temporal variation in habitat structure and shrubsteppe bird dynamics. Oecologia 47:1–9.

ROTENBERRY, J. T., AND J. A. WIENS. 1989. Reproductive biology of shrubsteppe passerine birds: geographical and temporal variation in clutch size, brood size, and fledging success. Condor 91:1–14.

ROTENBERRY, J. T., AND J. A. WIENS. 1991. Weather and reproductive variation in shrubsteppe sparrows: a hierarchical analysis. Ecology 72:1325–1335.

ROTENBERRY, J. T., AND J. A. WIENS. 1998. Foraging patch selection by shrubsteppe sparrows. Ecology 79:1160–1173.

SHERRY, T. W., AND R. T. HOLMES. 1995. Summer versus winter limitation of populations: what are the issues and what is the evidence. Pp. 85–120 *in* T. E. Martin and D. M. Finch (editors). Ecology and management of neotropical migratory birds. Oxford University Press, Oxford, U.K.

WIENS, J. A. 1981. Single-sample surveys of communities: are the revealed patterns real? American Naturalist 117:90–98.

WIENS, J. A. 1985. Habitat selection in variable environments: shrub-steppe birds. Pp. 227–251 *in* M. L. Cody (editor). Habitat selection in birds. Academic Press, New York, NY.

WIENS, J. A., AND J. T. ROTENBERRY. 1981a. Habitat associations and community structure of birds in shrubsteppe environments. Ecological Monographs 51:21–41.

WIENS, J. A., AND J. T. ROTENBERRY. 1981b. Censusing and the evaluation of avian habitat occupancy. Studies in Avian Biology 6:522–531.

WIENS, J. A., AND J. T. ROTENBERRY. 1985. Response of breeding passerine birds to rangeland alteration in a North American shrubsteppe locality. Journal of Applied Ecology 22:655–668.

WIENS, J. A., J. T. ROTENBERRY, AND B. VAN HORNE. 1986. A lesson in the limitations of field experiments: shrubsteppe birds and habitat alteration. Ecology 67:365–376.

Studies in Avian Biology No. 19:104–111, 1999.

SPATIAL DISTRIBUTION OF BREEDING PASSERINE BIRD HABITATS IN A SHRUBSTEPPE REGION OF SOUTHWESTERN IDAHO

STEVEN T. KNICK AND JOHN T. ROTENBERRY

Abstract. We mapped the spatial distribution of a habitat index for Sage Sparrows (*Amphispiza belli*), Brewer's Sparrows (*Spizella breweri*), Horned Larks (*Eremophila alpestris*), and Western Meadowlarks (*Sturnella neglecta*) in shrubsteppe habitats of southwestern Idaho. Landscape-level habitat associations of breeding passerine birds were determined from presence or absence at 119 randomly located points surveyed each year from 1992 through 1995. We developed a multivariate description of habitats used by each species from variables derived from coverages in a Geographical Information System. Habitat variables were number of shrub, agriculture, and hydrography cells, mean and standard deviation of shrub patch size, habitat richness, and a measure of spatial heterogeneity in a 1-kilometer radius around each survey point. We ranked each 50-meter cell in a Geographical Information System map by the generalized squared distance in multivariate space between values for habitat variables in the cell and the mean habitat vector for each species. We then generated a map of habitat probabilities of each species for a 200,000-hectare region in southwestern Idaho. In a verification survey at 39 sites, we correctly predicted presence or absence at approximately 80 percent of the sites for Sage and Brewer's sparrows and Western Meadowlarks but at only 36 percent of the sites for Horned Larks. Spatial distribution of habitats for breeding passerine birds was strongly related to distribution of large shrub patches. Because fire is rapidly converting shrublands to exotic annual grasslands in this region, we expect shrubland-obligate species to decline because of habitat loss and grassland species to become more predominant unless management practices change.

DISTRIBUCIÓN ESPACIAL DE HÁBITATS DE AVES PASERIFORMES EN REPRODUCCIÓN EN UNA REGIÓN DE ESTEPA ARBUSTIVA DEL SUROESTE DE IDAHO

Sinopsis. Delineamos mapas de distribución espacial de un índice de hábitat para el Gorrión de Artemisia (*Amphispiza belli*), el Gorrión de Brewer (*Spizella breweri*), la Alondra Cornuda (*Eremophila alpestris*) y el Pradero Occidental (*Sturnella neglecta*) en hábitats de estepa arbustiva en el suroeste de Idaho. Las relaciones de hábitat a escala de paisaje de los paseriformes reproductores se determinaron a partir de la presencia o ausencia observada en 119 puntos escogidos al azar, cada año entre 1992 y 1995. Desarrollamos una descripción multivariante de los hábitats utilizados por cada especie a partir de variables obtenidas de los datos de cobertura disponibles en un Sistema Geográfico de Información. Las variables de hábitat fueron: número de céldas arbustivas, agrícolas, e hidrográficas; media y desviación típica del tamaño de rodales con matorral; riqueza del hábitat; y una medición de la heterogeneidad espacial dentro de un radio de un kilómetro desde cada punto de censo. Ordenamos cada pixel de 50 metros de un mapa del Sistema Geográfico de Información de acuerdo con la distancia cuadrada generalizada entre el valor correspondiente a las variables de hábitat en el pixel y el valor medio correspondiente al vector hábitat de cada especie. Luego produjimos un mapa de probabilidades de hábitat para cada especie para una región de 200.000 hectáreas en el suroeste de Idaho. Censamos 39 sitios para verificar la presencia o ausencia de cada especie. Se predijeron correctamente en aproximadamente un 80 por ciento de los sitios para los Gorriones de Artemisia y de Brewer y para los Praderos Occidentales; sin embargo, sólo se predijo un 36 por ciento de los sitios para las Alondras Cornudas. La distribución espacial de hábitats para paseriformes reproductores se relacionó estrechamente con la distribución de rodales grandes de matorral. Como en esta región el fuego está convirtiendo rápidamente los matorrales a pastizales exóticos anuales, pensamos que, por la pérdida de hábitat, disminuirán las especies dependientes del matorral. Por otro lado, a menos que cambien las prácticas de manejo, esperamos que las especies dependientes de los pastizales se hagan más predominantes.

Key Words: Amphispiza belli; *Eremophila alpestris*; exotic annual grassland; Geographical Information System; habitat-selection model; shrubsteppe; *Spizella breweri*; *Sturnella neglecta*.

Interpreting the environment from a species' perspective is an important focus in studies of animal-habitat associations. Descriptions of habitat associations are well known for many species, and numerous statistical techniques exist to develop models of resource selection (e.g., John-son 1980; Alldredge and Ratti 1986, 1992; Manly et al. 1993). Recently, Geographical Information System (GIS) technology has advanced the capability to map the spatial distribution of single and multiple environmental variables. Just as realistic models have been developed to represent habitat use in a nonspatial context (Verner et al. 1986), it is now possible to describe the spatial distribution of elements in the landscape as perceived by an animal by mapping appropriate variables or indexes. It is then possible to manage landscapes for species based on concepts from theoretical biogeography, which have important implications for conservation biology (Urban and Shugart 1986, Temple and Cary 1988, Burkey 1989, Hansson and Angelstam 1991, Opdam 1991, Danielson 1992). For example, using maps of habitat distributions, managers can identify regions with high probability of use, maintain areas of sufficient size to contain viable populations, or identify habitat corridors for dispersal.

We studied four species of breeding passerines in a shrubsteppe region in southwestern Idaho. Two of the species, Sage Sparrow (*Amphispiza belli*) and Brewer's Sparrow (*Spizella breweri*), are shrubland obligates, and two, Horned Lark (*Eremophila alpestris*) and Western Meadowlark (*Sturnella neglecta*), are grassland species. Our first objective was to develop a resource-selection model for each species by combining field surveys for species presence with landscape variables derived from a classified GIS map. We then mapped the selection function for the entire study area to determine the spatial distribution of habitats potentially used by each species.

Our study involved several assumptions. We assumed that the scale and selection of environmental variables we measured were relevant to the species (Wiens 1989) and that our multivariate statistical model appropriately described the species-habitat associations (Rotenberry 1986, Rotenberry and Knick 1999). We also assumed that the relative probabilities of habitat configuration derived from the statistical model represented the probability that a species would fill available habitats (e.g., Fretwell 1972, Van Horne 1983, Hobbs and Hanley 1990, Vickery et al. 1992).

STUDY AREA

We conducted our study from 1992 through 1995 in a 200,000-ha region of shrubsteppe habitat in southwestern Idaho that included portions of the Snake River Birds of Prey National Conservation Area (116° W, 43° N). The primary management mandate of this area, which was designated as a national conservation area in 1994 (U.S. Public Law 103-64; 4 August 1994), is to maintain and conserve the high densities of nesting raptors and their prey (U.S. Department of the Interior 1979). Multiple uses, including livestock grazing and military training, are permitted if compatible with raptor-conservation management (Kochert and Pellant 1986, U.S. Department of the Interior 1995).

Wildfires are rapidly converting once-large expanses of big sagebrush (*Artemisia tridentata*), winterfat (*Kraschenninikovia lanata*), shadscale (*Atriplex confertifolia*), and other salt shrub (*Atriplex* spp.) communities in the Snake River plains into regions dominated by exotics such as cheatgrass (*Bromus tectorum*) or Russian thistle (*Salsola kali*; Whisenant 1990). As a result of numerous fires since 1980, the native shrub communities now are highly fragmented or have been converted to grassland (U.S. Department of the Interior 1996, Knick and Rotenberry 1997; Fig. 1). The highly flammable annual grasses increase fire frequency and reduce the potential for shrub reestablishment. More than 30% of the 76,910 ha that burned between 1980 and 1992 has reburned two to four times; human activities were responsible for 72% of the fire ignitions (U.S. Department of the Interior 1995).

METHODS

FIELD SURVEYS

We conducted unlimited-radius point-count surveys (Ralph et al. 1995) each year from 1992 through 1995 to determine habitat associations of breeding passerine birds. We established 119 sites by selecting random coordinates throughout the study area in an attempt to sample all habitats in proportion to their available distribution. Minimum distance between sites was more than 400 m, and we considered the sites spatially independent because 97% of all observations (N = 5,757) were estimated from a distance of less than 200 m. Final coordinates of each site were determined by Global Positioning System to an accuracy of less than 5 m (August et al. 1994). Order of sampling in each year was randomly determined.

Sites were sampled once each year between 0500 and 1000 on days with no precipitation and winds less than 12 km/hr. After waiting 2–5 min to reduce the disturbance from our arrival, we recorded all individuals we saw or heard at each site during a 5-min period. Sampling periods were 4 May–25 June 1992; 10 May–23 June 1993; 10 April–24 June 1994; and 3–29 May 1995. One observer participated in all 4 yr, one in 2 yr, and five in 1 yr. All observers participated in a 1- to 3-wk training before beginning surveys.

GIS COVERAGES

Our base coverage in the GIS was a vegetation map classified from Landsat thematic mapper satellite imagery (Knick et al. 1997). Resolution of the vegetation map was 50 m (resampled from 27-m cells in the original thematic mapper satellite image), and the study area contained 1,752,340 cells. After identifying water and agriculture areas, we classified each 50-m cell in the habitat map into one of five categories: sagebrush, winterfat, shadscale, disturbance (dominated by Russian thistle), or grasslands (including both cheatgrass and native grasses). Accuracy in separating shrub cells (>5% ground cover of shrub) from nonshrub cells was 80%; classification accuracy was 64% for classification of the five individual habitat classes (plus agriculture and water categories; Knick et al. 1997). Gross habitat characteristics such as percent shrub cover did not change during our study.

We derived variables that described both the composition and spatial heterogeneity of the landscape (Li

A.

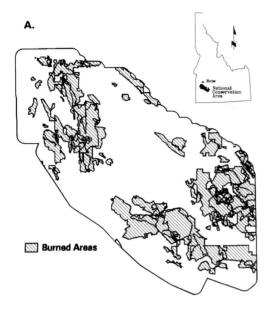

Burned Areas

B.

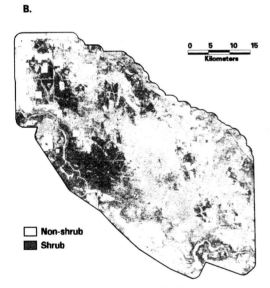

Non-shrub
Shrub

0   5   10   15
Kilometers

FIGURE 1. Locations in a 200,000-ha shrubsteppe region of southwestern Idaho of (A) areas that burned between 1980 and 1992 and (B) shrub patches and grassland in 1994. Burned areas were digitized from U.S. Bureau of Land Management fire boundaries on 1:24:000 quadrangle maps. Shrub and grasslands were classified from Landsat thematic mapper satellite imagery.

and Reynolds 1994; Table 1). We developed an index of habitat diversity from the number of habitats in a 1-km radius of each cell in the vegetation map. We also determined the number of shrub cells and the average size and standard deviation for shrub patches. We used the ratio of number of edges between shrub

and grass cells to total the number of edges in the 1-km radius as an estimate of landscape heterogeneity. Habitat diversity was the only variable derived from the full habitat classification, which contained the lower classification accuracy. For the other landscape variables we used the binary shrub/nonshrub classification.

We created a coverage of all agriculture fields from a composite of a 1979 vegetation map of the Snake River Birds of Prey National Conservation Area (U.S. Department of the Interior 1979), 1993 U.S. Bureau of Reclamation agriculture maps, and our classified satellite imagery. The composite agriculture map included areas of both actively growing and fallow vegetation. We also created a coverage of hydrography, to include wetlands, lakes, and ephemeral or permanent streams and rivers, from U.S. Geological Survey 1:100,000 digital line graphs. We used the number of agriculture and hydrography cells in the 1-km radius of each cell in our analyses.

HABITAT ASSOCIATIONS

We determined habitat associations for each species based on the mean values for the habitat variables at all sites where a species was detected. This multivariate habitat mean and the associated covariance matrix were then used to develop habitat maps for each species. We used a site in the analysis if a species was detected in any of the 4 yr of sampling. By including sites where a species was present in only 1 yr, we determined the optimistic range of habitat associations in our analysis because yearly variation in temporal persistence was related to habitat characteristics (Knick and Rotenberry 1995, Rotenberry and Knick 1999). Because of the relative ubiquity of Horned Larks, we defined presence of this species as more than four birds at a site.

Six of the seven variables were transformed to best approximate a normal distribution as determined by Kolmogorov-Smirnov tests. Distributions of all variables remained significantly different from normal (P < 0.05), but statistical power remained high because of large sample sizes in the GIS map. Although normality tests failed, we proceeded without meeting this assumption using the best approximations to a normal distribution to minimize the potential bias. We transformed average patch size and standard deviation by $\log_{10}(x + 1)$, number of shrub cells by $x^{0.4}$, landscape heterogeneity by $x^{0.8}$, habitat diversity by x^2, and hydrography by $x^{0.9}$. The distribution of the agriculture variable could not be improved and was not transformed.

HABITAT MAPS

We created maps of habitat distributions for each species by first determining the generalized squared distance (or Mahalanobis distance) between the landscape variables in each cell of the GIS map and the multivariate mean of those variables associated with a species (Clark et al. 1993, Knick and Dyer 1997). The generalized squared distance was then converted to a Chi-squared probability distribution with P (number of variables) − 1 = 6 degrees of freedom. Therefore, we simply rescaled the generalized squared distance, a dimensionless statistic, to a probability distribution be-

TABLE 1. LANDSCAPE-LEVEL VARIABLES USED IN AN ANALYSIS OF HABITAT SELECTION BY SAGE AND BREWER'S SPARROWS, HORNED LARKS, AND WESTERN MEADOWLARKS IN A SHRUBSTEPPE REGION IN SOUTHWESTERN IDAHO

Variable	Description
Agriculture	Number of 50-m agriculture cells
Habitat richness	Number of different habitats
Hydrography	Number of cells containing wetlands, lakes, or permanent or ephemeral streams and rivers
Shrubs	Number of 50-m cells classified in shrubland category
Mean shrub patch	Mean patch size of all shrubland patches in the 1-km radius
Shrub patch variance	Standard deviation of all shrubland patches in the 1-km radius
Habitat patchiness	Number of edges between shrubland and grassland cells

Note: All variables were determined for a 1-km radius around each 50-m cell in a GIS map of the study area.

tween 0 and 1. As such, we determined the probability that the variables at a cell were similar to the multivariate mean that described habitats associated with sites where a species was detected.

VERIFICATION SURVEYS

We conducted verification surveys in 1995 at an additional 39 sites located at random coordinates throughout the study area. Sites were classified into predicted absence or presence for each species based on a χ^2 probability of 0.5 for the cutpoint.

RESULTS

At 119 points surveyed annually from 1992 through 1995, we observed Sage Sparrows at 36 points, Brewer's Sparrows at 83, Horned Larks at 102, and Western Meadowlarks at 96. Habitats associated with Sage and Brewer's sparrows included large shrub patches and relatively lower amounts of edge between shrubland and grasslands than at habitats associated with Horned Larks and Western Meadowlarks (Table 2).

Maps of habitat probabilities for each cell reflected the strong association of Sage and Brewer's sparrows (Fig. 2) with existing shrublands (Fig. 1). At the landscape scale, burned areas were associated with low similarities to the mean habitat vectors at sites where we observed Sage and Brewer's sparrows (Fig. 1).

Maps generated from the χ^2 probability distribution of the generalized squared distances for Horned Larks and Western Meadowlarks were more conservative in predicting the spatial extent of habitats than we expected because of these species' ubiquity in the samples (Fig. 3). However, areas of predicted habitats for Horned Larks and Western Meadowlarks included both greater spatial extent and more grassland regions than maps generated for Sage and Brewer's sparrows.

Cumulative frequency distributions represented the proportion of the study area relative to the mean habitat vector for each species (Fig. 4). As expected, a smaller proportion of the habitat in the study area was similar to the mean habitat vector associated with Sage Sparrow, the least-observed and most habitat-specific species, when compared to Brewer's Sparrow, Horned Lark, or Western Meadowlark.

We correctly predicted presence or absence at 79% of the verification sites for Sage Sparrows and Western Meadowlarks, at 82% of the sites for Brewer's Sparrows, but at only 36% of the sites for Horned Larks (Table 3). In most classification errors, a species was present at a site where the selection model predicted absence. Horned Larks, present at 22 of 39 sites where

TABLE 2. SUMMARY STATISTICS FOR HABITAT VARIABLES AT SURVEY SITES IN SOUTHWESTERN IDAHO FOR SAGE AND BREWER'S SPARROWS, HORNED LARKS, AND WESTERN MEADOWLARKS

Habitat variable	Sage Sparrow (N = 36)		Brewer's Sparrow (N = 83)		Horned Lark (N = 102)		Western Meadowlark (N = 96)	
	$\bar{X}$	SE	$\bar{X}$	SE	$\bar{X}$	SE	$\bar{X}$	SE
Agriculture (no. cells)	21.3	13.0	34.0	11.8	28.2	9.6	36.6	11.0
Habitat richness	6.1	0.1	6.1	0.1	6.1	0.1	6.0	0.1
Hydrography (no. cells)	37.4	4.8	45.4	3.7	48.1	3.7	51.1	3.6
Shrubs (no. cells)	854.0	46.5	647.6	38.2	466.2	34.7	502.5	33.4
Mean shrub patch (km²)	47.0	9.1	30.2	5.2	22.6	4.6	14.5	2.5
Shrub patch variance	19.1	2.9	14.5	1.7	11.8	1.8	11.6	1.6
Habitat patchiness	405.6	33.2	439.6	22.4	462.5	22.6	471.3	21.2

Note: Sample sizes (N) are the number of sites where presence was recorded at 119 sites surveyed annually from 1992 through 1995.

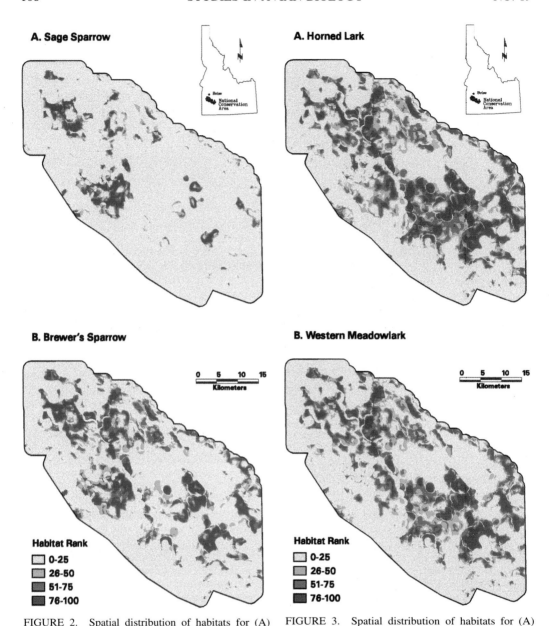

FIGURE 2. Spatial distribution of habitats for (A) Sage Sparrow and (B) Brewer's Sparrow in a 200,000-ha shrubsteppe region of southwestern Idaho. Habitat rank is the χ^2 probability that habitats in individual map cells were similar to the multivariate mean habitat vector associated with the species presence at survey sites (ranks closest to 100 have the highest probability of similarity).

FIGURE 3. Spatial distribution of habitats for (A) Horned Lark and (B) Western Meadowlark in a 200,000-ha shrubsteppe region of southwestern Idaho. Habitat rank is the χ^2 probability that habitats in individual map cells were similar to the multivariate mean habitat vector associated with the species presence at survey sites (ranks closest to 100 have the highest probability of similarity).

absence was predicted, represented the extreme in these errors (Table 3).

DISCUSSION

Spatial distribution of habitats for the two shrubland-obligate species, Sage and Brewer's sparrows, was clearly related to existing shrublands. Because large-scale fires have converted shrublands to exotic annual grasslands with increased fire frequency, we expect that habitats for shrubland-obligate species will continue to

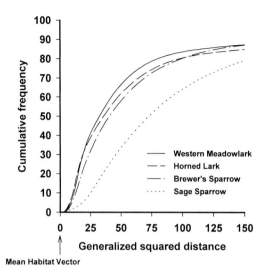

FIGURE 4. Cumulative frequency distribution of generalized squared distances for Sage and Brewer's sparrows, Horned Larks, and Western Meadowlarks in a 200,000-ha shrubsteppe region of southwestern Idaho. Relative shift in distribution toward the right indicates greater proportions of areas that are less similar to habitats (mean habitat vector) where the species was observed.

TABLE 3. ERROR MATRICES FOR PRESENCE OR ABSENCE PREDICTED BY RESOURCE-SELECTION MODELS DEVELOPED FOR SAGE AND BREWER'S SPARROWS, HORNED LARKS, AND WESTERN MEADOWLARKS AT 39 SITES IN A SHRUBSTEPPE REGION OF SOUTHWESTERN IDAHO

Species	Predicted	Known Absent	Present	Total
Sage Sparrow	Absent	27	5	32
	Present	3	4	7
	Total	30	9	39
Brewer's Sparrow	Absent	24	6	30
	Present	1	8	9
	Total	25	14	39
Horned Lark	Absent	12	22	34
	Present	3	2	5
	Total	15	24	39
Western Meadowlark	Absent	28	7	35
	Present	1	3	4
	Total	29	10	39

decline. We expect the current trajectory of habitat changes to have a particularly adverse effect on Sage Sparrow habitats.

Since 1979 fires have destroyed more than 30% of the existing shrublands in our study area (U.S. Department of the Interior 1996). We do not know the fire regime of presettlement periods, but large-scale fires, although present, likely were much less frequent than they now are because of the difference in grassland understory (Whisanant 1990). Because of cheatgrass invasion into this system in the late 1800s and early 1900s, continuous fuels are now omnipresent in the understory and facilitate firespread. In addition, cheatgrass cures earlier than native grasses, thus increasing the length of the fire season (Klemmedson and Smith 1964). The larger and more frequent fires in the present disturbance regime have either eliminated or widely dispersed the existing seed sources of shrub species (Knick and Rotenberry 1997). The potential for recovery of shrubs, such as sagebrush, is far outpaced by the rate of loss. Thus, the system has lost much of the once-dominant shrubland and now exists in a new grassland state that potentially represents a habitat sink from which shrub recovery by natural means of gradual recolonization by seedling establishment is unlikely or extremely long-term.

Our study demonstrated the potential of landscape-scale attributes to determine habitats for shrubland-obligate species; we correctly predicted presence/absence at approximately 80% of the verification points. Both species persisted in burned areas when measured at a local scale (< 10 ha; Petersen and Best 1987, 1999), but local plots still were embedded in larger-scale landscapes of shrubland. Loss of shrublands at our larger scale of investigation (1-km radius around each point) was reflected in complete absence of habitat for shrubland-obligate species, and those species were not present.

Our technique clearly represented the spatial distribution of habitat for shrubland-obligate specialists, such as Sage and Brewer's sparrows, and for Western Meadowlark, a grassland species. For these specialists, the mean and covariance matrix represented the distribution of the habitats used by the species. For more generalist species, however, such as Horned Lark, the mean and covariance matrix more likely represented the distribution of habitats in the study area rather than a species-habitat association. Thus, the generalized distance from the mean habitat vector may not represent the wide range (or variance) of habitats used by generalist species. As the species-habitat association becomes more general, the mapped distribution changes from the mean habitat vector of the species to represent the mean configuration of habitats in the study area.

Based on verification surveys, our habitat maps were consistently conservative in predicting species presence, despite using a relatively liberal definition of habitats used (species presence at a site in any of 4 yr) to define the multivariate mean habitat. By using a narrower definition, such as species presence at a site in all years, map predictions likely would underestimate further the actual distribution of habitats. Alternatively, we could change the χ^2 probability that defines presence or absence, or simply rescale the generalized squared distance into user-defined quantiles (e.g., Knick and Dyer 1997). When rescaled into quantiles, the categories then represent a percent of the study area in each class (e.g., the top 10% of the study area) rather than a probability of similarity to the multivariate habitat mean.

ACKNOWLEDGMENTS

Our study was funded by the Challenge Cost Share program of the U.S. Bureau of Land Management in cooperation with the University of California at Riverside and Boise State University and by the U.S. Fish and Wildlife Service and U.S. National Biological Service (now Biological Resources Division, U.S. Geological Survey). The vegetation map and GIS coverages were developed under the Global Climate Change programs of the U.S. Bureau of Land Management and U.S. National Biological Service. We appreciate administrative support from S. G. Coloff, M. R. Fuller, M. N. Kochert, and S. Sather-Blair. P. Bates, D. Dyer, W. Dyer, D. Johnson, G. Kaltenecker, T. Katzner, R. Lara, J. Younk, and T. Zarriello assisted with various aspects of the study. We appreciate the manuscript review by P. D. Vickery and two anonymous reviewers.

LITERATURE CITED

ALLDREDGE, J. R., AND J. T. RATTI. 1986. Comparison of some statistical techniques for analysis of resource selection. Journal of Wildlife Management 50:157–165.

ALLDREDGE, J. R., AND J. T. RATTI. 1992. Further comparison of some statistical techniques for analysis of resource selection. Journal of Wildlife Management 56:1–9.

AUGUST, P., J. MICHAUD, C. LABASH, AND C. SMITH. 1994. GPS for environmental applications: accuracy and precision of locational data. Photogrammetric Engineering and Remote Sensing 60:41–45.

BURKEY, T. V. 1989. Extinction in nature reserves: the effect of fragmentation and the importance of migration between reserve fragments. Oikos 55:75–81.

CLARK, J. D., J. E. DUNN, AND K. G. SMITH. 1993. A multivariate model of female black bear habitat use for a geographic information system. Journal of Wildlife Management 57:519–526.

DANIELSON, B. J. 1992. Habitat selection, interspecific interactions and landscape composition. Evolutionary Ecology 6:399–411.

FRETWELL, S. D. 1972. Populations in a seasonal environment. Princeton University Press, Princeton, NJ.

HANSSON, L., AND P. ANGELSTAM. 1991. Landscape ecology as a theoretical basis for nature conservation. Landscape Ecology 5:191–201.

HOBBS, N. T., AND T. A. HANLEY. 1990. Habitat evaluation: do use/availability data reflect carrying capacity? Journal of Wildlife Management 54:515–522.

JOHNSON, D. H. 1980. The comparison of usage and availability measurements for evaluating resource preference. Ecology 61:65–71.

KLEMMEDSON, J. O., AND J. G. SMITH. 1964. Cheatgrass (Bromus tectorum L.). Botanical Review 30:226–262.

KNICK, S. T., AND D. L. DYER. 1997. Distribution of black-tailed jackrabbit habitat determined by GIS in southwestern Idaho. Journal of Wildlife Management 61:75–85.

KNICK, S. T., AND J. T. ROTENBERRY. 1995. Landscape characteristics of fragmented shrubsteppe habitats and breeding passerine birds. Conservation Biology 9:1059–1071.

KNICK, S. T., AND J. T. ROTENBERRY. 1997. Landscape characteristics of disturbed shrubsteppe habitats in southwestern Idaho (U.S.A.). Landscape Ecology 12:287–297.

KNICK, S. T., J. T. ROTENBERRY, AND T. J. ZARRIELLO. 1997. Supervised classification of Landsat thematic mapper imagery in a semi-arid rangeland by nonparametric discriminant analysis. Photogrammetric Engineering and Remote Sensing 63:79–86.

KOCHERT, M. N., AND M. PELLANT. 1986. Multiple use in the Snake River Birds of Prey Area. Rangelands 8:217–220.

LI, H., AND J. F. REYNOLDS. 1994. A simulation experiment to quantify spatial heterogeneity in categorical maps. Ecology 75:2446–2455.

MANLY, B., L. McDONALD, AND D. THOMAS. 1993. Resource selection by animals. Chapman and Hall, London, U.K.

OPDAM, P. 1991. Metapopulation theory and habitat fragmentation: a review of holarctic breeding bird studies. Landscape Ecology 5:93–106.

PETERSEN, K. L., AND L. B. BEST. 1987. Effects of prescribed burning on nongame birds in a sagebrush community. Wildlife Society Bulletin 15:317–325.

PETERSEN, K. L., AND L. B. BEST. 1999. Design and duration of perturbation experiments: implications for data interpretation. Studies in Avian Biology 19:230–236.

RALPH, C. J., J. R. SAUER, AND S. DROEGE (EDITORS). 1995. Monitoring bird populations by point counts. USDA Forest Service Gen. Tech. Rep. PSW-GTR-149. USDA Forest Service, Albany, CA.

ROTENBERRY, J. T. 1986. Habitat relationships of shrubsteppe birds: even "good" models cannot predict the future. Pp. 217–221 in J. Verner, M. L. Morrison, and C. J. Ralph (editors). Wildlife 2000: modeling habitat relationships of terrestrial vertebrates. University of Wisconsin Press, Madison, WI.

ROTENBERRY, J. T., AND S. T. KNICK. 1999. Multiscale habitat associations of the Sage Sparrow: implications for conservation biology. Studies in Avian Biology 19:95–103.

TEMPLE, S. A., AND J. R. CARY. 1988. Modeling dynamics of habitat-interior bird populations in fragmented landscapes. Conservation Biology 2:340–347.

URBAN, D. L., AND H. H. SHUGART, JR. 1986. Avian demography in mosaic landscapes: modeling paradigm and preliminary results. Pp. 273–280 in J. Verner, M. L. Morrison, and C. J. Ralph (editors). Wildlife 2000: modeling habitat relationships of terrestrial vertebrates. University of Wisconsin Press, Madison, WI.

U.S. DEPARTMENT OF THE INTERIOR. 1979. Snake River Birds of Prey special research report to the Secretary of the Interior. U.S. Bureau of Land Management, Boise, ID.

U.S. DEPARTMENT OF THE INTERIOR. 1995. Snake River Birds of Prey National Conservation Area management plan. Bureau of Land Management, Lower Snake River District Office, Boise, ID.

U.S. DEPARTMENT OF THE INTERIOR. 1996. Effects of military training and fire in the Snake River Birds of Prey National Conservation Area. BLM/IDARNG research project final report. U.S. Geological Survey, Snake River Field Station, Boise, ID.

VAN HORNE, B. 1983. Density as a misleading indicator of habitat quality. Journal of Wildlife Management 47:893–901.

VERNER, J., M. L. MORRISON, AND C. J. RALPH (EDITORS). 1986. Wildlife 2000: modeling habitat relationships of terrestrial vertebrates. University of Wisconsin Press, Madison, WI.

VICKERY, P. D., M. L. HUNTER, JR., AND J. V. WELLS. 1992. Is density an indicator of breeding success? Auk 109:706–710.

WHISENANT, S. G. 1990. Changing fire frequencies on Idaho's Snake River plains: ecological and management implications. Pp. 4–10 *in* E. D. McArthur, E. M. Romney, S. D. Smith, and P. T. Tueller (editors). Proceedings: symposium on cheatgrass invasion, shrub die-off, and other aspects of shrub biology and management. USDA Forest Service Intermountain Research Station, Ogden, UT.

WIENS, J. A. 1989. Spatial scaling in ecology. Functional Ecology 3:385–397.

Studies in Avian Biology No. 19:112–121, 1999.

HABITAT RELATIONS AND BREEDING BIOLOGY
OF GRASSLAND BIRDS IN NEW YORK

CHRISTOPHER J. NORMENT, CHARLES D. ARDIZZONE, AND KATHLEEN HARTMAN

Abstract. In 1994 we began a study of the habitat relations and breeding biology of grassland birds in western New York. Most fields contained fewer than four grassland species, with Bobolink (*Dolichonyx oryzivorous*) and Savannah Sparrow (*Passerculus sandwichensis*) being the two most common species. Species of management concern in the Northeast, such as Henslow's Sparrow (*Ammodramus henslowii*) and Upland Sandpiper (*Bartramia longicauda*), were absent from the study area. Bird-habitat models generated through Principal Components Analysis and stepwise multiple regression indicated that field area, or variables correlated with area, explained most of the variation in overall grassland bird species richness (partial $r^2 = 0.43$) and abundance (partial $r^2 = 0.60$) and in the abundance of Bobolinks and Savannah Sparrows. Grassland birds were generally absent from fields smaller than 5 hectares. Areas with few shrubs and low horizontal heterogeneity supported more grassland bird species than did fields with more shrubs and high horizontal heterogeneity, and fields with shorter, less dense vegetation had more individuals than did fields with taller, dense vegetation. Few grassland birds occurred in fields planted in switchgrass (*Panicum virgatum*) monocultures. More than 90 percent of all known nesting pairs fledged young by the end of the first week in July. Nest success was generally high; the proportion of nests fledging one or more young was 0.76 for Savannah Sparrows, 0.54 for Bobolinks, and 0.67 for Eastern Meadowlarks (*Sturnella magna*).

Grassland bird populations in this study may benefit from management practices that increase field area, control shrub invasion, and encourage the growth of grasses other than switchgrass. The current low levels of grazing at Iroquois National Wildlife Refuge, with cattle allowed in pastures only after 15 July, do not appear to be harmful to grassland bird populations.

LAS RELACIONES ENTRE LOS HÁBITATS Y LA BIOLOGÍA REPRODUCTIVA
DE AVES DE PASTIZAL EN NUEVA YORK

Sinopsis. En 1994 iniciamos un estudio de las relaciones entre los hábitats y la biología reproductiva de aves de pastizal en el oeste de Nueva York. La mayoría de los campos tenían menos de cuatro especies de pastizal, con el Tordo Arrocero (*Dolichonyx oryzivorous*) y el Gorrión Sabanero (*Passerculus sandwichensis*) como las dos especies más comunes. Las especies de importancia para manejo en el noreste, como el Gorrión de Henslow (*Ammodramus henslowii*) y el Zarapito Ganga (*Bartramia longicauda*) estaban ausentes del área de estudio. Los modelos de hábitat para aves producidos por el Análisis de Componentes Principales y las regresiones múltiples de escala indicaron que el área del campo (o las variables correlacionadas con el área) daban cuenta de la mayor parte de la variación de la riqueza total de especies de aves de pastizal (parcial $r^2 = 0,43$), de la abundancia total de ellas (parcial $r^2 = 0,60$) y de la abundancia de los Tordos Arroceros y los Gorriones de Henslow. Las aves de pastizal generalmente estaban ausentes en los campos de menos de 5 hectáreas. Las áreas con pocos arbustos y una escasa heterogeneidad horizontal mantenían más especies de aves de pastizal que los campos con más arbustos y una abundante heterogeneidad horizontal; los campos con vegetación más baja y menos densa tenían más individuos que los campos con vegetación más alta y densa. Había pocas aves de pastizal en campos sembrados con monoculturas de *Panicum virgatum*. Más de un 90 por ciento de todas las parejas conocidas con nidos produjeron pollos para el fin de la primera semana de julio. El éxito de los nidos fue generalmente alto; la proporción de los nidos que produjeron un pollo o más fue 0,76 para los Gorriones Sabaneros, 0,54 para los Tordos Arroceros y 0,67 para los Praderos Orientales (*Sturnella magna*).

Las poblaciones de aves de pastizal pueden beneficiarse con las prácticas de manejo que aumenten el área de los campos, controlen la invasión de arbustos y estimulen el crecimiento de hierbas que no sean *Panicum virgatum*. Los bajos niveles actuales de apacentamiento en el Refugio Nacional de Fauna Iroquois, con ganado permitido en las praderas solamente después del 15 de julio, no parecen ser dañinos para las poblaciones de aves de pastizal.

Key Words: Bobolink; breeding biology; *Dolichonyx oryzivorous*; Eastern Meadowlark; grassland birds; habitat selection; New York; *Passerculus sandwichensis*; Savannah Sparrow; *Sturnella magna*.

Populations of many grassland bird species in the United States have declined significantly since the mid-1960s (Robbins et al. 1986, Knopf 1994). Although declines of North American breeding birds may vary across geographic regions (James et al. 1992; Peterjohn and Sauer 1994, 1999; Herkert 1995a), the trend evident for grassland birds is consistent across North America (Robbins et al. 1986, Bollinger and Gavin 1992, Smith and Smith 1992, Askins 1993, Peterjohn and Sauer 1999). Reasons for declines of grassland birds in the northeastern United

TABLE 1.   TYPES AND SIZES OF FIELDS CENSUSED FOR GRASSLAND BIRDS IN WESTERN NEW YORK, 1995

Habitat type	Sample sizes				Size (ha)
	Iroquois NWR[a]	Montezuma NWR[b]	Braddock Bay WMA	Total	
Cool-season grassland[c]	8	1		9	5.1–20.1
Warm-season grassland	6		1	7	1.3–44
Pasture	3			3	19.0–98.4
Fallow farm field	4	1		5	5.0–14.0
Forb-dominated field	5	2		7	3.0–32.9
Old field with shrubs	8	4		12	2.0–14.6
Total	34	8	1	43	1.3–98.4

[a] Includes Oak Orchard and Tonawanda WMAs.
[b] Includes NYSDEC lands in the Northern Montezuma Wetlands Complex.
[c] Habitat descriptions given in Appendix.

States include farmland abandonment, decline of hayfield area, and earlier and more frequent hay-cropping rotations (Andrle and Carroll 1988, Bollinger and Gavin 1992). Many species of grassland birds are area sensitive and are particularly vulnerable to loss of grassland habitat (Smith and Smith 1990, Vickery et al. 1994). In the Northeast, grassland habitat has declined by about 60% since the 1930s (Vickery et al. 1994).

In 1994 we began a study of grassland birds on lands in western New York administered by the U.S. Fish and Wildlife Service (USFWS) and New York State Department of Environmental Conservation (NYSDEC). Our objectives were to determine grassland bird species richness and abundance, breeding biology, and habitat relations on these lands. Studies on breeding biology focused on determining nest success and chronology, whereas bird-habitat relations were examined at both the local (vegetation) and landscape levels. Results of this study will be used to evaluate the status of grassland bird populations on public lands in the Great Lakes Plain of western New York and to suggest management alternatives to increase grassland bird populations in the region.

STUDY AREA

We began our study in May 1994 at Iroquois National Wildlife Refuge (NWR) and the contiguous NYSDEC Tonawanda and Oak Orchard Wildlife Management Areas (WMAs), located about 65 km west of Rochester, New York, in the Great Lakes Plain ecozone of New York (Andrle and Carroll 1988). The area comprises approximately 8,000 ha of wetlands and uplands that historically has been managed to provide habitat for breeding and migratory waterfowl (Iroquois NWR 1993). More than 1,000 ha of potential upland habitat for grassland birds also exist in the area. This potential habitat includes fields managed as cool-season grasslands, warm-season grasslands dominated by switchgrass (*Panicum virgatum*), old fields with a grass/forb/shrub mix, fallow farm fields, forb-dominated fields, and pastures (Iroquois NWR 1990; Table 1; see Appendix for a description of habitat types). The

various fields range in size from 0.5 to 98 ha, interspersed in a landscape matrix of wetlands, croplands, and hardwood forests.

In 1995 we expanded the study to include two additional sites: a 44-ha warm-season grassland at Beattie Point in the NYSDEC Braddock Bay WMA, 11 km west of Rochester, New York, and approximately 55 ha of upland habitat in the Northern Montezuma Wetlands Complex, about 50 km west of Syracuse, New York, and administered by the USFWS and NYSDEC. The grassland at Braddock Bay is on the southern shore of Lake Ontario and is bordered on three sides by extensive wetlands. The upland habitat in the Northern Montezuma Wetlands Complex is surrounded by a mixture of wetlands, agricultural fields, and deciduous forest.

METHODS

We determined grassland bird species abundance and richness using fixed 50-m-radius point counts. We established 59 census points in 34 fields in 1994 and 82 points (the same 59 points plus an additional 23) in 43 fields in 1995. These fields represented the range of shrub/grassland habitats found in the study area (Table 1). To control for area-related differences in sampling intensity, we placed no more than one census point in fields smaller than 10 ha and maintained a density of approximately one census point per 7 ha in larger fields. In fields with more than one census point, we separated point centers by at least 200 m to minimize recounts. Each point was censused five times a year for 10 min per census. We conducted censuses between 0600 and 1000 eastern standard time from 15 May to 1 July. For each point, we recorded the number of species, individuals per species, and total number of individuals seen and/or heard during the 10 min. For fields with more than one census point, we averaged bird abundance across points and censuses to obtain the mean number of individuals per census per point for the field. We also searched the study area for species of management concern at either the state or federal level (e.g., Henslow's Sparrow [*Ammodramus henslowii*] and Upland Sandpiper [*Bartramia longicauda*]) by walking transects and broadcasting songs in likely habitat.

We monitored nests of grassland and old-field species at Iroquois NWR in 1994, 1995, and 1996 to determine nest success and chronology for grassland birds; we restricted intensive nest searches and monitoring to this site because of time constraints. We located nests either by dragging ropes or by following birds to their nests. All nests located were marked with a small piece of flagging 5 m north of the nest and were checked at approximately 3-d intervals until fledging. We recorded the number of eggs and/or nestlings and checked for the presence of brood parasitism by Brown-headed Cowbirds (*Molothrus ater*). For species with a sample size larger than 10 per year, we used Mayfield's (1975) method to calculate nest success based on exposure.

We evaluated data from the 1995 field season on grassland bird-habitat relations at both the local, or infield, and landscape levels using methods similar to those of Wiens and Rotenberry (1981) and Pearson (1993). Between 18 and 25 May 1995, we measured vegetation at 10-m intervals along 50-m transects extending out from each census point in the four cardinal directions (N = 20 samples/point). At each sampling point we passed a 3-mm-diam, 1-m-long rod vertically through the vegetation perpendicular to the ground and counted the number of contacts made by four classes of vegetation (grass, forb, shrub, and dead). These measurements were used to derive 12 in-field variables: (1) mean vegetation height; (2) maximum vegetation height; (3) coefficient of variation of vegetation height, which is a measure of horizontal heterogeneity; (4) proportion of ground cover; (5) number of vegetation contacts ≤ 25 cm; (6) number of vegetation contacts > 25 cm; (7) total vegetation contacts; (8) total forb contacts; (9) total grass contacts; (10) total shrub contacts; (11) total dead contacts; and (12) total number of shrub stems intersected by the transects.

In 1995 we quantified 10 landscape-level variables using a combination of Geographic Information Systems (GIS) technology and interpretation of U.S. Department of Agriculture Agricultural Stabilization and Conservation Service (ASCS) 1:20,000 aerial photographs. For each field we calculated three variables: field area (which was log transformed before use in subsequent analyses), field perimeter, and distance from the center of the field to the nearest field-forest edge. We quantified seven additional landscape-matrix variables in a 500-m radius from the edge of each field. These variables were measured from ASCS aerial photographs with a simple dot grid transparent overlay and were based on the proportion of area occupied by seven different habitat types: (1) old field with shrubs, (2) forb-dominated field, (3) cool-season grassland and pasture, (4) wetland, (5) cropland, (6) deciduous forest, and (7) warm-season grassland. Habitat types were determined during ground surveys; patches were then classified based on the predominant habitat type (> 50%) in the patch.

The vegetation and landscape measurements from 1995 produced sets of 12 and 10 variables, respectively. We used Principal Components Analysis (PCA) to simplify the structure in each variable set by reducing the original number of variables to a smaller set of new, uncorrelated variables or axes (factors). All vegetation and landscape variables except proportion of ground cover were used in the PCAs; ground cover was excluded because it showed almost no variation among fields. PCAs were performed on correlation matrices; the initial solution was then rotated to provide a clearer interpretation of the loadings, and those factors with eigenvalues greater than 1.0 were used in subsequent analyses of bird-habitat relationships (Wiens and Rotenberry 1981, Pearson 1993). We then constructed statistical models to describe the variation in bird communities using factor scores and abundance/species-richness data for each field; abundance/species-richness data were based on means for all 1995 censuses in each field. We focused primarily on grassland birds, which included species in the North American grassland avifauna of Mengel 1970 (see also Knopf 1994), with the addition of Bobolink (*Dolichonyx oryzivorous*). Response variables included number of grassland species (hereafter referred to as "species") observed in the field during the season; mean number of grassland birds per census per point for each field; and for each common grassland species in the study area (Savannah Sparrow [*Passerculus sandwichensis*], Bobolink, and Eastern Meadowlark [*Sturnella magna*]), mean number of individuals per census per point for the field. Stepwise multiple regression was then used to select and evaluate the power of specific vegetation and landscape factors in explaining variation among fields in 1995 response variables. In addition, correlation coefficients were calculated for the relationship between the abundance of individual bird species and scores for each field on the most important factors (Wiens and Rotenberry 1981); for comparative purposes, nongrassland species were included in this analysis.

Although we restricted most bird-habitat analyses to the larger 1995 data set, we did test the 1994 data on species richness and abundance for their response to field area using simple linear regression.

RESULTS

Species Richness and Abundance

We observed five grassland bird species in the study area in 1994 and 1995: Northern Harrier (*Circus cyaneus*), Upland Sandpiper, Savannah Sparrow, Eastern Meadowlark, and Bobolink. Only the last three species were observed regularly (> 0.5 individuals/census/point) in at least one field.

Savannah Sparrows and Bobolinks were widely distributed throughout the study area, but Eastern Meadowlarks were observed regularly in only 4 of 34 fields censused in 1994 and in 4 of 43 fields censused in 1995. Other grassland species of management concern in the region, including Henslow's Sparrow, Grasshopper Sparrow (*Ammodramus savannarum*), and Vesper Sparrow (*Pooecetes gramineus*), were not observed in the study area, although Henslow's and Grasshopper sparrows have occurred sporadically at Iroquois NWR in the past (E. Derleth, pers. comm.).

The total number of species observed in a field and the average number of individuals per census per point increased with field area in both 1994 and 1995 (Table 2). We saw few species

TABLE 2. LINEAR CORRELATIONS (R^2) BETWEEN LOG OF FIELD AREA AND VARIOUS INDICES OF GRASSLAND BIRD ABUNDANCE IN WESTERN NEW YORK, 1994 AND 1995

	1994 (N = 34)	P	1995 (N = 43)	P
Species richness[a]	0.591	< 0.001	0.508	< 0.001
Number of individuals/census/point[a]				
Total grassland birds	0.604	< 0.001	0.365	< 0.001
Savannah Sparrow	0.551	< 0.001	0.354	< 0.001
Bobolink	0.395	< 0.001	0.261	< 0.001
Eastern Meadowlark	0.144	0.051	0.077	0.065

[a] Grassland species only (Northern Harrier, Upland Sandpiper, Savannah Sparrow, Bobolink, and Eastern Meadowlark).

or individuals in fields smaller than 5 ha (Fig. 1). The mean number of Savannah Sparrows and Bobolinks per census per point increased with area in 1994 and 1995 (Table 2, Fig. 2), with few individuals occurring in fields smaller than 5 ha. Abundance of these species did not increase, however, in larger old-field or warm-season grassland habitats (Fig. 2). The relationship between area and abundance was weak for Eastern Meadowlarks (Table 2), although this result may have been affected by the small number of fields where this species was recorded; it was not observed in fields smaller than 13 ha in either 1994 or 1995 (Fig. 2).

Grassland bird abundance and species richness were consistently lower in warm-season grasslands, including in the 44-ha field at Braddock Bay WMA, than in cool-season grasslands and pastures in the study area (Figs. 1 and 2). Common species in warm-season grasslands in-

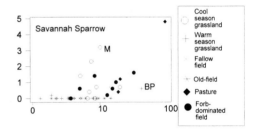

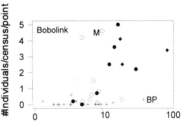

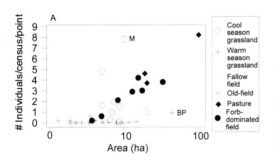

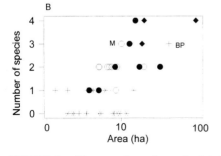

FIGURE 1. Mean number of grassland individuals per census per point (A) and number of grassland species (B) plotted against area (log transformed) in western New York fields, 1995. M = abandoned hayfield at Montezuma NWR; BP = Beattie Point warm-season grassland at Braddock Bay WMA (see "Results").

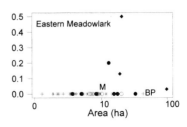

FIGURE 2. Mean number of individuals per census per point plotted against field area (log transformed) for Savannah Sparrows, Bobolinks, and Eastern Meadowlarks in western New York grasslands, 1995. M = abandoned hayfield at Montezuma NWR; BP = Beattie Point warm-season grassland at Braddock Bay WMA (see "Results").

TABLE 3. LANDSCAPE (L) FACTORS AND FACTOR LOADINGS GENERATED BY PRINCIPAL COMPONENTS ANALYSIS FOR GRASSLAND BIRDS IN WESTERN NEW YORK IN 1995

	Landscape factors				
	L1	L2	L3	L4	L5
Eigenvalue	2.831	2.676	1.291	1.276	1.221
Proportion of total variance explained	0.283	0.168	0.129	0.128	0.122
Cumulative proportion of variance explained	0.283	0.451	0.580	0.708	0.830
Variable					
Field area	0.551	−0.085	0.049	−0.180	−0.013
Field perimeter	0.532	−0.071	0.108	−0.279	−0.079
Distance to nearest field/forest edge	0.512	0.054	0.129	0.098	−0.106
Proportion warm-season grassland	−0.214	0.047	0.169	0.560	0.196
Proportion deciduous forest	0.192	−0.625	0.024	−0.035	−0.011
Proportion cool-season grassland	−0.150	−0.437	0.074	0.076	0.564
Proportion cropland	−0.148	0.014	−0.702	−0.189	−0.278
Proportion forb-dominated field	−0.114	0.203	−0.267	0.653	−0.098
Proportion old field	0.082	−0.019	0.576	0.052	−0.614
Proportion wetland	0.058	0.599	0.199	−0.308	0.402

Note: Only factors with eigenvalues > 1.0 are shown.

cluded Swamp Sparrow (*Melospiza georgiana*), Song Sparrow (*M. melodia*), and Field Sparrow (*Spizella pusilla*). Two species of management concern in the Northeast (Schneider and Pence 1992) used switchgrass fields during the study: Northern Harriers nested in switchgrass fields at Tonawanda and Braddock Bay WMAs, and Sedge Wrens (*Cistothorus platensis*) held territories in switchgrass fields at Iroquois NWR and at Braddock Bay WMA. The one field in the study area with a dense growth of alfalfa (*Medicago sativa*), a 10.1-ha former hayfield at Montezuma NWR, supported a much greater abundance of grassland birds than predicted on the basis of area alone (Fig. 1).

MULTIVARIATE ANALYSIS OF BIRD-HABITAT RELATIONSHIPS

PCA produced five landscape and three vegetation factors with eigenvalues greater than 1.0; these accounted for 83.0 and 77.6% of the total variation, respectively (Tables 3 and 4). These factors were interpreted by examining loadings on the original variables. Among the landscape factors, L1 clearly represented area, with three variables related to field area (field area, field perimeter, and distance from the center of a field to the nearest field/forest edge) having high positive loadings on the axis (Table 3). Fields with high scores on factor L2 were surrounded by

TABLE 4. VEGETATION (V) FACTORS AND FACTOR LOADINGS GENERATED BY PRINCIPAL COMPONENTS ANALYSIS FOR GRASSLAND BIRDS IN WESTERN NEW YORK IN 1995

	Vegetation factors		
	V1	V2	V3
Eigenvalue	4.299	3.136	1.214
Proportion of total variance explained	0.391	0.285	0.110
Cumulative proportion of variance explained	0.391	0.676	0.776
Variable			
Total vegetation contacts	−0.430	−0.229	0.027
Vegetation contacts > 25 cm	−0.415	−0.074	0.151
Mean vegetation height	−0.413	0.145	0.129
Total dead contacts	−0.402	−0.184	0.207
Maximum vegetation height	−0.323	0.351	0.180
Vegetation contacts ≤ 25 cm	−0.320	−0.293	−0.084
Total shrub contacts	−0.192	0.373	−0.533
Total shrub stems	−0.184	0.374	−0.523
Coefficient of variation of vegetation height	−0.126	0.391	0.209
Total grass contacts	−0.106	−0.365	−0.404
Total forb contacts	0.080	0.336	0.337

Note: Only factors with eigenvalues > 1.0 are shown.

TABLE 5. STEPWISE MULTIPLE REGRESSION MODELS OF GRASSLAND BIRD-HABITAT RELATIONSHIPS IN WESTERN NEW YORK

Bird variable	Habitat variables entered into model[a]	Partial r^2	r^2
Species richness	L1	0.43	0.51
	V2	0.08	
Abundance	L1	0.60	0.66
	V1	0.06	
Savannah Sparrow	L1	0.57	0.62
	V1	0.05	
Bobolink	L1	0.43	0.43
Eastern Meadowlark	No variables entered into model at P < 0.05		

Note: All variables given have P < 0.05; r^2 is the proportion of the total variation in the particular bird variable explained by the model.
[a] L1 = area, V2 = vegetation heterogeneity/shrub density, V1 = vegetation height/density.

large amounts of wetland habitat and small amounts of deciduous forest habitat. Factor L3 represented a gradient from increased shrubby old-field habitat to increased cropland. Fields with high positive scores on L4 had large amounts of forb-dominated fields and warm-season grasslands surrounding them; fields with high positive scores on L5 were surrounded by relatively large amounts of cool-season grassland and small amounts of old-field habitat (Table 3).

Vegetation factor V1 appeared to represent a gradient from tall, dense vegetation with a small amount of standing dead vegetation (negative factor scores on V1) to low, less dense vegetation (positive scores on V1; Table 4). Factor V2 represented a gradient from areas with less heterogeneous vegetation (negative scores on V2) and fewer shrubs to areas with greater horizontal heterogeneity, more shrubs, and less dense grass (positive scores on V2). Fields with high positive scores on factor V3 had greater forb cover and low grass and shrub cover. The vegetation factors should be interpreted cautiously, however, as loadings on the original variables were generally ≤ 0.500 (Table 4).

Bird-habitat models generated by stepwise multiple regression analysis suggested that most variation in grassland bird abundance and species richness was accounted for by the area variables (Table 5). Species richness was most strongly related to area (L1; partial $r^2 = 0.43$), with V2 (vegetation heterogeneity and shrub density) explaining an additional 8% of the variation (Table 5). Thus, larger areas with fewer shrubs, and consequently lower horizontal heterogeneity, tended to have more grassland birds species. A model incorporating area (L1) and vegetation height and density (V1) explained

66% of the among-field variation in grassland bird abundance (Table 5); larger fields with lower, less dense vegetation tended to have more individuals than did smaller fields with taller, dense vegetation. The variable related to field area (L1) was also most important in accounting for variation in abundance of Savannah Sparrows and Bobolinks; vegetation height and density (V1) explained only 5% of the variation in Savannah Sparrow abundance (Table 5). No model explained a significant amount of the variation in Eastern Meadowlark abundance. When variables L1 and V1 were forced into a stepwise multiple regression, they accounted for only 3.9% of the variation in Eastern Meadowlark abundance, even though the species was not seen in fields smaller than 13 ha (Fig. 2). This result may have been due to the small number of fields with meadowlarks. Although the vegetation heterogeneity and shrub density factor (V2) explained a significant amount of variation only in species richness (Table 5), there was no significant correlation between shrub density and grassland bird species abundance ($r^2 = 0.063$, P = 0.109). In general, fields with the most shrubs supported few grassland birds.

The distribution of bird species along gradients in habitat structure can also be illustrated with a three-dimensional plot of correlation coefficients for the relationship between the abundance of individual species and the L1, V1, and V2 factors (Fig. 3). Grassland birds were most abundant in large fields (high positive correlations with L1 factor scores), shorter, less dense vegetation (high positive correlations with V1 factor scores), and less shrub cover (negative correlations with V2 factor scores). In contrast, old-field species such as Song Sparrow, Common Yellowthroat (*Geothlypis trichas*), and Yellow Warbler (*Dendroica petechia*) were most abundant in smaller fields with denser vegetation and more shrubs (Fig. 3).

BREEDING BIOLOGY

Evidence of breeding (nests with eggs or young, or fledged young) was noted for Northern Harriers, Savannah Sparrows, Bobolinks, and Eastern Meadowlarks. In 1994, 1995, and 1996, we determined the outcome of 109 nests of three grassland bird species at Iroquois NWR (Table 6). The combined (1994–1996) proportion of successful nests was 0.76 for Savannah Sparrows, 0.54 for Bobolinks, and 0.67 for Eastern Meadowlarks (Table 6). The probability of survival to fledging (Mayfield 1975) was higher for Savannah Sparrows than for Bobolinks in both 1994 (0.795 vs. 0.646, respectively) and 1995 (0.709 vs. 0.139, respectively). The low survival probability for Bobolinks in 1995 was

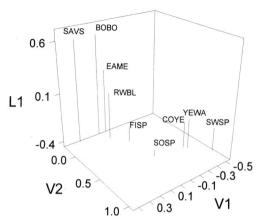

FIGURE 3. Plot of correlation coefficients for abundance (mean number of individuals/census/point) of individual species and L1, V1, and V2 factor scores for fields in western New York, 1995. See text for interpretation of axes. BOBO = Bobolink, COYE = Common Yellowthroat, EAME = Eastern Meadowlark, FISP = Field Sparrow, RWBL = Red-winged Blackbird (*Agelaius phoeniceus*), SAVS = Savannah Sparrow, SOSP = Song Sparrow, SWSP = Swamp Sparrow, YEWA = Yellow Warbler.

30 June for Bobolinks, 2 July for Eastern Meadowlarks, and 6 July for Savannah Sparrows. A pair of Northern Harriers nesting at Braddock Bay WMA initiated a clutch on 21 May 1995; fledging would have occurred at the end of July.

DISCUSSION

Our results suggest that the more widely distributed grassland species in western New York, especially Savannah Sparrow and Bobolink, have been sustaining breeding populations on state and federally administered lands in the study area. In 1994–1995, fields larger than 10 ha generally supported both species, with mean abundances of three or more individuals per census per point and relatively high rates of nest success. The proportion of successful Savannah Sparrow nests (0.76) was higher than has been reported for this species in Maine (0.33; Vickery et al. 1992), New Brunswick (0.40; Dixon 1978), or Michigan (0.52; Potter 1974). The proportion of successful Bobolink nests at Iroquois NWR (0.54) was within the range of values (< 0.38 to < 0.88) reported for sites in New York (Gavin and Bollinger 1988) and Wisconsin (Martin 1974). The proportion of successful Eastern Meadowlark nests (0.67) was higher than observed in three other studies (Lanyon 1957, Roseberry and Klimstra 1970, Granfors et al. 1996), although the sample size (N = 12) was too small to confidently evaluate nest success.

MANAGEMENT IMPLICATIONS

Our results emphasize the importance of habitat area for grassland bird species richness and abundance. This relationship has been observed elsewhere in the Northeast (Bollinger and Gavin 1992, Smith and Smith 1992, Vickery et al. 1994), and it suggests that managers should consider practices that will increase grassland area, such as hedgerow removal and consolidation of adjacent fields, as means of increasing grassland bird populations.

Increasing the size of fields in our study area may not attract species of management concern such as Grasshopper and Henslow's sparrows, however. Because fields of up to 98 ha already occur at Iroquois NWR, and because both Grass-

due to a high rate of nest loss early in the nestling period (five of nine active nests were depredated 1–5 d after hatching). There were no significant differences between the proportion of successful nests in pastures versus cool-season grasslands for either Savannah Sparrows (χ^2 = 0.781, df = 1, P = 0.377) or Bobolinks (χ^2 = 0.626, df = 1, P = 0.429) for all nests found in 1994–1996 (Table 6). None of the 109 nests located during the study were parasitized by Brown-headed Cowbirds.

Combined data on grassland bird breeding chronology for the 3-yr period indicated that most pairs initiated clutches during the second half of May and fledged young in mid-June. Bobolinks tended to initiate nesting somewhat later than Eastern Meadowlarks or Savannah Sparrows; median fledging dates for 1994–1996 were 10 June for Eastern Meadowlarks, 12 June for Savannah Sparrows, and 20 June for Bobolinks. Late fledging dates for known nests were

TABLE 6. PROPORTION OF SUCCESSFUL NESTS (AND SAMPLE SIZES) BY YEAR AND HABITAT TYPE FOR GRASSLAND SPECIES AT IROQUOIS NWR IN WESTERN NEW YORK, 1994–1996

Species	Proportion of successful nests					
	1994	1995	1996	Combined	Pasture	Cool-season grassland
Savannah Sparrow	0.81 (26)	0.72 (25)	0.71 (7)	0.76 (58)	0.77 (47)	0.64 (11)
Bobolink	0.63 (24)	0.40 (10)	0.40 (5)	0.54 (39)	0.47 (19)	0.60 (20)
Eastern Meadowlark	0.67 (3)	0.50 (2)	0.71 (7)	0.67 (12)	0.57 (7)	1.00 (2)

hopper and Henslow's sparrows have bred at Iroquois NWR in the past, their absence cannot be attributed to area effects alone. These species are found in fields as small as 11 and 30 ha, respectively, in the Finger Lakes National Forest in central New York (Smith and Smith 1990, 1992), and Grasshopper Sparrows have nested and fledged young in fields as small as 4 ha at Mendon Ponds County Park, near Rochester, New York (C. Norment, pers. obs.). The absence of these two species from our study area is more likely due to a combination of their specific habitat requirements (Wiens 1969, Smith and Smith 1990, Delaney and Linda 1994, Herkert 1995b) and their sporadic occurrence in the region. Given the absence of these species from Iroquois and Montezuma NWRs, attempting to manage primarily for species of concern at these refuges does not appear to be a reasonable objective. Habitat requirements and management options for these species should still be considered when developing management plans, however (Swanson 1996, Jones and Vickery 1997). Additionally, more effort should be devoted to analyzing the habitat preferences and management needs of the Eastern Meadowlark, which is declining across much of its range in the Northeast (Robbins et al. 1986, Bollinger and Gavin 1992). Although once described as "one of the commonest birds of the fields of western New York" (Beardslee and Mitchell 1965), this species is relatively uncommon in the study area.

Few vegetation variables significantly increased the explanatory power of the bird-habitat models. Shrub density, however, did appear to have a negative effect on both grassland bird species richness and abundance. Vegetation factor V2, which appeared to be related to shrub density, explained a significant amount of variation in species richness, and fields with large numbers of shrubs supported few grassland birds (Fig. 3). Also, the three-dimensional plot of the correlations between bird species abundances and L1 (area), V1 (vegetation height and density), and V2 (horizontal heterogeneity and shrub density) factor scores (Fig. 3) suggests that grassland birds are more abundant in fields with fewer shrubs and shorter, open vegetation. These observations indicate that increasing the frequency of disturbance by mowing may increase the abundance and richness of grassland birds in the study area.

Several fields on state and federal land in our study area have been planted in dense switchgrass monocultures to provide nesting cover for waterfowl (Iroquois NWR 1990). Our results indicate that switchgrass does not provide favorable habitat for most grassland birds; even the largest warm-season grassland (44 ha) had few

Bobolinks or Savannah Sparrows, and individuals of both species were confined to portions of the field with lower, less dense cover. In other regions, switchgrass also appears to support low numbers of grassland birds, especially of species that require open habitats (Volkert 1992; Prescott and Murphy 1995; R. C. Gatti, unpubl. data). Thus, although switchgrass fields may be more productive for nesting waterfowl than are cool-season grasslands in our study area (Estel 1989), they are not suitable for most grassland birds. The decision as to whether or not to plant and maintain fields with switchgrass monocultures should be based on the overall management goals for the area.

The relatively high abundance of grassland birds in pastures (Fig. 1) and the increased abundance of grassland birds observed in pastures in 1995 versus 1994, as opposed to the trend in cool-season grasslands (Table 3), suggest that grazing as practiced at Iroquois NWR is not detrimental to grassland birds in the area. The combination of low- to moderate-intensity grazing and mowing may be beneficial to grassland birds at Iroquois NWR because these practices retard succession and shrub establishment. Currently, cattle are allowed onto pastures at Iroquois NWR in mid-July and remain there until the end of October. Stocking rates range from 0.60 to 0.83 cattle per ha, which is similar to stocking rates at Finger Lakes National Forest in central New York, where species such as Grasshopper and Henslow's sparrows are relatively common (Smith and Smith 1990, 1992). Pastures at Iroquois NWR are also mowed, usually in August or September (S. Lor, pers. comm.). The absence at Iroquois NWR of cattle and other forms of disturbance, such as mowing, until at least mid-July means that grassland birds are able to raise at least one brood undisturbed. This observation supports the point that all forms of disturbance should be prohibited on pastures and other grasslands at least until birds have fledged their first broods (Andrle and Carroll 1988, Bollinger and Gavin 1992). For most species in the study area, an appropriate date for this would be 15 July, although switchgrass fields where Northern Harriers nest should not be mowed until early August (Beardslee and Mitchell 1965, Andrle and Carroll 1988).

Finally, management agencies should attempt to standardize field treatments such as mowing, herbicide application, and seeding. The current landscape on state and federally managed lands in our study area is a complex mosaic of deciduous forests, wetlands, and open fields in various stages of succession. Successional patterns have been influenced by a variety of treatments, with apparently little consideration given to replication and standardization of methods. Thus, understanding how succession and treatment effects influence grassland bird species richness and abundance in the study area has been complicated by the large number of treatment variables. For example, mowing has occurred with and without herbicide application, with and without disking, and with and without planting a variety of native or introduced cool-season grasses, thus making it difficult to separate the effects of the treatment variables. Successfully managing for grassland birds, or for any other wildlife, requires a clear understanding both of objectives and of how particular methods influence succession, habitats, and species.

ACKNOWLEDGMENTS

Funding for this project was provided by the U.S. Fish and Wildlife Service, New York State Department of Environmental Conservation, and Office of the Vice President for Academic Affairs and Scholarly Incentive Award Program of the State University of New York College at Brockport. D. Robinson, Jr., J. Romaneo, and B. Sheppard assisted with fieldwork. D. Tiller, S. Lor, and P. Caldwell of the U.S. Fish and Wildlife Service assisted with the project, as did D. Carroll and D. O'Dell of the New York State Department of Environmental Conservation. P. D. Vickery and two anonymous reviewers greatly improved the manuscript.

LITERATURE CITED

ANDRLE, R. F., AND J. R. CARROLL. 1988. The atlas of breeding birds in New York state. Cornell University Press, Ithaca, NY.
ASKINS, R. A. 1993. Population trends in grassland, shrubland, and forest birds in eastern North America. Current Ornithology 11:1–34.
BEARDSLEE, C. S., AND H. D. MITCHELL. 1965. Birds of the Niagara frontier region. Bulletin of the Buffalo Society of Natural History 22:1–478.
BOLLINGER, E. K., AND T. A. GAVIN. 1992. Eastern Bobolink populations: ecology and conservation in an agricultural landscape. Pp. 497–506 in J. M. Hagan III and D. W. Johnston (editors). Ecology and conservation of neotropical migrant landbirds. Smithsonian Institution Press, Washington, D.C.
DELANEY, M. F., AND S. B. LINDA. 1994. Characteristics of occupied and abandoned Florida Grasshopper Sparrow territories. Florida Field Naturalist 22:106–109.
DIXON, C. L. 1978. Breeding biology of the Savannah Sparrow on Kent Island. Auk 95:235–246.
ESTEL, B. L. 1989. Habitat use and nesting success of dabbling ducks in western New York grasslands. Master's thesis. Cornell University, Ithaca, NY.
GAVIN, T. A., AND E. K. BOLLINGER. 1988. Reproductive correlates of breeding site fidelity in Bobolinks (Dolichonyx oryzivorus). Ecology 69:96–103.
GRANFORS, D. A., K. E. CHURCH, AND L. M. SMITH. 1996. Eastern Meadowlarks nesting in rangelands and Conservation Reserve Program fields in Kansas. Journal of Field Ornithology 67:222–235.

HERKERT, J. R. 1995a. An analysis of midwestern breeding bird population trends: 1966–1993. American Midland Naturalist 134:41–50.
HERKERT, J. R. 1995b. Status and habitat selection of the Henslow's Sparrow in Illinois. Wilson Bulletin 106:35–45.
IROQUOIS NATIONAL WILDLIFE REFUGE. 1990. Grassland management plan. U.S. Fish and Wildlife Service, Alabama, NY.
IROQUOIS NATIONAL WILDLIFE REFUGE. 1993. Station management plan. U.S. Fish and Wildlife Service, Newton Corner, MA.
JAMES, F. C., D. A. WIEDENFIELD, AND C. E. MCCULLOCH. 1992. Trends in breeding populations of warblers: declines in the southern highlands and increases in the lowlands. Pp. 43–56 in J. M. Hagan III and D. W. Johnston (editors). Ecology and conservation of neotropical migrant landbirds. Smithsonian Institution Press, Washington, D.C.
JONES, A. L., AND P. D. VICKERY. 1997. Conserving grassland birds: managing large grasslands including conservation lands, airports, and landfills over 75 acres for grassland birds. Massachusetts Audubon Society, Lincoln, MA.
KNOPF, F. L. 1994. Avian assemblages on altered grasslands. Studies in Avian Biology 15:247–257.
LANYON, W. E. 1957. The comparative biology of the meadowlark (Sturnella) in Wisconsin. Nuttall Ornithological Club Publication 1. Cambridge, MA.
MARTIN, S. G. 1974. Adaptations for polygynous breeding in the Bobolink, Dolichonyx oryzivorus. American Zoologist 14:109–119.
MAYFIELD, H. F. 1975. Suggestions for calculating nest success. Wilson Bulletin 87:456–466.
MENGEL, R. M. 1970. The North American central plains as an isolating agent in bird speciation. Pp. 280–340 in W. Dort and J. K. Jones (editors). Pleistocene and recent environments of the central Great Plains. University of Kansas Press, Lawrence, KS.
PEARSON, S. M. 1993. The spatial extent and relative influence of landscape-level factors on wintering bird populations. Journal of Landscape Ecology 8:3–18.
PETERJOHN, B. G., AND J. R. SAUER. 1994. Population trends of woodland birds from the North American Breeding Bird Survey. Wildlife Society Bulletin 22:155–164.
PETERJOHN, B. G., AND J. R. SAUER. 1999. Population status of North American grassland birds from the North American Breeding Bird Survey, 1966–1996. Studies in Avian Biology 19:27–44.
POTTER, P. E. 1974. Breeding behavior of Savannah Sparrows in southeastern Michigan. Jack-Pine Warbler 52:50–63.
PRESCOTT, D. R. C., AND A. J. MURPHY. 1995. Bird populations and vegetation structure of tame dense nesting cover (DNC) in Alberta's aspen parkland. Alberta North American Waterfowl Management Plan Centre, Edmonton, AB.
ROBBINS, C. S., D. BYSTRAK, AND P. H. GEIGGLER. 1986. The Breeding Bird Survey: its first fifteen years, 1965–1979. U.S. Fish and Wildlife Service Resource Publication 157.

ROSEBERRY, J. L., AND W. D. KLIMSTRA. 1970. The nesting ecology and reproductive performance of the Eastern Meadowlark. Wilson Bulletin 82:243–267.

SCHNEIDER, K. J., AND D. M. PENCE. 1992. Migratory nongame birds of management concern in the northeast. U.S. Fish and Wildlife Service, Newton Corner, MA.

SMITH, C. R., AND D. J. SMITH. 1990. Summer bird species diversity and use of pastures by summer birds of the Finger Lake National Forest. Final report. Laboratory of Ornithology, Cornell University, Ithaca, NY.

SMITH, D. J., AND C. R. SMITH. 1992. Henslow's Sparrow and Grasshopper Sparrow: a comparison of habitat use in Finger Lakes National Forest, New York. Bird Observer 20:187–194.

SWANSON, D. A. 1996. Nesting ecology and nesting habitat requirements of Ohio's grassland-nesting birds: a literature review. Ohio Fish and Wildlife Report 13. Ohio Department of Natural Resources, Columbus, OH.

VICKERY, P. D., M. L. HUNTER, JR., AND S. M. MELVIN. 1994. Effects of habitat area on the distribution of grassland birds in Maine. Conservation Biology 8: 1087–1097.

VICKERY, P. D., M. L. HUNTER, JR., AND J. V. WELLS. 1992. Evidence of incidental nest predation and its effects on nests of threatened birds. Oikos 63:281–288.

VOLKERT, W. K. 1992. Response of grassland birds to a large-scale prairie planting project. Passenger Pigeon 54:191–196.

WIENS, J. A. 1969. An approach to the study of ecological relationships among grassland birds. Ornithological Monographs 8.

WIENS, J. A., AND J. T. ROTENBERRY. 1981. Habitat associations and community structure of birds in shrubsteppe environments. Ecological Monographs 51:21–41.

APPENDIX.   DESCRIPTION OF HABITAT TYPES OF FIELDS CENSUSED FOR GRASSLAND BIRDS IN WESTERN NEW YORK, 1994–1995

Habitat type	Description
Warm-season grassland	Grassland dominated by switchgrass (*Panicum virgatum*), which produces most or all of its growth in late spring or summer.
Cool-season grassland	Ungrazed grassland dominated by plants that produce the major portion of their growth in spring. Common grasses include timothy (*Phleum pratense*), brome-grass (*Bromus inermis*), orchard grass (*Dactylis glomerata*), and red-top (*Agrostis gigantea*). Common forbs include alfalfa (*Medicago sativa*), clover (*Trifolium* spp.), and birds-foot trefoil (*Lotus corniculatus*).
Pasture	Grazed grassland; common species are similar to those found in cool-season grasslands.
Fallow farm field	Agricultural land no longer being cultivated; dominated by early-successional grasses and forbs. Vegetation may be similar to that in cool-season grasslands, forb-dominated fields, or old fields with shrubs.
Forb-dominated field	May contain species found in cool-season grasslands, but forbs such as goldenrod (*Solidago* spp.), wild carrot (*Daucus carota*), and milkweed (*Asclepias* spp.) are common. Shrubs may also be present (cover < 5%).
Old field with shrubs	Formerly open habitat with a mix of grasses, forbs, and shrubs (cover > 5%). Common species include bramble (*Rubus* spp.), willow (*Salix* spp.), red osier dogwood (*Cornus stolonifera*), choke cherry (*Prunus virginiana*), Russian olive (*Elaeagnus angustifolia*), narrowleaf meadowsweet (*Spirea alba*), and arrowwood (*Viburnum* spp.).

Studies in Avian Biology No. 19:122–127, 1999.

EXPERIMENTAL ANALYSIS OF NEST PREDATION IN A NEW YORK GRASSLAND: EFFECTS OF HABITAT AND NEST DISTRIBUTION

Charles D. Ardizzone and Christopher J. Norment

Abstract. Depredation of artificial avian ground nests was studied in 1994 and 1995 on cool-season and warm-season grasslands in western New York State. The study examined the effects of habitat type and distance from forested edge on nest success in adjacent fields. Two experiments were conducted. The first examined the effects of nest distribution on nest success. Experimental predation rates were highest at the field-forest boundary, although there was no correlation between predation rate and distance from edge. Overall predation rates for cool-season grasslands differed significantly between years, with predation rates being higher during the 1995 field season. The second experiment examined the effects of dense nesting cover on nest success. Predation rates for nests in dense nesting cover varied among distance classes in 1995 but not in 1994; predation rates were also higher in 1995 than in 1994. Experimental rates of nest predation were similar in pasture/cool-season grasslands and warm-season grasslands in both years, suggesting that dense cover did not improve productivity of ground-nesting birds. Indirect evidence suggested that the primary predators along the forest-field boundaries were mammals, with birds and small mammals most frequently depredating nests away from the edge. This study suggests that dense nesting cover does not increase nesting success for small passerines on our study site.

ANÁLISIS EXPERIMENTAL DE DEPREDACIÓN DE NIDOS EN UN PASTIZAL EN NUEVA YORK: LOS EFECTOS DEL HÁBITAT Y DE LA DISTRIBUCIÓN DE NIDOS

Sinopsis. Se estudió la depredación de nidos avícolas artificiales en suelo durante 1994 y 1995 en pastizales de la estación fresca y de la estación cálida en el este del estado de Nueva York. El estudio examinó los efectos del tipo de hábitat y de la distancia desde el límite del bosque en el éxito de los nidos en campos adyacentes. Se hicieron dos experimentos. El primero revisó los efectos de la distribución de nidos en el éxito de los nidos. Las tasas experimentales de depredación fueron mayores en el límite del campo con el bosque, aunque no hubo correlación entre la tasa de depredación y la distancia del límite. Las tasas totales de depredación para los pastizales de estación fresca difirieron significativamente entre años, con las mayores tasas de depredación durante el período de investigación de 1995. El segundo experimento revisó los efectos de cobertura densa de los nidos en el éxito de los mismos. Las tasas de depredación para los nidos en la cobertura densa variaron en las diferentes clases de distancia en 1995 pero no en 1994; también las tasas de depredación fueron más altas en 1995 que en 1994. Las tasas experimentales de depredación de nidos fueron similares en prados/pastizales de estación fresca y pastizales de estación cálida en los dos años, lo que indica que la cobertura densa no mejoró la fertilidad de las aves que anidaron en el suelo. Evidencia indirecta indicó que los depredadores principales a lo largo del límite entre el campo y el bosque fueron mamíferos, y que aves y mamíferos pequeños depredaron los nidos fuera del límite con más frecuencia. Este estudio señala que la cobertura densa de nidos no incrementa el éxito de los nidos para las pequeñas aves paseriformes en el área de nuestro estudio.

Key Words: artificial nests; grassland birds; nest success; New York; predation.

Populations of several neotropical migrant song-birds have declined in many regions of North America since the mid- to late 1970s (Robbins et al. 1989). Significant negative trends have been noted for grassland and early successional bird species at regional and continental scales (Robbins et al. 1986, Hagan et al. 1992, Hussell et al. 1992, James et al. 1992, Herkert 1995). One of the most important factors contributing to the decline of grassland nesting birds is breeding-ground habitat loss (Herkert 1991, Warner 1994). This habitat loss has been attributed to changing land-use practices that have dramatically reduced the amount and quality of available grassland habitat, in part by increasing habitat fragmentation (Herkert 1991, Warner 1994).

Wildlife managers traditionally encouraged landscape fragmentation to maximize the amount of habitat interspersion and edge (Faaborg et al. 1993). Many biologists considered the edge between two adjacent habitat types to be a positive feature of the landscape for wildlife (Kremsater and Bunnell 1992), and wildlife refuge managers often created as much edge as possible with little concern for the effects of these actions on nongame birds (Noss 1983). More recently, wildlife biologists have challenged the idea that edge benefits most wildlife and have begun reexamining the effects of edge on neotropical migrant landbirds (Reese and Ratti 1988, Yahner 1988).

Increased isolation and fragmentation of breeding habitats can increase nest parasitism and nest predation (Wilcove 1985, Terborgh 1992). Nest predation is a primary source of nest loss for many avian species, accounting for a majority of all losses across a wide diversity of species, habitats, and geographic locations (Ricklefs 1969; Martin 1992, 1993). Depredation of avian nests may vary with habitat (Andrén and Angelstam 1988, Picman 1988), extent of habitat fragmentation (Wilcove 1985, Yahner and Scott 1988), degree of concealment provided by vegetation (Bowman and Harris 1980, Sugden and Beyersbergen 1986), and distance from edge (Gates and Gysel 1978, Wilcove 1985). Because increased predation along edges may cause species to reproduce well below levels necessary to maintain adequate population levels (Wilcove 1985), a full understanding of edge effects is needed if bird populations are to be managed successfully (Reese and Ratti 1988, Yahner 1988, Yahner and Scott 1988). In a review of 14 artificial- and 7 natural-nest predation studies, Paton (1994) concluded that more data are needed on nest predation rates between 100 and 200 m of the field-forest ecotone and that artificial nests should be placed at smaller increments (20–25 m) to quantify threshold edge effects. Because fragmentation and loss of grassland habitat, and concurrent creation of edge, are ongoing processes in New England and New York State (U.S. Department of Agriculture 1936–1991, Bollinger and Gavin 1992), we undertook this study to gather data on how nest-predation rates are affected by proximity to field-forest boundaries in two grassland habitat types in New York.

METHODS

Field work was conducted at the Iroquois National Wildlife Refuge (NWR), administered by the U.S. Fish and Wildlife Service, and at adjacent New York State wildlife management areas, administered by the New York State Department of Conservation. Together these areas comprise approximately 8,000 ha and contain a mosaic of habitat types including pastures/cool-season grasslands, warm-season grasslands dominated by switchgrass (*Panicum* spp.), old fields, marshes, fallow fields, deciduous forests, and wetlands. Grasslands ranging in size from less than 1 ha to 98 ha occur in some upland portions of the refuge and adjacent state-owned lands. Although the primary management objective of Iroquois NWR is to provide optimum conditions for resting, feeding, and nesting waterfowl (Iroquois NWR 1990), grassland habitats in the area support breeding populations of Savannah Sparrows (*Passerculus sandwichensis*), Bobolinks (*Dolichonyx oryzivorus*), Eastern Meadowlarks (*Sturnella magna*),

and Northern Harriers (*Circus cyaneus*). Many potential nest predators occur on the refuge and adjacent state-owned lands. Potential mammalian nest predators include raccoons (*Procyon lotor*), weasels (*Mustela* spp.), red foxes (*Vulpes vulpes*), and striped skunks (*Mephitis mephitis*; Iroquois NWR 1990). Potential avian nest predators include Blue Jays (*Cyanocitta cristata*) and American Crows (*Corvus brachyrhynchos*; Iroquois NWR 1990).

In early June of 1994 and 1995 we conducted two experiments to determine how predation rates on artificial nests are affected by proximity to field-forest boundaries and habitat type. Our first experiment examined the relationship between distance from the forest edge and nest success. In 1994 and 1995 we placed 21 transects of 7 artificial nest cups each perpendicular to the forest-field boundaries in pastures and cool-season grasslands, which are planted with native and introduced cool-season grasses that generally produce the major portion of their growth in winter and early spring. These pastures/cool-season grasslands ranged in area from 33 to 98 ha. The transects were separated from each other by at least 100 m. Artificial nest cups were placed 0, 25, 50, 75, 100, 125, and 150 m from the edge. Since markers may guide predators to nests (Picozzi 1975), nest cups were not marked in any way; instead, a small section of flagging was placed 5 m to one side of the beginning of each transect to facilitate relocation. Artificial nest cups were commercial wicker canary (*Serinus* sp.) nest cups (10.5 cm wide, 5 cm deep), each containing one Common Quail (*Coturnix coturnix*) egg. All eggs were mottled to some degree. Nest cups were checked once, at the end of 15 d, which is approximately the combined egg-laying and incubation period of many small passerines. We considered nests depredated if an egg was destroyed or removed from the nest cup.

Our second experiment examined effects of dense nesting cover on nest success. At Iroquois NWR, dense nesting cover occurs in small (<8 ha) warm-season grasslands, planted primarily in switchgrass, which produces most or all of its growth in late spring or summer and is usually dormant in winter. Experimental protocol followed that used in the first experiment. Transects were placed perpendicular to boundaries between forests and adjacent warm-season grasslands, were marked in a similar manner as in the first experiment, and were separated from one another by 100 m. Artificial nest cups were placed at 25-m increments. The small size of available warm-season grasslands limited the number of nest cups placed in each field and the distance of nest cups from the edge; all nest cups thus were within 100 m of the field-forest edge. Nest cups contained one Common Quail egg and were checked at the end of the 15-d period. Because of the small size of the warm-season grasslands, comparisons between the different habitats could have been confounded by area effects. In an attempt to partially control for area effects, comparisons of between-habitat predation rates included only those nests located 50 m or less from edge. This included most (80%; N = 122) of the nests placed in cool-season grasslands.

In addition to conducting artificial nest experiments, we also conducted intensive nest searches to locate grassland bird nests, from which natural predation

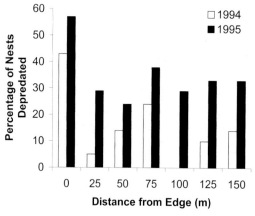

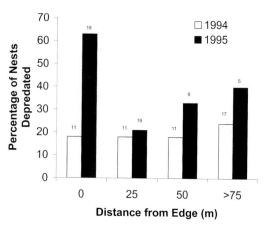

FIGURE 1. Nest-predation rates for artificial nests in pastures/cool-season grasslands at Iroquois NWR, Alabama, New York, 1994–1995. N = 21 at each distance for each year.

FIGURE 2. Nest-predation rates for artificial nests in warm-season grasslands at Iroquois NWR, Alabama, New York, 1994–1995. Sample sizes are indicated above bars.

rates could be compared to rates for artificial nests. Once located, each nest was marked with a numbered flag 5 m north of the nest. We revisited nests every 3–4 d until the nesting attempt ended. During each visit we recorded the number of eggs and/or nestlings in the nest and checked for the presence of brood parasitism by Brown-headed Cowbirds (*Molothrus ater*). Natural nests were considered successful if they fledged at least one young.

After all nesting attempts were completed, we returned to each nest to record local habitat characteristics. We recorded the height of vegetation at the nest cup and measured the height of vegetation surrounding the nest, sampling at 1-m increments along 5-m transects extending outward from the nest cup in the four cardinal directions (north, south, east, and west). At each sampling point we recorded the maximum height of vegetation. We also took Robel-pole measurements in the four cardinal directions to help determine the density of vegetation surrounding the nest (Robel et al. 1970).

Between-year and between-habitat effects were analyzed using χ^2 tests. The percentage of nests depredated at each distance in pastures/cool-season grasslands was analyzed using Spearman's rank correlation coefficient to determine if nest distribution had any effect on predation rates. Significance level was set at $\alpha = 0.05$.

RESULTS

Results of the first experiment showed that predation rates were highest at forest-field boundaries in both years. In 1994, 43% of all nests located at the edge were destroyed, and in 1995, 57% of all nests at the edge were destroyed (Fig. 1). Although predation rates were highest where the two habitats met, distance from edge was not related to nest-predation rates in any consistent manner; however, small sample sizes may have limited the power to detect pat-

terns in the data. Predation rates for 1994 differed significantly ($\chi^2 = 16.24$, df = 6, P = 0.0125) among the different distances; however, there was no significant correlation between predation rate and distance ($r_s = -0.324$, P > 0.05). In 1995 predation rates did not differ significantly among distances ($\chi^2 = 4.311$, df = 6, P = 0.635), and there was no significant correlation between predation rate and distance ($r_s = -0.073$, P > 0.05). Overall predation rates in pastures/cool-season grasslands were significantly higher in 1995 than in 1994 ($\chi^2 = 10.59$, df = 1, P = 0.001; Fig. 1).

Results of the second experiment showed that in 1994 there was no significant distance effect in warm-season grasslands ($\chi^2 = 6.74$, df = 3, P = 0.081). In 1995, however, predation rates differed significantly among distances ($\chi^2 = 11.95$, df = 3, P = 0.008), being highest at field-forest boundaries. Overall predation rates in warm-season grasslands were significantly higher in 1995 than in 1994 ($\chi^2 = 5.01$, df = 1, P = 0.025; Fig. 2).

Artificial-nest predation rates were similar in warm-season grasslands and pastures/cool-season grasslands in 1994 and 1995 (Table 1). Overall predation rates for nests located 50 m or less from the edge did not differ significantly between warm- and cool-season grasslands in 1994 ($\chi^2 = 0.82$, df = 1, P = 0.775) and 1995 ($\chi^2 = 2.108$, df = 1, P = 0.147).

Predation rates for artificial nests and natural nests that we followed were similar (Table 1). For example, in 1994 predation rates for artificial nests were 16% in cool-season grasslands and 20% in warm-season grasslands, whereas

TABLE 1. PREDATION RATES ON ARTIFICIAL AND NATURAL NESTS IN GRASSLAND HABITATS AT IROQUOIS NWR, ALABAMA, NEW YORK, 1994–1995

Habitat/species	1994		1995		Totals	
	% depredated	N	% depredated	N	% depredated	N
Artificial nests						
Cool-season grasslands/pastures	16	147	35	147	25	294
Warm-season grasslands	20	50	40	52	30	102
Savannah Sparrow nests	19	26	24	25	21	52
Bobolink nests	33	24	60	10	41	34

33% of Bobolink nests and 19% of Savannah Sparrow nests were depredated.

DISCUSSION

Several studies have demonstrated that nest predation decreases as distance from the forested edge increases (Gates and Gysel 1978, Wilcove 1985, Paton 1994). In our study, however, there was no significant correlation between predation rate and distance from edge, although the highest predation rates were observed at forest edge. This may be explained in several ways. First, a forest-grassland edge may function as a biological barrier and may concentrate predator activity along the wooded edge (Bider 1968, Johnson and Temple 1990). Raccoons use edges as travel lanes, which may increase nest predation (Fritzell 1978). Secondly, passerine nests may be destroyed incidentally as predators search for other prey items that are concentrated along edges (Vickery et al. 1992).

Several studies have concluded that depredation of avian nests may vary with habitat (Møller 1987, Andrén and Angelstam 1988, Picman 1988). Rates of artificial-nest predation in our study, however, were very similar between grassland habitat types, suggesting that dense nesting cover in warm-season grasslands will not significantly improve the productivity of nesting passerines. Warm-season grasslands in the study area also support few grassland bird species and individuals (Norment et al. 1999).

Significant increases in predation rates occurred in 1995 for both habitat types. These increases may be explained by the reduced density and height of vegetation in 1995 compared to 1994. Spring weather in western New York was cooler in 1995 than in 1994. There was also considerably less spring rainfall in 1995 than in 1994 (11.91 vs. 25.88 cm; SUNY Brockport Earth Science Dept., unpubl. data), leading to decreased vegetation growth. In our study area, most nest measurements related to height and density of vegetation were significantly smaller in 1995 than in 1994 (Table 2). Tall, dense vegetational cover may provide olfactory, visual, and physical barriers between predators and nests of ground-nesting birds (Bowman and Harris 1980, Redmond et al. 1982, Sugden and Beyersbergen 1986). Many studies have found that reduced vegetational cover increases rates of nest predation (e.g., Wray and Whitmore 1979, Bowman and Harris 1980, Peterson and Best 1987). Mankin and Warner (1992) found that rates of predation were strongly influenced by the level of nest concealment, regardless of the predator's search strategy. The lower degree of concealment provided by vegetation in 1995 in our study site may have allowed predators to find more nests (e.g., Bobolinks; Table 1). Also, the winter of 1994–1995 was very mild; total snowfall was 171 cm compared with 358 cm in the winter of 1993–1994 (SUNY Brockport Earth Science Dept., unpubl. data). This may have allowed an increase in the number of mammalian predators because of decreased winter mortality rates.

Most grassland habitats support a variety of

TABLE 2. BETWEEN-YEAR DIFFERENCE IN NEST-SITE CHARACTERISTICS AT IROQUOIS NWR, ALABAMA, NEW YORK, 1994–1995

Measurement	Bobolink			Savannah Sparrow		
	1994	1995	P[a]	1994	1995	P[a]
Robel pole ($\bar{X}$)	5.675	3.71	0.000	4.78	3.99	0.044
Height of nest-site vegetation (cm; $\bar{X}$)	54.10	43.30	0.035	44.80	46.40	0.700
Height of vegetation at nest (cm)	62.90	44.20	0.004	52.50	43.30	0.060
% of nests successful[b]	64.00	13.00		79.00	71.00	

[a] 2-sample t-test.

[b] Apparent nest success—nests fledging at least one young; percentages include nest abandonments.

predators that employ different foraging techniques and whose importance as nest predators may change annually (Gottfried and Thompson 1978, Vickery et al. 1992). In our study, many of the artificial nest cups located nearest the edge were moved or disturbed, most likely by relatively large mammalian predators such as striped skunks, raccoons, and opossums (*Didelphis virginiana*; Best 1978, Martin 1992). In contrast, most depredated nests away from the forest edge had not been disturbed and were missing only the egg, which suggests predation by snakes or birds (Best 1978, Picman 1988). Several depredated nests (N = 5) away from the field-forest boundary also contained punctured eggs, whereas others contained only eggshell fragments—damage most likely caused by small mammals or birds (Best 1978, Maxson and Oring 1978, Picman 1992).

Haskell (1995) suggested that artificial nest experiments using quail (*Coturnix*) eggs are inappropriate for investigating among-fragment differences in predation rates on nests of neotropical migrants because of the size differences between quail eggs and neotropical birds' eggs. Quail-egg experiments may underestimate predation rates because a quail egg's larger size partially excludes known small-mouthed mammalian egg predators (Haskell 1995). This may be true for nest-predation studies in forested sites; however, only a small percentage (0.2%) of our depredated artificial nests showed evidence of predation by small-mouthed mammals such as mice (*Peromyscus* spp.), and we saw little evidence of small-mouthed mammal predation on natural nests. Other authors (e.g., Angelstam 1986, Yahner and Voytko 1989) believe that in some situations artificial nests may actually be depredated at higher rates than natural nests because adult birds associated with natural nests conceal eggs while incubating and often defend nests against potential predators. Although results of artificial-nest predation experiments should not be generalized to predation rates on natural bird nests (Angelstam 1986, Roper 1992), artificial predation rates may provide an estimate of relative predation rates, which in turn may be useful in determining future management practices (Reitsma 1992, Paton 1994). In our study, predation rates for artificial and natural nests were similar.

Although dense nesting cover may be beneficial for nesting waterfowl in some cases (Clark and Nudds 1991), our study suggests that it does not appear to increase nesting success for small passerines at Iroquois NWR. Birds nesting in dense nesting cover at Iroquois NWR, including Song Sparrows (*Melospiza melodia*) and Swamp Sparrows (*M. georgiana*), suffer higher rates of nest predation than do grassland birds nesting in cool-season grasslands (C. J. Norment, unpubl. data). In nests away from the immediate vicinity of the field-forest boundary, we found no consistent relationship between distance from edge and nest success.

ACKNOWLEDGMENTS

The U.S. Fish and Wildlife Service and State University of New York College at Brockport provided financial support. K. Hartman, D. Robinson, Jr., J. Romaneo, and B. Sheppard helped with field work. D. Tiller and S. Lor of the U.S. Fish and Wildlife Service and T. D. Carroll of the New York State Department of Environmental Conservation facilitated field work.

LITERATURE CITED

ANDRÉN, H., AND P. ANGELSTAM. 1988. Elevated predation rates as an effect in habitat islands: experimental evidence. Ecology 69:544–547.

ANGELSTAM, P. 1986. Predation on ground-nesting birds' nest in relation to predator densities and habitat edge. Oikos 47:365–373.

BEST, L. B. 1978. Field Sparrow reproductive success and nesting ecology. Auk 95:9–22.

BIDER, J. R. 1968. Animal activity in uncontrolled terrestrial communities as determined by a sand transect technique. Ecological Monographs 38:269–308.

BOLLINGER, E. K., AND T. A. GAVIN. 1992. Eastern Bobolink populations: ecology and conservation in an agricultural landscape. Pp. 467–470 in J. M. Hagan III and D. W. Johnston (editors). Ecology and conservation of neotropical migrant landbirds. Smithsonian Institution Press, Washington, D.C.

BOWMAN, G. B., AND L. D. HARRIS. 1980. Effect of spatial heterogeneity on ground-nest depredation. Journal of Wildlife Management 44:806–813.

CLARK, R. G., AND T. D. NUDDS. 1991. Habitat patch size and duck nesting success: the crucial experiments have not been performed. Wildlife Society Bulletin 19:534–543.

FAABORG, J., M. BRITTINGHAM, T. DONOVAN, AND J. BLAKE. 1993. Habitat fragmentation in the temperate zone: a perspective for managers. Pp. 331–338 in D. M. Finch and P. W. Stangel (editors). Status and management of neotropical migratory birds. USDA Forest Service Gen. Tech. Rep. RM-229. USDA Forest Service Rocky Mountain Forest and Range Experimental Station, Fort Collins, CO.

FRITZELL, E. K. 1978. Habitat use by prairie raccoons during the waterfowl breeding season. Journal of Wildlife Management 42:118–127.

GATES, J. E., AND L. W. GYSEL. 1978. Avian nest dispersion and fledgling success in field-forest ecotones. Ecology 59:871–883.

GOTTFRIED, B. M., AND C. F. THOMPSON. 1978. Experimental analysis of nest predation in an old field habitat. Auk 95:304–312.

HAGAN, J. M., T. L. LLOYD-EVANS, J. L. ATWOOD, AND D. S. WOOD. 1992. Detecting population changes using migration count data: a comparative approach. Pp. 115–130 in J. M. Hagan III and D. W. Johnston (editors). Ecology and conservation of neotropical migrant landbirds. Smithsonian Institution Press, Washington, D.C.

HASKELL, D. G. 1995. Forest fragmentation and nest predation: are experiments with Japanese quail eggs misleading? Auk 112:767–770.

HERKERT, J. R. 1991. Prairie birds of Illinois: population response to two centuries of habitat change. Illinois Natural History Survey Bulletin 34:383–519.

HERKERT, J. R. 1995. An analysis of midwestern breeding bird population trends: 1966–1993. American Midland Naturalist 134:41–50.

HUSSELL, D. J. T., M. MATHER, AND P. SINCLAIR. 1992. Trends in numbers of tropical and temperate landbirds in migration at Long Point, Ontario, 1961–1988. Pp. 101–114 in J. M. Hagan III and D. W. Johnston (editors). Ecology and conservation of neotropical migrant landbirds. Smithsonian Institution Press, Washington, D.C.

IROQUOIS NATIONAL WILDLIFE REFUGE. 1990. Grassland management plan. U.S. Fish and Wildlife Service, Alabama, NY.

JAMES, F. C., D. A. WIDENFELD, AND C. MCCULLOCH. 1992. Trends in breeding populations of warblers: declines in the southern highlands and increases in the lowlands. Pp. 43–56 in J. M. Hagan III and D. W. Johnston (editors). Ecology and conservation of neotropical migrant landbirds. Smithsonian Institution Press, Washington, D.C.

JOHNSON, R. G., AND S. A. TEMPLE. 1990. Nest predation and brood parasitism of tallgrass prairie birds. Journal of Wildlife Management 54:106–111.

KREMSATER, L. L., AND F. L. BUNNELL. 1992. Testing responses to forest edges: the example of black-tailed deer. Canadian Journal of Zoology 70:2426–2435.

MANKIN, P. C., AND R. E. WARNER. 1992. Vulnerability of ground nests to predation on an agricultural habitat island in east-central Illinois. American Midland Naturalist 128:281–291.

MARTIN, T. E. 1992. Interactions of nest predation and food limitation in reproductive strategies. Current Ornithology 9:163–197.

MARTIN, T. E. 1993. Nest predation among vegetation layers and habitats: revising the dogmas. American Naturalist 141:897–913.

MAXSON, S. J., AND L. W. ORING. 1978. Mice as a source of egg loss among ground-nesting birds. Auk 95:582–584.

MØLLER, A. P. 1987. Egg predation as a selective factor for nest design: an experiment. Oikos 50:91–94.

NORMENT, C. J., C. D. ARDIZZONE, AND K. HARTMAN. 1999. Habitat relations and breeding biology of grassland birds in New York. Studies in Avian Biology 19:112–121.

NOSS, R. F. 1983. A regional landscape approach to maintain diversity. BioScience 33:700–706.

PATON, P. W. C. 1994. The effect of edge on avian nest success: how strong is the evidence? Conservation Biology 8:17–26.

PETERSON, K. L., AND L. B BEST. 1987. Effects of prescribed burning on nongame birds in sage-brush community. Wildlife Society Bulletin 15:317–329.

PICMAN, J. 1988. Experimental study of predation on eggs of ground-nesting birds: effects of habitat and nest distribution. Condor 90:124–131.

PICMAN, J. 1992. Egg destruction by Eastern Meadowlarks. Wilson Bulletin 104:520–525.

PICOZZI, N. 1975. Crow predation on marked nests. Journal of Wildlife Management 39:151–155.

REDMOND, G. W., D. M. KEPPIE, AND P. W. HERZOG. 1982. Vegetative structure, concealment, and success at nests of two races of Spruce Grouse. Canadian Journal of Zoology 60:670–675.

REESE, K. P., AND J. T. RATTI. 1988. Edge effect: a concept under scrutiny. Transactions of the North American Wildlife and Natural Resources Conference 53:127–136.

REITSMA, L. 1992. Is nest predation density dependent? A test using artificial nests. Canadian Journal of Zoology 70:2498–2500.

RICKLEFS, R. E. 1969. An analysis of nesting mortality in birds. Smithsonian Contributions in Zoology 9:1–48.

ROBBINS, C. S., D. BYSTRAK, AND P. H. GEISLER. 1986. The Breeding Bird Survey: its first fifteen years, 1966–1979. U.S. Fish and Wildlife Service Resource Publication 157.

ROBBINS, C. S., J. R. SAUER, R. GREENBERG, AND S. DROEGE. 1989. Population declines in North American birds that migrate to the neotropics. Proceedings of the National Academy of Sciences 86:7658–7662.

ROBEL, R. J., J. N. BRIGGS, A. D. DAYTON, AND L. C. HULBERT. 1970. Relationship between visual obstruction measurements and weight of grassland vegetation. Journal of Range Management 29:295–297.

ROPER, J. J. 1992. Nest predation experiments with quail eggs: too much to swallow? Oikos 65:528–530.

SUGDEN, L. G., AND G. W. BEYERSBERGEN. 1986. Effect of density and concealment on American Crow predation of simulated duck nests. Journal of Wildlife Management 50:9–14.

TERBORGH, J. W. 1992. Perspectives on the conservation of neotropical migrant landbirds. Pp. 7–12 in J. M. Hagan III and D. W. Johnston (editors). Ecology and conservation of neotropical migrant landbirds. Smithsonian Institution Press, Washington, D.C.

U.S. DEPARTMENT OF AGRICULTURE. 1936–1991. Agricultural statistics. U.S. Government Printing Office, Washington, D.C.

VICKERY, P. D., M. L. HUNTER, JR., AND J. V. WELLS. 1992. Evidence of incidental nest predation and its effects on nests of threatened grassland birds. Oikos 63:281–288.

WARNER, R. E. 1994. Agricultural land use and grassland habitat in Illinois: future shock for wildlife. Conservation Biology 8:147–461.

WILCOVE, D. S. 1985. Nest predation in forest tracts and the decline of migratory songbirds. Ecology 66:1211–1214.

WRAY, T., II, AND R. C. WHITMORE. 1979. Effects of vegetation on nesting success of Vesper Sparrows. Auk 96:802–805.

YAHNER, R. H. 1988. Changes in wildlife communities near edges. Conservation Biology 2:333–339.

YAHNER, R. H., AND D. P. SCOTT. 1988. Effects of forest fragmentation on depredation of artificial nests. Journal of Wildlife Management 52:158–161.

YAHNER, R. H., AND R. A. VOYTKO. 1989. Effects of nest-site selection on depredation of artificial nests. Journal of Wildlife Management 53:21–25.

Studies in Avian Biology No. 19:128–130, 1999.

SATELLITE BURROW USE BY BURROWING OWL CHICKS AND ITS INFLUENCE ON NEST FATE

MARTHA J. DESMOND AND JULIE A. SAVIDGE

Abstract. We examined the importance of satellite burrows to Burrowing Owls (*Athene cunicularia*) nesting in western Nebraska in 1991 and 1992. With few exceptions, prefledgling chicks used active black-tailed prairie dog (*Cynomys ludovicianus*) burrows either in greater proportion than their availability or in proportion to their availability within a 75-meter radius of the nest burrow. Successful owl nests (those fledging one or more chicks) had more active prairie-dog burrows within a 75-meter radius of the nest burrow than did unsuccessful nests. Efforts to control prairie-dog populations in the Great Plains states are detrimental to Burrowing Owl populations. State- and federally supported prairie-dog control programs should be reevaluated to ensure that adequate populations of prairie dogs and associated species can persist.

EL USO DE MADRIGUERAS ALTERNATIVAS DE LOS POLLOS DEL BÚHO LLANERO Y SU INFLUENCIA EN LA PRODUCCIÓN DEL NIDO

Sinopsis. Examinamos en 1991 y 1992 la importancia de las madrigueras alternativas para los Búhos Llaneros (*Athene cunicularia*) que hacen sus nidos en el oeste de Nebraska. Con pocas excepciones, los pollos en nido usaban madrigueras activas del perro llanero de cola negra (*Cynomys ludovicianus*) ya sea en proporción mayor a su disponibilidad o en proporción a ella dentro de un radio de 75 metros desde la madriguera del nido. Los nidos con éxito (aquellos que producen por lo menos un pollo volantón) tenían más madrigueras activas de perro llanero de cola negra dentro de un radio de 75 metros del nido que los nidos sin éxito. Los intentos para controlar las poblaciones del perro llanero de cola negra en los estados de la Gran Llanura han sido perjudiciales para las poblaciones de los Búhos Llaneros. Los programas de control del perro llanero de cola negra auspiciados por los gobiernos estatales y el gobierno federal requieren nuevas evaluaciones para asegurar la perduración adecuada de las poblaciones del perro llanero de cola negra y de sus especies asociadas.

Key Words: *Athene cunicularia*; *Cynomys ludovicianus;* prairie-dog colony; prairie-dog control; satellite burrow.

The western subspecies of Burrowing Owl (*Athene cunicularia hypugaea*) is a native grassland bird that depends heavily on black-tailed prairie dogs (*Cynomys ludovicianus*) for nest burrows in the Great Plains. Once abundant, black-tailed prairie dog populations have declined by 98% since the beginning of the twentieth century because of agriculture, disease, and control programs (Summers and Linder 1978, Miller et al. 1994). Today black-tailed prairie dog colonies are fragmented and degraded in quality. Federal- and state-sponsored control programs have played a major role in population reductions (Miller et al. 1990) and currently remain among the biggest threats to the fragmentation and loss of this ecosystem (Miller et al. 1994).

Most research on the nesting requirements of Burrowing Owls in prairie-dog ecosystems has addressed questions at the level of the prairie-dog colony (Butts 1973, Plumpton 1992, Hughes 1993, Pezzolesi 1994). Prairie-dog colonies are highly dynamic, and habitat characteristics can vary widely within a single town (Hoogland 1981). Little is known about owl nest choice within a town. Several authors have commented on satellite burrow use by Burrowing Owl

chicks (Thomsen 1971, Butts 1973, Thompson 1984, Plumpton 1992), but use has not been examined quantitatively.

Ten to 14 d after hatching, Burrowing Owl chicks begin to emerge from their nest burrow. Although initially reluctant to move past the immediate vicinity of the nest burrow, they are quickly distributed among neighboring burrows. On one occasion, an adult female was observed using food to lure chicks away from the nest burrow to nearby burrows (M. Desmond, pers. obs.); this occurred at dawn and took 0.5 hr. Although we have observed this behavior only once, we think it is a common behavior for distributing chicks among burrows. As chicks become older, they readily move among burrows on their own. Butts and Lewis (1982) and Green and Anthony (1989) have suggested that using satellite burrows may reduce overcrowding in the nest burrow or may be a response to ectoparasite loads. Because of their terrestrial nature and large broods, prefledgling Burrowing Owls are often highly visible and thus vulnerable to predation. Using satellite burrows may be a defense against predation, as an entire brood is less likely to be lost to a predator if chicks are distributed among several burrows (Desmond 1991).

This paper examines the importance of prairie dogs and particularly satellite burrows to prefledgling Burrowing Owls. We have observed both adult and young owls using active prairie-dog burrows. Burrow use is particularly important to prefledgling Burrowing Owls because of their vulnerability to predation. We hypothesized that chicks would be selective in their choice of satellite burrows, and we predicted that they would exhibit a preference for active rather than inactive prairie-dog burrows because active burrows are better maintained. We also predicted that Burrowing Owl nest fate would be positively influenced by the number of active prairie-dog burrows in the vicinity of nest burrows.

STUDY AREAS AND METHODS

Research was conducted in 16 black-tailed prairie dog colonies in Banner, Box Butte, Morrill, Scotts Bluff, and Sioux Counties in western Nebraska in the spring and summer of 1991 and 1992. We searched prairie-dog colonies for nesting Burrowing Owls throughout the month of May each year. We located nests by carefully observing towns when the owls were courting and by walking line transects through each town such that we covered the entire town. Burrowing Owl nests were easily located because of the owls' propensity to line their nest entrances with shredded cow or horse dung. We mapped satellite prairie-dog burrow use by prefledgling owl chicks on a weekly or biweekly basis, depending on the location of the site, for 51 of 60 successful nests. Nine nests were omitted because of logistical problems in getting to the sites often enough and for long enough periods to record burrow use. Successful nests were defined as nests that fledged one or more chicks (42 d posthatch; Haug 1985). We measured the distance and angle from each owl nest burrow to each satellite prairie-dog burrow used by chicks, and we recorded the status of each satellite burrow as either active or inactive. Sighting of a prairie dog, fresh fecal pellets, or digging indicated active prairie-dog burrows; the presence of live, unclipped vegetation on the mound, spider webs covering or in the burrow entrance, or the absence of fresh fecal pellets indicated inactive burrows.

In late July we counted all satellite burrows within 75 m of each nest burrow and recorded their status as active or inactive. We chose 75 m because this typically was the farthest distance chicks ranged from their nest before fledging. Most 75-m circles around nests were non-overlapping; there were a few instances, however, where nests were close enough that the 75-m circles partially overlapped. In the latter cases, the direction in which the chicks spread out from the nest burrow may have been influenced by the presence of other owls rather than the number of active burrows. We used Chi-square contingency analysis for each nest (N = 51) to determine if Burrowing Owl chicks used active prairie-dog burrows in proportion to their availability. A Student's t-test was used to determine if there was a difference between the number of active prairie-dog burrows surrounding successful and unsuccessful nest burrows.

RESULTS

Burrowing Owls used a mean ($\pm$ SE) of 10 $\pm$ 0.98 satellite prairie-dog burrows (range 0–36) within a 75-m radius of the nest. Chicks at 29 nest burrows exhibited a preference for active prairie-dog burrows ($P < 0.05$). Chicks at two nest burrows used active burrows less than expected ($P < 0.05$); however, both of these nests were in heavily controlled prairie-dog colonies that had few remaining prairie dogs. Chicks at 11 nest burrows used active prairie-dog burrows in proportion to their availability. For 7 of these 11 nests, nearly 100% of the satellite burrows within 75 m of the nest were active prairie-dog burrows. Nine nest burrows did not have any active prairie-dog burrows within 75 m of the nest.

We monitored 164 nests over the 2-yr period. Successful nests (fledging $\geq$ 1 chicks; N = 60) had more active prairie-dog burrows within a 75-m radius of the nest burrow ($\bar{X} \pm$ SE = 96 $\pm$ 5.1) than did unsuccessful nests (26 $\pm$ 3.8; N = 104; Student's t-test: t = 7.6, df = 162, P < 0.001).

DISCUSSION

Our data indicate that Burrowing Owl chicks preferentially used active prairie-dog burrows. Active prairie-dog burrows are better maintained than inactive burrows and therefore may be more suitable for owl occupation. In inactive burrows, vegetation may partially obstruct entrances, and tunnel systems may collapse with disuse. Burrow longevity is likely related to soil type (Thompson 1984) as well as to prairie-dog activity. In Oklahoma, Butts and Lewis (1982) noted that abandoned prairie-dog colonies were not recognizable as prairie-dog colonies within 3 yr of abandonment, and Butts (1973) observed that burrows were often useless to Burrowing Owls within 1 yr of a prairie-dog control program being instituted. Such observations indicate how quickly prairie-dog burrows may degenerate without active maintenance.

Prairie-dog activity in the vicinity of Burrowing Owl nests appears to strongly influence nest fate. In Colorado, Hughes (1993) found that Burrowing Owls nested at higher densities in towns where 90% or more of the prairie-dog burrows were active. Also in Colorado, Plumpton (1992) observed that Burrowing Owls nested in areas with higher burrow densities in 1 of the 2 yr of his study. Our results indicate that active prairie-dog burrow density in the immediate vicinity of a Burrowing Owl nest may have a strong impact on nest fate. Our mean of 96 active burrows within 75 m of successful nests was high compared to our mean of 26 for unsuccessful nests.

Burrowing Owls may benefit from the presence of prairie dogs. Prairie-dog alarm calls may alert the owls to predators. Also, the owls may benefit from the dilution effect. Predators may prey more heavily on prairie dogs because they are more abundant than Burrowing Owls (Desmond et al. 1995). Prairie dogs may also be a preferred food source because of their greater biomass. Numerous prairie-dog burrows in the vicinity of a Burrowing Owl nest allow an owl brood to be distributed among several burrows, reducing the chance that an entire brood will be lost to a predator.

Preferential use of active prairie-dog burrows by Burrowing Owl chicks, and the positive influence of prairie-dog activity on nest success, support the need to preserve prairie-dog colonies for Burrowing Owl populations. We suggest that conservation agencies closely monitor prairie-dog and associated owl populations. Such assessments should include the location of prairie-dog/Burrowing Owl colonies, sizes of colonies, and owl and prairie-dog densities. State- and federally supported control programs should be reevaluated to ensure that adequate populations of prairie dogs remain to support species associated with this ecosystem.

ACKNOWLEDGMENTS

F. Andelt, J. Dinan, T. Labedz, D. Virchow, and many Nebraska Ornithological Union members gave us information on Burrowing Owl nests and prairie-dog colony locations. Special thanks to the many landowners in the Nebraska panhandle who allowed access to their property. K. Church, T. Dean, P. D. Vickery, and an anonymous reviewer made helpful comments on this manuscript. Financial support was provided by grants from the University of Nebraska, Sigma Xi, Center for Great Plains Studies, and Nebraska Game and Parks Nongame Checkoff. This is journal series 11586 of the Agricultural Research Division, University of Nebraska-Lincoln.

LITERATURE CITED

BUTTS, K. O. 1973. Life history and habitat requirements of Burrowing Owls in western Oklahoma. M.S. thesis. Oklahoma State University, Stillwater, OK.

BUTTS, K. O., AND J. C. LEWIS. 1982. The importance of prairie dog towns to Burrowing Owls in Oklahoma. Proceedings of the Oklahoma Academy of Sciences 62:46–52.

DESMOND, M. J. 1991. Ecological aspects of Burrowing Owl nesting strategies in the Nebraska panhandle. M.S. thesis. University of Nebraska, Lincoln, NE.

DESMOND, M. J., J. A. SAVIDGE, AND T. F. SEIBERT. 1995. Spatial patterns of Burrowing Owl (*Speotyto cunicularia*) nests in black-tailed prairie dog (*Cynomys ludovicianus*) towns in western Nebraska. Canadian Journal of Zoology 73:1375–1379.

GREEN, G., AND R. ANTHONY. 1989. Nesting success and habitat relationships of Burrowing Owls in the Columbia Basin, Oregon. Condor 91:347–354.

HAUG, E. A. 1985. Observations on the breeding ecology of Burrowing Owls in Saskatchewan. M.S. thesis. University of Saskatchewan, Saskatoon, SK.

HOOGLAND, J. L. 1981. The evolution of coloniality in white-tailed and black-tailed prairie dogs (Sciuridae: *Cynomys leucurus* and *C. ludovicianus*). Ecology 62:252–272.

HUGHES, A. J. 1993. Breeding density and habitat preferences of the Burrowing Owl in northeastern Colorado. M.S. thesis. Colorado State University, Fort Collins, CO.

MILLER, B., G. CEBALLOS, AND R. READING. 1994. The prairie dog and biotic diversity. Conservation Biology 8:677–681.

MILLER, B., C. WEMMER, D. BIGGINS, AND R. READING. 1990. A proposal to conserve black-footed ferrets and the prairie dog ecosystem. Environmental Management 14:763–769.

PEZZOLESI, L. S. 1994. The western Burrowing Owl: increasing prairie dog abundance, foraging theory, and nest site fidelity. M.S. thesis. Texas Tech University, Lubbock, TX.

PLUMPTON, D. L. 1992. Aspects of nest site selection and habitat use by Burrowing Owls at the Rocky Mountain Arsenal, Colorado. M.S. thesis. Texas Tech University, Lubbock, TX.

SUMMERS, C. A., AND R. L. LINDER. 1978. Food habits of the black-tailed prairie dog in western South Dakota. Journal of Range Management 31:134–136.

THOMPSON, C. D. 1984. Selected aspects of Burrowing Owl ecology in central Wyoming. M.S. thesis. University of Wyoming, Laramie, WY.

THOMSEN, L. 1971. Behavior and ecology of Burrowing Owls on the Oakland Municipal Airport. Condor 67:125–139.

Studies in Avian Biology No. 19:131–136, 1999.

SONGBIRD ABUNDANCE IN GRASSLANDS AT A SUBURBAN INTERFACE ON THE COLORADO HIGH PLAINS

CARL E. BOCK, JANE H. BOCK, AND BARRY C. BENNETT

Abstract. We counted nesting songbirds for three summers on 62 200-meter-diameter plots on City of Boulder, Colorado, Open Space grasslands. Habitats included upland mixed-grass prairie and lowlands with tallgrass prairie and irrigated hayfields. Plots were located either at habitat edges adjacent to suburban developments or at least 200 meters interior to such edges. Grassland-nesting songbirds collectively were nearly twice as abundant on interior as on edge plots. Species significantly more abundant on interior plots, independent of habitat type, included Vesper Sparrow (*Pooecetes gramineus*), Savannah Sparrow (*Passerculus sandwichensis*), Grasshopper Sparrow (*Ammodramus savannarum*), Bobolink (*Dolichonyx oryzivorus*), and Western Meadowlark (*Sturnella neglecta*). By contrast, combined counts of five suburban species—American Robin (*Turdus migratorius*), European Starling (*Sturnus vulgaris*), Common Grackle (*Quiscalus quiscula*), House Finch (*Carpodacus mexicanus*), and House Sparrow (*Passer domesticus*)—were nearly five times greater on edge than on interior plots. If it is a goal to conserve native grassland birds on the western Great Plains, we conclude that grassland open-space systems in this region should be designed to reduce edges with suburban development. More research is needed to determine what causes edge effects, which might include increased nest predation, human interference with the nesting process, and increased competition with suburban species.

LA ABUNDANCIA DE AVES PASERIFORMES EN PASTIZALES EN UN LÍMITE SUBURBANO EN LA LLANURA ALTA DE COLORADO

Sinopsis. Contamos aves paseriformes durante tres veranos en 62 parcelas de 200 metros de diámetro en los pastizales Terreno Escampado de la Ciudad de Boulder, Colorado. Los hábitats incluyeron pradera alta de hierba mixta y tierra baja con pradera de hierba alta y campos regados de heno. Las parcelas se ubicaron ya sea en los límites de hábitats adyacentes a urbanizaciones de suburbios o a por los menos 200 metros al interior de esos límites. Las aves paseriformes fueron colectivamente casi dos veces más abundantes en las parcelas interiores que en aquéllas de los límites. Las especies significativamente más abundantes en las parcelas interiores, independientemente del tipo de hábitat, incluyeron el Gorrión Coliblanco (*Pooecetes gramineus*), el Gorrión Sabanero (*Passerculus sandwichensis*), el Gorrión Chapulín (*Ammodramus savannarum*), el Tordo Arrocero (*Dolichonyx oryzivorus*) y el Pradero Occidental (*Sturnella neglecta*). En cambio, las cifras combinadas de cinco especies suburbanas—el Zorzal Petirrojo (*Turdus migratorius*), el Estornino Europeo (*Sturnus vulgaris*), el Zanate Común (*Quiscalus quiscula*), el Fringílido Mexicano (*Carpodacus mexicanus*) y el Gorrión Doméstico (*Passer domesticus*)—fueron casi cinco veces mayores en las parcelas de los límites que en las parcelas interiores. Si es una prioridad conservar las aves nativas de pastizal en el oeste de la Gran Llanura, concluimos que los sistemas de terreno escampado para pastizales en esta región deben ser diseñados para reducir los límites de la urbanización de suburbios. Se necesitan más investigaciones para determinar lo que causa los efectos de los límites, que puede incluir una aumentada depredación de los nidos, la intervención humana en el proceso de nidaje y una mayor competencia con especies suburbanas.

Key Words: Colorado; edge effects; grassland birds; habitat fragmentation; prairie.

U.S. Fish and Wildlife Service Breeding Bird Surveys (now conducted by the Biological Resources Division of the U.S. Geological Survey) indicate widespread and substantial declines of grassland birds in North America since the mid-1960s (Peterjohn and Sauer 1993, Herkert 1995). Likely causes include habitat losses due to agricultural conversion and spreading urbanization (Knopf 1994). An additional factor may be that remaining patches of suitable habitat are too small and isolated to support viable populations of many species. Such landscape effects were evident in prairie remnants in Illinois and Maine, where various grassland birds were absent or scarce in relatively small prairies embed-ded in woodlands and croplands (Herkert 1994, Vickery et al. 1994).

Conserving and restoring grasslands and their bird populations on the western Great Plains also must take into account potential landscape effects. These grasslands, however, usually are not fragmented into discreet and isolated units like their prairie counterparts in the Midwest or Northeast. Rather, a background matrix of grasslands is variously interspersed with row crops, woodlots, and spreading urban fronts. Are western grassland bird populations affected by these landscape intrusions? Are the abundance and variety of endemic birds reduced in grasslands adjacent to human-created environments?

One rapidly urbanizing section of the western Great Plains lies at the eastern face of the Rocky Mountains in Colorado, from Fort Collins in the north to Pueblo in the south—the so-called Front Range Corridor (Alexander 1980, FitzSimmons 1985, Matthews 1992). Habitats being replaced by spreading suburbs for the most part are short-grass, mixed-grass, and occasional tallgrass prairies used primarily for livestock grazing and haying, with some irrigated row crops. The city of Boulder is one community in the Front Range Corridor that has a well-established Open Space program, designed to create a buffer against urban sprawl and to conserve endemic grassland flora and fauna (City of Boulder Open Space Department 1995, Zaslowsky 1995). More than 10,000 ha presently are included, making it the largest per-capita municipally owned open-space system in the United States (J. Crain, pers. comm.).

Most parcels of Boulder Open Space do not exist as isolated patches surrounded by suburban areas but rather as part of a belt of largely undeveloped land enclosing the city around its northern, eastern, and southern perimeters. Our objective in the present study was to test for edge effects (Harris 1988, Paton 1994) on bird abundance in open-space grasslands adjacent to this suburban front. We quantified relative abundances of birds in open-space grasslands and hayfields, comparing data from plots at habitat edges with those from plots located more to the interior of the protected lands. Our goal was to provide information on possible edge effects that might be useful to individuals and organizations planning similar open-space systems along the Front Range Corridor.

STUDY AREA

Boulder Open Space habitats include narrow riparian corridors along streams, tallgrass prairies and agricultural hayfields in adjacent lowland floodplains, and mixed grasslands on upland slopes and benches (Moir 1969, Santanachote 1992, Bock et al. 1995). Tallgrass stands include grasses typical of the true prairie to the east: big bluestem (*Andropogon gerardii*), little bluestem (*Schizachyrium scoparium*), switchgrass (*Panicum virgatum*), and Indian grass (*Sorghastrum nutans*). Boulder tallgrass stands are ungrazed in summer, but most are grazed by cattle in fall and winter.

Agricultural hayfields near Boulder support mixtures of alfalfa (*Medicago sativa*), sedges (*Carex* spp.), and various non-native pasture grasses, including smooth brome (*Bromus inermis*), meadow fescue (*Festuca pratensis*), orchard-grass (*Dactylis glomerata*), and timothy (*Phleum pratense*). Hayfields are flood-irrigated in spring and early summer, mowed in July, and sometimes grazed by cattle in fall and winter.

Upland habitats support diverse mixtures of short and midheight grasses, both native and introduced, along with a large variety of broad-leaved herbs. Yucca

(*Yucca glauca*) and prickly-pear cactus (*Opuntia* spp.) are common in some areas. Dominant grasses include blue grama (*Bouteloua gracilis*), western wheatgrass (*Agropyron smithii*), buffalograss (*Buchloë dactyloides*), needle grasses (*Stipa* spp.), and two exotics, Japanese brome (*Bromus japonicus*) and cheatgrass (*B. tectorum*). All upland sites have a history of livestock grazing, although some areas have been ungrazed for the past several years.

METHODS

Upland mixed grasslands supported very different avifaunas than lowland prairies and hayfields. Therefore, it was essential that our study plots include a mixture of both types of habitats, in both suburban edge and interior landscape settings. In the fall of 1993 we established 62 circular 200-m-diam plots on Boulder Open Space grasslands; 30 of the plots were in lowland hayfields and tallgrass prairies and 32 in upland mixed-grass prairies. Among the 32 upland plots, 22 were a minimum of 200 m from the nearest suburban edge and were designated interior plots, and 10 were directly adjacent to suburban housing developments. The 30 lowland plots were divided evenly between interior and suburban edge situations.

It is not clear how far apart bird count plots should be to be considered statistically independent (Verner 1985). Our plots were widely scattered over the 10,000 ha of open space, and no pair of plots was closer than 200 m. Each plot was marked with a single center stake, from which we conducted fixed-distance point counts between mid-May and mid-July in 1994, 1995, and 1996. During each count we recorded the number of birds we saw or heard over a 10-min period within 100 m of the plot center point. We made four counts per plot in 1994 and three counts per plot in 1995 and 1996.

As an index of relative abundance, we computed the average number of each species recorded per point count per plot, weighting each year's data equally to compute a single value for each species on each plot.

Interior versus edge plots were not evenly divided among lowland versus upland habitats because there has been more suburban development in lowland areas near Boulder. Furthermore, some birds were strongly associated with one or the other of the two habitat types. This made it possible to confuse landscape and habitat effects. For example, Lark Sparrows (*Chondestes grammacus*) were strongly associated with upland sites; because fewer upland than lowland plots were at suburban edges, this could have resulted in an impression that Lark Sparrows were avoiding grasslands in suburban landscape settings. Conversely, actual avoidance of edges could lead to the impression that Lark Sparrows were selecting uplands over lowlands. To control for the possibility of confusing landscape with habitat effects, we analyzed count data using two-way analysis of variance (ANOVA), with plot habitat (upland vs. lowland) and plot setting (interior vs. edge) as independent variables. By this method, resulting pairs of F-values for each species would reveal significant ($P < 0.05$) landscape effects independent of habitat, and vice versa.

Based on their likely nest locations, we identified three groups of songbirds using the 62 plots: 8 grass-

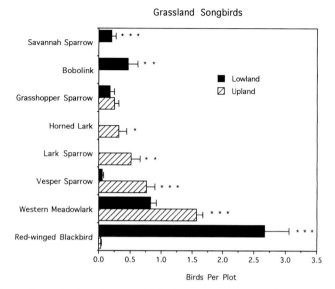

FIGURE 1.   Numbers of grassland-nesting songbirds (means + SE) counted per 100-m fixed-distance point count on 32 upland and 30 lowland grassland plots that are part of Boulder, Colorado, Open Space. Each plot was counted four times in summer 1994 and three times in summers 1995 and 1996. (* Significant difference between habitats independent of plot landscape setting, two-way ANOVA, P < 0.05; ** P < 0.01; *** P < 0.001.)

land species, 5 suburban species, and 17 other species. We made no systematic effort to locate nests, but incidental to point counts we did find nests of the eight grassland-nesting species. The five suburban species were all common in suburban environments in and near Boulder. The third group of 17 species did not nest in grasslands, nor were they specifically associated with suburban environments; nesting habitats for this group included cliffs and anthropogenic structures for swallows (*Hirundo* spp.) and riparian woodlands and shrublands for most of the remaining species.

RESULTS

GRASSLAND-NESTING SPECIES

Eight grassland-nesting species accounted for 46% of the songbird sightings on the 62 plots. Among these, Savannah Sparrows (*Passerculus sandwichensis*), Bobolinks (*Dolichonyx oryzivorus*), and Red-winged Blackbirds (*Agelaius phoeniceus*) were significantly more abundant on lowland than on upland plots, independent of plot proximity to suburban developments (Fig. 1). Horned Larks (*Eremophila alpestris*), Lark Sparrows, Vesper Sparrows (*Pooecetes gramineus*), and Western Meadowlarks (*Sturnella neglecta*) were more common in uplands, whereas Grasshopper Sparrows (*Ammodramus savannarum*) did not differ significantly between habitat types.

Among these same eight grassland-nesting species, all but Lark Sparrow, Horned Lark, and Red-winged Blackbird were significantly more abundant on interior plots not adjacent to suburbia, independent of plot habitat type (Fig. 2). We counted Lark Sparrows and Horned Larks much more frequently on interior plots, but their very high interplot variances resulted in a lack of statistical significance. Only Red-winged Blackbirds seemed unaffected by proximity to suburban edges. Combined counts of all eight grassland-nesting songbirds were 1.9 times higher on interior plots ($\bar{X}$ = 4.87, SE = 0.29) than on edge plots ($\bar{X}$ = 2.52, SE = 0.40), and this difference was highly significant, independent of habitat type (two-way ANOVA, F = 33.27, P < 0.0001, df = 1, 58).

SUBURBAN SPECIES

Five species nesting commonly in suburban habitats accounted for 30% of songbird sightings on our grassland plots. American Robins (*Turdus migratorius*), European Starlings (*Sturnus vulgaris*), and Common Grackles (*Quiscalus quiscula*) were more common in lowlands (Fig. 3), whereas House Sparrows (*Passer domesticus*) were more common in upland situations, and House Finches (*Carpodacus mexicanus*) did not differ between habitat types. Each of the five species was significantly more abundant on edge plots adjacent to suburban developments, independent of grassland habitat (Fig. 4). Combined counts of these five species were 4.9 times higher on edge plots ($\bar{X}$ = 4.72, SE = 0.43) than on

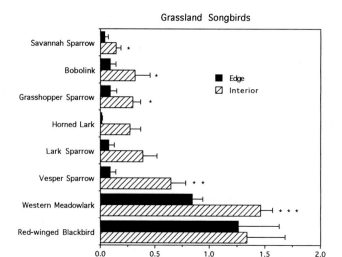

FIGURE 2. Numbers of grassland-nesting songbirds counted on 25 edge plots adjacent to suburban developments and 37 interior plots more than 200 m from suburban environments. (* Significant difference between landscape settings independent of plot habitat, two-way ANOVA, P < 0.05; ** P < 0.01; *** P < 0.001.)

interior plots ($\bar{X}$ = 0.97, SE = 0.26), and this difference was highly significant, independent of habitat type (two-way ANOVA, F = 67.70, P < 0.0001, df = 1, 58).

OTHER SONGBIRDS

Seventeen other songbird species accounted for 24% of our sightings on the 62 plots. None of these species nested in grasslands nor exclu-

sively in suburban habitats. Most common among these were Cliff Swallows (*Hirundo pyrrhonota*), Barn Swallows (*H. rustica*), and Black-billed Magpies (*Pica pica*), with much smaller numbers of various riparian and shrubland species such as Western Kingbirds (*Tyrannus verticalis*), Spotted Towhees (*Pipilo maculatus*), Bullock's Orioles (*Icterus bullockii*), and American Goldfinches (*Carduelis tristis*). Col-

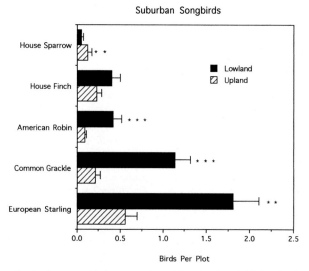

FIGURE 3. Numbers of suburban songbirds counted on 32 upland and 30 lowland grassland plots that are part of Boulder, Colorado, Open Space. (** Significant difference between habitats independent of plot landscape setting, two-way ANOVA, P < 0.01; *** P < 0.001.)

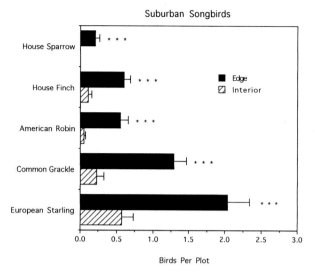

FIGURE 4. Numbers of suburban songbirds counted on 25 edge plots adjacent to suburban developments and 37 interior plots more than 200 m from suburban environments. (*** Significant difference between landscape settings independent of plot habitat, two-way ANOVA, $P < 0.001$.)

lectively, counts of these 17 species did not differ significantly between edge plots ($\bar{X}$ = 2.16, SE = 0.28) and interior plots ($\bar{X}$ = 1.87, SE = 0.25), independent of habitat type (two-way ANOVA, F = 0.24, P = 0.63, df = 1, 58).

DISCUSSION

Most of the grassland bird species in our study area avoided suburban edges, despite the fact that the grassland habitats of the edge plots did not differ from those of interior plots. Edge effects and the overall impacts of urbanization have been demonstrated primarily for woodland and forest birds in previous studies (Paton 1994, Blair 1996), but our results suggest they exist for grassland birds as well.

Overall abundance of grassland-nesting songbirds was nearly twice as high on interior plots as on plots adjacent to suburban environments. Five of the eight grassland species—Vesper Sparrow, Savannah Sparrow, Grasshopper Sparrow, Bobolink, and Western Meadowlark—were significantly less common in edge situations, and all five have been declining on a continental scale according to Breeding Bird Survey data (Knopf 1994, Herkert 1995). Some of these species have been found to be area sensitive in other prairie grasslands; examples include Savannah Sparrow, Grasshopper Sparrow, and Bobolink in Illinois (Herkert 1994) and Vesper Sparrow, Savannah Sparrow, Grasshopper Sparrow, and Bobolink in Maine (Vickery et al. 1994).

Our results strongly suggest that to enhance conservation of grassland-nesting birds, grass-

land open-space systems on the western Great Plains should be designed to reduce edges with suburban developments. More research is necessary, however, to determine why these edge effects occur.

Suburban songbirds foraged but did not nest on open-space grasslands adjacent to suburban developments. It is possible that resource competition with these suburban species resulted in reduced numbers of grassland birds at habitat edges. The fact that only grassland nesters and not the other grassland foragers were scarce in edge situations, however, suggests that nest predation (Martin 1993) and/or human nest interference (Knight and Gutzwiller 1995) were more likely factors. We observed very few Brown-headed Cowbirds (*Molothrus ater*) on Boulder Open Space grasslands, so nest parasitism seems unlikely to be involved. The logical next step in our research will be to compare reproductive success of grassland birds nesting in suburban edge versus interior situations, and to attempt to determine the possible causes of nesting failure in the different landscape settings.

ACKNOWLEDGMENTS

This study was supported by the Biological Resources Division of the U.S. Geological Survey, U.S. Fish and Wildlife Service, City of Boulder Open Space Department, and University of Colorado at Boulder, as participants in the Colorado Rockies Regional Cooperative. We thank H. Alden, J. Crain, S. Jones, D. Kuntz, C. Miller, R. Knight, and R. Schroeder for advice and assistance.

LITERATURE CITED

ALEXANDER, P. K. 1980. Urban sprawl and agricultural land loss along the Colorado Front Range. M.A. thesis. University of Colorado, Boulder, CO.

BLAIR, R. B. 1996. Land use and avian species diversity along an urban gradient. Ecological Applications 6:506–519.

BOCK, C. E., J. H. BOCK, AND B. C. BENNETT. 1995. The avifauna of remnant tallgrass prairie near Boulder, Colorado. Prairie Naturalist 27:147–157.

CITY OF BOULDER OPEN SPACE DEPARTMENT. 1995. City council draft of long range management policies. Open Space, Real Estate Department, Boulder, CO.

FITZSIMMONS, A. R. 1985. A geography of growth along the Colorado Front Range. M.A. thesis. University of Colorado, Boulder, CO.

HARRIS, L. D. 1988. Edge effects and conservation of biological diversity. Conservation Biology 2:330–332.

HERKERT, J. R. 1994. The effects of habitat fragmentation on midwestern grassland bird communities. Ecological Applications 4:461–471.

HERKERT, J. R. 1995. An analysis of midwestern breeding bird population trends: 1966–1993. American Midland Naturalist 134:41–50.

KNIGHT, R. L., AND K. G. GUTZWILLER (EDITORS). 1995. Wildlife and recreationists: coexistence through research and management. Island Press, Covelo, CA.

KNOPF, F. L. 1994. Avian assemblages on altered grasslands. Studies in Avian Biology 15:247–257.

MARTIN, T. E. 1993. Nest predation and nest sites. BioScience 43:523–532.

MATTHEWS, A. 1992. Where the buffalo roam. Grove Weidenfeld, New York, NY.

MOIR, W. H. 1969. Steppe communities in the foothills of the Colorado Front Range and their relative productivities. American Midland Naturalist 81:331–340.

PATON, P. W. C. 1994. The effect of edge on avian nest success: how strong is the evidence? Conservation Biology 8:17–26.

PETERJOHN, B. G., AND J. R. SAUER. 1993. North American Breeding Bird Survey annual summary 1990–1991. Bird Populations 1:1–15.

SANTANACHOTE, K. 1992. The vegetation cover, seed bank, seed rain, and seed reproduction of the relictual tallgrass prairie of Boulder County, Colorado. Ph.D. dissertation. University of Colorado, Boulder, CO.

VERNER, J. 1985. Assessment of counting techniques. Current Ornithology 2:247–302.

VICKERY, P. D., M. L. HUNTER, JR., AND S. M. MELVIN. 1994. Effects of habitat area on the distribution of grassland birds in Maine. Conservation Biology 8:1087–1097.

ZASLOWSKY, D. 1995. The battle of Boulder. Wilderness 58:25–33.

Studies in Avian Biology No. 19:137–143, 1999.

THERMAL ASPECTS OF NEST-SITE LOCATION FOR VESPER SPARROWS AND HORNED LARKS IN BRITISH COLUMBIA

KARI J. NELSON AND KATHY MARTIN

Abstract. During the 1994 and 1995 breeding seasons, we examined the orientation of Vesper Sparrow (*Pooecetes gramineus*) and Horned Lark (*Eremophila alpestris*) nests relative to vegetative cover in the Chilcotin grasslands of central British Columbia. To investigate the effects of nest placement on nest microclimate, we compared nest temperatures with (1) different orientations relative to single clumps of vegetative cover, (2) different orientations relative to multiple clumps of vegetative cover, and (3) different amounts of vegetative cover. Vegetation was located on the southwest side (180–260°) of 87 percent of nests of both species. The distribution of single clumps of vegetation (77 percent of nests) around nests of both species in both years differed significantly from a uniform distribution. Nests with either a single clump of vegetation on the southwest side or with more than one clump of vegetation on the southeast to southwest side had lower temperatures than did nests with vegetation on other sides; these nests also remained above the temperature that may be lethal to developing embryos (38 C) for shorter periods of time during the day than did other nests. Nests without vegetation on the east side warmed up more rapidly in the morning than did nests with vegetation on the northeast or southeast side. The height of the vegetation clump and the amount of cover it provided also influenced nest temperatures. Nests with more than 90 percent cover exceeded 38 C for only 1.25 hours at midday, whereas nests with less than 20 percent cover exceeded 38 C for 4.25 hours. The pattern of nest orientation displayed by Vesper Sparrows and Horned Larks in this study appeared to reflect selection for thermally advantageous nest sites.

LOS ASPECTOS TÉRMICOS DE LA UBICACIÓN DE NIDOS PARA LOS GORRIONES COLIBLANCOS Y LAS ALONDRAS CORNUDAS EN COLOMBIA BRITÁNICA

Sinopsis. Durante las temporadas reproductivas de 1994 y 1995, examinamos la orientación de los nidos del Gorrión Coliblanco (*Pooecetes gramineus*) y de la Alondra Cornuda (*Eremophila alpestris*) con relación a la cobertura vegetativa en los pastizales Chilcotin del centro de Colombia Británica, Canadá. Para investigar los efectos de la colocación de nidos en el microclima, comparamos las temperaturas de los nidos con (1) diferentes orientaciones con relación a matas sencillas de cobertura vegetativa, (2) diferentes orientaciones con relación a matas múltiples de cobertura vegetativa, y (3) diferentes cantidades de cobertura vegetativa. La vegetación se ubicaba al lado suroeste (180–260°) en un 87 por ciento de los nidos de ambas especies. La distribución de las matas sencillas de vegetación (un 77 por ciento de los nidos) alrededor de los nidos de ambas especies en los dos años difirió significativamente de una distribución uniforme. Los nidos que tenían o una mata sencilla al lado suroeste o más de una mata de vegetación al lado sureste a suroeste registraron temperaturas más bajas que los nidos con vegetación a los otros lados; estos nidos también tenían temperaturas más altas que la temperatura que puede ser mortal para los embriones en desarrollo (38 C) durante temporadas más cortas en el transcurso del día en comparación con la temporada que tenían los otros nidos. Los nidos que no tenían vegetación al lado este se calentaron más rápidamente en la mañana que los nidos con vegetación al lado noreste o sureste. La altura de la mata de vegetación y la cantidad de cobertura que ofrecía también influyeron en las temperaturas de los nidos. Los nidos que tenían cobertura de más de un 90 por ciento sobrepasaron los 38 C solamente por 1,25 horas alrededor del mediodía, mientras que los nidos con cobertura de menos de un 20 por ciento sobrepasaron los 38 C durante 4,25 horas. La tendencia en la orientación de los nidos que mostraron los Gorriones Coliblancos y las Alondras Cornudas en este estudio pareció reflejar una selección de sitios de nidos con ventajas térmicas.

Key Words: British Columbia; grassland birds; habitat selection; microclimate; nest placement; vegetative cover.

Choosing an appropriate nest site plays a critical role in the reproductive success of birds. Nest placement may influence the ability of predators to detect nests (Martin 1993) and the degree to which nests are sheltered from extreme environmental conditions (Walsberg 1985). Grassland environments are characterized by extreme environmental conditions, including intense solar radiation. Microclimatic conditions therefore may be a particularly important aspect of nest-site selection for open-nesting species in grassland habitats.

Studies of a wide variety of bird species have attributed nonrandom patterns of nest placement with respect to vegetative cover to protection from wind or solar radiation (Ricklefs and

Hainsworth 1969, Orr 1970, Austin 1976, Cannings 1981, Cannings and Threlfall 1981, Verbeek 1981, Zerba and Morton 1983a, Facemire et al. 1990, Petersen and Best 1991). Few of these studies, however, have documented the influence of nest orientation on nest microclimate (but see With and Webb 1993). Our study is part of an ongoing investigation into thermal aspects of nest placement of Horned Larks (*Eremophila alpestris*) and Vesper Sparrows (*Pooecetes gramineus*) in the Chilcotin grasslands of British Columbia. In this paper we test the hypothesis that these species orient their nests nonrandomly with respect to vegetative cover. To illustrate the effects of nest-site selection on nest microclimate, we compare nest temperatures obtained from nests with (1) different orientations relative to single clumps of vegetative cover, (2) different orientations relative to multiple clumps of vegetative cover, and (3) different amounts of vegetative cover.

STUDY SITES

Field work was conducted during the 1994 and 1995 breeding seasons at Becher's Prairie near Riske Creek, British Columbia (51°58' N, 122°32' W). Becher's Prairie has an elevation of approximately 1,000 m and consists of grassland habitats interspersed with small lakes and copses (trembling aspen [*Populus tremuloides*], Douglas-fir [*Pseudotsuga menziesii*], and lodgepole pine [*Pinus contorta*]). The dominant vegetation in the area is bluebunch wheatgrass (*Elymus spicata*), June grass (*Koeleria macrantha*), porcupine grass (*Stipa curtiseta*), and Kentucky bluegrass (*Poa pratensis*).

We sampled six sites ranging in size from 36 to 74 ha and comprising a total of 364 ha. Grazing by domestic cattle has occurred on most grasslands in the system, and fire is presently being reintroduced as a range-management tool to reduce forest encroachment and enhance forage production. Vesper Sparrows and Horned Larks are the most common breeding passerines in the area.

METHODS

We located Horned Lark and Vesper Sparrow nests by flushing females from nests while walking through the study sites or by rope-dragging (Labisky 1957). The majority of nests of both species were located immediately adjacent to (i.e., touching) the base of perennial bunchgrasses (porcupine grass or bluebunch wheatgrass; K. Nelson, unpubl. data). Individual plants of these species form discrete, densely tufted clumps of vegetation. After a nest was vacated, we determined the orientation (relative to true north) of any clumps of vegetation (i.e., individual plants) touching it by measuring the compass direction of a line bisecting the center of the nest and the center of the vegetation clump(s). In the few cases (N = 10) where a nest was completely surrounded by vegetation, we did not measure the orientation of individual clumps.

Calculations of descriptive statistics and significance tests for data from circular distributions (i.e., orientation of vegetation relative to nests) followed Zar 1984.

Differences between mean angles of orientation of vegetation relative to nests were determined using the Watson-Williams test, and Rayleigh's test was used to determine whether the distribution of vegetation around nests was uniform.

We quantified the amount of nest concealment using a 6.5-cm-diam ball marked with a grid of 61 dots (2 mm diam). The dots were drawn on the ball so they would appear equidistant (8 mm apart) when viewed from a distance of 1 m. This ball fit snugly into the nest cups of both species, thus providing an objective, readily repeatable method of measuring nest concealment. Overhead cover was determined by placing the ball in the nest cup with the grid axes oriented along each of the four cardinal compass directions. The number of dots visible from a height of 1 m above the nest was counted, and the proportion of the nest concealed was calculated by dividing the number of dots not visible by the total number of dots. We also measured the maximum height of the vegetation clump(s) adjoining the nest.

In 1995 we measured nest temperatures by placing a single HOBO™ data logger (temperature range -37 to $+46$ C) inside nest cups as soon as possible after they were vacated. Nest temperatures were recorded every 5–6 min over a 6- or 8-d period. A maximum of 13 nests could be monitored at one time, so data were collected over six separate time periods during the summer. In total, we recorded temperature profiles for 49 Vesper Sparrow nests and 16 Horned Lark nests.

In this paper we present temperature data from nests with single clumps of vegetation on the southwest, northwest, northeast, or southeast side; with multiple vegetation clumps on different sides; and with different amounts of vegetative cover. To control as much as possible for the effects of weather, we present nest temperatures obtained only on clear days, and we limit direct comparisons to data collected on the same day. To facilitate comparisons between nests, the temperature presumed lethal for embryos (38 C; Zerba and Morton 1983b) appears on all plots of nest temperatures. To provide an indication of the range of temperatures potentially experienced by birds and nests in this system, we also present temperature data recorded by a HOBO data logger that was placed on the ground in an exposed location on a clear day.

RESULTS

Nest Orientation

We located a total of 122 nests in 1994 and 1995: 19 Horned Lark and 103 Vesper Sparrow. We found 77% of nests of both species (17 Horned Lark, 77 Vesper Sparrow) at the base of a single clump of vegetation. For these nests, there was no significant difference between years in the mean angle of orientation of vegetation relative to nests of either species (Horned Lark: $F_{1,16} = 3.27$, $P > 0.05$; Vesper Sparrow: $F_{1,76} = 2.69$, $P > 0.10$). There was also no significant difference between species in the mean angle of orientation of vegetation relative to nests for both years combined ($F_{1,93} = 0.43$, $P > 0.25$). The distribution of single clumps of

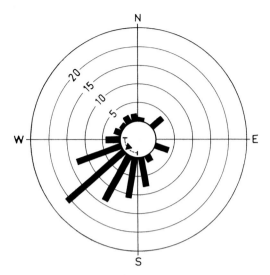

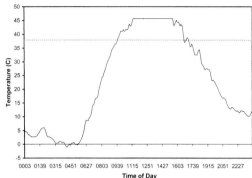

FIGURE 2. Temperature profile from a HOBO data logger placed in an exposed location on the ground on a clear day (3 June 1995). The dotted horizontal line (38 C) represents the presumed lethal temperature for embryos.

FIGURE 1. Frequency distribution of the orientation of single clumps of vegetation relative to Vesper Sparrow and Horned Lark nests (center of figure). N represents true north, the triangle represents the mean angle of orientation of vegetation relative to nests, and the dashed lines represent the angular deviation.

vegetation around nests of both species in both years was significantly nonuniform (mean angle = 230.4°, s = 33.6°, z_{94} = 40.09, P < 0.001; Fig. 1).

We found 23% of nests (2 Horned Lark, 26 Vesper Sparrow) adjoining more than one clump of vegetation. Ten of these nests were completely surrounded by vegetation, and one was under a branch. The other 17 nests with multiple clumps of vegetation all had one clump of vegetation on the southwest side of the nest.

TEMPERATURE PROFILES

Temperatures recorded in an exposed location on the ground on 3 June 1995 ranged from below 0 C before dawn to 45.7 C (the maximum recordable temperature on the HOBO data logger) at midday (Fig. 2). For more than 7 hr between 0942 and 1647, the temperature exceeded 38 C. During this time, eggs exposed to the sun would rapidly have exceeded temperatures presumed lethal for embryos (Zerba and Morton 1983b), and adults incubating eggs or sheltering young would have needed to expend energy cooling themselves and their eggs or young (Grant 1982). Although we collected temperature data in an exposed location on only one day, the results clearly demonstrate the temperature extremes to which birds and nests in this area may be exposed. In all cases where maximum temperatures were recorded, actual temperatures were probably at least 10 degrees higher.

Nest temperatures differ depending on how long and during what time of day nests are exposed to solar radiation. To examine the influence of nest orientation relative to vegetative cover on nest temperatures, we selected nests that were as similar as possible with respect to height of vegetation beside the nest and amount of nest concealment (Table 1). We collected temperature data for only one nest with vegetation on the northeast side and one nest with vegetation on the northwest side (because nests with these orientations were rare). We compared temperatures from these nests to temperatures obtained on the same day from nests with vegetation on the opposite sides of the nest (southwest and southeast sides, respectively).

On 15 June 1995, temperatures in the nest with vegetation on the southwest side (N5) rose much more rapidly in the morning than did temperatures in the nest with vegetation on the northeast side (KN2; Fig. 3A). Temperatures in N5 reached a peak of 30.2 C in 4.5 hr, at 1008. Temperatures in KN2 did not surpass 30.2 C until 1147 (6.25 hr after warming began) and rose gradually to the maximum recordable temperature of 45.7 C between 1417 and 1502. Temperatures in KN2 were above 38 C for less than 3 hr (from 1307 to 1553).

Temperatures in nests with vegetation on the northwest side (N31) and southeast side (N23) were recorded later in the season, on 19 July 1995 (Fig. 3B). Temperatures in these nests were approximately 5 degrees higher at 2400 than they were in nests with vegetation on the southwest and northeast sides (Fig. 3A). Temperatures rose more rapidly in N31 than in N23, surpassing 38 C by 1040 (4.75 hr after the nest began to heat up) and remained above this temperature for 6 hr (until 1645). Temperatures in N31

TABLE 1. ORIENTATION OF VEGETATION RELATIVE TO NESTS (COMPASS DIRECTION), HEIGHT OF VEGETATION, AND AMOUNT OF VEGETATIVE COVER FOR EACH OF THE NESTS USED IN COMPARISONS OF NEST TEMPERATURES

Comparison	Nest	Species[a]	Compass direction	Height (cm)	% nest cover
Orientation of single clumps (Fig. 3)	KN2	VESP	56°	41	77
	N5	VESP	227°	33	58.4
	N23	VESP	117°	27.5	42.6
	N31	VESP	318°	32	63.9
Orientation of multiple clumps (Fig. 4)	KN7	VESP	84/169/238°	33/35/31	63.9
	KN3	VESP	128/236°	21.5/33	37.7
	N4	VESP	211/297°	32.5/35	91.8
	N6	VESP	168/236/310°	37/33/34	98.4
Size of clump (Fig. 5)	KN13	HOLA	225°	16	18
	N1	VESP	222°	33	39.3
	RN3	VESP	219°	57	90.2

[a] VESP = Vesper Sparrow, HOLA = Horned Lark.

reached the maximum recordable temperature (45.7 C) at 1118 and dropped below this temperature at 1521. Temperatures in N23 did not surpass 38 C until 1254 (>2 hr later than in N31), reached the maximum recordable temperature at 1430, and dropped below 38 C at the

same time as in N31 (1645). Both of these nests cooled at similar rates.

The effect of orientation of multiple clumps of vegetation on nest temperatures was recorded on 15 and 28 June 1995 and is illustrated in Fig. 4. Nest KN7 had vegetation on the east, south, and southwest sides, whereas KN3 had vegetation on the southeast and southwest sides. These

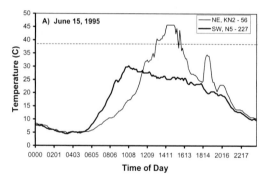

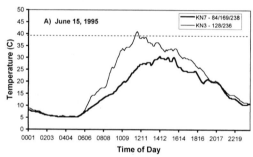

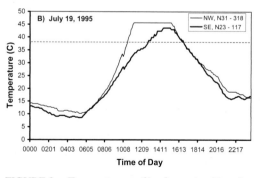

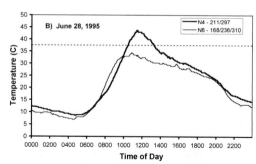

FIGURE 3. Temperature profiles for nests with a single clump of vegetation on (A) the southwest or northeast side and (B) the northwest or southeast side. The dotted horizontal line (38 C) represents the presumed lethal temperature for embryos. Numbers following nest identification codes are compass orientation (in degrees) of vegetation relative to nests.

FIGURE 4. Temperature profiles for nests surrounded by more than one clump of vegetation; all nests have vegetation on the southwest side. The dotted horizontal line (38 C) represents the presumed lethal temperature for embryos. Numbers following nest identification codes are compass orientation (in degrees) of vegetation relative to nests.

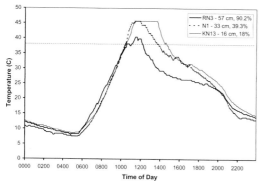

FIGURE 5. Temperature profiles recorded on 28 June 1995 for nests with different amounts of vegetative cover; all nests have vegetation on the southwest side. The dotted horizontal line (38 C) represents the presumed lethal temperature for embryos. Numbers following nest identification codes are height of vegetation and percentage of vegetative cover for each nest.

differences were reflected in a more rapid rise in temperatures in KN3 than in KN7, with temperatures in KN3 reaching a peak of 41.1 C at 1145, which was 5.75 hr after temperatures began to rise (Fig. 4A). Temperatures in KN7 peaked at a much lower temperature (30.6 C) 2.5 hr later (at 1412). Temperatures in KN3 remained above 38 C for just over 1 hr at midday (from 1126 to 1249).

Rapid increases in morning temperatures were displayed on 28 June 1995 by two nests (N4 and N6) with no vegetation on their northeast, east, or southeast sides (Fig. 4B). These nests heated at similar rates, but temperatures in N6 peaked at 34.5 C at 1053, whereas temperatures in N4 continued to rise, peaking at 43.7 C at 1126. Temperatures in N4 remained above 38 C for 2.75 hr (from 1033 to 1317). The difference in temperature profiles for these two nests is explained by the presence of an additional clump of vegetation on the south side of N6.

To examine how the amount of cover influenced nest microclimate, we compared temperature data from three nests that all had vegetation on the southwest side but that differed with respect to height of vegetative cover and amount of nest concealment (Table 1, Fig. 5). All three nests heated at similar rates on the morning of 28 June 1995. The nest with the largest clump of vegetation and the most cover (RN3) remained above 38 C for only 1.75 hr and reached a lower maximum temperature (40.5 C) than did the other two nests (N1 and KN13). N1 and KN13 reached the maximum recordable temperatures (45.7 C) by 1125, but KN13, which had the least vegetative cover, remained at this tem-

perature for a longer period of time (2.25 hr compared with 0.5 hr for N1). Temperatures in KN13 also remained above 38 C for the longest period during the hottest time of the day.

DISCUSSION

During the breeding season, grassland environments, particularly at northern latitudes, are characterized by extreme environmental conditions, including cold nights and hot days. Most of the heat transfer between eggs or nestlings in open-nesting species occurs through convection and short-wave radiation (Webb and King 1983). In grasslands, two of the most important aspects of nest-site location should thus be protection from wind and protection from solar radiation (With and Webb 1993).

The pattern of nest orientation relative to vegetative cover displayed by Vesper Sparrows and Horned Larks in our study was similar to that reported for several other open-nesting species in a variety of ecosystems (Cannings 1981; Cannings and Threlfall 1981; Verbeek 1981; Walsberg 1981; Zerba and Morton 1983a; Petersen and Best 1985, 1991; With and Webb 1993). In some of these ecosystems, prevailing winds are from the southwest, and the observed pattern of nest orientation has been attributed either to protection from wind (Cannings 1981, Cannings and Threlfall 1981) or to protection from wind and/or afternoon sun (Zerba and Morton 1983a, Petersen and Best 1985). With and Webb (1993) measured wind profiles in nests of three species of birds in shortgrass prairie and found that the orientation of nests relative to vegetative cover did not correspond to the degree to which they were protected from prevailing winds. Nests of Lark Buntings (*Calamospiza melanocorys*) were placed on the leeward side of shrubs but experienced higher relative wind velocities (in the nest cup, compared with ambient conditions) than did the more exposed nests of Horned Larks and McCown's Longspurs (*Calcarius mccownii*). These results, in conjunction with the similarity in nest orientation displayed by different species in such a wide variety of ecosystems, suggest that protecting nests from solar radiation may be more important to open-nesting species than protecting nests from wind.

Several researchers have suggested that by placing nests on the northeast side of vegetation, birds maximize exposure to morning sun and minimize exposure to afternoon sun (Walsberg and King 1978, Verbeek 1981, Walsberg 1981, Petersen and Best 1991). At Becher's Prairie during the breeding season, the sun rises in the northeast and sets in the northwest. Nests with vegetation on the southwest side are thus exposed to sun in the morning but are shaded during the hottest time of the day. Our temperature data obtained from nests with different orientations showed that nests with vegetation on the southwest side heated up rapidly in the morning but remained cooler in the afternoon than did nests with vegetation on the northeast, southeast, or northwest sides. Wiebe and Martin (1997) documented a similar pattern of heating and cooling in White-tailed Ptarmigan (*Lagopus leucurus*) nests exposed to morning sun but shaded from afternoon sun. We believe that these microclimatic conditions provide the most thermally advantageous environment for eggs, nestlings, and attending adult birds.

Exposure of the nest to direct sun may result in dramatic changes in nest attentiveness during incubation (Zerba and Morton 1983b). Female Mountain White-crowned Sparrows (*Zonotrichia leucophrys oriantha*) remained on nests exposed to direct sun to prevent embryos from reaching lethal temperatures (Zerba and Morton 1983a, b). A female with consecutive nests in the same breeding season had lower attentiveness during midday, and took longer and more frequent foraging bouts, at the nest that was more shaded than at the nest that was exposed to direct sun (Zerba and Morton 1983b). The lower afternoon temperatures that we recorded at Becher's Prairie in nests with vegetation on the southwest side should allow incubating adults to take more and longer foraging bouts during this time period than if vegetation were located on the northeast, southeast, or northwest side of the nest. In exposed nests, White-tailed Ptarmigan avoided taking incubation recesses during midday, when nest temperatures could rise above 45 C (Wiebe and Martin 1997). Lower afternoon temperatures should also be important during the nestling period, when foraging demands on attending adults are high. If nestlings are exposed to direct sun, adults must forego foraging opportunities to provide shade for nestlings, and they must expend energy to cool themselves and their young.

We found that nests with vegetation on the south and southwest sides but not on the east side had an additional advantage in that they heated up more quickly during the early morning than did other nests. If nests are exposed to direct sun during this period, eggs should cool less rapidly when adults leave the nest than if they were shaded. In fact, egg temperatures increase at rates directly related to ambient temperatures when eggs are exposed to direct sun (Zerba and Morton 1983a). Females may be able to take advantage of solar heating of eggs by increasing the length of their foraging bouts. Long foraging bouts and extended periods of nest attentiveness appear to be the most energy-

efficient strategies for adults tending nests alone (Vleck 1981).

The most thermally favorable nest sites at Becher's Prairie appear to be those with several clumps of vegetation arranged around the southeast to west sides of the nest. These nests, however, accounted for only 5% of the 122 nests we found. The high percentage of nests (77%) we found beside a single clump of vegetation could indicate that sites with multiple clumps are limited in availability, or that they are less preferred because predation risk is higher. Nests with multiple clumps may also be under-represented in our sample because they were more difficult to find.

Differences in nest orientation may or may not result in differences in reproductive success. Nests of Verdins (*Auriparus flaviceps*) and Cactus Wrens (*Campylorhynchus brunneicapillus*) that were oriented into prevailing winds had higher success rates than did nests that were "incorrectly" oriented (Austin 1974, 1976). Verbeek (1981) compared success of Water Pipit (*Anthus spinoletta*) nests with different orientations and found no significant difference between nests oriented in the mean direction and other nests. If adults are able to adjust their nest-attendance behavior to provide protection for eggs and young, then effects of nest orientation may not be reflected in differences in embryo viability and nestling survival. Differences in nest orientation are more likely to be reflected in differences in nestling growth rates and post-fledging survival, and/or in sublethal behavioral costs to attending adults. Adults that expend less energy shading eggs and young from extreme heat and are able to take more and longer foraging recesses may be in better condition when young fledge and at the end of the breeding season. These factors may in turn influence renesting ability and adult survival probabilities, respectively. We plan to monitor Horned Lark and Vesper Sparrow nests through the incubation and nestling periods to determine how nest orientation influences nest-attendance behavior and renesting ability. Experiments involving manipulation of vegetative cover around nests would also provide valuable information on the importance of nesting cover to reproductive success and survival.

We found that other important determinants of nest temperature were the height and amount of cover provided by sheltering vegetation. A nest located beside a small clump of vegetation with little overhead cover was afforded scant protection from direct sun, even though the vegetation was located on the southwest side of the nest. Practices, such as prescribed burning, that remove standing litter from previous years' growth effectively eliminate large clumps of bunchgrass. We plan to investigate the impact of grassland fires on the availability of thermally advantageous nest sites for Horned Larks and Vesper Sparrows.

ACKNOWLEDGMENTS

This work was made possible by a Natural Sciences and Engineering Research Council (NSERC) postgraduate scholarship to K. Nelson and an NSERC operating research grant to K. Martin. S. Taylor and R. Handler were enthusiastic and dedicated field assistants. Special thanks to F. Knezevich and J. Young for generous logistical support; to T. Hooper for her time and advice; and to G. Huffman, N. McDonald, and K. McDonald for permission to conduct research on their land. L. B. Best and an anonymous reviewer provided valuable comments.

LITERATURE CITED

AUSTIN, G. T. 1974. Nesting success of the Cactus Wren in relation to nest orientation. Condor 76:216–217.

AUSTIN, G. T. 1976. Behavioral adaptations of the Verdin to the desert. Auk 93:245–262.

CANNINGS, R. J. 1981. Notes on the nesting of Horned Larks on the Chilcotin Plateau of British Columbia. Murrelet 62:21–23.

CANNINGS, R. J., AND W. THRELFALL. 1981. Horned Lark breeding biology at Cape St. Mary's, Newfoundland. Wilson Bulletin 93:519–530.

FACEMIRE, C. F., M. E. FACEMIRE, AND M. C. FACEMIRE. 1990. Wind as a factor in the orientation of entrances of Cactus Wren nests. Condor 92:1073–1075.

GRANT, G. S. 1982. Avian incubation: egg temperature, nest humidity, and behavioral thermoregulation in a hot environment. Ornithological Monographs 30:1–75.

LABISKY, R. F. 1957. Relation of hay harvesting to duck nesting under a refuge-permittee system. Journal of Wildlife Management 21:194–200.

MARTIN, T. E. 1993. Nest predation, nest sites and birds: new perspectives on old patterns. BioScience 43:523–532.

ORR, Y. 1970. Temperature measurements at the nest of the Desert Lark (*Ammomanes deserti deserti*). Condor 72:476–478.

PETERSEN, K. J., AND L. B. BEST. 1985. Nest-site selection by Sage Sparrows. Condor 87:217–221.

PETERSEN, K. J., AND L. B. BEST. 1991. Nest-site selection by Sage Thrashers in southeastern Idaho. Great Basin Naturalist 51:261–266.

RICKLEFS, R. E., AND F. R. HAINSWORTH. 1969. Temperature regulation in nestling Cactus Wrens: the nest environment. Condor 71:32–37.

VERBEEK, N. A. M. 1981. Nesting success and orientation of Water Pipit *Anthus spinoletta* nests. Ornis Scandinavica 12:37–39.

VLECK, C. M. 1981. Energetic costs of incubation in the Zebra Finch. Condor 83:229–237.

WALSBERG, G. E. 1981. Nest-site selection and the radiative environment of the Warbling Vireo. Condor 83:86–88.

WALSBERG, G. E. 1985. Physiological consequences of microhabitat selection. Pp. 389–413 *in* M. L. Cody (editor). Habitat selection in birds. Academic Press, New York, NY.

WALSBERG, G. E., AND J. R. KING. 1978. The heat budget of incubating Mountain White-crowned Sparrows (*Zonotrichia leucophrys oriantha*) in Oregon. Physiological Zoology 51:92–103.

WEBB, D. R., AND J. R. KING. 1983. An analysis of the heat budgets of the eggs and nest of the White-crowned Sparrow, *Zonotrichia leucophrys,* in relation to parental attentiveness. Physiological Zoology 56:493–505.

WIEBE, K. L., AND K. MARTIN. 1997. Effects of predation, body condition and temperature on incubation rhythms of White-tailed Ptarmigan *Lagopus leucurus.* Wildlife Biology 3:219–227.

WITH, K. A., AND D. R. WEBB. 1993. Microclimate of ground nests: the relative importance of radiative cover and wind breaks for three grassland species. Condor 95:401–413.

ZAR, J. H. 1984. Biostatistical Analysis. 2d ed. Prentice Hall, Englewood Cliffs, NJ.

ZERBA, E., AND M. L. MORTON. 1983a. Dynamics of incubation in Mountain White-crowned Sparrows. Condor 85:1–11.

ZERBA, E., AND M. L. MORTON. 1983b. The rhythm of incubation from egg laying to hatching in Mountain White-crowned Sparrows. Ornis Scandinavica 14:188–197.

Studies in Avian Biology No. 19:144–148, 1999.

THE EFFECTS OF SUMMER BURNS ON BREEDING FLORIDA GRASSHOPPER AND BACHMAN'S SPARROWS

W. Gregory Shriver, Peter D. Vickery, and Dustin W. Perkins

Abstract. The dry prairie grasslands of central Florida once dominated the landscape from Lake Kissimmee to Lake Okeechobee, encompassing 1.1 million hectares. These prairies have been largely reduced to four protected sites, where the federally endangered Florida Grasshopper Sparrow (*Ammodramus savannarum floridanus*) and Bachman's Sparrow (*Aimophila aestivalis*) are year-round residents. Management of dry prairie habitat has usually involved late-fall and winter prescribed burns to maintain habitat in an early successional state, which is preferred by these sparrows. Naturally ignited fires on dry prairie ecosystems, however, occur most frequently in summer. Because this grassland evolved with summer wildfires, we sought to understand how prescribed summer burns affected the two rare emberizid sparrows that breed and winter there. Between 1994 and 1996 we studied the effects of prescribed summer fires on Florida Grasshopper and Bachman's sparrows at the Kissimmee Prairie Sanctuary and Three Lakes Wildlife Management Area. Grasshopper Sparrows were more sensitive to timing of prescribed fires than were Bachman's Sparrows. Both species increased in density following mid-June fires, but only Bachman's Sparrows responded positively to July fires. We found that both species occupied burned areas one week after burning and remained reproductively active into September.

LOS EFECTOS DE INCENDIOS ESTIVALES EN LOS GORRIONES REPRODUCTIVOS *AMMODRAMUS SAVANNARUM FLORIDANUS* Y *AIMOPHILA AESTIVALIS*

Sinopsis. En otro tiempo los pastizales secos de las llanuras del centro de Florida dominaban el paisaje desde el Lago Kissimmee al Lago Okeechobee, abarcando 1,1 millones de hectáreas. Estas llanuras se redujeron considerablemente a cuatro lugares protegidos, donde residen todo el año dos gorriones clasificados En Peligro: *Ammodramus savannarum floridanus* y *Aimophila aestivalis*. El manejo del hábitat de llanura seca normalmente incluye incendios intencionales durante el fin del otoño y el invierno para mantener el hábitat en un estado preliminar de sucesión, que estos gorriones prefieren. Sin embargo, los fuegos de ignición natural de los sistemas ecológicos de llanura seca ocurren con mayor frecuencia en verano. Dado que este pastizal evolucionó con fuegos estivales, procuramos entender como los fuegos estivales intencionales afectaban a estos dos gorriones escasos que se reproducen y que pasan el invierno allí. Entre 1994 y 1996 estudiamos los efectos de los fuegos estivales intencionales en los gorriones *Ammodramus savannarum floridanus* y *Aimophila aestivalis* en el Santuario Kissimmee de Llanura y en el Area de Manejo de Fauna Tres Lagos. Los gorriones *Aimophila aestivalis* fueron más sensibles a la programación de los fuegos intencionales que los gorriones *Ammodramus savannarum floridanus*. Ambas especies aumentaron en densidad después de los fuegos de mediados de junio, pero sólo los gorriones *Aimophila aestivalis* respondieron positivamente a los fuegos en julio. Descubrimos que ambas especies ocuparon áreas quemadas una semana después del fuego y permanecieron activas reproductivamente hasta septiembre.

Key Words: Aimophila aestivalis; Ammodramus savannarum floridanus; Bachman's Sparrow; Florida Grasshopper Sparrow; prairie management; prescribed fire.

The dry prairie of central Florida is an endemic grassland system composed of pyrogenic plant associations that have evolved with frequent natural fires (Snyder et al. 1990). The natural fire frequency of this system appears to be every 1–4 yr, a slightly higher frequency than occurs in mesic flatwoods, which contain a pine (*Pinus*) overstory (Florida Natural Areas Inventory 1990). Fires on dry prairie were ignited naturally by lightning, primarily during the summer months when thunderstorms are most frequent (Snyder et al. 1990). Plants of the dry prairie are dependent on these summer fires. For example, wire grass (*Aristida beyrinchium*), the dominant grass in this habitat, flowers and sets seed more profusely after summer fires than after winter

fires (Lewis 1964). It is likely that the fauna of this system also adapted to this pattern of frequent summer fire.

The Florida Grasshopper Sparrow (*Ammodramus savannarum floridanus*), a federally endangered grassland sparrow endemic to central Florida dry prairie (Federal Register 1986), has evolved in this fire-adapted ecosystem and prefers areas burned within the past 24 mo (Delany et al. 1985, Delany and Cox 1986, Walsh et al. 1995). Federal guidelines recommend prescribed burns as part of a management plan to maintain and enhance populations of this endemic sparrow (U.S. Fish and Wildlife Service 1988). Nearly all prescribed fires, however, have been conducted in late fall or winter (e.g., Walsh et al. 1995), to reduce potential nest mortality resulting from fire. Questions concerning whether the season of pre-scribed burns (winter vs. summer) affects the Florida Grasshopper Sparrow's breeding biology and, ultimately, potential recovery have not been carefully examined or tested in the field.

Bachman's Sparrow (*Aimophila aestivalis*) is also a resident breeder of the dry prairies of cen-tral Florida. Historically this species has been as-sociated with mature longleaf pine (*Pinus palus-tris*) forests with grassy, open understories (Brooks 1938, Stoddard 1978, Haggerty 1986). Dunning and Watts (1990) reported that Bach-man's Sparrows consistently occupied areas with abundant grasses and forbs in the vegetative layer 1 m above ground but with reduced vegetation in the layer 2–4 m above ground. For breeding Bachman's Sparrows, the age class of the canopy was not as important a predictor of occupancy as was the structure of the vegetation in the first meter above ground (Dunning and Watts 1990).

The objectives of this study were to determine how prescribed summer burns affect breeding densities and phenology of these two species. Having documented the extension of the breed-ing season after summer fires (Shriver et al. 1996), we sought to determine if the prolonged singing period (to early September) on burned areas observed in the initial study reflected ac-tual breeding activity.

METHODS

Between 1994 and 1996 we measured sparrow re-sponse to summer fire using standard spot-map cen-susing methods (International Bird Census Committee 1970). All plots were rectangular (8–18 ha), more than 100 m from any other plot, and more than 50 m from unsuitable habitat (e.g., wetlands, tropical hammocks). Plots were censused every 4–8 d from March to Sep-tember, and a territory was defined as an area where a male was present for 4+ wk (Vickery et al. 1992). The breeding success of each territory was ranked based on observed breeding behaviors (Vickery et al. 1992). We used three-way analysis of variance (ANOVA) to test for differences in sparrow densities between burned and unburned plots, study sites, and years.

STUDY SITES

KISSIMMEE PRAIRIE SANCTUARY

The National Audubon Society Ordway-Whittell Kissimmee Prairie Sanctuary in Okeechobee County (27°34′ N, 80°58′ W) is a 3,071-ha portion of prairie habitat that historically covered much of central Flor-ida. As part of our study on the breeding biology of these two species, we established eight plots (92 ha total) in three burn units at this site. In June 1992 more than 75% of the sanctuary was burned by a lightning-ignited fire (S. Hedges, pers. comm.). Since that time, Kissimmee Prairie has been managed on a 2-yr sum-mer-fire rotation. During our research, specific plots were burned and then left for 2 yr or more before the next prescribed burning; thus, they changed burn status

from one year to the next. Both treatment and control areas were not burned for at least 2 yr in all years of this study.

We conducted three prescribed burns at Kissimmee Prairie between 1994 and 1996 and measured Grass-hopper and Bachman's sparrow densities before and after all burns. On 15 July 1994, a 250-ha unit was burned; three plots (35 ha) were located in the burn unit and two plots (33 ha) in the unburned unit. On 30 June 1995, a 240-ha unit was burned; three plots (39 ha) were burned, and two plots (16 ha) were not burned. On 17 June 1996, a 112-ha unit was burned; two plots (16 ha) were burned, and three plots (35 ha) were unburned.

THREE LAKES WILDLIFE MANAGEMENT AREA

Approximately 4,000 ha of dry prairie occur on the southern portion of Three Lakes Wildlife Management Area (WMA) in Osceola County (27°47′ N, 81°06′ W). This property is owned and managed by the Florida Game and Fresh Water Fish Commission which, prior to our research, conducted a 2- to 3-yr fire rotation in the fall and winter. During our study, all plots had not been burned for at least 2 yr prior to summer burning.

We conducted three prescribed burns at Three Lakes WMA between 1994 and 1996 and measured Grass-hopper and Bachman's sparrow densities before and after all burns. On 22 June 1994, three plots (26 ha) were burned, and three unburned plots (31 ha) served as controls. On 31 July 1995, three plots (43 ha) were burned, and three unburned plots (31 ha) served as controls. On 17 June 1996, three plots (30 ha) were burned, and two plots (16 ha) served as controls.

RESULTS

When all six burns were analyzed together, there was no clear difference in Grasshopper Sparrow densities on burned spot-map plots compared to unburned plots (Table 1, Fig. 1). There were increases in Grasshopper Sparrow densities, however, following three mid-June fires (Fig. 1, A–C). When mid-June fires were tested alone (Fig. 1, A–C), densities between burned and unburned areas differed (F = 4.26, df = 1, P = 0.05). Grasshopper Sparrow terri-tory densities did not increase on plots that were burned later than 29 June (Fig. 1, D–F). There was a significant interaction between year, site, and burn treatment for changes in Grasshopper Sparrow densities (Table 1).

Grasshopper Sparrows established territories on burned areas within 1 wk of mid-June fires. Males were observed singing and aggressively defending territories in areas that were vacant before the burn. We observed females in terri-tories, suggesting that Grasshopper Sparrows were breeding on burned areas. On 23 July 1996 we discovered a nest with four nestlings at Three Lakes WMA. This nest was located on a plot that was burned 17 June 1996. The nest was considered successful: four nestlings were ob-served on 29 July, and the nest was empty on 5

TABLE 1. THREE-WAY ANOVA FOR CHANGES IN FLORIDA GRASSHOPPER SPARROW BREEDING DENSITY AFTER SUMMER PRESCRIBED FIRES AT KISSIMMEE PRAIRIE AND THREE LAKES WMA, FLORIDA, 1994–1996

Source	Sum of squares	df	Mean square	F-ratio	P
Burn	0.025	1	0.025	0.010	0.919
Site	13.541	1	13.541	5.599	0.026
Year	64.751	2	32.375	13.386	0.000
Burn × Year × Site	16.959	2	8.479	3.506	0.045
Error	60.466	25	2.419		

August. This was the first confirmed breeding by Florida Grasshopper Sparrows on prairie fragments that were burned in summer.

Bachman's Sparrows were observed singing on burned plots within 1 wk of prescribed fires, and densities on burned plots increased after fires conducted from 17 June to 31 July (Table 2, Fig. 2). At Kissimmee Prairie in 1994 and 1995, females were observed with males in burned territories. At Three Lakes WMA in 1994–1996, juvenile Bachman's Sparrows were observed in postburn territories more than 5 wk after the fires. There was a significant interaction between year and site for changes in Bachman's Sparrow densities (Table 2).

DISCUSSION

The dry prairie of central Florida is a pyrogenic assemblage of grasses, forbs, and shrubs that depends on fire to maintain the composition and structure of the vegetation. The season in which fire occurs has profound effects on vegetation structure and phenology. Lewis (1964) reported that wire grass in South Florida flowered profusely after summer fires but exhibited little or no response after winter fires. The flow-

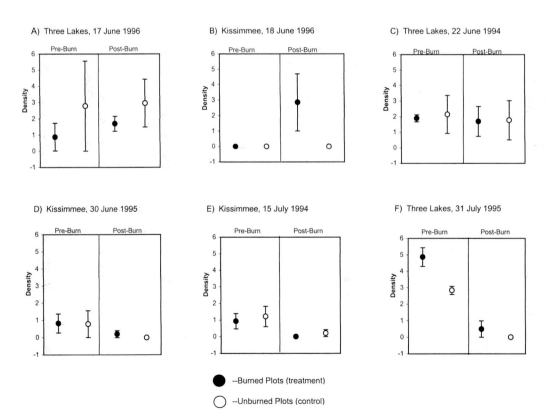

FIGURE 1. Mean number (± 1 SE) of Florida Grasshopper Sparrow territories per 10 ha ("Density") before and after summer prescribed fires. Graphs (A–F) are ordered by seasonal date of fire to show how timing of burning influenced sparrow response.

TABLE 2. THREE-WAY ANOVA FOR CHANGES IN BACHMAN'S SPARROW BREEDING DENSITY AFTER SUMMER PRESCRIBED FIRES AT KISSIMMEE PRAIRIE AND THREE LAKES WMA, FLORIDA, 1994–1996

Source	Sum of squares	df	Mean square	F-ratio	P
Burn	16.662	1	16.662	19.830	0.000
Site	3.529	1	3.529	4.201	0.051
Year	0.238	2	0.119	0.142	0.868
Year × Site	6.524	2	3.262	3.882	0.034
Error	21.005	25	0.840		

ering of the dominant grass on the prairie has a profound effect on the structure of the vegetation; flower stalks exceed 1 m on summer burns but are nonexistent on winter burns (W. G. Shriver, pers. obs.). These changes in vegetative structure may affect breeding sparrow populations and may have important implications for endangered-species management.

For Florida Grasshopper Sparrows, it is important to consider the timing of summer burns when attempting to predict sparrow response. As the length of the "typical" breeding season for Florida Grasshopper Sparrows on winter-burned areas is reported to end in mid-July (Delany et al. 1985), hormone levels at this time in the breeding season may drop below a point such that breeding is no longer possible. This study demonstrates that Florida Grasshopper Sparrows were breeding only on plots that were burned in mid-June. Florida Grasshopper Sparrows established territories but did not initiate late-season breeding activity after the late June or July burns. Although we indicated that there was a positive response to a 15 July burn (Shriver et al. 1996), the more extensive spot-map data demonstrated that these birds did not establish territories for a period of 4 wk or more.

Bachman's Sparrows were not sensitive to timing of summer burns. We measured higher territory densities on burned areas regardless of when the burns occurred. Bachman's Sparrows in central Arkansas were reported to continue breeding into October (Haggerty 1986), much later than Florida Grasshopper Sparrows. The longer breeding season documented for Bach-

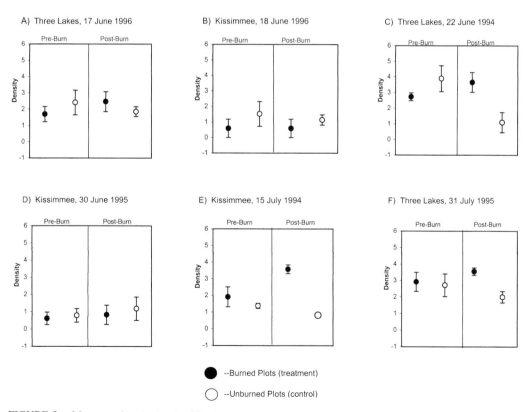

FIGURE 2. Mean number (± 1 SE) of Bachman's Sparrow territories per 10 ha ("Density") before and after summer prescribed fires. Graphs (A–F) are ordered by seasonal date of fire to show how timing of burning influenced sparrow response.

man's Sparrows may explain why they responded positively to late-season burns and Grasshopper Sparrows did not.

We think the year and site interaction we detected for both species was caused by the 1995 burn at Kissimmee Prairie where severe inundation resulted in low sparrow densities during this breeding season (Figs. 1 and 2D). For Grasshopper Sparrows, the inclusion of burn treatment in the interaction term is explained by the variability in sparrow densities in relation to the timing of fires.

Our previous research indicated that Grasshopper Sparrows on burned areas extended their breeding activity into September, whereas on unburned areas breeding ended in late July (Shriver et al. 1996). We have now documented that Florida Grasshopper Sparrows will successfully breed after mid-June burns, indicating that this species is not simply extending singing behavior but is actively breeding later into the season on summer-burn areas. This extension of the breeding season has important implications for endangered-species management and the long-term persistence of this subspecies. If this grassland ecosystem is adapted to summer fires, continuous winter burning may be not be the appropriate management tool for species endemic to this system.

We recommend incorporating mid-June burns into fire-management regimes where Florida Grasshopper and Bachman's sparrows coexist. Both sparrows responded favorably to mid-June burns, whereas only Bachman's Sparrows exhibited a positive response to late-season burns. These two species are sympatric throughout the range of the Florida Grasshopper Sparrow. Management practices that are adopted for the endangered Florida Grasshopper Sparrow therefore will inevitably affect and should benefit Bachman's Sparrows.

ACKNOWLEDGMENTS

This research was funded by the Natural Resource Flight at Avon Park Air Force Range, Avon Park, Florida, and The Nature Conservancy Lake Wales Ridge Office, Lake Wales, Florida. We thank L. Backus, J. Barret, C. Zan, R. Renfrew, E. Chapman, T. Dean, M. Scheuerell, C. Collins, and B. Pranty for help with data collection. S. Hedges and P. Gray of Kissimmee Prairie Sanctuary and the National Audubon Society, D. Darrow and the Three Lakes WMA staff, and B. Progulsky are all warmly acknowledged. Special thanks to S. Van Hook for his time, equipment, and expertise in prescribed fire. This manuscript benefited from careful review by D. Kroodsma, C. Griffin, R. Bowman, T. Engstrom, and J. Herkert.

LITERATURE CITED

BROOKS, M. 1938. Bachman's Sparrow in the northern portion of its range. Wilson Bulletin 50:86–109.

DELANY, M. F., AND J. A. COX. 1986. Florida Grasshopper Sparrow breeding distribution and abundance in 1984. Florida Field Naturalist 14:100–104.

DELANY, M. F., H. M. STEVENSON, AND R. MCCRACKEN. 1985. Distribution, abundance, and habitat of the Florida Grasshopper Sparrow. Journal of Wildlife Management 49:626–631.

DUNNING, J. B., AND B. D. WATTS. 1990. Regional differences in habitat occupancy by Bachman's Sparrow. Auk 107:463–472.

FEDERAL REGISTER. 1986. Endangered and threatened wildlife and plants; determination of endangered status of the Florida grasshopper sparrow. Federal Register 51(147):27492–27495.

FLORIDA NATURAL AREAS INVENTORY. 1990. Guide to the natural communities of Florida. Florida Natural Areas Inventory and Florida Department of Natural Resources, Tallahassee, FL.

HAGGERTY, T. M. 1986. Reproductive ecology of Bachman's Sparrow (Aimophila aestivalis) in central Arkansas. Ph.D. dissertation. University of Arkansas, Fayetteville, AR.

INTERNATIONAL BIRD CENSUS COMMITTEE. 1970. An international standard for a mapping method in bird census work recommended by the International Bird Census Committee. Audubon Field Notes 24:722–726.

LEWIS, C. E. 1964. Forage response to month of burning. USDA Forest Service Research Note SE-35. USDA Forest Service Southeastern Forest Experiment Station, Asheville, NC.

SHRIVER, W. G., P. D. VICKERY, AND S. A. HEDGES. 1996. Effects of summer burns on Florida Grasshopper Sparrows. Florida Field Naturalist 24:68–73.

SNYDER, J. R., A. HERNDON, AND W. B. ROBERTSON, JR. 1990. Pp. 230–274 in R. L. Myers and J. J. Ewel (editors). Ecosystems of Florida. University of Central Florida Press, Orlando, FL.

STODDARD, H. L. 1978. Birds of Grady County, Georgia. Bulletin of the Tall Timbers Research Station 21:1–175.

U. S. FISH AND WILDLIFE SERVICE. 1988. Recovery plan for Florida Grasshopper Sparrow. U.S. Fish and Wildlife Service, Atlanta, GA.

VICKERY, P. D., M. L. HUNTER, JR., AND J. V. WELLS. 1992. Use of a new reproductive index to evaluate relationship between habitat quality and breeding success. Auk 109:697–705.

WALSH, P. B., D. A. DARROW, AND J. G. DYESS. 1995. Habitat selection by Florida Grasshopper Sparrows in response to fire. Annual Conference of the Southeast Association of Fish and Wildlife Agencies 49: 342–349.

Studies in Avian Biology No. 19:149–159, 1999.

EFFECTS OF FIRE AND HERBICIDE TREATMENT ON HABITAT SELECTION IN GRASSLAND BIRDS IN SOUTHERN MAINE

PETER D. VICKERY, MALCOLM L. HUNTER, JR., AND JEFFREY V. WELLS

Abstract. We studied habitat selection of grassland birds nesting on a 240-hectare grassland in southern Maine. The site was commercially managed for blueberry (*Vaccinium*) production, which involved prescribed burning and herbicide spraying. These management practices profoundly affected vegetation physiognomy and influenced patterns of habitat selection of nesting species. There were clear differences in the types of habitat birds selected; four species preferred sites with both tall and short graminoid cover, whereas three species preferred sparse cover. Despite general similarities in each of these two groups, habitat selection for each species was generally characterized by a unique suite of vegetation features rather than distinct values for any particular habitat parameter.

Territory densities of five breeding species were strongly influenced by management practices at this site. Species that preferred grass cover were adversely affected by herbicide spraying; these effects persisted for two to six years, depending on the number of herbicide applications and the species. In particular, Eastern Meadowlark (*Sturnella magna*) densities had not recovered six years after spraying. In unsprayed plots, densities of six species declined with time since fire; densities of one species, Field Sparrow (*Spizella pusilla*), increased with time since fire; and densities of Eastern Meadowlarks were unaffected by time since fire.

LOS EFECTOS DEL FUEGO Y DEL TRATAMIENTO DE HERBICIDA EN LA SELECCIÓN DE HÁBITAT POR AVES DE PASTIZAL EN EL SUR DE MAINE

Sinopsis. Estudiamos la selección de hábitat por aves de pastizal en un prado en el sur de Maine. Se explotaba comercialmente el sitio para la producción del arándano (*Vaccinium*), que comprendía fuegos programados y fumigación con herbicidas. Estas prácticas de manejo afectaron profundamente la fisiognomía de la vegetación e influyeron en las normas de la selección de hábitat de las especies en anidaje. Hubo diferencias claras en los tipos de hábitat que las aves seleccionaron; cuatro especies prefirieron sitios con cobertura de hierbas alta y corta, mientras que tres especies prefirieron los de cobertura escasa. A pesar de las similitudes generales en cada uno de estos dos grupos, la selección de hábitat para cada especie se caracterizó por un conjunto único de rasgos vegetativos y no por valores distintos para algún parámetro de hábitat en particular. Las prácticas de manejo en este sitio influyeron en gran medida en las densidades de los territorios de cinco especies en reproducción. La fumigación de herbicidas afectó desfavorablemente las especies que prefirieron cobertura de hierbas; estos efectos persistieron por dos a seis años, según el número de aplicaciones de herbicidas y la especie. En particular, las densidades del Pradero Común (*Sturnella magna*) no se habían recuperado seis años después de las fumigaciones. En las parcelas sin fumigación, las densidades de seis especies disminuyeron con el tiempo después del fuego; las densidades de una especie, el Gorrión Llanaro (*Spizella pusilla*), aumentaron con el tiempo después del fuego; y las densidades del Pradero Común no experimentaron cambios con el tiempo después del fuego.

Key Words: burn; fire; grassland birds; habitat selection; herbicide spray; Maine.

Although extensive research has sought to determine what constitutes high-quality habitat for a wide variety of bird species (e.g., Cody 1985), various limitations to observed patterns of habitat occupancy have been described (Verner et al. 1986). These include inter- and intraspecific competition (Cody 1974; Diamond 1978; Rosenzweig 1981, 1985); population density (Fretwell and Lucas 1970; Zimmerman 1971; Wiens 1977, 1985; Karr and Freemark 1983); habitat area, shape, and isolation (Robbins 1979, Whitcomb et al. 1981, Robbins et al. 1989); site tenacity (Hildén 1965, Wiens and Rotenberry 1985); predation (Roseberry and Klimstra 1970, Slagsvold 1980); and anthropogenic factors (Robbins et al. 1986, Bollinger 1988).

In addition, resource abundance is often patchy, unpredictable, and not necessarily coincident with habitat structure (Rotenberry and Wiens 1980, Cody 1985). Thus, attraction to abundant, spatially variable resources may be more important than vegetation physiognomy when individuals select habitat. Finally, in some ecosystems there may be sufficient annual variation to make habitat selection more diffuse (Rotenberry and Wiens 1980); instead of a "single optimum expression of habitat selection, there may be an optimality plateau, within which various expressions of habitat selection may be adaptively equivalent" (Wiens 1985:244).

If vegetation and resources are highly variable in certain ecosystems and the linkage between a species and its habitat is imprecise, one would generally predict a broad "optimal plateau" for the species breeding in these ecosystems. Conversely, there may be a smaller "optimal plateau" for species breeding in more stable environments (Vickery et al. 1992a).

Controlled, manipulative studies of avian habitat use in grassland or shrubsteppe systems have often been limited by the size of the experimental units, which can make it difficult to predict population responses (Best 1972, Wiens and Rotenberry 1981, Morse 1985, Wiens et al. 1986, Petersen and Best 1987). In an effort to overcome this difficulty, we selected a broader spatial and temporal scale and established permanent plots, covering a total of 120 ha, which we followed for 8 yr. Commercial management of a native shrub, lowbush blueberry (*Vaccinium angustifolium*), for berry production in southern Maine used prescribed burning and herbicide spraying to reduce competing shrubs, graminoids, and forbs. These habitat manipulations profoundly affect the vegetation structure and composition (Yarborough and Bhowmik 1989) and thus provided the opportunity to conduct a partially controlled experiment on a scale that was large enough to elucidate some of the processes by which grassland birds occupy habitat.

METHODS

STUDY AREA AND HABITAT MANIPULATION

The study site, a 240-ha sandplain grassland situated on a broad glacial-marine delta with thick sand deposits, supports a xeric native flora, notably graminoids (poverty grass [*Danthonia spicata*], little bluestem [*Schizachyrium scoparium*], and sedge [*Carex pensylvanica*]), shrubs (lowbush blueberry and chokeberry [*Aronia* spp.]), and forbs (northern blazing star [*Liatris scariosa* var. *novae-angliae*], whorled loosestrife [*Lysimachia quadrifolia*], and goldenrod [*Solidago* spp.]; see Vickery et al. 1992b). The site is located in Kennebunk, York County, Maine (43°23′ N, 70°37′ W) and was managed for commercial blueberry production until 1987. During the first phase of our study (1984–1986), the site was managed on a biennial rotation; approximately 50% was mowed and burned each year (= burn-year plots). Blueberries were harvested in the portion that was burned the previous year (= production-year plots). Beginning in 1984, the herbicide hexazinone (Velpar®) was used at the rate of approximately 4 kg per ha to increase blueberry production by reducing or eliminating competing shrubs, forbs, and graminoids (Yarborough and Bhowmik 1989). Herbicide was applied in April, in the same cycle as the burning operation. In the second phase of the study (1987–1991), there was no active management for berry production.

EXPERIMENTAL DESIGN

We examined avian habitat occupancy at two different spatial scales: the scale of individual territories (1–5 ha for all species except Upland Sandpiper [*Bartramia longicauda*]) and the scale at which the habitat manipulation occurred (plot = 6–24 ha). For territo-

ries, defined as the number of males singing and defending small areas for 4 wk or more, we assessed whether each species selected particular physiognomic features by measuring nine habitat parameters for each territory. We then compared these measurements with measurements taken in unoccupied quadrats in the grassland.

We then wanted to see if densities were affected by large-scale habitat manipulations. If populations of grassland birds breeding at this site did respond to changes in habitat, we would expect changes in territory density to be reflected at the larger scale. If birds were not selecting particular features of the habitat, however, we would expect no clear relationship between territory density and blueberry management practices. To determine which, if either, of these alternatives predominated, we estimated territory density in relation to these habitat management practices. We could make this distinction because each treatment changed in space and time during the first phase of this study (1984–1986). We distinguished between breeding territory (= breeding site) fidelity and philopatry (= return to general breeding area) and recognized that use of territory density to elucidate patterns of habitat occupancy should not be equated with habitat quality (Van Horne 1983, Vickery et al. 1992c).

We placed 10 permanent plots (6–24 ha), covering 120 ha and marked into quadrats with a 50-m-interval grid, on different parts of the site. Plots were sited to fall within a particular management unit and were 50 m or more from any management border. To examine the relationship between occupancy and habitat structure, territories for each species were spot-mapped (International Bird Census Committee 1970) using at least 8 replicate censuses on 10 plots for the first 3 yr (1984–1986) of the study. We used counter-singing of neighboring males and presence on frequently used song perches to estimate the perimeter of each territory for each species during this period. A quadrat was defined as being in a male's territory if 50% or more of that territory fell within a quadrat. For Upland Sandpipers, we simply delineated high-use areas for each pair. In the second part of the study (1987–1991), we used three to six censuses to determine the number of territories per species per plot. The reduced number of censuses during this part of the study did not allow us to accurately delineate the shape and size of individual territories, but it did allow us to calculate the number of territories for each species per plot, which in turn enabled us to examine each species' pattern of habitat occupancy in this changing environment.

We followed avian occupancy patterns in three primary treatments: plots that had received zero, one, or two herbicide applications. We then followed the status of these plots for 8 yr. We were thus able to observe bird occupancy in plots all the way from burn year (N = 17) to 8 yr postburn (N = 1; Table 1). A burn-year plot was defined as a site in its first growing season immediately following a management burn. Because a burn-year plot became a production-year plot the following summer, it was impossible to follow burn-year treatment effects for more than 1 yr. For example, a plot that was burned in early spring 1984, and thus considered a burn-year plot during the 1984 breeding season, was a first-year production-year plot in 1985.

TABLE 1. NUMBER OF MANAGEMENT UNITS ON PLOTS AT KENNEBUNK, MAINE, 1984–1991

Years since burn	Herbicide application		
	0 spray	1 spray	2 sprays
0	8	6	3
1	12	7	3
2	4	3	3
3	4	3	3
4	4	3	3
5	4	1	1
6	1	1	0
7	1	0	0
8	1	0	0

If this plot was not burned in April 1986, it became a second-year production-year plot in 1986. Because early-successional habitats experience frequent disturbance regimes, we defined control plots as first-year production-year plots that had never been sprayed with herbicide (N = 12).

Vegetation cover was estimated visually for every 50- × 50-m quadrat during the first 3 yr of intensive study (1984–1986) using a modification of the Braun-Blanquet réleve method (Mueller-Dombois and Ellenberg 1974; for detailed description, see Vickery et al. 1992a). Thereafter, from 1987 to 1991, we used the same method for 30–50% of the quadrats in a checkerboard fashion. All estimates were conducted in mid-July and August, once vegetation growth had stabilized. Graminoid, forb, and shrub cover were estimated in three strata: 0–2 cm, >2–20 cm (short cover), and >20–60 cm (tall cover). Bare ground, litter, and lichen and moss were estimated in the 0- to 2-cm stratum. Because lowbush blueberry was a dominant shrub and its rhizomatous, matlike growth habit differed from that of other low shrubs, it was estimated separately in the >2- to 20-cm stratum. Vegetative cover was estimated in the following units: < 3 stems per quadrat; < 0.1%; 0.1–1%; >1–5%; >5–15%; >15–25%; >25–50%; >50–75%; and > 75%. Only vegetation parameters with more than 5% mean cover were used for analysis. Cover percentages were transformed to midpoint percentages, and these percentages were arcsin transformed for all parametric analyses (Zar 1984).

Bird species breeding at the site included Upland Sandpiper, Horned Lark (*Eremophila alpestris*), Field Sparrow (*Spizella pusilla*), Vesper Sparrow (*Pooecetes gramineus*), Savannah Sparrow (*Passerculus sandwichensis*), Grasshopper Sparrow (*Ammodramus savannarum*), Bobolink (*Dolichonyx oryzivorus*), and Eastern Meadowlark (*Sturnella magna*). Field Sparrows were present only in the second phase of the study (1987–1991), once active management at the site had ceased and the height and abundance of shrubs had increased.

Because commercial operators had been managing this site for many years, we were unable to make this a randomized experiment. Although we did not seek to influence blueberry management for avian or habitat-related reasons, we did negotiate with the blueberry managers to ensure that each permanent plot fell completely within an operational area of the management practice. Because the site was physiographically homogeneous and the vegetation prior to herbicide application was similar, we do not think failure to meet the assumption of randomness vitiated our results.

STATISTICAL ANALYSIS

We first used the detailed spot-map data (1984–1986) to determine which habitat variables were selected by each species (except Field Sparrow) breeding at this site. We used multivariate analysis of variance (ANOVA) to determine which vegetation parameters helped discriminate occupied habitat from unoccupied areas (Wilkinson 1990). Because species-habitat relationships were examined over a 3-yr period (1984–1986), and most treatments occurred in all 3 yr, we included the potential effect of annual variation (year effect) in this analysis (see Table 2 for sample sizes).

In a separate analysis, we used Spearman rank correlation to determine if specific habitat variables were associated with each species' density at the site. We used data from the entire study period (8 yr) for this analysis. To compensate for the possibility of increased Type I error for these eight analyses (one for each species), Bonferroni adjustment of significance level was set at P = 0.00625.

To examine habitat occupancy at the broader scale at which blueberry management occurred, we used repeated measure ANOVA to test for differences between territory density in plots that had never been sprayed with herbicide versus plots that had been sprayed once or twice (Wilkinson et al. 1996). Because sample sizes were notably uneven, especially 5–8 yr postburn (Table 1), this analysis was limited to the first 4 yr after the treatment, which was the period when differences, if they existed, were greatest. We then analyzed the importance of management effects for each year by contrasting specific management effects within the same year (Wilkinson 1990). We then used Spearman rank correlation to determine if territory densities for any of these species changed over time after burn/herbicide treatment. Because we were specifically interested in learning if Grasshopper and Savannah sparrow densities changed over time in unsprayed plots, we used repeated measures ANOVA to compare the first 4 yr postburn to the 5- to 8-yr postburn period.

RESULTS

EFFECTS OF BURNING AND HERBICIDE SPRAYING ON VEGETATION PHYSIOGNOMY

Burning and herbicide spraying had profound effects on grassland vegetation. Herbicide spraying reduced forb and short shrub cover for 3–4 yr (Fig. 1). Short shrub cover was greatly reduced on plots that were sprayed twice and began to recover only 4–6 yr postspray. Tall shrub cover was sharply reduced for 3 yr in plots that were sprayed twice but then increased more rapidly. This appeared to be an example of "vegetative release" common in herbicide applications in commercial forestry (Walstad and Kuch 1987). Herbicide application had a positive effect on blueberry cover for 3 yr. Thereafter, blueberry cover declined, probably as a result of

TABLE 2.　Vegetation Measurements (percent cover; mean ± SE) for Grassland Birds Breeding at Kennebunk, Maine, 1984–1986

Habitat parameters	Species					
	Upland Sandpiper		Horned Lark		Vesper Sparrow	
	Territory	Nonterritory	Territory	Nonterritory	Territory	Nonterritory
N	405	233	186	449	434	204
Bare ground	23.5 (0.9)	20.6 (0.7)	32.8 (1.2)[a,b]	27.3 (0.7)	31.8 (0.8)[a,b]	23.9 (1.0)
Litter	29.2 (0.8)[a,b]	33.6 (0.6)	33.4 (1.1)	31.4 (0.6)	30.9 (0.6)[a,b]	34.2 (1.0)
Graminoid (2–20 cm)	22.1 (0.8)	21.2 (0.6)	20.2 (0.9)[a]	24.1 (0.6)	21.2 (0.6)[a,b]	32.9 (0.5)
Graminoid (>20–60 cm)	20.9 (1.0)	23.5 (0.8)	21.5 (1.2)	22.4 (0.7)	20.9 (0.7)	22.4 (1.1)
Forb (2–20 cm)	15.3 (0.9)	15.1 (0.8)	14.9 (1.1)	15.3 (0.7)	15.0 (0.7)	15.5 (1.1)
Forb (>20–60 cm)	25.7 (0.9)	27.8 (0.8)	25.1 (1.1)	27.7 (0.7)	25.8 (0.7)	28.2 (1.0)
Blueberry	27.2 (1.1)[a]	31.9 (0.8)	31.7 (1.0)[a,b]	29.5 (0.8)	30.1 (0.8)	30.4 (1.1)
Shrub (2–20 cm)	15.4 (1.1)	17.0 (0.9)	11.6 (1.2)[a,b]	18.5 (0.8)	16.6 (0.8)[a]	20.5 (0.8)
Shrub (>20–60 cm)	21.7 (1.0)	23.6 (0.8)	17.1 (1.1)[a]	24.9 (0.7)	20.9 (0.7)	23.5 (1.1)

[a] Significant difference (P < 0.05) between territory and nonterritory.
[b] Significant difference (P < 0.05) in year effect.

increased competition with other plants (Fig. 1). Increased nutrient availability and reduced competition after fire appeared to benefit short and tall forbs in unsprayed plots (Wright and Bailey 1982, Smith et al. 1988). Tall graminoids also responded favorably to fire, but this effect was also apparent in plots that were sprayed (Fig. 1). Tall graminoids consisted primarily of little bluestem, which was the only grass species not adversely affected by spraying.

The decline in short shrubs in unsprayed plots 4 yr postburn was probably a result of successional effects; after 3 yr these shrubs grew into the tall shrub category (Fig. 1).

PATTERNS OF HABITAT SELECTION AT KENNEBUNK

Multivariate ANOVA revealed a major division in the way species occupied habitat at this site. Savannah and Grasshopper sparrows, Eastern Meadowlarks, and Bobolinks selected sites with greater amounts of both short and tall vegetation cover, particularly graminoid cover, whereas Upland Sandpipers, Horned Larks, and Vesper Sparrows preferred sites with generally sparse cover (Table 2). Savannah and Grasshopper sparrows, Bobolinks, and Eastern Meadowlarks all selected sites with significantly greater amounts of graminoid cover (Table 2). These four species also appeared to be more discriminating in their habitat requirements, or at least territories that were occupied by these species were described by a greater number of significant habitat parameters (Table 2). Savannah Sparrows selected areas with increased short graminoid, tall graminoid, and short forb cover and less litter, blueberry, short shrub, and tall shrub cover (Table 2). Grasshopper Sparrows chose habitat with increased short graminoid, tall forb, and short shrub cover and less litter

and blueberry cover. Bobolinks chose sites with increased tall graminoid, tall forb, and blueberry cover and reduced tall shrub cover (Table 2). Eastern Meadowlarks selected sites with increased short graminoid and shrub cover, both short and tall forb cover, and decreased litter and blueberry cover.

Selection of habitat by Horned Larks and Vesper Sparrows was similar. Both species chose sites with increased bare ground and reduced short graminoid and shrub cover. Vesper Sparrows also selected sites with increased litter cover, whereas Horned Larks were positively associated with increased blueberry cover (Table 2). In general, Upland Sandpipers were not highly selective but did occupy areas with sparse litter and blueberry cover (Table 2).

All seven species showed considerable year-to-year variation in the habitats they occupied. Overall, there was significant annual variation in 22 of 33 of the habitat parameters that showed differences between used and unoccupied habitat. These between-year differences ranged between 2.8 and 10.9%.

Although each species selected certain sites that were associated with particular vegetative characteristics, Spearman rank analysis revealed few clear correlations between a species' density and any habitat parameter. None of the four species associated with grass cover showed correlations with any habitat parameters. Upland Sandpiper densities were positively associated with bare ground (r_s = 0.457, P < 0.005) and were negatively associated with tall forbs (r_s = −0.531, P < 0.005) and tall shrubs (r_s = −0.734, P < 0.001). Horned Lark densities were negatively correlated with short graminoid cover (r_s = −0.532, P < 0.005) and tall forb (r_s = −0.466, P < 0.005) and tall shrub cover (r_s = −0.637, P < 0.005). Field Sparrow density was

TABLE 2. EXTENDED.

Species							
Savannah Sparrow		Grasshopper Sparrow		Bobolink		Eastern Meadowlark	
Territory	Nonterritory	Territory	Nonterritory	Territory	Nonterritory	Territory	Nonterritory
283	355	319	318	261	377	121	517
22.1 (1.0)	23.2 (0.6)	23.7 (0.9)	22.4 (0.6)	21.8 (0.8)	23.5 (0.7)	24.5 (1.2)	22.4 (0.6)
28.8 (0.8)[a,b]	33.2 (0.6)	28.6 (0.7)[a,b]	33.7 (0.7)	30.8 (0.6)	32.8 (0.7)	26.0 (0.8)[a,b]	33.4 (0.6)
29.3 (0.7)[a,b]	20.9 (0.6)	24.1 (0.8)[a,b]	20.2 (0.6)	21.8 (0.8)	21.3 (0.6)	27.1 (1.1)[a,b]	20.2 (0.5)
25.7 (1.0)[a]	21.0 (0.8)	22.6 (0.9)	20.9 (0.8)	23.4 (0.9)[a]	20.2 (0.8)	21.4 (1.0)	21.5 (0.7)
16.8 (1.1)[a,b]	14.5 (0.7)	14.6 (0.9)	15.4 (0.8)	15.8 (0.9)	14.7 (0.8)	18.3 (1.3)[a,b]	14.4 (0.7)
27.4 (1.0)	27.1 (0.7)	28.7 (0.9)[a,b]	26.3 (0.7)	29.5 (0.8)[a,b]	26.3 (0.8)	31.2 (1.1)[a,b]	26.2 (0.7)
26.7 (1.2)[a]	31.6 (0.8)	26.4 (1.0)[a]	30.3 (0.8)	32.6 (1.0)[a,b]	29.2 (0.9)	26.7 (1.4)[a]	31.0 (0.7)
18.2 (1.3)[a,b]	22.1 (0.7)	20.1 (1.2)[a,b]	16.1 (0.9)	17.1 (1.1)	15.9 (0.9)	20.2 (1.6)[a]	15.5 (0.7)
19.7 (1.1)[a]	22.9 (0.7)	20.6 (0.9)	22.9 (0.8)	24.1 (0.9)[a,b]	16.9 (0.8)	20.0 (1.2)	22.4 (0.7)

negatively associated with bare ground ($r_s = -0.551$, $P < 0.005$), tall graminoids ($r_s = -0.467$, $P < 0.005$), and tall forbs ($r_s = -0.512$, $P < 0.005$) and was positively associated with litter ($r_s = 0.603$, $P < 0.005$), short graminoids ($r_s = 0.663$, $P < 0.001$), and tall shrubs ($r_s = 0.519$, $P < 0.005$).

EFFECTS OF HABITAT MANIPULATION ON HABITAT SELECTION PATTERNS

Herbicide use reduced densities of Savannah and Grasshopper sparrows, Bobolinks, and Eastern Meadowlarks, whereas Horned Lark densities increased with herbicide use (Table 3). Herbicide use did not affect Upland Sandpiper or Vesper Sparrow densities (Table 3). In sprayed plots, Savannah Sparrow and Bobolink densities increased with time since burning and herbicide use, whereas Upland Sandpiper and Horned Lark densities declined with time since burning and herbicide use.

Burn effects

Prescribed burning reduced burn-year densities for Savannah and Grasshopper sparrows, Bobolinks, and Eastern Meadowlarks such that,

except for Savannah Sparrows, there was no difference between unsprayed and sprayed (1 or 2 herbicide applications) treatments; all four of these species showed similar declines on treated plots compared to control plots (Fig. 2). This decline persisted for only 1 yr for unsprayed plots, however (Fig. 2). Bobolink densities were highest in treated and control plots 1–2 yr post-burn.

Densities of Upland Sandpipers, Horned Larks, and Vesper Sparrows were generally greatest in the burn year or first year thereafter (Fig. 3). Horned Larks only occurred on burn-year plots in unsprayed areas (Fig. 3).

Herbicide effects

In plots sprayed with herbicide, territory densities were sharply reduced for the four species that were positively associated with graminoid cover (Fig. 2). Eastern Meadowlark densities were consistently greater in unsprayed than in sprayed plots (Fig. 2). Densities of Savannah Sparrows, Grasshopper Sparrows, and Bobolinks were also negatively affected by spraying, at least initially (Fig. 2). Depending on the spe-

TABLE 3. REPEATED MEASURES ANALYSIS OF VARIANCE FOR EFFECTS OF HERBICIDE USE ON GRASSLAND BIRD TERRITORY DENSITY AT KENNEBUNK, MAINE, 1984–1991

	Herbicide effect			
Species	df	F-ratio	P	Response to herbicide
Upland Sandpiper	2, 6	1.579	ns[a]	
Horned Lark	2, 6	5.639	0.035	+
Vesper Sparrow	2, 6	0.563	ns	
Savannah Sparrow	2, 6	9.451	0.014	−
Grasshopper Sparrow	2, 6	10.809	0.003	−
Bobolink	2, 6	9.454	0.014	−
Eastern Meadowlark	2, 6	28.013	0.001	−

[a] Nonsignificant ($P > 0.05$).

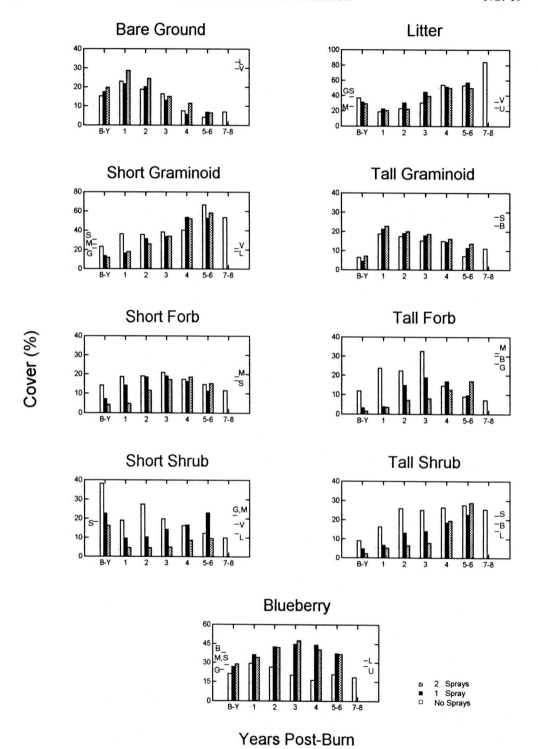

FIGURE 1.   Mean cover values (percent) of nine habitat variables measured at Kennebunk, Maine, 1984–1991. Depending on the number of applications, herbicide spray reduced cover of short graminoid, short and tall forbs, and short and tall shrubs for 2–6 yr. Letters and bars represent mean cover values of significant habitat variables associated with four species that preferred extensive graminoid cover (Savannah Sparrow [S], Grasshopper Sparrow [G], Eastern Meadowlark [M], and Bobolink [B]) and three species that preferred sparser cover (Upland Sandpiper [U], Horned Lark [L], and Vesper Sparrow [V]).

cies and number of herbicide applications, these effects persisted for 2–6 yr (Fig. 2).

Eastern Meadowlark densities appeared to be negatively affected by herbicide-induced reductions in short graminoid and short and tall forb cover and increases in blueberry cover (Fig. 1). Increased litter and decreased tall forb cover in years 5–8 did not seem to affect meadowlark densities, even though the birds selected habitat with reduced litter and greater tall forb cover (Fig. 1). This suggests that this species was tolerant of changes in these two parameters but that herbicide-induced reduction in short graminoid cover, coupled with increased blueberry cover, effectively limited habitat use by meadowlarks.

Savannah and Grasshopper sparrows displayed a similar pattern. As a result of herbicide spray, especially two applications, densities were reduced to levels that were similar to, or lower than, those found in unsprayed burn-year plots (Fig. 2). In sprayed plots, it took Savannah Sparrow densities 2–3 yr to recover to control-plot levels (Fig. 2). It took Grasshopper Sparrow densities 5 yr to recover to control-plot levels after spraying (Fig. 2). The number of herbicide applications (1–2) did not seem to affect the duration of this recovery period, though Grasshopper Sparrow densities were initially greater in plots that had been sprayed only once (Fig. 2). For both species, herbicide-induced decreases in short graminoid and short shrub cover apparently limited the amount of available habitat for 2 yr postspray. An increase in litter coupled with decreases in tall forb and short shrub cover appeared to affect Grasshopper Sparrows more than 4 yr postspray.

Bobolink densities in plots that were sprayed twice did not recover to control-plot densities until 5 yr after treatment (Fig. 2). The near absence of tall forbs and tall shrubs in these plots appeared to have a negative effect on Bobolinks for 4 yr (Fig. 2). The steady decline in tall graminoids and tall forbs (years 4–8) appeared to have a negative effect on Bobolink densities in unsprayed plots (Fig. 2).

Horned Larks occurred only in plots that were burned or burned and sprayed, or in production-year plots that had been recently sprayed; they never occurred in unsprayed production-year

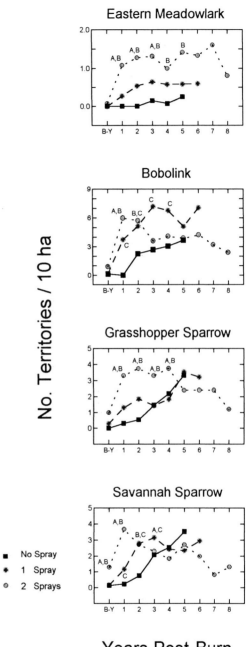

$\rightarrow$

FIGURE 2. Mean nesting densities of four species that were positively associated with graminoid cover were adversely affected by herbicide spray at Kennebunk, Maine, 1984–1991. Eastern Meadowlark densities had not recovered 6 yr after spraying. Depending on the number of herbicide applications, Grasshopper Sparrow, Savannah Sparrow, and Bobolink densities were reduced for 2–5 yr. "A" indicates difference (P < 0.05) between unsprayed and single-spray plots; "B" indicates difference between unsprayed plots and plots sprayed twice; "C" indicates difference between plots sprayed once versus twice. Irrespective of herbicide treatment (0, 1, or 2 applications), densities on burn-year plots differed (P < 0.05) from those on control plots (unsprayed 1 yr postburn). Standard errors (not shown) were less than 0.2 territories per 10 ha for all significant differences.

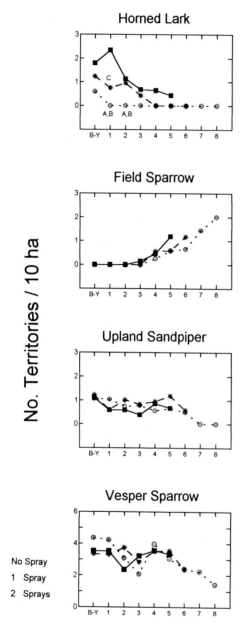

No. Territories / 10 ha

Horned Lark

Field Sparrow

Upland Sandpiper

Vesper Sparrow

■ No Spray
✳ 1 Spray
⊕ 2 Sprays

Years Post-Burn

FIGURE 3. Mean nesting densities of four species that were not adversely affected by herbicide use at Kennebunk, Maine, 1984–1991. Burning and spraying benefited Horned Larks; they occurred only in plots that had been recently burned or burned and sprayed. Field Sparrows did not nest in recently burned or sprayed plots but started to occupy territories 3 yr post-burn. "A" indicates difference (P < 0.05) between un-sprayed and single-spray plots; "B" indicates difference between unsprayed plots and plots sprayed twice;

plots (Fig. 3). Not surprisingly, extensive bare ground and reduced graminoid cover provided preferred habitat for Horned Larks (Table 2). Upland Sandpipers and Vesper Sparrows were unaffected by spraying (Fig. 3).

Successional effects

Savannah and Grasshopper sparrow densities in unsprayed plots declined notably 4–5 yr post-burn (Fig. 2). Grasshopper Sparrow densities in unsprayed plots were greater in the first 4 yr than in the latter 4 yr of the study (F = 4.871; df = 1, 3; P = 0.031); Savannah Sparrow densities displayed a similar pattern (F = 3.289; df = 1, 3; P = 0.074). Both species appeared to be adversely affected by the combination of increased litter and short graminoid cover and diminished short shrub cover 5–8 yr postfire (Fig. 1).

Upland Sandpiper, Horned Lark, and Vesper Sparrow densities generally declined as the time since the most recent fire increased (Fig. 3). In unsprayed areas, densities for all three species declined with time since the most recent burn (Upland Sandpiper: r_s = 0.255, P = 0.003; Horned Lark: r_s = 0.230, P = 0.004; Vesper Sparrow: r_s = 0.193, P = 0.01). It was likely that increased litter coupled with reductions in bare ground and increased tall shrub cover reduced habitat suitability for Upland Sandpipers (Fig. 1). The reduction in bare ground and increased litter cover and short graminoid cover appeared to reduce habitat suitability for Vesper Sparrows (Figs. 1 and 3).

Field Sparrows did not occur on recently burned or sprayed plots but occurred in low densities on plots 3 yr postburn; they increased steadily thereafter (r_s = 0.243, P = 0.002; Fig. 3). Densities were greater in sprayed plots 4–6 yr postspray than in unsprayed plots. This appeared to reflect the increased tall shrub cover, which this species prefers, in these plots (Evans 1978; Figs. 1 and 3).

DISCUSSION

HABITAT SELECTION BY GRASSLAND BIRDS

Grasshopper and Savannah sparrows, Bobolinks, and Eastern Meadowlarks all had similar cover values for significant, occupied habitat parameters. On average, these cover values were quite different from those for Upland Sandpip-

←

"C" indicates difference between plots sprayed once versus twice. Standard errors (not shown) were less than 0.02 territories per 10 ha for all significant differences.

ers, Horned Larks, and Vesper Sparrows (Table 2). Interestingly, the habitat for each species was defined by a unique set of significant vegetation parameters rather than any notably different measures of a shared habitat variable.

Although certain habitat parameters were closely associated with a species' occupancy of this site, there was significant between-year variation (3–10%) in cover values for more than half of these parameters. Wiens (1973) found similar variability for Grasshopper and Savannah sparrows in Wisconsin, suggesting flexibility in the habitat-selection process—an "optimality plateau" rather than a "single optimum expression of habitat selection" (Wiens 1985: 244).

The breadth and configuration of an "optimality plateau," however, may depend on the scale or resolution of the study (Wiens 1981). In our study, density was used to infer coarse-grain patterns of "acceptable" or "adequate" breeding habitat but not to make fine-grain distinctions of high-, medium-, or low-quality habitats (Van Horne 1983). Previous research at Kennebunk determined that there was less variability in vegetation cover values for highly successful territories compared with territories in general for three breeding Emberizid sparrows (Vickery et al. 1992a). Thus, a plateau that appears to be a flat tableland at a general level of resolution may in fact be more patchy and three-dimensional when examined at a finer scale.

EFFECTS OF BURNING AND HERBICIDE SPRAYING

Use of prescribed burns and herbicides had profound effects on vegetation physiognomy at Kennebunk, and these changes in turn affected patterns of territory occupancy by grassland birds.

Although prescribed burning reduced densities of nesting Grasshopper and Savannah sparrows, Bobolinks, and Eastern Meadowlarks, this effect was temporary and persisted for only 1 yr. Thus, for most species, burning appeared to be a key disturbance factor that led to high densities of these species over the subsequent 2–4 yr. The general pattern at Kennebunk was similar to the response to fire by the same species in North Dakota; populations were depressed immediately after burning but had highest densities 2–5 yr postfire and then gradually declined (Cody 1985, Johnson 1997). High burn frequency was also essential in creating and maintaining breeding habitat for Horned Larks. This disturbance, however, precluded Field Sparrows from establishing territories at Kennebunk; the species was not present until the latter years of our study (1987–1991) when active management had ceased and successional effects were apparent.

Herbicide spraying had a more prolonged effect on reducing population densities for Grasshopper and Savannah sparrows, Bobolinks, and Eastern Meadowlarks. Except for Eastern Meadowlarks, which had not recovered in 6 yr, there was a general pattern of recovery that took 2–6 yr depending on the number of herbicide applications. These results follow the same general pattern found in forest systems sprayed with herbicide; avian declines are usually short-term (see Lautenschlager 1991 for review).

There is a notable difference, however, between the use of herbicides in forestry and in blueberry agriculture. In forest conifer-release programs, herbicides are usually applied only once (Lautenschlager 1991), whereas they are usually applied biennially on commercial lowbush blueberry fields. Furthermore, many blueberry fields have been sprayed four or more times in the past decade. More than 90% of Maine's commercial blueberry fields have been sprayed with herbicide (D. Yarborough, pers. comm.), whereas less than 10% of Maine's forests have been sprayed (R. A. Lautenschlager, pers. comm.). Persistent biennial use of herbicides would presumably lead to permanent depression of breeding populations for at least five of the bird species we examined. Such declines are likely to have profound effects on populations of these species, several of which are rare or regionally threatened grassland birds (Vickery 1992, Vickery et al. 1994).

ACKNOWLEDGMENTS

The authors warmly acknowledge E. and O. Campbell and Coastal Blueberry, Inc., for permission to conduct this study on private land. Major financial support was provided to the primary author through Switzer Environmental Fellowships and Switzer Environmental Leadership Grants. Additional financial support was provided by The Nature Conservancy (Maine Chapter and Eastern Regional Office), Nongame Project of the Maine Department of Inland Fisheries and Wildlife, Maine Department of Agriculture (Board of Pesticides Control), F. I. Dupont, Inc., and Maine Audubon Society. The Massachusetts Audubon Society provided additional time and support for the project. W. Halteman provided assistance in data analysis. J. Gibbs, W. E. Glanz, J. R. Herkert, G. L. Jacobson, Jr., N. T. Wheelwright, A. S. White, J. L. Zimmerman, and an anonymous reviewer provided valuable suggestions. Critical logistical support was provided by D. Coonradt and B. Vickery. R. Denny and B. Vickery provided encouragement and support for which they are gratefully and warmly acknowledged.

LITERATURE CITED

BEST, L. B. 1972. First-year effects of sagebrush control on two sparrows. Journal of Wildlife Management 36:534–544.

BOLLINGER, E. K. 1988. Breeding dispersion and reproductive success of Bobolinks in an agricultural landscape. Ph.D. dissertation. Cornell University, Ithaca, NY.

CODY, M. L. 1974. Competition and the structure of bird communities. Princeton University Press, Princeton, NJ.

CODY, M. L. 1985. Habitat selection in grassland and open-country birds. Pp. 191–226 in M. L. Cody (editor). Habitat selection in birds. Academic Press, Orlando, FL.

DIAMOND, J. M. 1978. Niche shifts and the rediscovery of interspecific competition. American Scientist 66: 322–331.

EVANS, E. W. 1978. Nesting responses of Field Sparrows (*Spizella pusilla*) to plant succession on a Michigan old field. Condor 80:34–40.

FRETWELL, S. D., AND H. L. LUCAS, JR. 1970. On territorial behavior and other factors influencing habitat distribution in birds I. Theoretical development. Acta Biotheoretica 19:16–36.

HILDÉN, O. 1965. Habitat selection in birds. Annales Zoologica Fennica 2:53–75.

INTERNATIONAL BIRD CENSUS COMMITTEE. 1970. An international standard for a mapping method in bird census work recommended by the International Bird Census Committee. Audubon Field Notes 24:722–726.

JOHNSON, D. H. 1997. Effects of fire on bird populations in mixed-grass prairie. Pp. 181–206 in F. L. Knopf and F. B. Samson (editors). Ecology and conservation of Great Plains vertebrates. Springer-Verlag, New York, NY.

KARR, J. R., AND K. E. FREEMARK. 1983. Habitat selection and environmental gradients: dynamics in the "stable" tropics. Ecology 64:1481–1494.

LAUTENSCHLAGER, R. A. 1991. Response of wildlife in northern ecosystems to conifer release with herbicides. Maine Agricultural Experimental Station Miscellaneous Report 362, Orono, ME.

MORSE, D. H. 1985. Habitat selection in North American parulid warblers. Pp. 131–157 in M. L. Cody (editor). Habitat selection in birds. Academic Press, Orlando, FL.

MUELLER-DOMBOIS, D., AND H. ELLENBERG. 1974. Aims and methods of vegetation ecology. John Wiley and Sons, New York, NY.

PETERSEN, K. L., AND L. B. BEST. 1987. Effects of prescribed burning on nongame birds in a sagebrush community. Wildlife Society Bulletin 15:317–329.

ROBBINS, C. S. 1979. Effect of forest fragmentation on bird populations. Pp. 198–212 in R. M. DeGraaf and K. E. Evans (editors). Management of north central and northeastern forests for nongame birds. USDA Forest Service Gen. Tech. Rep. NC-51. USDA Forest Service North Central Forest Experimental Station, St. Paul, MN.

ROBBINS, C. S., D. BYSTRACK, AND P. H. GEISSLER. 1986. The Breeding Bird Survey: its first fifteen years, 1965–1979. U.S. Fish and Wildlife Service Resource Publication 157.

ROBBINS, C. S., D. K. DAWSON, AND B. A. DOWELL. 1989. Habitat area requirements of breeding forest birds of the middle Atlantic states. Wildlife Monographs 103:1–34.

ROSEBERRY, J. L., AND W. D. KLIMSTRA. 1970. The nesting ecology and reproductive performance of the Eastern Meadowlark. Wilson Bulletin 82:243–267.

ROSENZWEIG, M. L. 1981. A theory of habitat selection. Ecology 62:327–335.

ROSENZWEIG, M. L. 1985. Some theoretical aspects of habitat selection. Pp. 517–540 in M. L. Cody (editor). Habitat selection in birds. Academic Press, Orlando, FL.

ROTENBERRY, J. T., AND J. A. WIENS. 1980. Temporal variation in habitat structure and shrubsteppe bird dynamics. Oecologia 47:1–9.

SLAGSVOLD, T. 1980. Habitat selection in birds: on the presence of other bird species with special regard to *Turdus pilaris*. Journal of Animal Ecology 49:523–536.

SMITH, C. T., J. W. HORNBECK, AND M. L. McCORMACK, JR. 1988. Changes in nutrient cycling following aerial application of triclopyr to release spruce-fir. Proceedings of the Northeastern Weed Scientific Society 42:94–99.

VAN HORNE, B. 1983. Density as a misleading indicator of habitat quality. Journal of Wildlife Management 47:893–901.

VERNER, J., M. L. MORRISON, AND C. J. RALPH (EDITORS). 1986. Wildlife 2000: modeling habitat relationships of terrestrial vertebrates. University of Wisconsin Press, Madison, WI.

VICKERY, P. D. 1992. A regional analysis of endangered, threatened, and special-concern birds in the northeastern United States. Transactions of the Northeast Section of the Wildlife Society 48:1–10.

VICKERY, P. D., M. L. HUNTER, JR., AND S. M. MELVIN. 1994. Effects of habitat area on the distribution of grassland birds in Maine. Conservation Biology 8: 1087–1097.

VICKERY, P. D., M. L. HUNTER, JR., AND J. V. WELLS. 1992a. Use of a new reproductive index to evaluate relationship between habitat quality and breeding success. Auk 109:697–705.

VICKERY, P. D., M. L. HUNTER, JR., AND J. V. WELLS. 1992b. Evidence of incidental nest predation and its effects on nests of threatened grassland birds. Oikos 63:281–288.

VICKERY, P. D., M. L. HUNTER, JR., AND J. V. WELLS. 1992c. Is density an indicator of breeding success? Auk 109:706–710.

WALSTAD, J. D., AND P. J. KUCH. 1987. Forest vegetation management for conifer production. John Wiley and Sons, New York, NY.

WHITCOMB, R. F., C. S. ROBBINS, J. F. LYNCH, B. L. WHITCOMB, M. K. KLIMKIEWICZ, AND D. BYSTRAK. 1981. Effects of forest fragmentation on avifauna of the eastern deciduous forest. Pp. 125–205 in R. L. Burgess and D. M. Sharpe (editors). Forest island dynamics in man-dominated landscapes. Springer-Verlag, New York, NY.

WIENS, J. A. 1973. Interterritorial habitat variation in Grasshopper and Savannah sparrows. Ecology 54: 877–884.

WIENS, J. A. 1977. On competition and variable environments. American Scientist 65:590–597.

WIENS, J. A. 1981. Scale problems in avian censusing. Studies in Avian Biology 6:513–521.

WIENS, J. A. 1985. Habitat selection in variable environments: shrub-steppe birds. Pp. 227–251 in M. L.

Cody (editor). Habitat selection in birds. Academic Press, New York, NY.

WIENS, J. A., AND J. T. ROTENBERRY. 1981. Habitat associations and community structure of birds in shrubsteppe environments. Ecological Monographs 5:21–41.

WIENS, J. A., AND J. T. ROTENBERRY. 1985. Response of breeding passerine birds to rangeland alteration in a North American shrubsteppe locality. Journal of Applied Ecology 22:655–668.

WIENS, J. A., J. T. ROTENBERRY, AND B. VAN HORNE. 1986. A lesson in the limitations of field experiments: shrubsteppe birds and habitat alteration. Ecology 67:365–376.

WILKINSON, L. 1990. Systat: the system for statistics. Systat, Inc., Evanston, IL.

WILKINSON, L., G. BLANK, AND C. GRUBER. 1996. Desktop data analysis with Systat. Prentice-Hall, Englewood Cliffs, NJ.

WRIGHT, H. A., AND A. W. BAILEY. 1982. Fire ecology: United States and southern Canada. John Wiley and Sons, New York, NY.

YARBOROUGH, D. E., AND P. C. BHOWMIK. 1989. Effect of hexazinone on weed populations and on lowbush blueberries in Maine. Acta Horticulturae 241:344–349.

ZAR, J. H. 1984. Biostatistical analysis. Prentice-Hall, Englewood Cliffs, NJ.

ZIMMERMAN, J. L. 1971. The territory and its density dependent effect on *Spiza americana.* Auk 88:591–612.

Studies in Avian Biology No. 19:160–164, 1999.

HENSLOW'S SPARROW RESPONSE TO PRESCRIBED FIRE IN AN ILLINOIS PRAIRIE REMNANT

James R. Herkert and William D. Glass

Abstract. We studied the effects of prescribed fire on Henslow's Sparrows (*Ammodramus henslowii*) breeding in a native prairie remnant in northeastern Illinois in 1991–1996. Portions of this prairie were burned in four of the six years of our study. Henslow's Sparrow distributions were influenced by time since the last fire and location in the prairie (census-point effect). Sparrows usually did not occur in burned areas during the first growing season postfire and colonized adjacent unburned sections of the prairie as other sections were burned. Henslow's Sparrows were rarely recorded at some census points regardless of their burn history. The birds appeared to exhibit a hierarchical pattern of habitat occupancy, with use of secondary portions of the prairie being greatest in years of high overall abundance or when burning made primary areas unsuitable. Sparrow abundance tended to increase in years when spring precipitation in the current year exceeded that of the preceding year and to decline in years when spring precipitation declined. Although Henslow's Sparrows were sensitive to fire, our data suggest that numbers can be maintained, and even increased, on large prairies actively managed with prescribed fire.

LA RESPUESTA DEL GORRIÓN DE HENSLOW A INCENDIOS PROGRAMADOS EN UN REMANENTE DE LLANURA EN ILLINOIS

Sinopsis. Estudiamos los efectos de incendios programados para el Gorrión de Henslow (*Ammodramus henslowii*) en reproducción en un remanente de llanura nativa en el noreste de Illinois entre 1991 y 1996. Se quemaron porciones de esta llanura en cuatro de los seis años de nuestro estudio. El tiempo desde el último incendio y la ubicación en la llanura (efecto del punto de censo) influyeron en las distribuciones del Gorrión de Henslow. Normalmente no había gorriones en áreas quemadas durante la primera estación de cultivo después del incendio, por lo que colonizaron secciones contiguas no quemadas en la llanura cuando se incendiaron otras secciones. Raramente se registraron Gorriones de Henslow en algunos puntos de censo, a pesar de su experiencia de quema. Parecía que las aves exhibieron un sistema jerárquico de ocupación de hábitat, con un uso mayor de porciones secundarias de la llanura durante los años de alta abundancia general o cuando las quemas convirtieron las áreas primarias en zonas inadecuadas. Cuando la precipitación en la primavera del año en curso sobrepasó la del año anterior la abundancia de gorriones tendía a aumentar; por el contrario, cuando la precipitación en la primavera disminuyó, la abundancia de gorriones tendía a disminuir. Aunque los Gorriones de Henslow fueron sensibles al fuego, nuestros datos sugirieron que se puede mantener las cifras de gorriones, e incluso aumentarlas, en llanuras grandes controladas activamente con incendios programados.

Key Words: Ammodramus henslowii; habitat selection; Henslow's Sparrow; Illinois; prescribed fire.

Henslow's Sparrows (*Ammodramus henslowii*) breed in the northeastern and eastcentral United States and southern Canada (Hands et al. 1989). Populations are scattered and local in distribution, however, throughout the breeding range (Pruitt 1996). Since the late 1960s, populations have declined (Sauer et al. 1996, Herkert 1997, Peterjohn and Sauer 1999) and the breeding range of this species is currently contracting, particularly in the northeast and eastern portions of the range (Pruitt 1996). Loss and degradation of grassland habitats are thought to be major factors contributing to these declines (Pruitt 1996). Because of this species' overall rarity and declining populations, its rangewide population status is uncertain (U.S. Fish and Wildlife Service 1995, Pruitt 1996). As a result, it is important to understand more fully this species' breeding ecology.

Henslow's Sparrows prefer tall, dense grasslands with well-developed litter and standing dead residual vegetation (Wiens 1969, Robins 1971, Skinner et al. 1984, Zimmerman 1988, Sample 1989, Herkert 1994, Mazur 1996). Several commonly employed grassland-management activities, such as prescribed fire, grazing, and mowing, generally remove or reduce tall, dense vegetation and/or litter and frequently lead to short-term reductions in Henslow's Sparrows (e.g., Skinner et al. 1984, Zimmerman 1988, Sample 1989, Herkert 1994, Swengel 1996). In some situations, prescribed fire may even extirpate populations from small sites (e.g., Minney 1994). Although fire is known to reduce Henslow's Sparrow numbers at the local level (i.e., within particular transects; Zimmerman 1988, Herkert 1994, Swengel 1996), little is known about how this species responds to fire at broader scales.

To effectively design and implement conservation strategies to benefit Henslow's Sparrows, a more thorough understanding of this species' broad-scale response to prescribed fire and other common grassland-management practices is needed. Our study examined the site-level response of Henslow's Sparrows to prescribed burning on a large native-prairie remnant in Illinois.

METHODS

We studied the effects of prescribed fire on Henslow's Sparrows between 1991 and 1996 at Goose Lake Prairie State Natural Area, a 650-plus-ha tallgrass-prairie remnant in Grundy County, northeastern Illinois. The study area was divided into three burn units, and portions of it were burned in 4 of the 6 yr of our study. The northwest (NW) burn unit was approximately 300 ha and was burned twice during the study; the entire unit was burned in 1992, and 240 ha were burned in 1996. The southern (S) burn unit was approximately 125 ha and was burned once, in 1993. The northeast (NE) burn unit was approximately 250 ha and was burned once, in 1994.

We surveyed Henslow's Sparrows using 10-min point counts. We conducted 11 point counts two to three times each year between 23 May and 12 July at permanently marked locations evenly distributed at approximately 0.8-km intervals. At each point we recorded all singing males detected. Because Henslow's Sparrows are rarely detected beyond 150 m of census points (J. R. Herkert and S. K. Robinson, unpubl. data), we could not have detected males at more than one census point.

We used one-way analysis of variance (ANOVA) to test the effect of prescribed fire on relative abundance of Henslow's Sparrows. Each census point was classified into one of five burn categories based on the time since last burning. Burn 1 sites had been burned the previous April (1–2 mo before censusing); Burn 2 sites were entering their second growing season postfire (13–14 mo postfire at the time of censusing); Burn 3 sites were entering their third growing season postfire (25–26 mo); Burn 4 sites were entering their fourth growing season postfire (37–38 mo); and Burn 5 sites had not been burned in more than 4 yr. Because Henslow's Sparrows were not uniformly distributed in the study area and their numbers varied from year to year, census points and years were used as blocking variables in the ANOVA model.

In 1995 and 1996 we sampled vegetation at all census points and recorded vegetation height-density, litter depth, and shrub/tree density. Height-density was measured at 10 randomly located sites at each census point using a Robel pole (Robel et al. 1970). At each sample location we recorded the height at which 90% of the pole (approximately 2.5 cm wide, 1.5 m high, and marked in 10-cm intervals) became obscured by vegetation from a viewing distance of 4 m in each of the four cardinal directions. Litter depth was measured (in centimeters) as the distance between the ground and the top of the horizontal litter layer at 40 randomly located points at each census point. Shrub/tree density was measured by counting all shrubs or trees taller than 2 m and within 100 m of the census point. We

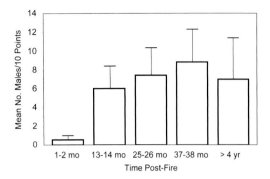

FIGURE 1.   Mean number ($\pm$ SE) of Henslow's Sparrow males recorded at census points in different years postfire. Burn 1 = 1–2 mo postfire, Burn 2 = 13–14 mo postfire, Burn 3 = 25–26 mo postfire, Burn 4 = 37–38 mo postfire, and Burn 5 = > 4 yr postfire.

used a t-test to compare vegetation features at census points where Henslow's Sparrows were recorded with points where the species was not recorded and to compare vegetation features between burned (Burn 1) and unburned (Burns 2–5) areas.

We examined the potential effect of precipitation on Henslow's Sparrow abundance by comparing sparrow abundance at the site with three measures of precipitation: annual (1 June previous year to 31 May current year), January–April (1 January–31 April), and April–May (1 April–31 May). Precipitation data were collected at the Channahon Recording Station, approximately 10 km east of the study area.

RESULTS

Henslow's Sparrow distributions were significantly influenced by burning (F = 3.49; df = 1, 49; P = 0.0010) and location in the prairie (census-point effect; F = 4.44; df = 10, 49; P < 0.0002). Preliminary analyses indicated that abundance among Burn 2, Burn 3, Burn 4, and Burn 5 areas did not differ (P > 0.20), so these categories were combined for analyses (Burn 2+, including results reported above). Henslow's Sparrows were generally absent from recently burned areas (Burn 1; Fig. 1). Their relative abundance in Burn 2 areas (second season postfire) was approximately 10 times greater than it was in Burn 1 areas but approximately 20% lower than it was in Burn 3 areas (third season postfire; Fig. 1). Henslow's Sparrow numbers at the study site increased between 1991 and 1996, with peak numbers recorded in 1995 (Fig. 2).

Henslow's Sparrows were not uniformly distributed among census points, and they were rarely recorded at some census points regardless of their burn history. For example, census points in the NW burn unit consistently had higher sparrow numbers than did census points in other burn units, except in years when the NW unit was burned (Fig. 3).

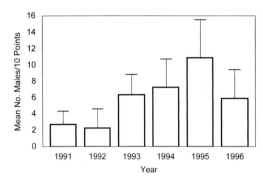

FIGURE 2. Mean number (± SE) of Henslow's Sparrow males recorded at census points at Goose Lake Prairie, Illinois, 1991–1996.

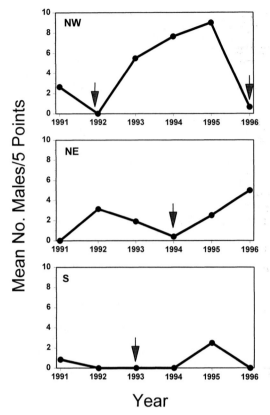

FIGURE 3. Mean number of Henslow's Sparrow males in three burn units at Goose Lake Prairie, Illinois, 1991–1996. The NW burn unit was approximately 300 ha and contained five census points; the NE burn unit was approximately 250 ha and contained four census points; and the S burn unit was approximately 125 ha and contained two census points. The NW burn unit was burned in 1992 and 1996, the NE unit in 1994, and the S unit in 1993.

Our comparison of vegetation features in 1995–1996 found little difference in vegetation height-density or litter depth between occupied and unoccupied census points during these 2 yr (Table 1). Density of tall (≥ 2 m) shrubs and/or trees was more than 70% greater at unoccupied sites than it was at occupied sites (Table 1). Burning reduced vegetation height-density and litter depth (Table 2).

Variation in annual abundance of Henslow's Sparrows in the three burn units suggests that this species colonized adjacent unburned sections of prairie when other sections were burned (Fig. 3). Sparrow densities in the NE burn unit showed three increases of more than 50% (1992, 1995, 1996; Fig. 3). Two of these years (1992, 1996) were years in which the adjacent NW burn unit was burned. The third year, 1995, was the year the NE burn unit changed from Burn 1 to Burn 2 and was also the year of highest overall sparrow abundance (Fig. 2). The only increase of more than 50% in the NW burn unit was in 1993, following the 1992 burn of the NW unit and coincident with the 1993 burn of the S burn unit. A smaller increase (approximately 40%) was observed in the NW burn unit in 1994, the year the adjacent NE unit was burned. No apparent shifts in sparrow numbers in the S burn unit were evident in relation to burning in adjacent blocks, although use of this unit also was highest in 1995, the year of highest overall abundance (Fig. 3).

Annual Henslow's Sparrow abundance was most strongly associated with total January–April precipitation ($r = 0.51$, $P = 0.296$, $N = 6$

TABLE 1. COMPARISON OF HABITAT FEATURES BETWEEN OCCUPIED AND UNOCCUPIED CENSUS POINTS AT GOOSE LAKE PRAIRIE, ILLINOIS, 1995–1996

	Occupied (N = 10)		Unoccupied (N = 10)			
	Mean	(SE)	Mean	(SE)	t	P
Height-density (VOR[a])	3.4	(0.2)	3.6	(0.3)	0.37	0.72
Litter depth (cm)	3.5	(0.7)	3.5	(0.8)	0.01	0.99
Shrub density (no./3.1 ha)	3.6	(1.9)	6.2	(2.0)	0.92	0.37

Note: Figures are vegetative means and standard errors (SE) for measurements taken at census points where Henslow's Sparrows were either present or absent. Comparisons between means were conducted with a t-test.

[a] VOR = Visual Obstruction Reading.

TABLE 2.   COMPARISON OF HABITAT FEATURES BETWEEN BURNED AND UNBURNED CENSUS POINTS AT GOOSE LAKE PRAIRIE, ILLINOIS, 1995–1996

	Burned (N = 4)		Unburned (N = 16)			
	Mean	(SE)	Mean	(SE)	t	P
Height-density (VOR[a])	2.7	(0.1)	3.7	(0.2)	3.7	0.002
Litter depth (cm)	2.1	(0.7)	4.2	(0.6)	2.0	0.062

Note: Figures are vegetative means and standard errors (SE) for measurements taken at census points where Henslow's Sparrows were either present or absent and for measurements taken in burned (Burn 1) and unburned (Burn 2–5) areas. Comparisons between means were conducted with a t-test. Shrub density was not compared between burned and unburned points since burning did not have an immediate effect on shrubs or trees taller than 2 m.
[a] VOR = Visual Obstruction Reading.

yr). Sparrow abundance generally increased in years when spring precipitation in the current year exceeded that of the preceding year and declined when there was less spring precipitation (Fig. 4). Precipitation also may have influenced sparrow abundance following burning; abundance in Burn 1 areas was highest in the wettest burn year (1996) and lowest in the driest burn year (1992; Fig. 5).

DISCUSSION

Henslow's Sparrows shifted their distributions in response to prescribed burning, colonizing adjacent unburned areas as portions of the prairie were burned. Their use of management units peaked when adjacent burn units were burned; abundances in both the NE and NW burn units were generally high in years when an adjacent burn unit had been burned (Fig. 3).

Henslow's Sparrows appeared to exhibit a hierarchical pattern of habitat occupancy (see O'Connor 1981). Use of secondary portions of the study site (NE and S burn units) was greatest in years of high overall sparrow abundance (e.g., 1995) or in years when burning made the principal area (NW burn unit, based on abundance) unsuitable. In both years when the NW burn unit was burned, Henslow's Sparrow numbers on the adjacent NE burn unit increased by more than 50%. Although these data suggest a shifting population, a study of a marked population of birds at this site would be necessary to establish this pattern conclusively.

The avoidance of recently burned sections of prairie exhibited by Henslow's Sparrows in our study is consistent with previous work (Zimmerman 1988, 1992; Herkert 1994). Recolonization of this species following burning (Fig. 1) was more rapid in our study, however, than was previously reported for this site (e.g., Herkert 1994). Herkert (1994) previously reported that Henslow's Sparrow densities in prairie areas in their second season postfire were less than half that of areas in their third or greater growing season postfire. In this study, Henslow's Sparrow numbers were only 20% lower in prairie areas in their second season postfire than they were in areas in their third season postfire, and 32% lower than they were in areas in their fourth season postfire (Fig. 1).

Local features also played a role in determining distribution patterns. Some census points rarely had sparrows, regardless of the management history of the surrounding area. Local fea-

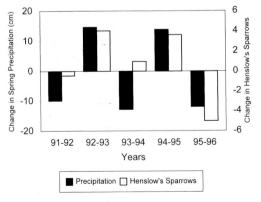

FIGURE 4.   Relationship between changes in Henslow's Sparrow abundance and January–April precipitation. Numbers represent changes in precipitation (centimeters) and in Henslow's Sparrows (mean total abundance) between successive years.

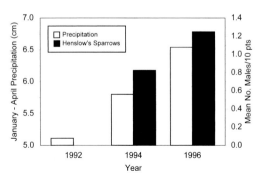

FIGURE 5.   Henslow's Sparrow abundance in burn-year (Burn 1) areas in relation to January–April precipitation (centimeters).

tures that make some portions of this prairie more attractive than others for this species are not well understood. Sparrows at this site appeared to favor the NW management unit; at least estimated densities in this area were higher than they were in other sections. Our analyses of vegetation features among occupied and unoccupied areas in 1995–1996 suggest that differences in vegetation height-density or litter depth, two factors reported to strongly influence Henslow's Sparrow abundance (Zimmerman 1988, Herkert 1994), were probably not responsible for differences in abundance among particular census points, since there was little difference in these variables between occupied and unoccupied areas (Table 1). These data suggest that there may be structurally suitable habitat at this site that is unoccupied in some years.

Even though large portions (up to 300 ha) of this prairie were burned in 4 of 6 yr, the overall Henslow's Sparrow population at this site increased during our study (Fig. 2). This trend suggests that burning did not have an adverse effect on sparrows at this site when assessed at a broad scale, and that although this species was sensitive to burning, numbers can be maintained and even increased on large prairies actively managed with prescribed fire. Maintaining Henslow's Sparrow numbers on a site may be accomplished by using a rotational burning system in which small portions (usually no more than 20–30%) of a given site are burned in any particular year. Burn units should also be designed to ensure that areas known to be suitable for Henslow's Sparrows are available (in the appropriate burn status) in all burn-rotation situations. Managers interested in Henslow's Sparrow management should avoid burning all portions of an area known to be used by this species in the same year.

Additional research is needed to assess the response of Henslow's Sparrows to prescribed burns on smaller prairies. Until more is known about the broad-scale movements of this species in smaller prairies, caution should be applied when burning small sites known to support breeding Henslow's Sparrows.

ACKNOWLEDGMENTS

We thank the Illinois Department of Natural Resources and Illinois Nature Preserves Commission for allowing us to work at Goose Lake Prairie. We also thank the Illinois Water Survey for providing us with precipitation data. L. Igl, P. D. Vickery, and one anonymous reviewer provided us many helpful comments on an earlier version of this manuscript.

LITERATURE CITED

HANDS, H. M., R. D. DROBNEY, AND M. R. RYAN. 1989. Status of the Henslow's Sparrow in the northcentral United States. U.S. Fish and Wildlife Service, Twin Cities, MN.

HERKERT, J. R. 1994. Status and habitat selection of the Henslow's Sparrow in Illinois. Wilson Bulletin 106:35–45.

HERKERT, J. R. 1997. Population trends of the Henslow's Sparrow in relation to the Conservation Reserve Program in Illinois, 1975–1995. Journal of Field Ornithology 68:235–244.

MAZUR, R. 1996. Implications of field management for Henslow's Sparrow habitat at Saratoga National Historic Park, New York. M.S. thesis. State University of New York, Syracuse, NY.

MINNEY, D. 1994. Breeding Bird Census: tallgrass prairie remnant. Journal of Field Ornithology 65 (supplement):123.

O'CONNOR, R. J. 1981. Habitat correlates of bird distribution in British census plots. Studies in Avian Biology 6:533–537.

PETERJOHN, B. G., AND J. R. SAUER. 1999. Population status of North American grassland birds from the North American Breeding Bird Survey, 1966–1996. Studies in Avian Biology 19:27–44.

PRUITT, L. 1996. Henslow's Sparrow status assessment. U. S. Fish and Wildlife Service, Bloomington Field Office, Bloomington, IN.

ROBEL, R. J., J. N. BRIGGS, A. D. DAYTON, AND L. C. HULBERT. 1970. Relationships between visual obstruction measurements and weight of grassland vegetation. Journal of Range Management 23:295–297.

ROBINS, J. D. 1971. A study of Henslow's Sparrow in Michigan. Wilson Bulletin. 83:39–48.

SAMPLE, D. W. 1989. Grassland birds in southern Wisconsin: habitat preference, population trends, and response to land use changes. M.S. thesis. University of Wisconsin, Madison, WI.

SAUER, J. R., S. SCHWARTZ, B. G. PETERJOHN, AND J. E. HINES. 1996. The North American Breeding Bird Survey home page. Ver. 94.3: www.mbr.nbs.gov/bbs/bbs96t3.htm. U.S. Geological Survey, Patuxent Wildlife Research Center, Laurel, MD.

SKINNER, R. M., T. S. BASKETT, AND M. D. BLENDEN. 1984. Bird habitat on Missouri prairies. Terrestrial series #14, Missouri Department of Conservation, Jefferson City, MO.

SWENGEL, S. R. 1996. Management response of three species of declining sparrows in tallgrass prairie. Bird Conservation International 6:241–253.

U.S. FISH AND WILDLIFE SERVICE. 1995. Migratory nongame birds of management concern in the United States: the 1995 list. U.S. Fish and Wildlife Service, Office of Migratory Bird Management, Washington, D.C.

WIENS, J. A. 1969. An approach to the study of ecological relationships among grassland birds. Ornithological Monographs no. 8.

ZIMMERMAN, J. L. 1988. Breeding season habitat selection by the Henslow's Sparrow (Ammodramus henslowii) in Kansas. Wilson Bulletin 100:17–24.

ZIMMERMAN, J. L. 1992. Density-independent factors affecting the avian diversity of the tallgrass prairie community. Wilson Bulletin 104:85–94.

Studies in Avian Biology No. 19:165–170, 1999.

EFFECTS OF PRESCRIBED BURNING AND GRAZING ON NESTING AND REPRODUCTIVE SUCCESS OF THREE GRASSLAND PASSERINE SPECIES IN TALLGRASS PRAIRIE

RONALD W. ROHRBAUGH, JR., DAN L. REINKING, DONALD H. WOLFE, STEVE K. SHERROD, AND M. ALAN JENKINS

Abstract. In 1992 the George M. Sutton Avian Research Center initiated a five-year project to examine the nesting ecology of birds using tallgrass-prairie habitats in Oklahoma. The project was designed to help determine why grassland bird populations in the southern Great Plains are experiencing widespread and rapid declines. One of our objectives was to determine the effects of contemporary fire and grazing regimes on the nesting ecology of birds breeding in tallgrass prairie. From 1993 to 1995 we monitored nests on six 16.2-hectare plots at The Nature Conservancy's Tallgrass Prairie Preserve in Osage County, Oklahoma. Three of these plots were undisturbed (unburned and ungrazed), and three were disturbed (burned and/or grazed) during each year of the study. We monitored nesting success, clutch size, and fledging rates at each of 313 Eastern Meadowlark (*Sturnella magna*), Grasshopper Sparrow (*Ammodramus savannarum*), and Dickcissel (*Spiza americana*) nests on the six plots. We observed 42, 12, and 87 Eastern Meadowlark, Grasshopper Sparrow, and Dickcissel nests, respectively, on undisturbed plots and 60, 26, and 86 nests, respectively, on disturbed plots. On undisturbed plots, the average Mayfield probabilities of nesting success for the incubation and brood-rearing periods combined were 0.17, 0.17, and 0.19 for Eastern Meadowlarks, Grasshopper Sparrows, and Dickcissels, respectively; the average probabilities of success on disturbed plots were 0.07, 0.06, and 0.06, respectively. Clutch sizes and fledging rates from successful nests were not statistically different between plot types. These results suggest that physiologically the reproductive performance of these species was not affected by burning and grazing; however, rates of nesting success for Eastern Meadowlarks and Dickcissels may be negatively affected by these activities. Through cooperative efforts with private landowners, we are currently developing management recommendations to mitigate the effects of burning and grazing on these species.

LOS EFECTOS DE FUEGO PROGRAMADO Y DE APACENTAMIENTO EN EL NIDAJE Y EN EL ÉXITO REPRODUCTIVO DE TRES ESPECIES PASERIFORMES DE PASTIZAL EN PRADERA DE HIERBA ALTA

Sinopsis. En 1992 el Centro George M. Sutton de Investigaciones Avícolas inició un proyecto de cinco años para examinar la ecología del nidaje de aves que utilizan hábitats en las praderas de hierba alta en Oklahoma. Se diseñó el proyecto para determinar por qué las poblaciones de aves de pastizal en el sur de la Gran Llanura experimentan rápidas y extensas disminuciones. Uno de nuestros objetivos fue determinar los efectos de regímenes contemporáneos de fuego y de apacentamiento en la ecología del nidaje de aves que se reproducen en pradera de hierba alta. Entre 1993 y 1995 vigilamos nidos en seis parcelas de 16,2 hectáreas en la Reserva de Pradera de Hierba Alta de The Nature Conservancy en el Condado de Osage, Oklahoma. Tres de estas parcelas no fueron alteradas (ausencia de fuego y de apacentamiento), y tres fueron alteradas (con fuego y/o con apacentamiento) durante cada año del estudio. Recolectamos datos del éxito de los nidos, del tamaño de la nidada y del número de polluelos volantones en 313 nidos del Pradero Común (*Sturnella magna*), del Gorrión Chapulín (*Ammodramus savannarum*) y del Arrocero Americano (*Spiza americana*) en las seis parcelas. Observamos 42, 12 y 87 nidos del Pradero Común, del Gorrión Chapulín y del Arrocero Americano, respectivamente, en parcelas sin alteraciones y 60, 26 y 86 nidos, respectivamente, en parcelas con alteraciones. En las parcelas sin alteraciones, las probabilidades promedio Mayfield de éxito del nido para los períodos combinados de incubación y de cría fueron 0,17, 0,17 y 0,19 para los Praderos Comunes, los Gorriones Chapulines y los Arroceros Americanos, respectivamente; las probabilidades promedio de éxito en las parcelas con alteraciones fueron 0,07, 0,06 y 0,06, respectivamente. Los tamaños de la nidada y los números de polluelos volantones de los nidos exitosos no se diferenciaron estadísticamente entre los tipos de parcela. Estos resultados indican que la capacidad reproductiva de estas especies no fue influida fisiológicamente por el fuego o por el apacentamiento; sin embargo, el éxito de los nidos de los Praderos Comunes y de los Arroceros Americanos puede ser influido negativamente por estas actividades. Hoy estamos elaborando recomendaciones de manejo por medio de colaboraciones con los propietarios, para atenuar los efectos del fuego y del apacentamiento en estas especies.

Key Words: fire; grazing; nest success; prescribed burning; tallgrass prairie.

Grassland birds are declining faster than any other behavioral or ecological group of avian species in North America (Knopf 1994, Peterjohn et al. 1994). Biologists have postulated several reasons for the geographically widespread and precipitous decline of grassland birds, including habitat loss, changes in agricultural and ranching practices, pesticide use, and habitat loss and persecution on the wintering grounds (Bock et al. 1993, Gard et al. 1993, Rodenhouse

STUDIES IN AVIAN BIOLOGY

et al. 1993). In many grassland areas, prescribed burning and grazing of prairie habitats may affect populations of grassland birds.

Grazing is a major land use in the United States, particularly in the West where 70% of the land area in 11 western states is grazed by livestock (Fleischner 1994). In regions where tallgrass prairie persists, such as portions of Oklahoma, prescribed burning is frequently associated with cattle grazing. Tallgrass-prairie rangeland is often burned in the spring to encourage the subsequent growth of highly nutritious and palatable grasses such as big bluestem (*Andropogon gerardi*), little bluestem (*Schizachyrium scoparium*), Indian grass (*Sorghastrum nutans*), and switchgrass (*Panicum virgatum*; scientific names in accordance with Great Plains Flora Association 1986). Spring burning also discourages the growth of woody plants and undesirable forbs. These prescribed burns typically occur in March and April, and many areas are burned annually or biennially. After spring burning, relatively high densities of cattle are placed in pastures to forage for approximately 100 d. This grazing regime is known as early intensive stocking (Smith and Owensby 1978).

Tallgrass-prairie habitats have evolved with grazing and fire. Historically, grazing occurred by bison (*Bison bison*), elk (*Cervus elaphus*), and pronghorn (*Antilocapra americana*), and fires were ignited by lightning strikes and Native Americans (J. H. Shaw and M. Lee, unpubl. data). These natural and anthropogenic fires are believed to have occurred most frequently in late summer and early fall in areas where fuel had accumulated because of a lack of recent fire (J. H. Shaw and M. Lee, unpubl. data). Although there is no way to determine accurately how natural grazing and fire regimes affected grassland birds in past centuries, we do know that grazing and fire shaped the prairie into a mosaic of habitats that probably differed spatially and temporally in age, structure, and floral and faunal compositions. This mosaic presumably created suitable habitat for populations of wintering and breeding birds with diverse habitat requirements. The effect of fire and/or grazing on grassland vegetation and the breeding biology of birds has been the subject of several studies, including Wiens 1973; Whitmore 1981; Johnson and Temple 1986, 1990; Zimmerman 1988, 1996; and Herkert 1994. Specific management recommendations that may be drawn or inferred from these studies are often interspecifically contradictory, with a particular burning or grazing regime benefiting one species to the detriment of another.

Our objective was to determine how contemporary grazing and burning practices in tallgrass-prairie habitats affect the nesting and re-

TABLE 1. TREATMENTS AND LIVESTOCK DENSITIES (HEAD/HECTARE) FOR THREE 16.2-HA TREATED PLOTS AT THE NATURE CONSERVANCY'S TALLGRASS PRAIRIE PRESERVE IN NORTHCENTRAL OKLAHOMA, 1992–1995

Plot number	Year			
	1992	1993	1994	1995
T1	UD	BG	BG	BG
	NA	0.99	1.11	1.09
T2	UD	BG	BG	GR
	NA	0.98	0.82	0.86
T3	UD	BG	BG	GR
	NA	0.98	0.82	0.86

Note: UD = undisturbed, BG = burned and grazed, GR = grazed, NA = not applicable.

productive success of Eastern Meadowlarks (*Sturnella magna*), Grasshopper Sparrows (*Ammodramus savannarum*), and Dickcissels (*Spiza americana*). We chose these species because they commonly nest in undisturbed as well as burned and grazed prairie and are showing significant population declines in several regions of North America (Peterjohn et al. 1994, 1995). Furthermore, Eastern Meadowlarks, Grasshopper Sparrows, and Dickcissels represent three migratory classes: residents, temperate-zone migrants, and neotropical migrants, respectively.

STUDY AREA

Field work was conducted during 1993–1995 at The Nature Conservancy's Tallgrass Prairie Preserve in Osage County, northcentral Oklahoma. The Nature Conservancy manages this area with prescribed burning as well as grazing by cattle and bison. The 14,800-ha preserve is mainly contiguous tallgrass prairie interspersed with riparian forests and blackjack oak (*Quercus marilandica*) and post oak (*Q. stellata*) thickets and savannas. Common herbaceous plant species include switchgrass, Indian grass, little bluestem, big bluestem, common broomweed (*Gutierrezia dracunculoides*), dogbane (*Apocynum cannabinum*), ironweed (*Veronia baldwinii*), aster (*Aster* spp.), goldenrod (*Solidago* spp.), and lespedeza (*Lespedeza* spp.).

We conducted our research in six 16.2-ha square study plots. Three of these plots were undisturbed (no fire or grazing) since at least 1990. The remaining three plots were considered disturbed and were undisturbed, grazed, or burned and grazed during 1992–1995 (Table 1). Treated plots were burned in March, and cattle were placed on them in late April to early May of each year. When placed on the plots, cattle were either yearling heifers or steers weighing approximately 227 kg each. The mean duration that cattle grazed on treated plots was 99.5 d, and the mean stock density was 0.95 head per hectare.

Disturbed and undisturbed plots were located in contiguous tallgrass prairie that was dominated by herbaceous plants. The greatest distance between disturbed and undisturbed plots was 8.6 km and the shortest distance was 1.1 km, as measured on U.S. Geological Survey topographical maps.

METHODS

Each plot contained 13 north-south and 13 east-west transect lines set at 33.5-m intervals. A 41-cm-long wooden stake was driven into the ground at the intersection of each transect line to identify the 169 grid-point locations. These semipermanently marked grid points aided in nest relocation. We began searching for nests in mid-April and continued through July of each year. Nests were located by systematic searching and observation of flushes and carries of nesting material, food, and fecal sacs to and from nests. When we discovered a nest, we recorded the grid-point coordinates and discreetly marked the location with vinyl flagging approximately 10 m from the nest. Nests were monitored at 3- to 4-d intervals until fledging or failure to determine rates of nesting and reproductive success. Nest-searching effort was similar among treatments and years. We followed guidelines outlined by Ralph et al. 1993 to minimize observer-related effects on rates of predation caused by nest monitoring.

We compared numbers of nests observed, mean clutch sizes, numbers of young fledged, and Mayfield probabilities of nesting success between disturbed and undisturbed plots for each of the three species. Clutch size was defined as the maximum number of eggs contained in successful nests or the number of eggs contained in a nest when the female began incubating. Number of young fledged from successful nests was estimated based on the number of young last observed in those nests. We calculated Mayfield probabilities for the incubation, brood-rearing, and combined phases of the nesting cycle for each species (Mayfield 1961, 1975). Mayfield probabilities for the combined phase were calculated by multiplying the incubation-phase probability by the brood-rearing-phase probability. Mayfield probabilities were computed using the Mayfield Nesting Success Modeling System developed by WordTech Systems, Inc. The numbers of incubation and brood-rearing days used in the Mayfield calculations for Eastern Meadowlarks, Grasshopper Sparrows, and Dickcissels were 14 and 11, 11 and 9, and 12 and 9, respectively.

Differences in number of nests observed between plot types and among years were tested for significance using Student's t-test and chi-square contingency tables, respectively. Differences in clutch sizes and number of young fledged among years and between plot types were tested for significance using univariate analyses of variance (ANOVA). Differences in Mayfield probabilities between plot types were tested for significance using chi-square tests of independence, based on procedures similar to those outlined by Dow 1978. Differences for all statistical tests were considered to be significant at alpha levels ≤ 0.05.

RESULTS

We observed 42, 12, and 87 Eastern Meadowlark (EAME), Grasshopper Sparrow (GRSP), and Dickcissel (DICK) nests, respectively, on undisturbed plots and 60, 26, and 86 nests, respectively, on disturbed plots. The mean number of nests observed for each species did not differ significantly between undisturbed and disturbed plots for the 3 yr combined (EAME: t = -2.04,

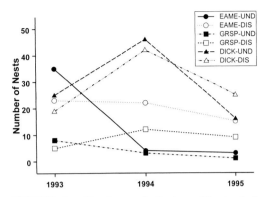

FIGURE 1. Numbers of Eastern Meadowlark (EAME), Grasshopper Sparrow (GRSP), and Dickcissel (DICK) nests observed on six 16.2-ha undisturbed (UND) and disturbed (DIS) tallgrass-prairie study plots in northcentral Oklahoma, 1993–1995.

df = 4, P = 0.11; GRSP: t = -2.40, df = 4, P = 0.07; DICK: t = 0.02, df = 4, P = 0.98). However, the number of Eastern Meadowlark and Grasshopper Sparrow nests differed significantly among years on undisturbed plots. We observed significantly fewer Eastern Meadowlark ($\chi^2 = 20.40$, df = 2, P < 0.01) and Grasshopper Sparrow ($\chi^2 = 8.49$, df = 2, P = 0.01) nests than expected on undisturbed plots in 1994 and 1995 (Fig. 1).

Overall mean clutch sizes for Eastern Meadowlarks, Grasshopper Sparrows, and Dickcissels were 4.3 (N = 70, SE ± 0.10), 4.2 (N = 32, SE ± 0.20), and 3.8 (N = 102, SE ± 0.08), respectively. Mean clutch sizes for the three species were not significantly different between undisturbed and disturbed plots (EAME: $F_{1,68} = 0.49$, P = 0.48; GRSP: $F_{1,30} = 0.11$, P = 0.75; DICK: $F_{1,100} = 1.77$, P = 0.19). Similarly, the average number of young fledged from successful nests was not significantly different between plot types (EAME: $F_{1,22} = 0.32$, P = 0.58; GRSP: $F_{1,4} = 0.00$, P = 1.00; DICK: $F_{1,33} = 2.56$, P = 0.12). The average number of young fledged from successful nests was 3.3 (N = 24, SE ± 0.24), 3.7 (N = 6, SE ± 0.42), and 2.8 (N = 35, SE ± 0.17) for Eastern Meadowlarks, Grasshopper Sparrows, and Dickcissels, respectively.

Mayfield probabilities of nesting success for Eastern Meadowlarks were significantly higher on undisturbed plots in the brood-rearing period ($\chi^2 = 6.02$, df = 1, P = 0.01) but did not vary significantly in the incubation ($\chi^2 = 0.07$, df = 1, P = 0.79) and combined ($\chi^2 = 1.47$, df = 1, P = 0.23) periods (Fig. 2). Mayfield probabilities of nesting success for Grasshopper Sparrows were not significantly different between undisturbed and disturbed plots for any of the three phases of the nesting cycle (incubation: $\chi^2 = $

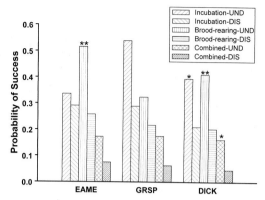

FIGURE 2. Mayfield probabilities of nesting success for Eastern Meadowlarks (EAME), Grasshopper Sparrows (GRSP), and Dickcissels (DICK) on undisturbed (UND) versus disturbed (DIS) tallgrass-prairie plots during incubation, brood-rearing, and combined phases of the nesting cycle in northcentral Oklahoma, 1993–1995. * Denotes $P \leq 0.05$ difference between plot types, ** denotes $P \leq 0.01$ difference between plot types.

1.27, df = 1, P = 0.26; brood-rearing: $\chi^2 = 0.09$, df = 1, P = 0.76; combined: $\chi^2 = 0.24$, df = 1, P = 0.62; Fig. 2). However, Mayfield probabilities of nesting success for Dickcissels were significantly lower on disturbed plots during all three phases of the nesting cycle (incubation: $\chi^2 = 5.66$, df = 1, P = 0.02; brood-rearing: $\chi^2 = 6.41$, df = 1, P = 0.01; combined: $\chi^2 = 5.56$, df = 1, P = 0.02; Fig. 2).

On disturbed plots, at least 13.5, 9.1, and 1.5% of Eastern Meadowlark, Grasshopper Sparrow, and Dickcissel nests, respectively, were trampled by cattle.

DISCUSSION

The temporal decline in numbers of Eastern Meadowlark and Grasshopper Sparrow nests on undisturbed plots was probably due largely to changes in the vegetation profile and composition owing to ecological succession, although finding nests in the denser vegetation of undisturbed plots was also more difficult. Ecological succession of grassland habitats following disturbances is known to affect the composition and structure of grassland bird communities (Johnson and Temple 1990, Herkert 1994, Zimmerman 1996). In the absence of disturbances such as burning, grazing, or mowing, tallgrass prairie becomes more densely vegetated with forbs and woody plant species (Gibson and Hulbert 1987, Hulbert 1988). For example, the mean density of woody plants on undisturbed plots in our study was 10,287 per hectare, whereas the mean on disturbed plots was 4,344 per hectare

(George M. Sutton Avian Research Center, unpubl. data). Eastern Meadowlarks and Grasshopper Sparrows are most frequently associated with habitats characterized by vegetation with low to intermediate density and height (Whitmore 1981; Herkert et al. 1993; George M. Sutton Avian Research Center, unpubl. data). Thus, over time, increasing vegetation density and height may have rendered control plots less suitable for use by nesting Eastern Meadowlarks and Grasshopper Sparrows.

In addition to preferring vegetation of low to intermediate height, Eastern Meadowlarks also prefer habitats with low forb-to-grass ratios. These habitats are most often created by episodes of periodic fire. We speculate that because of a lack of fire, habitat conditions on our undisturbed plots were probably unfavorable for Eastern Meadowlarks in 1994 and 1995, thus explaining the low numbers of nests observed in those years. Herkert (1994) noted that Grasshopper Sparrows were more abundant in recently burned areas than in areas in their third or later growing season since last burning. The number of Grasshopper Sparrow nests on our undisturbed plots was probably declining when we initiated our study in 1993, as this was at least the third consecutive year since these plots had been burned.

Whitmore (1981), Zimmerman (1988), and Herkert (1994) noted the importance of periodic fire in maintaining suitable habitat for several species of grassland birds. Johnson and Temple (1990) observed higher probabilities of nesting success for Western Meadowlarks (*Sturnella neglecta*) and Grasshopper Sparrows in recently burned (1 yr postburn) prairie than in prairie that had not been burned in at least 2 yr. Zimmerman (1996) reported lower nesting-success probabilities for Eastern Meadowlarks, Grasshopper Sparrows, and Dickcissels in burned and grazed prairie. We found no evidence that annual spring burning negatively affected the reproductive performance of Grasshopper Sparrows. In addition, the increase in relative abundance of Eastern Meadowlarks in burned areas may have offset the slightly lower rate of nesting success meadowlarks experienced in these areas. Furthermore, the 13.5% of Eastern Meadowlark nests that failed on our disturbed plots because of trampling by cattle was an effect that was not a direct result of burning, although burned areas were then preferentially grazed if livestock were subsequently introduced. Therefore, we concur with Whitmore (1981), Zimmerman (1988), and Herkert (1994) and suggest that a regime of rotational prescribed burning would benefit these avian species by providing a mosaic of habitats in various stages of ecological succession.

In our study it was difficult to isolate the effects of grazing from the effects of burning. For Eastern Meadowlarks, trampling of nests by cattle coupled with higher rates of predation (62% on disturbed plots, 50% on undisturbed plots) accounted for the lower rate of nesting success on burned and grazed plots. Dickcissels are less susceptible to trampling because they nest an average of 21.7 cm (N = 738, range 0–540, SE ± 1.64) above the ground (George M. Sutton Avian Research Center, unpubl. data). The primary causes of lower nesting success by Dickcissels on disturbed plots were higher rates of nest predation (75% on disturbed plots, 64% on undisturbed plots) and abandonment (5% on disturbed plots, 1% on undisturbed plots).

We are currently analyzing data on habitat structure and predation to determine if spatial heterogeneity and specific habitat characteristics are related to nesting success or avian community composition and structure. In addition, we are analyzing nest, point-count, habitat, and insect data from these and 12 other tallgrass-prairie study plots on privately owned ranches and The Nature Conservancy's Tallgrass Prairie Preserve. These plots have been burned and/or grazed by bison or cattle during the past 5 yr. Results of these analyses combined with results reported in this paper will be used to draw specific conclusions regarding the effects of burning and grazing on the nesting ecology of tallgrass-prairie avifauna. Conclusions from our studies combined with input from ranchers will be used to formulate conservation strategies for grassland birds that incorporate the financial and logistical needs of private landowners.

ACKNOWLEDGMENTS

We are grateful to The Nature Conservancy, particularly B. Hamilton, and to local ranchers for cooperating with us and providing access to land. We thank the National Fish and Wildlife Foundation and U.S. Fish and Wildlife Service for financial support. We also thank the many other foundations, corporations, organizations, and individuals—too numerous to list—whose contributions support the George M. Sutton Avian Research Center. J. Herkert, J. Zimmerman, and an anonymous reviewer provided helpful comments on the manuscript. Last but by no means least, we thank the many seasonal field biologists who have helped collect and enter data.

LITERATURE CITED

BOCK, C. E., V. A. SAAB, T. D. RICH, AND D. S. DOBKIN. 1993. Effects of livestock grazing on neotropical migratory landbirds in western North America. Pp. 296–309 *in* D. M. Finch and P. W. Stangel (editors). Status and management of neotropical migratory birds. USDA Forest Service Gen. Tech. Rep. RM-229. USDA Forest Service Rocky Mountain Forest and Range Experimental Station, Fort Collins, CO.

DOW, D. D. 1978. A test of significance for Mayfield's method of calculating nest success. Wilson Bulletin 90:291–295.

FLEISCHNER, T. L. 1994. Ecological costs of livestock grazing in western North America. Conservation Biology 8:629–644.

GARD, N. W., M. J. HOOPER, AND R. S. BENNETT. 1993. Effects of pesticides and contaminants on neotropical migrants. Pp. 310–314 *in* D. M. Finch and P. W. Stangel (editors). Status and management of neotropical migratory birds. USDA Forest Service Gen. Tech. Rep. RM-229. USDA Forest Service Rocky Mountain Forest and Range Experimental Station, Fort Collins, CO.

GIBSON, D. J., AND L. C. HULBERT. 1987. Effects of fire, topography and year-to-year climate variation on species composition in tallgrass prairie. Vegetation 72:175–185.

GREAT PLAINS FLORA ASSOCIATION. 1986. Flora of the Great Plains. University Press of Kansas, Lawrence, KS.

HERKERT, J. R. 1994. Breeding bird communities of midwestern prairie fragments: the effects of prescribed burning and habitat-area. Natural Areas Journal 14:128–135.

HERKERT, J. R., R. E. SZAFONI, V. M. KLEEN, AND J. E. SCHWEGMAN. 1993. Habitat establishment, enhancement and management for forest and grassland birds in Illinois. Natural Heritage Technical Publication no. 1. Division of Natural Heritage, Illinois Department of Conservation, Springfield, IL.

HULBERT, L. C. 1988. Causes of fire effects in tallgrass prairie. Ecology 69:46–58.

JOHNSON, R. G., AND S. A. TEMPLE. 1986. Assessing habitat quality for birds nesting in fragmented tallgrass prairies. Pp. 245–250 *in* J. A. Verner, M. L. Morrison, and C. J. Ralph (editors). Wildlife 2000: modeling habitat relationships of terrestrial vertebrates. University of Wisconsin Press, Madison, WI.

JOHNSON, R. G., AND S. A. TEMPLE. 1990. Nest predation and brood parasitism of tallgrass prairie birds. Journal of Wildlife Management 54:106–111.

KNOPF, F. L. 1994. Avian assemblages on altered grasslands. Studies in Avian Biology 15:247–257.

MAYFIELD, H. F. 1961. Nesting success calculated from exposure. Wilson Bulletin 73:255–261.

MAYFIELD, H. F. 1975. Suggestions for calculating nesting success. Wilson Bulletin 87:456–466.

PETERJOHN, B. G., J. R. SAUER, AND W. A. LINK. 1994. The 1992 and 1993 summary of the North American Breeding Bird Survey. Bird Populations 2:46–61.

PETERJOHN, B. G., J. R. SAUER, AND C. S. ROBBINS. 1995. Populations trends from the North American Breeding Bird Survey. Pp. 3–39 *in* T. E. Martin and D. M. Finch (editors). Ecology and management of neotropical migratory birds. Oxford University Press, New York, NY.

RALPH, C. J., G. R. GEUPEL, P. PYLE, T. E. MARTIN, AND D. F. DESANTE. 1993. Handbook of field methods for monitoring landbirds. USDA Forest Service Gen. Tech. Rep. PSW-GTR-144. USDA Forest Service Pacific Southwest Research Station, Albany, CA.

RODENHOUSE, N. L., L. B. BEST, R. J. O'CONNOR, AND E. K. BOLLINGER. 1993. Effects of temperate agriculture on neotropical migrant landbirds. Pp. 280–295 *in* D. M. Finch and P. W. Stangel (editors). Status and management of neotropical migratory birds. USDA Forest Service Gen. Tech. Rep. RM-229. USDA Forest Service Rocky Mountain Forest and Range Experimental Station, Fort Collins, CO.

SMITH, E. F., AND C. E. OWENSBY. 1978. Intensive early stocking and season-long stocking of Kansas Flint Hills range. Journal of Range Management 31:14–17.

WHITMORE, R. C. 1981. Structural characteristics of Grasshopper Sparrow habitat. Journal of Wildlife Management 45:811–814.

WIENS, J. A. 1973. Pattern and process in grassland bird communities. Ecological Monographs 43:237–270.

ZIMMERMAN, J. L. 1988. Breeding season habitat selection by the Henslow's Sparrow (*Ammodramus henslowii*) in Kansas. Wilson Bulletin 100:17–24.

ZIMMERMAN, J. L. 1996. Avian community responses to fire, grazing, and drought in the tallgrass prairie. Pp. 167–180 *in* F. Knopf and F. B. Samson (editors). Ecology and conservation of Great Plains vertebrates. Springer-Verlag, New York, NY.

Studies in Avian Biology No. 19:171–177, 1999.

RELATIONSHIP OF FIRE HISTORY TO TERRITORY SIZE, BREEDING DENSITY, AND HABITAT OF BAIRD'S SPARROW IN NORTH DAKOTA

MAIKEN WINTER

Abstract. Prescribed fire often is used to manage prairies, but its effects on many grassland birds are not well documented. In 1993 I compared breeding density, territory size, and habitat of Baird's Sparrows (*Ammodramus bairdii*) among three different fire regimes in mixed-grass prairie in North Dakota: areas not burned in more than 80 years, areas burned twice since the late 1970s, and areas burned four times since the late 1970s. Baird's Sparrows were absent on unburned areas. They occurred at moderate densities ($\bar{X}$ = 6.9 males/100 hectares) on two-burn areas; these areas were characterized by relatively high vegetation ($\bar{X}$ = 18.5 centimeters), relatively deep litter ($\bar{X}$ = 2.8 centimeters), and an absence of bare soil. Higher Baird's Sparrow densities ($\bar{X}$ = 20 males/100 hectares) were found on four-burn areas where litter was low ($\bar{X}$ = 0.08 centimeters), vegetation relatively short ($\bar{X}$ = 13.8 centimeters), and the percentage of canopy coverage by bare soil relatively large ($\bar{X}$ = 11.4 percent). Mean territory size was significantly smaller in four-burn areas ($\bar{X}$ = 1.2 hectares) than in two-burn areas ($\bar{X}$ = 1.5 hectares). Prescribed burning favorably changed habitat structure for Baird's Sparrow, as indicated by a clear tie between occurrence of burning and that of the species; observed changes in density and territory size with frequent burning further suggested a positive link between fire and Baird's Sparrows in northwestern North Dakota.

LA RELACIÓN DE LA HISTORIA DE FUEGO CON EL TAMAÑO DE TERRITORIO, CON LA DENSIDAD DE REPRODUCCIÓN Y CON EL HÁBITAT DEL GORRIÓN DE BAIRD EN DAKOTA DEL NORTE

Sinopsis. El fuego programado se usa con frecuencia para manejar llanuras, pero sus efectos no han sido bien documentados para muchas aves de pastizal. En 1993 comparé la densidad de reproducción, el tamaño de territorio y el hábitat de los Gorriones de Baird (*Ammodramus bairdii*) entre tres diferentes regímenes de fuego en llanura de hierbas mixtas en Dakota del Norte: áreas no quemadas en más de 80 años, áreas quemadas dos veces desde fines de los años 70, y áreas quemadas cuatro veces desde fines de los años 70. Los Gorriones de Baird estuvieron ausentes en las áreas no quemadas. Se detectaron en densidades moderadas ($\bar{X}$ = 6,9 machos/100 hectáreas) en áreas de dos quemadas; estas áreas se caracterizaron por una vegetación relativamente alta ($\bar{X}$ = 18,5 centímetros), una cobertura de hojas relativamente honda ($\bar{X}$ = 2,8 centímetros) y una ausencia de suelo abierto. Se encontraron densidades más altas de Gorriones de Baird ($\bar{X}$ = 20 machos/100 hectáreas) en áreas de cuatro quemadas donde la cobertura de hojas era menor ($\bar{X}$ = 0,08 centímetros), la vegetación relativamente baja ($\bar{X}$ = 13,8 centímetros) y el porcentaje de suelo abierto relativamente mayor ($\bar{X}$ = 11,4 por ciento). El tamaño promedio de territorio fue significativamente más pequeño en áreas de cuatro quemadas ($\bar{X}$ = 1,2 hectáreas) que en áreas de dos quemadas ($\bar{X}$ = 1,5 hectáreas). El fuego programado cambió favorablemente la estructura de hábitat para el Gorrión de Baird, indicado por una clara conexión entre la incidencia de quemadas y la presencia de la especie; los cambios observados en densidad y tamaño de territorio con quemadas frecuentes indicaron aun más una conexión positiva entre el fuego y los Gorriones de Baird en el noroeste de Dakota del Norte.

Key Words: *Ammodramus bairdii*; avian density; Baird's Sparrow; fire effects; mixed-grass prairie.

Baird's Sparrows (*Ammodramus bairdii*) are endemic to the northern Great Plains (Johnsgard 1978). Early reports indicate that the species was common in the northern mixed-grass prairie in the late 1800s (Coues 1878); it still is common in some areas, such as the Missouri Coteau of North Dakota (Stewart 1975, Kantrud 1981). Since the arrival of European farmers in the early 1900s, Baird's Sparrow abundance has decreased considerably (DeSmet and Conrad 1991). This decline has been attributed to the conversion of prairie to farmland, overgrazing, invasion by exotic plants, and fire suppression (Higgins et al. 1989, Dobkin 1992, Sauer and

Droege 1992, Goossen et al. 1993, Jones and Green 1997).

Fire suppression can decrease habitat suitability for grassland breeding birds by altering the dominant vegetation of prairies from grasses and forbs to mostly woody vegetation (Higgins et al. 1989). This deterioration of prairie ecosystems can be prevented or reversed by using prescribed burning (Wright and Bailey 1982, Collins and Wallace 1990). Wise use of prescribed burning, however, requires a knowledge of the habitat requirements of grassland species and of the effects of fire on habitat. The breeding habitat of Baird's Sparrow has been well characterized in

Canada (Dale 1983, Sousa and McDonal 1983, Wershler 1987, DeSmet and Conrad 1991, Anstey et al. 1995, Davis et al. 1996), but few studies have investigated the habitat needs of this species elsewhere (Green 1992, Winter 1994, Madden 1996, Jones and Green 1997). Moreover, there has been almost no documentation of fire effects on the distribution and habitat of the species, particularly where multiple burns have occurred over many years. The objective of my study was to describe the effect of fire history on density and territory size of Baird's Sparrow in the mixed-grass prairie of northwestern North Dakota. Knowledge of the impact of fire may aid in decisions on the use of prescribed burning as a management tool in this area.

STUDY AREA AND METHODS

The study was conducted at Lostwood National Wildlife Refuge (NWR), 109 km^2 of predominantly native mixed-grass prairie (*Stipa* spp., *Agropyron* spp.) on the Missouri Coteau in northwestern North Dakota (48°35' N, 102°25' W). Mean annual precipitation at Lostwood NWR is about 42 cm and occurs mostly as rainfall from April through September (Smith et al. 1993). The Missouri Coteau is characterized by rolling hills and numerous shallow wetlands which are relics of the last ice age (Freers 1973). Native mixed-grass prairie at Lostwood NWR has been greatly altered since the early 1900s. Only 30% of its land had been broken for agriculture before the refuge was established in 1935, but the native prairie has changed in plant species composition, mostly as a result of fire exclusion. Native fire-adapted grass and forb communities have been replaced by woody vegetation, especially western snowberry (*Symphoricarpos occidentalis*) and quaking aspen (*Populus tremuloides*), and by introduced grasses such as Kentucky bluegrass (*Poa pratensis*) and smooth brome (*Bromus inermis*). Since the late 1970s, the refuge's uplands have been managed mainly with prescribed fire and short-duration grazing. As a result, about 20% of its prairie currently approximates presettlement conditions (K. Smith, pers. comm.).

I selected study plots by subdividing each legal section (2.59 km^2) of Lostwood NWR into 16 subsections (each 16 ha in size). From those subsections I randomly selected 18 as study plots for each of three burn categories: five unburned areas (zero-burn), five areas burned twice since the late 1970s (two-burn), and eight areas burned four times since the late 1970s (four-burn). Each 16-ha plot was marked with wooden stakes at 50-m intervals along its 400- × 400-m border. Most two-burn plots were burned before 1992, whereas most four-burn plots were last burned in 1992. It was thus not possible to distinguish between the effect of the number of times an area had been burned and the time since an area had last been burned. I present analyses here based only on the number of times areas had been burned. These results closely parallel those of the effect of the time since areas were last burned (Winter 1994).

The available habitat in each study plot was char-

acterized by measuring the vegetation in a randomly chosen 100- × 100-m subplot during 11–16 May 1993. I placed two perpendicular 80-m transects through the middle of each subplot, along which I quantified vegetation at 8-m intervals. The variables measured were mean vegetation height, maximum vegetation height, litter depth, and visual obstruction (Robel et al. 1970); vegetation height and litter depth were measured in centimeters, visual obstruction in decimeters. Litter was defined as horizontally lying dead plant material. The mean values of these vegetation characteristics in each plot were compared between burn areas using analysis of variance. Since the comparisons were not orthogonal, and thus not independent, I lowered the type I error of statistical significance by using the Tukey-Kramer procedure (Sokal and Rohlf 1995). One two-burn and two four-burn plots were excluded from this analysis because the time since they had last been burned, and thus their vegetation characteristics, greatly differed from all other plots (Winter 1994).

I determined density of Baird's Sparrows by linear transect censuses (Emlen 1977) conducted between 30 min before sunrise and about 1000 during 1–30 June. I defined density as the number of singing males per 100 ha and included only males whose territories were more than half inside the plot (Moore 1980). Censuses were not conducted on days with rain, fog, or wind velocities greater than about 25 km/hr. I used a modified flush technique to outline territory boundaries (Wiens 1969, Winter 1994). Each territory was mapped 2–5 times during the season (depending on the detectability of the territory holder) between 1 and 30 June, and its location was marked on an aerial photograph (1:7920). Territory size was determined by measuring the circumference of each territory with a digital planimeter (PLACOM, no. 50408, Los Angeles, California; Greer and Anderson 1989). The mean size of several outlines of the same territory was used in further analyses.

Between 30 June and 24 July, I measured vegetation attributes along a transect through the longest axis of each territory. A sampling point was located randomly in each 10-m interval of the transect by taking a random number of steps along the transect interval and then stepping a random distance to the left or right (selected by coin toss), perpendicular to the transect (Noon 1981). At each sampling point I quantified mean vegetation height, maximum vegetation height, litter depth, visual obstruction, and soil and vegetation cover, as well as the number of woody stems in a 20- × 50-cm Daubenmire frame (Daubenmire 1959). Because vegetation measurements in one territory were not independent of each other, data were pooled for each territory (Smith and Connors 1986).

Density and territory size in two- and four-burn areas were compared with a t-test. Relationships between density or territory size and vegetation parameters were investigated with simple and stepwise multiple regression (Sokal and Rohlf 1995). I calculated regressions of density on median vegetation values for each plot in which Baird's Sparrows were found (pooled vegetation values from one to three territory-transects per plot) and regressions of territory size on the median vegetation values for each territory. A principal component analysis (PCA) was used to summa-

TABLE 1. MEAN DENSITY AND TERRITORY SIZE OF SINGING MALE BAIRD'S SPARROWS ON TWO DIFFERENT BURN AREAS AT LOSTWOOD NWR, NORTH DAKOTA, 1993

Area	Density/100 ha				Territory size (ha)			
	Mean (SE)	N	t	P	Mean (SE)	N	t	P
2-burn	6.9 (4.11)	4	2.53	0.03	1.5 (0.33)	11	2.60	0.01
4-burn	20.0 (3.11)	7			1.2 (0.06)			

rize habitat characteristics of territories. The first two principal components were then used for principal component regression (Maurer 1986), with territory size as the dependent variable. All study plots where Baird's Sparrows did not occur (all unburned plots, one two-burn plot, and one four-burn plot; see Winter 1994) were excluded from regression and principal component analyses. I set alpha at 0.05 for all analyses.

RESULTS

Baird's Sparrow density and territory size differed significantly among areas with different fire histories (Table 1). The species was absent from all unburned plots and occurred in lower numbers and occupied larger territories in two-burn areas than in four-burn areas. Plot vegetation differed greatly among areas with different fire histories (Table 2); visual obstruction readings, vegetation height, and litter depth decreased with fire frequency. Density of Baird's Sparrows in two- and four-burn areas was related to several vegetation variables. Density was positively related to maximum and mean vegetation height (maximum height: $R^2 = 0.42$, F = 6.47, P = 0.03; mean height: $R^2 = 0.48$, F = 6.44, P = 0.03; N = 11), although maximum and mean height were not correlated to each other (P > 0.05). Litter depth and mean vegetation height were the only variables selected by the stepwise regression analysis. Litter depth alone accounted for more than half the total variance in density, with density decreasing with increasing litter depth (Fig. 1). This negative relationship between density and litter depth was only true at intermediate litter depths (0.5–2.5 cm), however, whereas density declined at minimum and maximum litter depths (Winter 1994). After mean height was added to the stepwise model, 82.8% of the variation in Baird's Sparrow density was explained.

Territories in two-burn areas were characterized by high scores on the first principal component (PC I) and large sizes (1.07–2.25 ha), whereas territories in four-burn areas mainly had negative scores on PC I and were smaller in size (0.8–1.69 ha; Fig. 2). PC I represented a continuum from low values representing relatively tall vegetation and little or no litter to high values representing low vegetation and relatively deep litter (Table 3). It explained 26.2% of the variation in territory size; the higher the scores of PC I, the larger the territories (Fig. 2). Almost as much variability was explained by simple linear regression with litter depth as the explanatory variable ($R^2 = 0.22$, F = 7.97, P = 0.009, N = 30 territories), suggesting that quantity of litter is an important factor influencing territory size. The second principal component (PC II), which reflected a continuum from low to high cover by forbs, woody plants, and introduced grasses, did not explain any variation in territory size ($R^2 = 0.00$, F = 0.00, P = 0.98). The amount of dead plant material, which is summarized in PC I (Table 3), thus seemed to influence territory size more than did vegetation height or types of vegetation cover. Plot B, a

TABLE 2. MEANS AND STANDARD ERRORS FOR VEGETATION VARIABLES MEASURED IN RANDOM SUBPLOTS AT LOSTWOOD NWR, NORTH DAKOTA, 1993

Plots	Visual obstruction (dm)	Maximum height (cm)	Mean height (cm)	Litter depth (cm)
0-burn (N = 5)	1.63 (0.42)	42.8 (6.03)	23.9 (3.53)	3.3 (0.46)
2-burn (N = 4)	1.37 (0.20)	39.5 (3.18)	18.5 (1.30)	2.8 (0.39)
4-burn (N = 6)	0.63 (0.22)	30.2 (4.48)	13.8 (2.37)	0.08 (0.05)
F (df = 14)	4.16*	1.93	3.85*	31.34**
Differences[a]	0b > 4b	—	0b > 4b	0b > 2b > 4b

Note: Means from 20 vegetation measurements in each plot were compared among all burn areas using analysis of variance, adjusting for nonindependence with the Tukey-Kramer procedure.
[a] 0b = no burns, 2b = burned twice since the late 1970s, 4b = burned 4 times since the late 1970s.
* P ≤ 0.05, ** P ≤ 0.001.

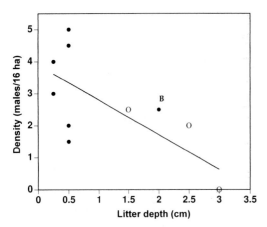

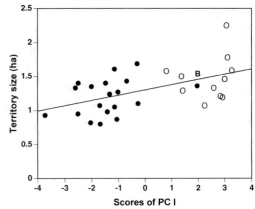

FIGURE 1. Regression of Baird's Sparrow density on litter depth in two-burn areas (open circles) and four-burn areas (solid circles; $R^2 = 0.55$, $F = 11.11$, $P = 0.009$, $df = 1, 9$). Only plots in which Baird's Sparrows occurred were included in the analysis. Plot B deviated from other four-burn areas because it had last been burned before 1992.

FIGURE 2. Regression of territory size on PC I in territories in two-burn areas (open circles) and four-burn areas (solid circles; $R^2 = 0.26$, $F = 9.96$, $P = 0.004$, $df = 1, 28$). Plots with high scores on PC I are characterized by relatively deep litter and little or no cover by bare soil. Plot B deviated from other four-burn areas because it had last been burned before 1992.

four-burn area that was only partly burned in 1992, deviated from the otherwise consistent separation between two- and four-burn areas. The high accumulation of litter in this plot (median = 2 cm vs. 0.25–0.61 cm in all other four-burn areas in which Baird's Sparrows occurred) accounted for the similarity of this plot with two-burn areas.

DISCUSSION

The prescribed fire regime at Lostwood NWR had a profound effect on the distribution of Baird's Sparrow. The species was absent from unburned areas, where litter and vegetation were higher than in two- and four-burn areas. Highest densities were found on four-burn areas, where litter depth and vegetation height were relatively low. This result is surprising since most four-burn areas had been burned the previous year, and vegetation cover, and thus nesting sites and concealment from predators, is reduced by fire (Pylypec 1991; but see Johnson and Temple 1990 for other grassland birds). Therefore, densities of many grassland birds are usually low the first year after a fire (Madden 1996, Johnson 1997). This typical short-term fire effect may have been overridden by the unusually wet year of 1993, which resulted in relatively lush vegetation at Lostwood NWR (K. Smith, pers. comm.). Although many bird species do not immediately respond to habitat change because of site tenacity (Rotenberry and Wiens 1980, Wiens 1989), such "tracking inertia" (Wiens et al. 1987) does not seem to apply to Baird's Spar-

TABLE 3. FACTOR LOADINGS OF PRINCIPAL COMPONENTS DERIVED FROM VARIABLES MEASURED ALONG TERRITORY TRANSECTS (N = 30 TERRITORIES) AT LOSTWOOD NWR, NORTH DAKOTA, 1993

	PC I	PC II
Eigenvalue	4.62	2.58
Percentage of total variance	0.27	0.15
Correlations with original variable:		
Topography		
Elevation	0.13	−0.03
Slope	0.12	0.07
Structure		
Visual obstruction	0.16	0.11
Maximum height	−0.29	0.18
Mean height	−0.21	0.44
Litter depth	0.43	0.17
Total number of hits	0.33	0.36
Hits at the first 10 cm of the Wiens pole	0.40	0.21
Cover		
Bunchgrass	−0.01	0.18
Native rhizomatous grass	0.06	−0.42
Introduced rhizomatous grass	0.03	−0.35
Forb	0.03	−0.35
Wood	0.19	−0.22
Litter	0.36	0.12
Soil	−0.34	0.09
Distance to:		
Shrub	0.01	0.14
Woodland	−0.00	0.05

rows. This species appears to be highly nomadic (Green 1992), and therefore its density and territory size probably directly reflect its annual habitat choice. Such high plasticity in habitat choice has also been reported for other grassland-nesting birds (Cody 1985, Igl and Johnson 1995) and is assumed to be an adaptation to the highly dynamic habitat of the Great Plains.

Territory size and density of Baird's Sparrows were inversely related; territories in two-burn areas were larger than in four-burn areas, whereas density was lower in two- than in four-burn areas. Although density does not necessarily indicate habitat quality (Van Horne 1983), high densities and small territories in four-burn areas suggest that vegetation in areas with several prescribed burns is more suitable for breeding Baird's Sparrows than in areas with few or no prescribed burns. This notion was supported by the significant relationship between density or territory size and vegetation variables on two- and four-burn areas. Low litter depth, as was typical in four-burn areas, was consistently associated with high Baird's Sparrow densities and small territories. Baird's Sparrows were absent, however, from areas where litter was not present at all. They thus preferred an intermediate litter depth, which may be a compromise between foraging efficiency and availability of nest cover (Winter 1994). Litter depth thus strongly influenced the distribution of Baird's Sparrows, as described in other studies (Sousa and McDonal 1983, Renken and Dinsmore 1987, Anstey et al. 1995, Madden 1996).

My observations support those of previous studies that have described Baird's Sparrow as sensitive to vegetation characteristics of its habitat and thus as a highly restricted grassland bird (Kantrud and Kologiski 1983, Goossen et al. 1993). Recent observations of Baird's Sparrows in alfalfa (*Medicago sativa*) fields and other cultivated areas, however, suggest the species may be more adaptable to habitat change than previously thought (DeSmet and Conrad 1991, Davis et al. 1996), but it is not known if these areas support successful breeding. It is also not known if the effect of fire on Baird's Sparrow differs between large and small prairie fragments, as has been shown by Herkert (1994) for bird communities in tall-grass prairie fragments in Illinois. The absence of Baird's Sparrow on unburned habitats in my study clearly documents that prescribed fire is necessary to sustain populations of Baird's Sparrow at Lostwood NWR in northwestern North Dakota. These findings may not apply to more western parts of the species' breeding range, where annual precipitation and thus plant growth and litter accumulation are less. One must thus be cautious when applying results of a spatially restricted study to a broader scale (Raphael et al. 1987, Wiens et al. 1987, Fox 1992). These results, however, should compel land managers to further explore prescribed burning as a management tool for Baird's Sparrow throughout the eastern part of its breeding range in the northern mixed-grass prairie.

ACKNOWLEDGMENTS

I thank K. Schmidt-Koenig and H. Wiley for advising this study. Special thanks are due K. Smith and B. Murphy who helped during the field season, B. Madden who shared both joys and frustrations, M. Green who introduced me to one of the most beautiful places I know, and B. Stewart whose delicious pancakes maintained my energy. B. Murphy, K. Smith, D. Johnson, S. Jones, M. Green, H. Wiley, J. Faaborg, W. Hochachka, and F. Uhlman made many suggestions that greatly improved the manuscript. My work was supported by the U.S. Fish and Wildlife Service and a stipend given by the Tübinger Studentenstiftung/Germany.

LITERATURE CITED

ANSTEY, D. A., S. K. DAVIS, D. C. DUNCAN, AND M. SKEEL. 1995. Distribution and habitat requirements of eight grassland songbird species in southern Saskatchewan. Saskatchewan Wetland Conservation Corporation, Regina, SK.

CODY, M. L. 1985. Habitat selection in grassland and open-country birds. Pp. 191–226 *in* M. L. Cody (editor). Habitat selection in birds. Academic Press, Orlando, FL.

COLLINS, S. L., AND L. M. WALLACE (EDITORS). 1990. Fire in North-American tallgrass prairies. University of Oklahoma Press, Norman, OK.

COUES, E. 1878. Field notes on birds observed in Dakota and Montana along the forty-ninth parallel during the seasons of 1873 and 1874. U.S. Geologic and Geographic Survey Territorial Bulletin 4:545–661.

DALE, B. 1983. Habitat relationships of seven species of passerine birds at Last Mountain Lake, Saskatchewan. Master's thesis. University of Regina, Regina, SK.

DAUBENMIRE, R. 1959. A canopy-coverage method of vegetational analysis. Northwest Scientist 33:43–63.

DAVIS, S. K., D. C. DUNCAN, AND M. A. SKEEL. 1996. Abundance of Baird's Sparrows, *Ammodramus bairdii,* in native prairie and introduced vegetation. Blue Jay 54:185–191.

DESMET, K. D., AND M. P. CONRAD. 1991. Management and research needs for Baird's Sparrows and other grassland species in Manitoba. Pp. 83–86 *in* G. L. Holroyd, G. Burns, and H. C. Smith (editors). Proceedings of the second endangered species and prairie conservation workshop. Occasional Paper 15, Provincial Museum of Alberta, Edmonton, AB.

DOBKIN, D. S. 1992. Neotropical migrant landbirds in the northern Rockies and Great Plains. USDA Forest Service Northern Region, Missoula, MT.

EMLEN, J. T. 1977. Estimating breeding bird densities from transect counts. Auk 94:455–468.

Fox, J. 1992. The problem of scale in community resource management. Environmental Management 16:289–297.

Freers, T. F. 1973. Geology of Burke County, North Dakota. Geological Survey Bulletin 55.

Goossen, J. P., S. Brechtel, K. D. DeSmet, D. Hjertaas, and C. Wershler. 1993. Canadian Baird's Sparrow recovery plan. Recovery of nationally endangered wildlife. Report no. 3, Canadian Wildlife Federation, Ottawa, ON.

Green, M. T. 1992. Adaptations of Baird's Sparrows (*Ammodramus bairdii*) to grasslands: acoustic communication and nomadism. Ph.D. dissertation. University of North Carolina, Chapel Hill, NC.

Greer, R. D., and S. H. Anderson. 1989. Relationships between population demography of McCown's Longspur and habitat resources. Condor 91:609–619.

Herkert, J. R. 1994. Breeding bird communities of midwestern prairie fragments: the effect of prescribed burning and habitat-area. Natural Areas Journal 14:128–135.

Higgins, K. F., A. D. Kruse, and J. L. Piehl. 1989. Effects of fire in the northern Great Plains. South Dakota State University Extension Circular no. 761. South Dakota State University, Brookings, SD.

Igl, L. D., and D. H. Johnson. 1995. Dramatic increase of Le Conte's Sparrow in Conservation Reserve Program fields in the northern Great Plains. Prairie Naturalist 27:89–94.

Johnsgard, P. A. 1978. The ornithogeography of the Great Plains states. Prairie Naturalist 10:97–112.

Johnson, D. H. 1997. Effects of fire on bird populations in mixed-grass prairie. Pp. 181–206 *in* F. L. Knopf and F. B. Samson (editors). Ecology and conservation of Great Plains vertebrates. Springer-Verlag, New York, NY.

Johnson, R. G., and S. A. Temple. 1990. Nest predation and brood parasitism of tallgrass prairie birds. Journal of Wildlife Management 54:106–111.

Jones, S. L., and M. T. Green. 1997. Baird's Sparrow status assessment and conservation plan. Administrative report, U.S. Fish and Wildlife Service, Denver, CO.

Kantrud, H. A. 1981. Grazing intensity effects on the breeding avifauna of North Dakota native grasslands. Canadian Field-Naturalist 95:404–417.

Kantrud, H. A., and R. L. Kologiski. 1983. Avian associations of the northern Great Plains grasslands. Journal of Biogeography 10:331–350.

Madden, E. M. 1996. Passerine communities and bird-habitat relationships on prescribe-burned, mixed-grass prairie in North Dakota. Master's thesis. Montana State University, Bozeman, MT.

Maurer, B. A. 1986. Predicting habitat quality for grassland birds using density-habitat correlations. Journal of Wildlife Management 50:556–565.

Moore, M. C. 1980. Habitat structure in relation to population density and timing of breeding in Prairie Warblers. Wilson Bulletin 92:177–187.

Noon, B. B. 1981. Techniques for sampling avian habitats. Pp. 42–52 *in* D. E. Capen (editor). The use of multivariate statistics in studies of wildlife habitat. USDA Forest Service Gen. Tech. Rep. GTR RM-

87. USDA Forest Service Rocky Mountain Forest and Range Experimental Station, Fort Collins, CO.

Pylypec, B. 1991. Impacts of fire on bird populations in a fescue prairie. Canadian Field-Naturalist 105:346–349.

Raphael, M. G., M. L. Morrison, and M. P. Yoder-Williams. 1987. Breeding bird populations during twenty-five years of postfire succession in the Sierra Nevada. Condor 89:614–626.

Renken, R. B., and J. J. Dinsmore. 1987. Nongame bird communities on managed grasslands in North Dakota. Canadian Field-Naturalist 101:551–557.

Robel, R. J., J. N. Briggs, A. D. Dayton, and L. C. Hulbert. 1970. Relationship between visual obstruction measurements and weight of grassland vegetation. Journal of Range Management 23:295–297.

Rotenberry, J. T., and J. A. Wiens. 1980. Habitat structure, patchiness and avian communities in North American steppe vegetation: a multivariate analysis. Ecology 61:1228–1250.

Sauer, J. R., and S. Droege. 1992. Geographic patterns in population trends of neotropical migrants in North America. Pp. 26–42 *in* J. M. Hagan III and D. W. Johnston (editors). Ecology and conservation of neotropical migrant landbirds. Smithsonian Institution Press, Washington, D.C.

Smith, K. A., R. K. Murphy, D. L. Michaelson, and W. C. Viehl. 1993. Habitat and predation management for nesting Piping Plovers at Lostwood National Wildlife Refuge, North Dakota. Prairie Naturalist 25:139–147.

Smith, K. G., and P. G. Conners. 1986. Building predictive models of species occurrence from total-count transect data and habitat measurements. Pp. 45–50 *in* J. Verner, M. L. Morrison, and C. J. Ralph (editors). Wildlife 2000: modeling habitat relationships of terrestrial vertebrates. University of Wisconsin Press, Madison, WI.

Sokal, R. R., and F. J. Rohlf. 1995. Biometry. 3d ed. W. H. Freeman, New York, NY.

Sousa, P. J., and W. N. McDonal. 1983. Habitat suitability index models: Baird's Sparrow. U.S. Fish and Wildlife Service, Western Energy and Land Use Team, Fort Collins, CO.

Stewart, R. E. 1975. Breeding birds of North Dakota. Tri-College Center for Environmental Studies, Fargo, ND.

Van Horne, B. 1983. Density as a misleading indicator of habitat quality. Journal of Wildlife Management 47:893–901.

Wershler, C. 1987. Baird's Sparrow. Pp. 283–284 *in* G. L. Holroyd, W. B. McGillivray, P. H. R. Stepney, D. M. Ealey, G. C. Trottier, and K. E. Ebhart (editors). Proceedings of the workshop on endangered species in the prairie provinces. Natural History Occasional Paper 9, Provincial Museum of Alberta, Edmonton, AB.

Wiens, J. A. 1969. An approach to the study of ecological relationships among grassland birds. Ornithological Monographs 8.

Wiens, J. A. 1989. The ecology of bird communities. Vols. 1 and 2. Cambridge Studies in Ecology. Cambridge University Press, Cambridge, U.K.

Wiens, J. A., J. T. Rotenberry, and B. Van Horne.

1987. Habitat occupancy patterns of North American shrubsteppe birds: the effect of spatial scale. Oikos 48:132–147.

WINTER, M. 1994. Habitat selection of Baird's Sparrows in the northern mixed-grass prairie. Diplomarbeit der Fakultät für Biologie der Universität Tübingen, Tübingen, Germany.

WRIGHT, H. A., AND A. W. BAILEY. 1982. Fire ecology: United States and southern Canada. John Wiley and Sons, New York, NY.

Studies in Avian Biology No. 19:178–186, 1999.

LE CONTE'S SPARROWS BREEDING IN CONSERVATION RESERVE PROGRAM FIELDS: PRECIPITATION AND PATTERNS OF POPULATION CHANGE

Lawrence D. Igl and Douglas H. Johnson

Abstract. Breeding Le Conte's Sparrows (*Ammodramus leconteii*) were studied from 1990 to 1996 in perennial grasslands established on fields enrolled in the Conservation Reserve Program in the northern Great Plains. The status of Le Conte's Sparrow in these grasslands changed from that of an uncommon breeding species in 1990–1993 to that of one of the most abundant breeding species in 1994–1996. Numerical population lows and highs coincided with drought and amelioration of drought conditions, respectively. Our results emphasize the importance of rangewide conservation efforts and long-term observations of grassland birds.

PROCREACIÓN DEL GORRIÓN DE LE CONTE EN CAMPOS DEL PROGRAMA DE CONSERVACIÓN EN RESERVAS: PRECIPITACIONES Y ESQUEMAS DE CAMBIO DE LA POBLACIÓN

Sinopsis. Desde 1990 a 1996, los Gorriones de Le Conte (*Ammodramus leconteii*) se estudiaron durante su estación de reproducción en los pastizales perennes establecidos en terrenos del Programa de Conservación en Reservas en el norte de la Gran Llanura. La condición del Gorrión de Le Conte en estos pastizales cambió desde una especie poco común entre 1990 y 1993, a una de las especies más abundantes entre 1994 y 1996. Los números de población mínimos y máximos coincidieron con la sequía y el mejoramiento de las condiciones de sequía, respectivamente. Nuestros resultados ponen en relieve la importancia de las campañas conservacionistas del gorrión a gran escala y de las observaciones a largo plazo de las aves de pastizal.

Key Words: *Ammodramus leconteii*; climate; Conservation Reserve Program; drought; grassland; Great Plains; Le Conte's Sparrow; populations; precipitation.

The climate of the North American Great Plains is highly dynamic, with great year-to-year variability in precipitation and periodic, often extreme, wet and dry cycles (Bragg 1995). Drought is a major force of ecological disturbance on the Great Plains and has played a key role in directing the evolution of the grassland biota of this region (Knopf and Samson 1997). Although grassland birds may differ in their responses to environmental variations (Rotenberry and Wiens 1991), climatic variability and concomitant unpredictability of resources strongly influence populations of grassland birds across space and time (Wiens 1974, 1986; Cody 1985). Not surprisingly, breeding bird populations on the Great Plains are highly dynamic, exhibiting considerable annual variation in composition, abundance, and distribution (Johnson and Grier 1988, George et al. 1992, Zimmerman 1992, Igl and Johnson 1997).

Recently, interest in grassland birds has increased with the recognition that many species are declining both continentally (Droege and Sauer 1994) and globally (Goriup 1988). Identification of the specific factors associated with grassland bird declines in North America, however, remains largely enigmatic (Herkert 1997), and it is complicated by the considerable annual fluctuations in grassland bird distribution and abundance (Igl and Johnson 1997). Although there is evidence that land-use changes on the breeding grounds may have contributed to grassland bird declines (e.g., Igl and Johnson 1997), there also is an indication that long-term drought conditions may have influenced recent population changes of some breeding birds on the Great Plains (Droege and Sauer 1989, Peterjohn and Sauer 1993, Bethke and Nudds 1995, Igl and Johnson 1997).

Le Conte's Sparrow (*Ammodramus leconteii*) is a secretive grassland bird that breeds in central and southern Canada and the northcentral United States (Murray 1969). It winters primarily in the southern United States (Peterson 1980, 1990). Like populations of many grassland breeding birds in North America (Fretwell 1986, Igl and Johnson 1997), Le Conte's Sparrow populations exhibit numerical highs and lows depending on local moisture conditions (Peabody 1901, Stewart 1975, Knapton 1979, Zimmer 1979, Madden 1996). This observation, however, is based largely on anecdotal evidence or short-term observations. Long-term studies of Le Conte's Sparrow populations are limited. Le Conte's Sparrow is poorly represented on the North American Breeding Bird Survey (BBS) because of small sample sizes, poor coverage in the northern portion of its breeding range, and

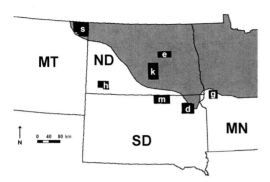

FIGURE 1.   Breeding range (shaded area; Peterson 1980, 1990) of Le Conte's Sparrow in the area of our study in relation to the counties (solid areas) in which Le Conte's Sparrows were observed in CRP fields in the northern Great Plains. North Dakota: h = Hettinger County, e = Eddy County, k = Kidder County; Montana: s = Sheridan County; South Dakota: m = McPherson County, d = Day County; Minnesota: g = Grant County.

the species' furtive behavior (Sauer et al. 1995). Moreover, dramatic fluctuations in Le Conte's Sparrow abundance tend to obscure the species' long-term population trends on the BBS (Sauer et al. 1995).

In this paper we examine long-term population changes of Le Conte's Sparrows breeding in perennial grassland fields enrolled in the Conservation Reserve Program (CRP) on the northern Great Plains. We discuss patterns of population change of Le Conte's Sparrows associated with changes in precipitation and moisture conditions.

METHODS

The CRP of the 1985 Food Security Act removed millions of hectares of highly erodable and environmentally sensitive land from crop production and established perennial grassland for a 10-yr period (Young and Osborn 1990). We surveyed breeding birds from 1990 to 1996 in CRP grassland fields in nine counties in North Dakota, South Dakota, Minnesota, and Montana (Johnson and Schwartz 1993a, b). Le Conte's Sparrows were recorded in only seven of these counties. Herein we report data from those seven counties: Sheridan County, Montana; McPherson and Day Counties, South Dakota; Eddy, Hettinger, and Kidder Counties, North Dakota; and Grant County, Minnesota (Fig. 1). In these counties we surveyed 181 fields (3,565 ha) in 1990; 263 fields (4,843 ha) in 1991; 296 fields (5,468 ha) in 1992; 292 fields (5,360 ha) in 1993; 293 fields (5,369 ha) in 1994; 293 fields (5,369 ha) in 1995; and 290 fields (5,233 ha) in 1996. We selected fields with well-established vegetation because they offered more mature cover and thus a better perspective on long-term, rather than transient, effects. Once a field was selected, we surveyed it in subsequent years unless permission for further access was denied or the field was planted to small grains or row

crops. We did not select any new CRP fields after 1993.

In the northern Great Plains, most CRP fields were left idle during their contract period, although in nearly every year some CRP fields in the northern Great Plains were released for emergency haying and grazing because of drought or flooding in the region. In this study, these disturbances occurred from 1993 through 1996, and in only a small number of fields each year. The highest percentage of disturbance was in 1996 when 15% of the CRP fields in our study were wholly or partially hayed or, in rare cases, grazed. Although the conditions for releasing CRP lands for emergency haying and grazing varied from year to year, in every year the perturbations occurred after the birds were surveyed (15 July or later).

We surveyed breeding birds using a minor modification of the strip transect procedures used by Stewart and Kantrud (1972) and Igl and Johnson (1997). This method allows a fairly rapid assessment of the breeding birds in a field. Fields were surveyed once each year by one or two observers on foot. Small (≤32 ha) fields usually were surveyed by a single observer; large fields typically were surveyed by two observers, each covering about half of the field. The number and configuration of transects varied depending on field size and shape. Care was taken to avoid double-counting birds. We tallied all breeding pairs, based on singing or calling males, females, observed pairs, or presence of an active nest. We avoided censusing birds in adverse weather conditions (precipitation or winds > 24 km/hr). Surveys began about dawn and continued until midafternoon. Although some surveys were conducted outside the time of most active bird vocalizations (early morning or late evening), Stewart and Kantrud (1972) concluded that singing and other activities of open-country birds were not appreciably affected by time of day during the peak of the breeding season (also see Vickery 1995). We conducted surveys from late May to early July each year, which coincided with the peak breeding season of Le Conte's Sparrow (Stewart and Kantrud 1972, Stewart 1975).

We likely missed some breeding Le Conte's Sparrows in our single annual survey of CRP fields (see Järvinen and Lokki 1978). We used the same technique each year, however, so any bias, other than differences in observers, should be consistent. Stewart and Kantrud (1972) felt justified in estimating bird populations in open habitats using single counts because many species have behavioral adaptations (e.g., elevated perches, flight songs, synchronous displays) that tend to increase their detectability compared with birds inhabiting wooded areas (also see Cody 1985).

For each county we obtained data for long-term (1961–1990) average precipitation (May of previous year to April of current year) and annual deviations from the average, 1989–1996, taken at the nearest national weather station (National Oceanic and Atmospheric Administration [NOAA] 1987–1996). To describe moisture conditions in the study area, we obtained regional data for the Palmer Drought Severity Index (PDSI) for May of each year (NOAA 1997). The PDSI incorporates information on both moisture and temperature and expresses the severity of a wet (positive values) or dry (negative values) period by incor-

TABLE 1. NUMBER OF BREEDING PAIRS OF LE CONTE'S SPARROWS OBSERVED IN CONSERVATION RESERVE PROGRAM FIELDS IN THE NORTHERN GREAT PLAINS, 1990–1996

County	Number of breeding pairs						
	1990	1991	1992	1993	1994	1995	1996
Sheridan, MT	0	0	8	0	52	76	99
Eddy, ND	0	1	0	0	206	694	529
Kidder, ND	0	0	0	1	26	148	184
Hettinger, ND	0	0	0	0	0	0	7
McPherson, SD	0	0	0	0	0	47	106
Day, SD	0	0	0	0	2	101	190
Grant, MN	0	0	0	2	4	74	25
Totals	0	1	8	3	290	1,140	1,140

porating past and present conditions. Specifically, PDSI values of 0 to −0.5 indicate normal moisture conditions, −0.5 to −1.0 incipient drought, −1.0 to −2.0 mild drought, −2.0 to −3.0 moderate drought, −3.0 to −4.0 severe drought, and less than −4.0 extreme drought. Similar terms are associated with positive values and wet spells.

RESULTS

Between 1990 and 1996 we recorded 111 species of birds using CRP grassland fields in the northern Great Plains during the breeding season (L. Igl and D. Johnson, unpubl. data). The number of Le Conte's Sparrows in CRP fields was relatively low in 1990–1993 compared with 1994–1996; fewer than 1% of all breeding pairs were observed in the first 4 of the 7 yr (Table 1). Le Conte's Sparrows were not observed in any CRP field that we surveyed in 1990, the first year of this study. Between 1994 and 1996, Le Conte's Sparrow was one of the most abundant species in CRP fields in the northern Great Plains (Igl and Johnson 1995; L. Igl and D. Johnson, unpubl. data).

Most of the Le Conte's Sparrow's breeding range occurs north of our study area (Stewart 1975; Peterson 1980, 1990; AOU 1983; Janssen 1987; South Dakota Ornithologists' Union [SDOU] 1991; Montana Bird Distribution Committee [MBDC] 1996). Also, Le Conte's Sparrow abundance was not uniform across the region of the study (Table 1, Figs. 1 and 2). The species was most common in 1994–1996 in Eddy and Kidder Counties, North Dakota (Fig. 1), in the interior (albeit southern) portion of the species' breeding range. Le Conte's Sparrows were least abundant in the other five counties, which occur on the southern edge of (Day County, South Dakota; Grant County, Minnesota; and Sheridan County, Montana) or outside (Hettinger County, North Dakota, and McPherson County, South Dakota) the species' known breeding range (Stewart 1975; Peterson 1980, 1990; AOU 1983; Janssen 1987; SDOU 1991; MBDC 1996).

Our study included some of the driest and wettest years on record in the northern Great Plains (NOAA 1987–1996, 1997). Between 1987 and mid-1993, drought conditions occurred over much of the study area (Table 2, Fig. 2). Numerical increases of Le Conte's Sparrows began in 1994, coincident with dramatic increases in precipitation (Tables 1 and 2, Fig. 2). Changes in Le Conte's Sparrow densities generally paralleled changes in moisture conditions for the two counties in the interior of the species' breeding range (Fig. 2). Le Conte's Sparrows, however, exhibited a time lag or delayed numerical response to improved moisture conditions in all counties, especially those on the edge of or outside the species' typical breeding range (Fig. 2). In the extralimital counties (McPherson County, South Dakota, and Hettinger County, North Dakota), colonization of CRP fields coincided with dramatic increases in abundance in the interior of the species' breeding range (Tables 1 and 2, Fig. 2). Le Conte's Sparrows were absent from CRP fields in McPherson County until 1995 and in Hettinger County until 1996.

DISCUSSION

Between 1990 and 1996 we recorded four species of Ammodramus sparrows in the grassland habitats established by the CRP in the northern Great Plains: Baird's Sparrow (A. bairdii), Grasshopper Sparrow (A. savannarum), Nelson's Sharp-tailed Sparrow (A. nelsoni), and Le Conte's Sparrow (Johnson and Schwartz 1993a, b). Le Conte's Sparrow is among the most poorly known of these sympatric Ammodramus sparrows (Ehrlich et al. 1988). This likely reflects the species' secretive behavior, weak insect-like song, cryptic appearance, and sporadic distribution and abundance (Walkinshaw 1968, Murray 1969), as well as a general misconception about its habitat affinities (Robbins 1969, 1991). Le Conte's Sparrows also tend to be most vocal in the evening or at night (Murray 1969), a period when few observers visit the

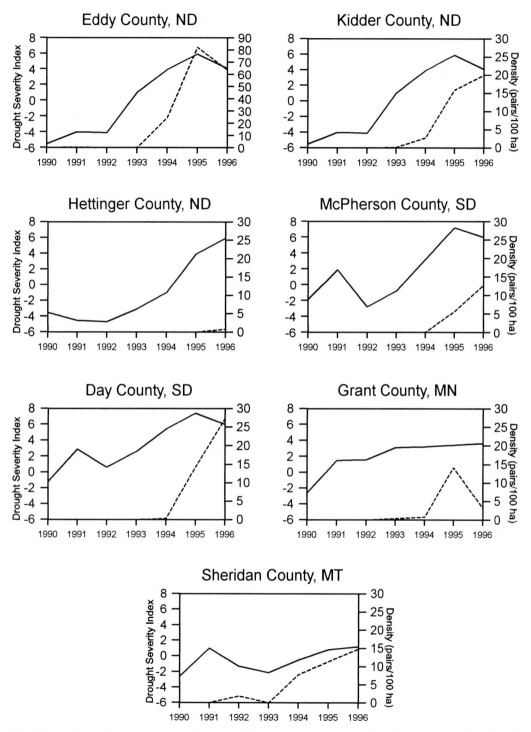

FIGURE 2. Palmer Drought Severity Index (solid lines) and breeding densities (dashed lines) of Le Conte's Sparrows in CRP fields in seven counties in the northern Great Plains, 1990–1996.

TABLE 2. LONG-TERM (1961–1990) AVERAGE PRECIPITATION IN CENTIMETERS (MAY OF PREVIOUS YEAR TO APRIL OF CURRENT YEAR) AND ANNUAL DEVIATIONS FROM THE AVERAGE PRECIPITATION, 1989–1996, TAKEN AT THE NATIONAL WEATHER STATION NEAREST EACH STUDY AREA

County	Long-term average	Deviation from the long-term average						
		1989–90	1990–91	1991–92	1992–93	1993–94	1994–95	1995–96
Sheridan, MT	32.39	−8.36	+1.57	+10.26	−6.38	+24.92	+2.03	+0.15
Eddy, ND	45.72	+0.58	−2.11	+3.71	−8.33	+22.81	+9.00	+9.45
Kidder, ND	41.10	−13.87	+6.35	+1.83	−7.67	+19.66	+15.42	+11.40
Hettinger, ND	41.88	−13.43	−11.68	−9.34	−13.86	+20.25	+0.64	+4.04
McPherson, SD	40.18	−10.41	+12.57	−9.02	+18.03	+39.29	+15.22	+19.38
Day, SD	53.49	+3.91	+1.40	+11.94	−6.30	+30.10	+12.27	+2.26
Grant, MN	64.72	−3.40	−3.38	+5.61	−1.37	+0.25	−4.50	−3.46

species' preferred breeding habitats (Sauer et al. 1995).

During the breeding season, Le Conte's Sparrows generally prefer moister grassland habitats than Baird's or Grasshopper sparrows and drier habitats than Nelson's Sharp-tailed Sparrows (AOU 1983). Although Le Conte's Sparrows tend to avoid areas with permanent standing water, their affinity for tall, dense vegetation in wet meadows and wetland edges has frequently been noted (Davis 1952, Murray 1969, Stewart 1975, Graber and Graber 1976, SDOU 1991). This has resulted in the species being known more as a wetland or wet-meadow species than as a grassland species (Johnsgard 1979, Maxwell et al. 1988).

It is less well known that moist habitats are not necessary for Le Conte's Sparrows during the breeding season (Walkinshaw 1937, Robbins 1969, Cooper 1984). Although Mengel (1970) did not consider Le Conte's Sparrow to be an endemic or secondary grassland bird, he grouped it with other marsh-inhabiting species (e.g., Nelson's Sharp-tailed Sparrow) that have secondary preferences for moist or dry grasslands. This flexibility in habitat selection presumably is not of recent origin (e.g., in response to changes in agriculture) and likely reflects the similarity in grassland-like vegetation structure that is characteristic of both wetlands and grasslands in the species' breeding range. Nonetheless, changes in land use after European settlement probably have influenced the distribution of suitable habitats for this species (Lowther 1996).

In addition to breeding in native prairie, Le Conte's Sparrows regularly breed in other upland grass areas, including pasture, hayland, and retired cropland (Stewart 1975, AOU 1983, Cooper 1984, Renken and Dinsmore 1987, Robbins 1991, Hartley 1994, Igl and Johnson 1995, Madden 1996, Prescott and Murphy 1996). The grassland habitats established by the CRP are similar to the upland habitats used by Le Conte's

Sparrows elsewhere in their breeding range. Although vegetation composition varied considerably among fields and counties (Johnson and Schwartz 1993b, Igl and Johnson 1995), most CRP land in this study was planted to a mixture of grasses (mostly cool season) and legumes. In Saskatchewan, Hartley (1994) reported that Le Conte's Sparrow was the second most abundant species in native prairie and the most abundant species in grasslands dominated by grass-legume mixtures and managed for waterfowl production. In Alberta, Prescott and Murphy (1996) reported that Le Conte's Sparrows were more common in pastures dominated by exotic grasses and legumes than in native pastures. In North Dakota, Renken and Dinsmore (1987) found Le Conte's Sparrows in grasslands dominated by grass-legume mixtures and managed for waterfowl production, but in contrast to Hartley (1994) and Prescott and Murphy (1996), they did not find this species in native mixed-grass prairie. Also in North Dakota, Madden (1996) noted the species' affinity for areas dominated by broad-leaved exotic grasses over native prairie.

In semiarid environments such as the northern Great Plains, extreme wet or dry conditions may cause increases, decreases, or no changes in bird populations (e.g., George et al. 1992). Our results indicate that the dramatic population increases of Le Conte's Sparrows during the breeding season coincided with the occurrence of wet conditions (or the amelioration of drought conditions) in the northern Great Plains. This finding was consistent with the anecdotal, but somewhat vague, reports of Peabody (1901), Stewart (1975), Knapton (1979), and Zimmer (1979), each suggesting that Le Conte's Sparrows were more abundant or common during wet years than dry years. Madden (1996) also reported dramatic increases in Le Conte's Sparrow abundance in North Dakota between 1993 and 1994, and she attributed these increases to improved moisture conditions in the region. Le

Conte's Sparrows also appear to respond to wet conditions during migration and on their wintering grounds (Grzybowski 1980, Lowther 1996). Although climatic variability may have been a factor leading to these dramatic fluctuations in Le Conte's Sparrow distribution and abundance, our data shed little light on the mechanisms underlying these patterns of population change. Nonetheless, these large population fluctuations suggest strong selection for coping with unpredictable resources in a variable environment.

In general, most birds do not respond directly to a climatic condition such as a prolonged wet or dry period; instead their response is indirect and tempered by the direct effects of climate on primary and secondary production (Wiens 1986, Rotenberry et al. 1995). The suitability of grassland habitats for birds is strongly influenced by floristic composition and vegetation structure (Cody 1985) as well as food resource availability (Wiens 1986, George et al. 1992). Although we did not collect data on annual changes in vegetation structure or food resource availability in the CRP grassland fields, it is reasonable to assume that the extreme variations in moisture availability influenced primary and secondary resources in these grasslands (Wiens 1986, George et al. 1992). Unlike habitats dominated by woody perennials, grasslands are dominated by mostly herbaceous vegetation (grasses, annuals, and some perennials), which responds relatively quickly to climate changes (Wiens 1986). A species' response to a climatic condition, however, may not be immediate. Primary and secondary resources may change through time in response to environmental variation. Additional time lags occur in the conversion of these changes in resources into variations in grassland bird abundance (Wiens 1986).

Data from this study indicate that Le Conte's Sparrows are capable of locating available habitat opportunistically. Dramatic changes of this nature in distribution and abundance have been documented for other grassland and wetland species that breed in the Great Plains and winter elsewhere (e.g., George et al. 1992, Zimmerman 1992). Johnson and Grier (1988) found that grassland-nesting ducks migrating north to their breeding grounds tend to fill breeding habitat in the southern portion of their breeding ranges first. During dry years, however, several species of ducks arriving on the breeding grounds respond by over-flying southern portions of their breeding range, apparently in search of more suitable habitat in the northern portion of the range (Johnson and Grier 1988). Similarly, Baird's Sparrows are more common in northern portions of their breeding range when areas in the southern portions of the range are experiencing drought conditions, and they are less common in the north when areas in the south are experiencing wet conditions (Kantrud and Faanes 1979). Roth (1979) and others (Oberholser and Kinkaid 1974, Robbins and Van Velzen 1974, Fretwell 1986) also alluded to this pattern for Dickcissels (*Spiza americana*), which nest in the extreme southern portion of their range during wet years, when herbaceous vegetation is lush, but continue north during dry years when conditions are poor for nesting. Roth (1979) suggested that this behavior represents past selection to compensate for unpredictable weather and vegetation conditions.

Although the concept of climate-driven shifts in grassland bird populations is pervasive in the literature, our understanding of these population fluctuations and their conservation implications is poor. Skagen and Knopf (1994) suggested that species that use disjunct patches of changing habitat in an irregular fashion may be the most difficult species to protect in the Great Plains. The large fluctuations in the abundance and distribution of Le Conte's Sparrows emphasize the importance of large-scale conservation efforts such as the CRP for grassland birds. Although the CRP is primarily an agricultural commodities program, many grassland birds have benefited from the network of perennial grasslands established by this program throughout the Great Plains (Johnson and Schwartz 1993a, b; Kantrud 1993; Reynolds et al. 1994; Johnson and Igl 1995; Patterson and Best 1996). The dramatic increase in Le Conte's Sparrow abundance in CRP fields since 1994, however, suggests that these perennial grasslands in the southern portion of the species' breeding range may be an important breeding habitat for this species only under moist conditions (Igl and Johnson 1995). Thus, conservation of grassland birds poses a special challenge that requires an assessment of a species' habitat needs in different portions of its breeding range under various conditions. Managers and policy makers should recognize that negative impacts (e.g., loss and fragmentation of grassland habitat) in a portion of the Great Plains could affect grassland birds that use that area only under certain conditions. Unfortunately, some conservation and land set-aside programs, such as the CRP, terminate at international or political borders, whereas breeding ranges and annual shifts in grassland bird populations may involve two or more countries (Johnson and Grier 1988).

In the early years of this study, it was readily apparent that the densities of breeding birds in a county reflected the uneven geographical distributions of a particular species (Johnson and Schwartz 1993b). Data from more recent years also indicate the value of long-term over short-term approaches to studies of grassland breeding birds. In this study, Le Conte's Sparrows were absent or rare in some years and abundant in others. Wiens (1974) noted similar changes in Grasshopper Sparrow populations in Texas; Grasshopper Sparrows were rare or absent during a severe and widespread drought but abundant the year after the drought. Because grassland bird populations fluctuate naturally and dramatically, short-term studies may provide a misleading picture of a changing population captured at one point in time (Wiens 1986). Additionally, a species' response to climatic variation may not be immediate; it may take 1 yr or more for a numerical response to occur. Thus, the probability of observing patterns of population change associated with changes in climate increases with longer term observations.

ACKNOWLEDGMENTS

We thank C. J. Johnson, R. L. Manson, L. A. Murphy, K. L. Richardson, M. D. Schwartz, C. M. Shoemaker, M. L. Sondreal, J. M. Steiner, and K. A. Ward for assistance in the field. Without the cooperation of the numerous landowners and operators who allowed access to their property, this study would not have been possible. We appreciate the cooperation of the U.S. Department of Agriculture's Farm Service Agency (formerly Agricultural Stabilization and Conservation Service) state directors and the executive directors and staffs of county Farm Service Agency offices who provided information on CRP fields. H. A. Kantrud, D. L. Larson, D. W. Sample, M. D. Schwartz, P. D. Vickery, and one anonymous reviewer provided helpful comments that greatly improved this paper.

LITERATURE CITED

AMERICAN ORNITHOLOGISTS' UNION. 1983. Check-list of North American birds. 6th ed. American Ornithologists' Union, Washington, D.C.

BETHKE, R. W., AND T. D. NUDDS. 1995. Effects of climate change and land use on duck abundance in Canadian prairie-parkland. Ecological Applications 5:588–600.

BRAGG, T. B. 1995. The physical environment of Great Plains grasslands. Pp. 49–81 in A. Joern and K. H. Keeler (editors). The changing prairie: North American grasslands. Oxford University Press, New York, NY.

CODY, M. L. 1985. Habitat selection in grassland and open-country birds. Pp. 191–226 in M. L. Cody (editor). Habitat selection in birds. Academic Press, Orlando, FL.

COOPER, S. 1984. Habitat and size of the Le Conte's Sparrow's territory. Loon 56:162–165.

DAVIS, D. E. 1952. Le Conte's Sparrow in western Montana. Condor 54:115–116.

DROEGE, S., AND J. R. SAUER. 1989. North American Breeding Bird Survey annual summary 1988. U.S. Fish and Wildlife Service Biological Report 89(13).

DROEGE, S., AND J. R. SAUER. 1994. Are more North American species decreasing than increasing? Pp.

297–306 in E. J. M. Hagemeijer and T. J. Verstrael (editors). Bird numbers 1992: distribution, monitoring and ecological aspects. Proceedings of the 12th International Conference of IBCC and EOAC, Noordwijkerhout, Netherlands. Statistics Netherlands, Voorburg/Heerlen, and SOVON, Beek-Ubbergen, Netherlands.

EHRLICH, P. R., D. S. DOBKIN, AND D. WHEYE. 1988. The birder's handbook: a field guide to the natural history of North American birds. Simon and Schuster, New York, NY.

FRETWELL, S. 1986. Distribution and abundance of the Dickcissel. Current Ornithology 4:211–242.

GEORGE, T. L., A. C. FOWLER, R. L. KNIGHT, AND L. C. MCEWEN. 1992. Impacts of a severe drought on grassland birds in western North Dakota. Ecological Applications 2:275–284.

GORIUP, P. D. (EDITOR). 1988. Ecology and conservation of grassland birds. ICBP Technical Publication no. 7. International Council for Bird Preservation, Cambridge, U.K.

GRABER, J. W., AND R. R. GRABER. 1976. Environmental evaluations using birds and their habitats. Illinois Natural History Survey Biological Notes no. 97.

GRZYBOWSKI, J. A. 1980. Ecological relationships among grassland birds during winter. Ph.D. dissertation. University of Oklahoma, Norman, OK.

HARTLEY, M. J. 1994. Passerine abundance and productivity indices in grasslands managed for waterfowl nesting cover in Saskatchewan, Canada. M.S. thesis. Louisiana State University, Baton Rouge, LA.

HERKERT, J. R. 1997. Bobolink Dolichonyx oryzivorus population declines in agricultural landscapes in the midwestern USA. Biological Conservation 80:107–112.

IGL, L. D., AND D. H. JOHNSON. 1995. Dramatic increase in Le Conte's Sparrow in Conservation Reserve Program fields in the northern Great Plains. Prairie Naturalist 27:89–94.

IGL, L. D., AND D. H. JOHNSON. 1997. Changes in breeding bird populations in North Dakota: 1967 to 1992–93. Auk 114:74–92.

JANSSEN, R. B. 1987. Birds in Minnesota. University of Minnesota Press, Minneapolis, MN.

JÄRVINEN, O., AND J. LOKKI. 1978. Indices of community structure in bird censuses based on a single visit: effect of variation in species efficiency. Ornis Scandinavica 9:87–93.

JOHNSGARD, P. A. 1979. Birds of the Great Plains: breeding species and their distributions. University of Nebraska Press, Lincoln, NE.

JOHNSON, D. H., AND J. W. GRIER. 1988. Determinants of breeding distributions of ducks. Wildlife Monograph 100:1–37.

JOHNSON, D. H., AND L. D. IGL. 1995. Contributions of the Conservation Reserve Program to populations of breeding birds in North Dakota. Wilson Bulletin 107:709–718.

JOHNSON, D. H., AND M. D. SCHWARTZ. 1993a. The Conservation Reserve Program and grassland birds. Conservation Biology 7:934–937.

JOHNSON, D. H., AND M. D. SCHWARTZ. 1993b. The Conservation Reserve Program: habitat for grassland birds. Great Plains Research 3:273–295.

KANTRUD, H. A. 1993. Duck nest success on Conservation Reserve Program land in the prairie pothole region. Journal of Soil and Water Conservation 48: 238–242.

KANTRUD, H. A., AND C. A. FAANES. 1979. Range expansion of Baird's Sparrow in South Dakota. Prairie Naturalist 11:111–112.

KNAPTON, R. W. 1979. Birds of the Gainsborough-Lyleton region (Saskatchewan and Manitoba). Special Publication no. 10, Saskatchewan Natural History Society, Regina, SK.

KNOPF, F. L., AND F. B. SAMSON. 1997. Conservation of grassland vertebrates. Pp. 273–289 *in* F. L. Knopf and F. B. Samson (editors). Ecology and conservation of Great Plains vertebrates. Springer-Verlag, New York, NY.

LOWTHER, P. E. 1996. Le Conte's Sparrow (*Ammodramus leconteii*). *In* A. Poole and F. Gill (editors). The birds of North America, no. 224. Academy of Natural Sciences, Philadelphia, PA, and American Ornithologists' Union, Washington, D.C.

MADDEN, E. M. 1996. Passerine communities and bird-habitat relationships on prescribe-burn, mixed-grass prairie in North Dakota. M.S. thesis. Montana State University, Bozeman, MT.

MAXWELL, T. C, D. E. MADDEN, AND R. C. DAWKINS. 1988. Status of Le Conte's Sparrow, *Ammodramus leconteii* (Emberizidae), wintering in western Texas. Southwestern Naturalist 33:373–375.

MENGEL, R. M. 1970. The North American central plains as an isolating agent in bird speciation. Pp. 280–340 *in* W. Dort and J. K. Jones (editors). Pleistocene and recent environments of the central Great Plains. University of Kansas Press, Lawrence, KS.

MONTANA BIRD DISTRIBUTION COMMITTEE. 1996. P. D. Skaar's Montana bird distribution. 5th ed. Special Publication no. 3, Montana Natural Heritage Program, Helena, MT.

MURRAY, B. G., JR. 1969. A comparative study of the Le Conte's and Sharp-tailed sparrows. Auk 86:199–231.

NATIONAL OCEANIC AND ATMOSPHERIC ADMINISTRATION. 1987–1996. Climatological data for Minnesota, Montana, North Dakota, and South Dakota. U.S. Department of Commerce, Asheville, NC.

NATIONAL OCEANIC AND ATMOSPHERIC ADMINISTRATION. 1997. National Climatic Data Center home page: climate division precipitation, temperature, and drought data. Www.ncdc.noaa.gov/onlineprod/drought/xmgr.html.

OBERHOLSER, H. C., AND E. B. KINKAID, JR. 1974. The birdlife of Texas. University of Texas Press, Austin, TX.

PATTERSON, M. P., AND L. B. BEST. 1996. Bird abundance and nesting success in Iowa CRP fields: the importance of vegetation structure and composition. American Midland Naturalist 135:153–167.

PEABODY, P. B. 1901. Nesting habits of Le Conte's Sparrow. Auk 18:129–134.

PETERJOHN, B. G., AND J. R. SAUER. 1993. North American Breeding Bird Survey annual summary, 1990–1991. Bird Populations 1:52–67.

PETERSON, R. T. 1980. A field guide to the birds. 4th ed. Houghton Mifflin, Boston, MA.

PETERSON, R. T. 1990. A field guide to western birds. 3d ed. Houghton Mifflin, Boston, MA.

PRESCOTT, D. R. C., AND A. J. MURPHY. 1996. Habitat associations of grassland birds on native and tame pastures in the aspen parkland of Alberta. Alberta North American Waterfowl Management Plan Centre, Edmonton, AB.

RENKEN, R. B., AND J. J. DINSMORE. 1987. Nongame bird communities on managed grasslands in North Dakota. Canadian Field-Naturalist 101:551–557.

REYNOLDS, R. E., T. L. SHAFFER, J. R. SAUER, AND B. G. PETERJOHN. 1994. Conservation Reserve Program: benefit for grassland birds in the northern plains. Transactions of the North American Wildlife and Natural Resources Conference 59:328–336.

ROBBINS, C. S., AND W. T. VAN VELZEN. 1974. Progress report on the North American Breeding Bird Survey. Acta Ornithologica 14:170–191.

ROBBINS, S. 1969. New light on the Le Conte's Sparrow. Passenger Pigeon 31:267–274.

ROBBINS, S. D., JR. 1991. Wisconsin birdlife. University of Wisconsin Press, Madison, WI.

ROTENBERRY, J. T., R. J. COOPER, J. M. WUNDERLE, AND K. G. SMITH. 1995. When and how are populations limited? The roles of insect outbreaks, fire, and other natural perturbations. Pp. 55–84 *in* T. E. Martin and D. M. Finch (editors). Ecology and management of neotropical migratory birds: a synthesis and review of critical issues. Oxford University Press, New York, NY.

ROTENBERRY, J. T., AND J. A. WIENS. 1991. Weather and reproductive variation in shrubsteppe sparrows: a hierarchical analysis. Ecology 72:1325–1335.

ROTH, R. R. 1979. Vegetation as a determinant in avian ecology. Pp. 162–175 *in* D. L. Drawe (editor). Proceedings of the First Welder Wildlife Foundation Symposium. Contribution B-7, Welder Wildlife Foundation, Sinton, TX.

SAUER, J. R., B. G. PETERJOHN, S. SCHWARTZ, AND J. E. HINES. 1995. The grassland bird home page. Ver. 95.0: www.mbr.nbs.gov/bbs/grass/grass.htm. U.S. Geological Survey, Patuxent Wildlife Research Center, Laurel, MD.

SKAGEN, S. K., AND F. L. KNOPF. 1994. Migrating shorebirds and habitat dynamics at a prairie wetland complex. Wilson Bulletin 106:91–105.

SOUTH DAKOTA ORNITHOLOGISTS' UNION. 1991. The birds of South Dakota. Northern State University Press, Aberdeen, SD.

STEWART, R. E. 1975. Breeding birds of North Dakota. Tri-College Center for Environmental Studies, Fargo, ND.

STEWART, R. E., AND H. A. KANTRUD. 1972. Population estimates of breeding birds in North Dakota. Auk 89:766–788.

VICKERY, P. D. 1995. Grassland bird detectability in New England. U.S. Fish and Wildlife Service, Hadley, MA.

WALKINSHAW, L. H. 1937. Le Conte's Sparrows breeding in Michigan and South Dakota. Auk 54:309–320.

WALKINSHAW, L. H. 1968. Le Conte's Sparrow. Pp. 765–778 *in* A. C. Bent (editor). Life histories of North American cardinals, grosbeaks, buntings, towhees, finches, sparrows, and allies. U.S. National Museum Bulletin 237, pt. 2.

WIENS, J. A. 1974. Climatic instability and the "ecological saturation" of bird communities in North American grasslands. Condor 76:385–400.

WIENS, J. A. 1986. Spatial scale and temporal variation in studies of shrubsteppe birds. Pp. 159–172 *in* T. J. Case and J. M. Diamond (editors). Community ecology. Harper and Row, New York, NY.

YOUNG, E. C., AND C. T. OSBORN. 1990. Costs and benefits of the Conservation Reserve Program. Journal of Soil and Water Conservation 45:370–373.

ZIMMER, K. J. 1979. A birder's guide to North Dakota. L & P Press, Denver, CO.

ZIMMERMAN, J. L. 1992. Density-independent factors affecting the avian diversity of the tallgrass prairie community. Wilson Bulletin 104:85–94.

Studies in Avian Biology No. 19:187–195, 1999.

DENSITY AND FLEDGING SUCCESS OF GRASSLAND BIRDS IN CONSERVATION RESERVE PROGRAM FIELDS IN NORTH DAKOTA AND WEST-CENTRAL MINNESOTA

ROLF R. KOFORD

Abstract. The Conservation Reserve Program, initiated in 1985, was designed primarily to reduce soil erosion and crop surpluses. A secondary benefit was the provision of habitat for wildlife. Grassland bird populations, many of which declined in the decades prior to the Conservation Reserve Program, may have benefited from the Conservation Reserve Program if reproduction in this newly available habitat has been at least as high as it would have been in the absence of the Conservation Reserve Program. On study areas in North Dakota and Minnesota, I examined breeding densities and fledging success of grassland birds in Conservation Reserve Program fields and in an alternative habitat of similar structure, idle grassland fields on federal Waterfowl Production Areas. Fields were 10 to 25 hectares in size. The avifaunas of these two habitats were similar, although brush-dependent species were more abundant on Waterfowl Production Areas. The common species in these habitats included ones whose continental populations have declined, such as Grasshopper Sparrow (*Ammodramus savannarum*), Savannah Sparrow (*Passerculus sandwichensis*), and Bobolink (*Dolichonyx oryzivorus*). These ground-nesting species were pooled with other ground nesters in an analysis of fledging success, which revealed no significant differences between habitats, between states, or among years (1991–1993). Predation was the primary cause of nest failure. I concluded that Conservation Reserve Program fields in this region were suitable breeding habitat for several species whose populations had declined prior to the Conservation Reserve Program era. This habitat appeared to be as secure for nests of ground-nesting birds as another suitable habitat in North Dakota and Minnesota.

LA DENSIDAD Y EL ÉXITO DE LOS POLLUELOS VOLANTONES DE AVES DE PASTIZAL EN CAMPOS DEL PROGRAMA DE RESERVAS DE CONSERVACIÓN EN DAKOTA DEL NORTE Y EN EL OESTE CENTRAL DE MINNESOTA

Sinopsis. El Programa de Reservas de Conservación, iniciado en 1985, fue diseñado principalmente para reducir la erosión de la tierra y los excedentes de cosechas. La disposición de hábitat para la fauna silvestre constituyó un beneficio secundario. Las poblaciones de aves de pastizal, muchas de las cuales disminuyeron durante las décadas anteriores al Programa de Reservas de Conservación, pueden haberse beneficiado con el Programa de Reservas de Conservación si su reproducción en este nuevo hábitat disponible ha sido por lo menos tan alta como habría sido sin el Programa de Reservas de Conservación. En áreas de estudio en Dakota del Norte y en Minnesota examiné las densidades reproductivas y el éxito de los polluelos volantones de aves de pastizal en campos del Programa de Reservas de Conservación y en otro hábitat de estructura similar: los campos de pastizal fuera de producción en Áreas de Producción para Aves Acuáticas del gobierno federal. El tamaño de los campos varió entre 10 y 25 hectáreas. Las avifaunas de estos dos hábitats fueron similares, aunque las especies que dependían de broza fueron más abundantes en las Áreas de Producción para Aves Acuáticas. Las especies comunes en estos hábitats incluyeron algunas poblaciones continentales que han disminuido, como el Gorrión Chapulín (*Ammodramus savannarum*), el Gorrión Sabanero (*Passerculus sandwichensis*) y el Tordo Arrocero (*Dolichonyx oryzivorus*). Estas especies que anidan en suelo fueron reunidas con otras especies que anidan en suelo en un análisis del éxito de los polluelos volantones, que no reveló ninguna diferencia significativa entre hábitats, entre estados o entre años (1991–1993). La depredación fue la causa principal del fracaso de los nidos. Concluí que los campos del Programa de Reservas de Conservación en esta región fueron el hábitat adecuado de reproducción para varias especies cuyas poblaciones habían disminuido antes del Programa de Reservas de Conservación. Para los nidos de las aves que anidan en suelo este hábitat parecía ser tan seguro como otro hábitat adecuado en Dakota del Norte y en Minnesota.

Key Words: Bobolink; Conservation Reserve Program; Grasshopper Sparrow; grassland birds; habitat quality; nest success; North Dakota; Minnesota; productivity; Savanna Sparrow; Waterfowl Production Areas.

Several species of grassland birds are significantly less numerous in North America in the mid-1990s than they were in the mid-1960s, when extensive population monitoring began with the North American Breeding Bird Survey (BBS). More grassland species have undergone population declines than have other classes of birds (Askins 1993, Knopf 1994, Peterjohn et al. 1994, Herkert 1995).

Several factors may have contributed to these widespread declines. One important factor has been loss of habitat (Askins 1993, Herkert

1995). Although most of the original prairie was lost long before the BBS started, habitat loss has continued in recent decades (Herkert 1991, Samson and Knopf 1994). Grassland birds now breed in many kinds of grassland habitat that are structurally similar to various types of prairie vegetation. Recent population declines in the northeastern United States may be due largely to loss of old-field habitats that have undergone succession to woody vegetation unsuitable for grassland birds (Askins 1993). Habitat loss in the Midwest has been due to loss of pasture and hayland, along with a general loss of strip cover as farming has become more intensive (Herkert 1991, Askins 1993, Herkert et al. 1996). Alfalfa (*Medicago sativa*) has generally replaced more diverse vegetation as the primary source of hay (Bollinger et al. 1990, Warner 1994, Herkert et al. 1996). Older hayfields, which provide more diverse habitat, are usually not promoted by current practices (Bollinger 1995). Few species nest in row crops and small-grain fields, although many species nest in alfalfa fields, pastures, and idle grassland (Best et al. 1995). Finally, many of the small fields common in current agricultural landscapes do not attract the full suite of breeding grassland birds, perhaps because some species are area sensitive (Herkert 1994, Vickery et al. 1994, Warner 1994).

Low quality of suitable nesting habitat may have contributed to population declines of grassland birds (Askins 1993). Prairie remnants and fields of non-native grassland, although suitable for nesting, may be of lower quality than large expanses of prairie. Small fields have a high ratio of edge to area, and many fields have wooded edges that may contribute to high frequencies of nest predation and brood parasitism by Brown-headed Cowbirds (*Molothrus ater*; Best 1978; Gates and Gysel 1978; Graber and Graber 1983; Johnson and Temple 1986, 1990).

If habitat loss, fragmentation, and degradation have contributed to population declines, then restoration of large amounts of grassland would be expected to slow or reverse those declines. The Conservation Reserve Program (CRP), administered by the U.S. Department of Agriculture (USDA), dramatically increased the amount of grassland in the late 1980s, particularly in the tall- and mixed-grass regions of the central United States. The addition of this habitat presents the opportunity to evaluate the benefit to birds of restoring a large amount of grassland habitat.

The potential benefit from the CRP is enormous. This program has taken millions of hectares of highly erodible cropland, almost a tenth of U.S. cropland, out of production under 10-yr contracts (Johnson and Schwartz 1993). Except in the southeastern United States, most of this land was seeded with perennial grasses and legumes, creating suitable feeding and nesting habitat for some bird species but possibly eliminating some habitat for a few species that nest in cropland and very short vegetation (Basore et al. 1986, Johnson and Igl 1995, King and Savidge 1995). Fields enrolled in the CRP cannot be grazed but can be partially hayed in weather-related emergencies. Johnson and Schwartz (1993) examined bird use of CRP fields in the northern Great Plains and found that most grassland species had higher breeding densities in CRP fields than had been reported for cropland.

Among the species that have higher breeding densities in CRP fields than in cropland are several that declined in the central United States from 1966 to 1990 according to BBS data (Johnson and Schwartz 1993, Johnson and Igl 1995). These declining species include Grasshopper Sparrow (*Ammodramus savannarum*), Baird's Sparrow (*A. bairdii*), Clay-colored Sparrow (*Spizella pallida*), Dickcissel (*Spiza americana*), Lark Bunting (*Calamospiza melanocorys*), and Bobolink (*Dolichonyx oryzivorus*). Savannah Sparrow (*Passerculus sandwichensis*), which also had higher densities in CRP fields, has experienced a continental population decline (Peterjohn et al. 1994). Other studies have confirmed the widespread use of CRP fields by grassland birds (Granfors 1992, Millenbah 1993, Klute 1994, Patterson and Best 1996). The potential of the CRP to slow or reverse declines of these species (e.g., Reynolds et al. 1994) depends on whether birds nesting in CRP fields have higher reproductive success than they would have had in the absence of the CRP. Ducks such as the Mallard (*Anas platyrhynchos*), which also declined during the 1980s, had relatively high hatching success in CRP fields compared with hatching success on Waterfowl Production Area (WPA) fields (Kantrud 1993, Reynolds et al. 1994).

To compare CRP fields with another grassland habitat frequently used by grassland birds that have declined, I studied birds in CRP fields and in idle grasslands on WPA fields. Numerous WPA fields, mostly small tracts of grassland and wetlands in the U.S. prairie pothole region, are managed by the U.S. Fish and Wildlife Service (USFWS) to provide nesting and brood-rearing habitat for waterfowl. These fields attract all of the declining species listed above (Renken and Dinsmore 1987), although these species rarely nest in cropland, the habitat that CRP fields have replaced (Johnson and Schwartz 1993, Best et al. 1995). Thus, addition of CRP fields to the landscape has provided these species, which typically nest in hayfields and pastureland (Best et al. 1995), with an additional habitat they may find suitable for nesting.

To determine how similar the avifaunas of CRP and WPA fields were, I estimated densities of breeding birds on the study areas. I also estimated fledging success. Variation in fledging success probably contributes greatly to variation in reproductive success, and techniques for monitoring nests are better developed than are techniques for estimating survival of juveniles.

METHODS

STUDY AREAS

I selected two study areas: Stutsman County in east-central North Dakota and Stevens and western Pope Counties in west-central Minnesota. These areas were chosen to represent mixed- and tallgrass regions of the northeastern Great Plains, respectively, and were studied from 1991 to 1993.

In each study area I identified idle WPAs with well-established grassland comprising at least 10 ha. Idle WPAs were not subjected to disturbance from farming activities, although normal management activities continued, such as prescribed burning (1 field, 1 yr) and mowing to control weeds (2 fields, 3 yr). Furthermore, idle WPAs did not experience variation in densities of breeding birds associated with variation in grazing intensity (Kantrud 1981, Kantrud and Kologiski 1982, Renken and Dinsmore 1987, Bowen and Kruse 1993). From the identified WPAs, I selected six in North Dakota and five in Minnesota that were dispersed throughout the study areas. All 11 WPA fields were bordered by potential perch sites (e.g., trees, fences, power lines) for Brown-headed Cowbirds, and some, especially the native-prairie fields, had woody vegetation in the field. Minnesota fields had been seeded with several native warm-season grasses. North Dakota fields were either native prairie (four fields, invaded by cool-season exotic grasses) or had been seeded with cool-season grasses in the 1970s (two fields).

With the assistance of personnel in the Farm Service Agency (formerly Agricultural Stabilization and Conservation Service) and Natural Resources Conservation Service (formerly Soil Conservation Service), both agencies of the USDA, I identified the CRP fields in the vicinity of each selected WPA. I chose the CRP field closest to a selected WPA field that met four criteria: (1) it was not adjacent to a selected WPA field, (2) it comprised 10–16 ha, (3) it was enrolled in the CRP prior to 1989, and (4) it had potential cowbird perches on at least one side. In a few cases I had to use a portion of a larger field because a field smaller than 16 ha was not available. All CRP fields were dominated by cool-season grasses.

The same WPA and CRP fields were studied in all 3 yr (1991–1993) except for one CRP field that was replaced by a nearby field in 1992 after the initial field was flooded in 1991.

ESTIMATING DENSITY

Each year, birds were counted twice on each field between 26 May and 23 July. I established parallel transect lines 100 m apart to cover the entire field. Data were collected on distance (using rangefinders) and angle relative to the transect line for each bird seen, according to truncated line-transect methodology (Burnham et al. 1980, Buckland et al. 1993). This method used counts of observed birds to derive density estimates that accounted for birds that were not observed. The primary assumption was that all birds on the transect line itself were seen. Detectability decreased with perpendicular distance from the transect line, and the method estimated the shape of this detection function. Another assumption was that each individual bird was counted only once, where it was first observed. We attempted to track the movements of birds that were observed flying from one transect to another, although this was especially difficult for male Bobolinks early in the nesting season (see below). To minimize the likelihood of double-counting birds that moved unobserved between transects, we avoided surveying adjacent transects consecutively. Transect lines were walked at a pace of 1.5–2.0 km/hr between sunrise and 1300 central daylight time (Dawson 1981). Surveys were not conducted during rain, if the temperature was below 0 C or above 32 C, or when the wind speed exceeded 30 km/hr (Dawson 1981).

Density was estimated from 1992 data with program DISTANCE (Buckland et al. 1993) using a polynomial function to model the detectability function. This program emphasizes estimation of parameters rather than tests of hypotheses. The 95% confidence intervals were tabulated for the density estimates. Densities are likely to be truly different if their confidence intervals do not overlap.

For most species, I report estimates from the first count each year because the second count may have been confounded by the inclusion of some fledglings. The exception was the Bobolink, for which I report data from the second count each year. Estimated densities of Bobolinks were notably higher in the first count. Bollinger et al. (1988) noted that Bobolink densities were easily overestimated with transect methodologies. To the extent that this overestimation was related to the frequent long-distance flights of males early in the nesting season, the estimates from the second count probably more accurately reflect the breeding densities for this species. The estimates were intended to represent species nesting in the study fields. Thus, I have not reported densities of Yellow-headed Blackbirds (*Xanthocephalus xanthocephalus*), which frequently were seen foraging in our study fields in Minnesota.

ESTIMATING FLEDGING SUCCESS

Most nests were found with the aid of a 25-m rope, weighted with sections of chain and aluminum pipe. Two people pulled the rope, and one to three observers walked behind the rope to observe birds that flushed from nests and to find the nests. Two nest searches were conducted in 1991 and three in 1992 and 1993. Some nests were found opportunistically or incidental to other field activities. We identified the nesting species from the appearance of the flushed bird, eggs, or nestlings. We placed flagged wires 4 m from each nest in a randomly selected cardinal direction and marked nest locations on field maps. Nestling ages, estimated by noting body size and development (Bent 1942:350;

TABLE 1.   NUMBERS SEEN, ESTIMATED DENSITIES (BIRDS/10 HA), AND 95% CONFIDENCE INTERVALS (CI) FOR DENSITY ESTIMATES FOR BIRDS COUNTED ON CONSERVATION RESERVE PROGRAM (CRP) OR WATERFOWL PRODUCTION AREA (WPA) FIELDS IN STUTSMAN COUNTY, NORTH DAKOTA, AND STEVENS AND POPE COUNTIES, MINNESOTA

State	CRP			WPA		
Species	N	Density	CI	N	Density	CI
North Dakota						
Eastern Kingbird	0	–		18	3.4	1.9–6.3
Common Yellowthroat	6	–		0	–	
Clay-colored Sparrow	4	–		24	4.9	2.4–9.9
Savannah Sparrow	13	2.4	1.0–5.8	10	–	
Grasshopper Sparrow	45	8.0	4.1–15.6	14	2.1	1.2–4.0
Bobolink	7	–		6	–	
Red-winged Blackbird	58	10.8	5.5–20.7	3	–	
Western Meadowlark	9	–		4	–	
Brown-headed Cowbird	7	–		11	2.5	0.8–7.3
Minnesota						
Common Yellowthroat	7	–		1	–	
Clay-colored Sparrow	1	–		15	4.7	1.5–14.0
Savannah Sparrow	13	3.6	1.9–6.8	41	12.3	8.8–17.3
Grasshopper Sparrow	19	4.2	1.6–11.1	6	–	
Bobolink	13	4.5	1.8–11.3	13	3.7	1.2–11.1
Red-winged Blackbird	11	5.9	1.3–25.7	2	–	
Western Meadowlark	0	–		1	–	
Brown-headed Cowbird	10	–		1	–	

Note: Estimates are from the first survey, 27 May–15 June 1992, except for Bobolink estimates, which are from the second survey, 11 June–9 July 1992. Densities were estimated only for species in which more than 10 individuals were seen.

1968:171–172; Fairfield 1968:1643–1644; Smith 1968:732), were used to estimate fledging dates.

Nests were visited at intervals of 3–7 d. The final visit was shortly before fledging (i.e., 6–8 d old). Late nest visits (>8 d) were avoided so that field personnel did not induce nestlings to leave the nest prematurely and did not have to judge whether or not any young had fledged from an empty nest. Such judgment would have required analysis of the appearance of the nest and the parental behavior of the adults, both of which might have been subject to error.

Fledging success is the probability that a nesting attempt (i.e., at least one egg laid) will produce at least one fledgling. I estimated fledging success with the Mayfield (1975) method for the entire nesting cycle, that is, not analyzing egg and nestling stages separately. Altricial species that nest on the ground were pooled for statistical analysis, to maximize the power of statistical tests. Ground nesters probably share many of the same nest predators. To estimate fledging success, I raised the estimated daily survival rates of nests to the 25th, 27th, or 29th power (Ehrlich et al. 1988).

Field personnel assigned each nest failure to the most likely cause. If eggs or nestlings were missing or damaged in a manner consistent with predation, failure was attributed to predation. If the nest was unattended and there was no change in the number of host eggs between visits, failure was attributed to abandonment. Abandonment between the first and second nest visit was attributed to investigator disturbance unless cowbird eggs had been added, in which case abandonment was attributed to cowbird parasitism. Other abandonments were not attributed to a specific cause, although some may in fact have been due to cowbird parasitism (see Elliott 1978, Koford et al. in press).

I used a Summary procedure (SAS Institute 1987) to tabulate fledging success by species for each study area and field type. I used a General Linear Model procedure (SAS Institute 1987) to examine variation in daily survival rates of nests of altricial ground-nesting birds between field types (CRP vs. WPA), between study areas (North Dakota vs. Minnesota), and among years (1991, 1992, and 1993). The response variable was an angular transformation (Steel and Torrie 1980) of daily survival rates of nests, weighted by exposure days. Fields were the sampling units. I used a blocked design structure with pairs of fields in each study area as blocks (Milliken and Johnson 1984). A repeated-measures analysis of variance was conducted to account for the non-independence of the fields, which were sampled in all 3 yr (Milliken and Johnson 1984). Statistical significance was indicated by $P < 0.05$. Least squares means (Milliken and Johnson 1984, SAS Institute 1987) were used in the analysis because samples of nests were not available from all fields in all years. Least squares means are the expected values of class or subclass means that would be expected for a balanced design and may be substantially different from arithmetic means. Nests that had apparently been abandoned because of investigator disturbance (N = 6) were not analyzed.

RESULTS

DENSITY

Nine species were fairly common in the grassland study fields (Table 1). In North Dakota, Eastern Kingbirds (*Tyrannus tyrannus*) and Clay-colored Sparrows, both of which nest in shrubs, were more abundant in WPA than in

TABLE 2.   Estimated fledging success of grassland birds for which at least 10 nests were monitored in 1991–1993 on Conservation Reserve Program (CRP) and Waterfowl Production Area (WPA) fields in Stutsman County, North Dakota, and Stevens and Pope Counties, Minnesota

| State | CRP | | | | WPA | | | |
Species	N	Exposure days	DSR	Fledging success (%)	N	Exposure days	DSR	Fledging success (%)
North Dakota								
Mourning Dove[a]	7	75.0	0.920	8.9[b]	3	41.0	1.0	100.0[b]
Clay-colored Sparrow	8	81.0	0.975	53.5[c]	49	422.5	0.934	18.0[c]
Vesper Sparrow[a]	6	59.0	0.949	27.1[c]	7	71.5	0.944	21.3[c]
Savannah Sparrow[a]	4	30.0	0.933	15.5	4	55.0	0.945	22.0
Grasshopper Sparrow[a]	38	347.5	0.950	28.5[c]	14	116.5	0.914	10.6[c]
Song Sparrow[a]	0	–	–	–	0	–	–	–
Bobolink[a]	8	78.5	0.975	47.3[b]	7	60.5	0.901	6.0[b]
Red-winged Blackbird	70	634.0	0.921	10.9	9	79.0	0.937	17.1
Western Meadowlark[a]	20	207.5	0.952	23.9[b]	13	79.5	0.874	2.0[b]
Minnesota								
Mourning Dove[a]	0	–	–	–	1	5.0	0.800	0.2[b]
Clay-colored Sparrow	1	11.0	0.909	9.2[c]	24	309.0	0.968	43.9[c]
Vesper Sparrow[a]	1	5.0	0.800	0.4[c]	1	2.0	0.500	0.0[c]
Savannah Sparrow[a]	12	81.0	0.864	1.9	30	259.0	0.950	24.9
Grasshopper Sparrow[a]	13	98.0	0.918	11.9[c]	1	16.0	1.0	100.0[c]
Song Sparrow[a]	8	74.0	0.946	22.3	9	66.5	0.910	7.8
Bobolink[a]	16	154.5	0.922	9.6[b]	31	269.5	0.926	10.7[b]
Red-winged Blackbird	25	153.0	0.856	1.5	1	7.0	1.0	100.0
Western Meadowlark[a]	6	88.5	0.955	26.1[b]	3	37.5	0.973	45.7[b]

Note: Number of nests (N), exposure days, daily survival rate (DSR) of nests, and fledging success (Mayfield estimate) are presented. Nesting cycles were assumed to be 27 d unless otherwise noted.
[a] Ground nests.
[b] 29-d nesting cycle assumed.
[c] 25-d nesting cycle assumed.

CRP fields. All of the Clay-colored Sparrows observed in WPA fields were in native-prairie fields that had western snowberry (*Symphoricarpos occidentalis*) shrubs. Grasshopper Sparrows and Red-winged Blackbirds (*Agelaius phoeniceus*), by contrast, were more abundant in CRP than in WPA fields. On about half of these CRP fields, Red-winged Blackbirds were by far the most abundant breeding birds; on the other fields their numbers ranged from zero to three birds per field. These differences are largely due to the variation among fields in the presence of vegetation such as sweetclover (*Melilotus* spp.), which supports nests and serves as song perches. Sweetclover, a biennial, would be expected to decline in abundance over time in many CRP fields.

In Minnesota, Clay-colored and Savannah sparrows were more abundant in WPA than in CRP fields. Almost all of the Clay-colored Sparrows seen in WPA fields were in one field; many nested in sweetclover. It is possible that Savannah Sparrows preferred the denser cover associated with WPA fields, which were dominated by warm-season grasses. Most CRP fields were dominated by cool-season grasses such as smooth brome (*Bromus inermis*).

FLEDGING SUCCESS

Estimates of fledging success were obtained for 657 nests, including 166 nests of precocial species (mostly dabbling ducks) which were not the focus of this paper. Among the altricial species for which at least 10 nests were monitored, estimated fledging success was variable (Table 2). A total of 263 ground nests, mostly of Savannah Sparrows, Grasshopper Sparrows, and Bobolinks (see Table 2), were pooled and analyzed statistically for differences in daily survival rate. There were no significant differences in fledging success between field types (P = 0.65), between states (P = 0.67), or among years (P = 0.06). None of the interaction terms was significant. I therefore failed to reject the primary null hypothesis of interest, that fledging success of ground nesters was the same in the two types of fields.

The great variability in daily survival rate of ground nests (Table 2) affected the reliability of the estimated daily survival rates of ground nests in the two field types (Table 3). The standard errors associated with the mean daily survival rates were quite large.

Predation was the overwhelming cause of nest

TABLE 3.   LEAST SQUARES MEAN DAILY SURVIVAL RATES (DSR) ± 1 SE FOR NESTS OF GROUND-NESTING SPECIES IN CONSERVATION RESERVE PROGRAM (CRP) AND WATERFOWL PRODUCTION AREA (WPA) FIELDS IN STUTSMAN COUNTY, NORTH DAKOTA, AND STEVENS AND POPE COUNTIES, MINNESOTA

Field type	DSR	DSR − 1 SE	DSR + 1 SE	Fledging success (%) for 27-d cycle
CRP	0.9458	0.9338	0.9566	22
WPA	0.9527	0.9417	0.9627	27

failure. For the nine species in Table 2, predation accounted for 80–96% of the nest losses. For most destroyed nests we have no information on the identity of nest predators. On two occasions we saw garter snakes (*Thamnophis* sp.) eating nestlings.

DISCUSSION

DENSITY

The CRP fields attracted the same species as did the WPA fields, with the exception of the Eastern Kingbird, which I did not observe in CRP fields. This species, however, was observed in CRP fields by Johnson and Schwartz (1993). Two species, Eastern Kingbird and Clay-colored Sparrow, appeared to be much more abundant in WPA fields. These species nest in shrubs, which occurred in some of the WPA fields but not in CRP fields. The CRP fields, which had been tilled before being enrolled in the CRP, had not been invaded by much woody vegetation. The dearth of Clay-colored Sparrows in CRP fields contrasts with counts as high as 12 indicated pairs per 100 ha (countywide average) reported by Johnson and Schwartz (1993) for CRP fields in the same general area.

Bobolinks and Savannah Sparrows, whose densities were similar in the two states, occurred in both CRP and WPA fields. These species were two of the most abundant in alfalfa-wheatgrass (*Agropyron* spp.) mixtures in North Dakota WPAs studied by Renken and Dinsmore (1987). In Minnesota the density of Savannah Sparrows was higher in WPA than in CRP fields. Grasshopper Sparrow densities were not significantly different between states, but in Minnesota they were higher in CRP than in WPA fields. Renken and Dinsmore (1987) found this species to be more abundant in native prairie than in alfalfa-wheatgrass mixtures.

FLEDGING SUCCESS

I found no significant difference in fledging success of ground nesters between WPA and CRP fields, leading me to conclude that fledging success was similar in these two kinds of fields. This similarity indicates that CRP fields provided nesting cover as safe for ground nesters as the other habitat I examined. Patterson and Best

(1996) estimated 30% fledging success (assuming a 23-d nesting cycle) for Grasshopper Sparrows in CRP fields in Iowa, which is very similar to the 28% fledging success calculated from the mean daily survival rate of ground nests in CRP fields (Table 3), assuming a 23-d cycle. Studies that have compared fledging success in CRP fields and pastures have found no significant differences between these habitats (Granfors 1992, Klute 1994). Thus, available evidence suggests that CRP fields are equivalent in quality to pastures and WPAs for the grassland birds that are common in CRP fields. In general, pasture and rangeland are much more common in midwestern landscapes than are CRP fields (Koford and Best 1996). The CRP fields appear to be better nesting habitat than hayfields, which also attract grassland birds. Fledging success tends to be low in hayfields because of nest losses from mowing operations (Bollinger et al. 1990).

Demonstrating that some habitats were of equivalent quality during the CRP era is not conclusive evidence that birds nesting in CRP fields had higher fledging success than they would have had in the absence of the CRP. The extensive CRP cover could have affected the distribution of birds and predators, making fledging success in suitable habitats different from what it would have been in the absence of the CRP. If one assumes, however, that recent estimates of fledging success in habitats other than CRP fields are similar to levels of fledging success in those habitats before the CRP era, and similar to what they would have been without the CRP, then the CRP has probably benefited grassland birds. The additional cover provided by CRP fields may have lowered breeding densities in all habitats, with possible benefits if reproduction is density dependent. The additional habitat also may have allowed birds to breed that otherwise would not have, such as second-year birds, thereby supporting higher population growth overall. The effect of loss of CRP habitat would be substantial for grassland species that nest in the dense cover provided by CRP fields (see also Johnson and Igl 1995).

Estimated fledging success of 22–27% (Table 3) appears to be relatively low but may be sufficient to maintain stable populations without immigration. Given this range of fledging success, if all pairs renested up to four times after failed nesting attempts, the percentage of pairs producing at least one fledgling in a nesting season would be 63% $(1.0 - [0.78]^4)$ to 72% $(1.0 - [0.73]^4)$. If each of these successful pairs fledged 3 young, the average production per pair in the population would be 1.9–2.1 fledglings per season. This level of reproduction is at the low end of the range expected for a stable population. Sherry and Holmes (1995) estimated that a pair of neotropical migrants would have to produce 1.7–4 fledglings per season to balance mortality. Rodenhouse et al. (1995), assuming only two nesting attempts, estimated that production of three fledglings would be necessary. More data are needed on mortality, renesting frequency, and double-brooding before definitive conclusions can be reached regarding the adequacy of fledging success in the CRP and WPA fields studied.

The relatively low estimated fledging success of grassland birds in this and other studies (Rodenhouse et al. 1995) raises questions about whether these estimates are accurate. It is possible that investigator effects caused the fledging-success estimates to be biased (Bart 1977, Westmoreland and Best 1985, Major 1990). Comparisons between treatments, as was done in this study, would be valid even if the estimates of fledging success were biased, assuming that biases were similar in all fields studied.

It is desirable to have studies of fledging success in CRP fields and other habitats from various geographic regions (e.g., Granfors 1992, Millenbah 1993, Klute 1994, Patterson and Best 1996). In parts of North Dakota and Minnesota, at least, this study indicates that the CRP provided nesting cover at least as safe as one other habitat. This suggests that declining species of grassland birds have probably benefited from this program which has converted so much former cropland to attractive nesting cover for grassland birds.

ACKNOWLEDGMENTS

I appreciate the hard work of my field assistants: J. Bates, B. Bolduan, D. Burt, L. Cox, J. Evanoff, S. Garcia, A. Halvorson, T. Hansted, J. Henderson, B. Hockenberry, L. Hoxtell, L. Huff, J. Hughes, T. Jenni, L. Joyal, D. Laird, K. MacDonald, G. Machart, R. Manson, W. Meeks, M. Moodie, K. Mullen, H. Muller, S. Norland, C. Shoemaker, E. Sincox, D. Storm, P. Sweet, L. Quinlan, W. Widdowson, and J. Woleslagle. I also appreciate the cooperation and congeniality of P. Arnold, G. Bober, C. Luna, and A. Radtke of the USFWS. K. Krueger and others in offices of the Farm Service Agency and Natural Resources Conservation Service were helpful. The study would have been impossible without the cooperation of numerous landowners who allowed us to study birds on their CRP fields. B. Bowen assisted with data analysis. J. Lokemoen shared ideas on study techniques. I appreciate the helpful comments on this paper by B. Bowen, L. Igl, and E. Klaas.

LITERATURE CITED

ASKINS, R. A. 1993. Population trends in grassland, shrubland, and forest birds in eastern North America. Current Ornithology 11:1–34.

BART, J. 1977. Impact of human visitations on avian nesting success. Living Bird 16:187–192.

BASORE, N. S., L. B. BEST, AND J. B. WOOLEY, JR. 1986. Bird nesting in Iowa no-tillage and tilled cropland. Journal of Wildlife Management 50:19–28.

BENT, A. C. 1942. Life histories of North American flycatchers, larks, swallows, and their allies. U.S. National Museum Bulletin 179.

BENT, A. C. 1968. Life histories of North American cardinals, grosbeaks, buntings, towhees, finches, sparrows, and allies. U.S. National Museum Bulletin 237.

BEST, L. B. 1978. Field Sparrow reproductive success and nesting ecology. Auk 95:9–22.

BEST, L. B., K. E. FREEMARK, J. J. DINSMORE, AND M. CAMP. 1995. A review and synthesis of bird habitat use in agricultural landscapes of Iowa. American Midland Naturalist 134:1–29.

BOLLINGER, E. K. 1995. Successional changes and habitat selection in hayfield bird communities. Auk 112: 720–730.

BOLLINGER, E. K., P. B. BOLLINGER, AND T. A. GAVIN. 1990. Effects of hay-cropping on eastern populations of the Bobolink. Wildlife Society Bulletin 18: 142–150.

BOLLINGER, E. K., T. A. GAVIN, AND D. C. MCINTYRE. 1988. Comparison of transects and circular-plots for estimating Bobolink densities. Journal of Wildlife Management 52:777–786.

BOWEN, B. S., AND A. KRUSE. 1993. Effects of grazing on nesting by Upland Sandpipers in southcentral North Dakota. Journal of Wildlife Management 57: 291–301.

BUCKLAND, S. T., D. R. ANDERSON, K. P. BURNHAM, AND J. L. LAAKE. 1993. Distance sampling: estimating abundance of biological populations. Chapman and Hall, London, U.K.

BURNHAM, K. P., D. R. ANDERSON, AND J. L. LAAKE. 1980. Estimation of density from line transect sampling of biological populations. Wildlife Monographs no. 72.

DAWSON, D. G. 1981. Counting birds for a relative measure (index) of density. Studies in Avian Biology 6:12–16.

EHRLICH, P. R., D. S. DOBKIN, AND D. WHEYE. 1988. The birder's handbook: a field guide to the natural history of North American birds. Simon & Schuster, New York, NY.

ELLIOTT, P. F. 1978. Cowbird parasitism in the Kansas tallgrass prairie. Auk 95:161–167.

FAIRFIELD, G. M. 1968. *Calcarius ornatus* (Townsend) Chestnut-collared Longspur. U.S. National Museum Bulletin 237, pt. 3:1635–1652.

GATES, J. E., AND L. W. GYSEL. 1978. Avian nest dispersion and fledging success in field-forest ecotones. Ecology 59:871–883.

GRABER, R. R., AND J. W. GRABER. 1983. The declining grassland birds. Illinois Natural History Survey Reports no. 227.

GRANFORS, D. A. 1992. The impact of the Conservation Reserve Program on Eastern Meadowlark production and validation of the Eastern Meadowlark habitat suitability index model. M.S. thesis. Texas Tech University, Lubbock, TX.

HERKERT, J. R. 1991. Prairie birds of Illinois: population response to two centuries of habitat change. Illinois Natural History Survey Bulletin 34:393–399.

HERKERT, J. R. 1994. The effects of habitat fragmentation on midwestern grassland bird communities. Ecological Applications 4:461–471.

HERKERT, J. R. 1995. An analysis of midwestern breeding bird population trends: 1966–1993. American Midland Naturalist 134:41–50.

HERKERT, J. R., D. W. SAMPLE, AND R. E. WARNER. 1996. Management of midwestern grassland landscapes for the conservation of migratory birds. Pp. 89–116 in F. R. Thompson III (editor). Management of midwestern landscapes for the conservation of neotropical migratory birds. USDA Forest Service Gen. Tech. Rep. NC-187. USDA Forest Service North Central Forest Experiment Station, St. Paul, MN.

JOHNSON, D. H., AND L. D. IGL. 1995. Contributions of the Conservation Reserve Program to populations of breeding birds in North Dakota. Wilson Bulletin 107:709–718.

JOHNSON, D. H., AND M. D. SCHWARTZ. 1993. The Conservation Reserve Program and grassland birds. Conservation Biology 7:934–937.

JOHNSON, R. G., AND S. A. TEMPLE. 1986. Assessing habitat quality for birds nesting in fragmented tallgrass prairies. Pp. 245–249 in J. Verner, M. L. Morrison, and C. J. Ralph (editors). Wildlife 2000: modeling habitat relationships of terrestrial vertebrates. University of Wisconsin Press, Madison, WI.

JOHNSON, R. G., AND S. A. TEMPLE. 1990. Nest predation and brood parasitism of tallgrass prairie birds. Journal of Wildlife Management 54:106–111.

KANTRUD, H. A. 1981. Grazing intensity effects on the breeding avifauna of North Dakota native grasslands. Canadian Field-Naturalist 95:404–417.

KANTRUD, H. A. 1993. Duck nest success on Conservation Reserve Program land in the prairie pothole region. Journal of Soil and Water Conservation 48:238–242.

KANTRUD, H. A., AND R. L. KOLOGISKI. 1982. Effects of soils and grazing on breeding birds of uncultivated upland grasslands of the northern Great Plains. U.S. Fish and Wildlife Service Wildlife Research Report 15:1–33, Washington, D.C.

KING, J. W., AND J. A. SAVIDGE. 1995. Effects of the Conservation Reserve Program on wildlife in southeast Nebraska. Wildlife Society Bulletin 23:377–385.

KLUTE, D. S. 1994. Avian community structure, reproductive success, vegetation structure, and food availability in burned CRP fields and grazed pastures in northeastern Kansas. M.S. thesis. Kansas State University, Manhattan, KS.

KNOPF, F. L. 1994. Avian assemblages on altered grasslands. Studies in Avian Biology 15:247–257.

KOFORD, R. R., AND L. B. BEST. 1996. Management of agricultural landscapes for the conservation of neotropical migratory birds. Pp. 68–88 in F. R. Thompson III (editor). Management of midwestern landscapes for the conservation of neotropical migratory birds. USDA Forest Service Gen. Tech. Rep. NC-187. USDA Forest Service North Central Forest Experiment Station, St. Paul, MN.

KOFORD, R. R., B. S. BOWEN, J. L. LOKEMOEN, AND A. KRUSE. In press. Cowbird parasitism in grassland and cropland in North Dakota. In T. Cook, S. K. Robinson, S. I. Rothstein, S. G. Sealy, and J. N. M. Smith (editors). The ecology and management of cowbirds. University of Texas Press, Austin, TX.

MAJOR, R. E. 1990. The effect of human observers on the intensity of nest predation. Ibis 132:608–612.

MAYFIELD, H. 1975. Suggestions for calculating nest success. Wilson Bulletin 87:456–466.

MILLENBAH, K. F. 1993. The effects of different age classes of fields enrolled in the Conservation Reserve Program in Michigan on avian diversity, density, and productivity. M.S. thesis. Michigan State University, East Lansing, MI.

MILLIKEN, G. A., AND D. E. JOHNSON. 1984. Analysis of messy data. Van Nostrand Reinhold, New York, NY.

PATTERSON, M. P., AND L. B. BEST. 1996. Bird abundance and nest success in Iowa CRP fields: the importance of vegetation structure and composition. American Midland Naturalist 135:153–167.

PETERJOHN, B. G., J. R. SAUER, AND W. A. LINK. 1994. The 1992 and 1993 summary of the North American Breeding Bird Survey. Bird Populations 2:46–61.

RENKEN, R. B., AND J. J. DINSMORE. 1987. Nongame bird communities on managed grasslands in North Dakota. Canadian Field-Naturalist 101:551–557.

REYNOLDS, R. E., T. L. SHAFFER, J. R. SAUER, AND B. G. PETERJOHN. 1994. Conservation Reserve Program: benefit for grassland birds in the northern plains. Transactions of the North American Wildlife and Natural Resources Conference 59:328–336.

RODENHOUSE, N. L., L. B. BEST, R. J. O'CONNOR, AND E. K. BOLLINGER. 1995. Effects of agricultural practices and farmland structures on neotropical migratory birds. Pp. 269–293 in T. E. Martin and D. M. Finch (editors). Ecology and management of neotropical migratory birds: a synthesis and review of critical issues. Oxford University Press, Oxford, U.K.

SAMSON, F., AND F. KNOPF. 1994. Prairie conservation in North America. BioScience 44:418–421.

SAS INSTITUTE. 1987. SAS/STAT guide for personal computers, version 6. SAS Institute, Cary, NC.

SHERRY, T. W., AND R. T. HOLMES. 1995. Summer versus winter limitation of populations: what are the issues and what is the evidence? Pp. 85–120 in T. E. Martin and D. M. Finch (editors). Ecology and management of neotropical migratory birds: a synthesis and review of critical issues. Oxford University Press, Oxford, U.K.

SMITH, R. L. 1968. *Ammodramus savannarum* (Gmelin) Grasshopper Sparrow. U.S. National Museum Bulletin 237, pt. 2:725–745.

STEEL, R. G. D., AND J. H. TORRIE. 1980. Principles and procedures of statistics. 2d ed. McGraw-Hill, New York, NY.

VICKERY, P. D., M. L. HUNTER, JR., AND S. M. MELVIN. 1994. Effects of habitat area on the distribution of grassland birds in Maine. Conservation Biology 8: 1087–1097.

WARNER, R. E. 1994. Agricultural land use and grassland habitat in Illinois: future shock for midwestern birds? Conservation Biology 8:147–156.

WESTMORELAND, D., AND L. B. BEST. 1985. The effect of disturbance on Mourning Dove nesting success. Auk 102:774–780.

Studies in Avian Biology No. 19:196–202, 1999.

NESTING BIRDS AND GRAZING CATTLE: ACCOMMODATING BOTH ON MIDWESTERN PASTURES

STANLEY A. TEMPLE, BRICK M. FEVOLD, LAURA K. PAINE, DANIEL J. UNDERSANDER, AND DAVID W. SAMPLE

Abstract. We measured the diversity, density, nest success, and productivity of grassland birds on three types of sites in southwestern Wisconsin: ungrazed grasslands, continuously grazed pastures, and rotationally grazed pastures. We found that diversity, density, nest success, and productivity were highest on ungrazed grasslands. Continuously grazed pastures had the lowest diversity and density but intermediate nest success and productivity. Rotationally grazed pastures had intermediate diversities and densities but the lowest nest success and productivity. We recommend a grassland management regime in which areas of ungrazed grassland and rotationally grazed pastures are maintained in a 1:2 ratio on farms during the nesting season (15 May–1 July). Our data suggest that such a management regime would result in per-farm avian productivity that is higher than on continuously grazed and rotationally grazed pastures and much higher than that reported for frequently mowed hayfields.

EL ANIDAJE DE AVES Y EL APACENTAMIENTO DE GANADO: COMO ACOMODAR A LOS DOS EN LAS PASTURAS DEL MEDIOOESTE

Sinopsis. Medimos la diversidad, la densidad, el éxito de los nidos y la productividad de aves de pastizal en tres tipos de lugares en el sudoeste de Wisconsin: los pastizales no apacentados, las pasturas continuamente apacentadas y las pasturas apacentadas en rotación. Encontramos que la diversidad, la densidad, el éxito de los nidos y la productividad fueron mayores en los pastizales no apacentados. La diversidad y la densidad fueron menores en las pasturas continuamente apacentadas, pero el éxito de los nidos y la productividad fueron medianos. Encontramos que las diversidades y las densidades fueron medianas en las pasturas apacentadas en rotación, pero asimismo, también tuvieron el menor éxito de los nidos y la menor productividad. Recomendamos un régimen de manejo de los pastizales en el que las áreas de pastizales no apacentados y las pasturas apacentadas en rotación se mantengan en una proporción 1:2 en los terrenos agrícolas durante la estación de anidaje (15 mayo–1 julio). Nuestros datos sugieren que tal régimen de manejo daría por resultado una productividad avícola por granja mayor que en las pasturas continuamente apacentadas y las apacentadas en rotación, y mucho mayor que la registrada en los henares frecuentemente segados.

Key Words: grassland birds; nesting success; pasture management; population densities; rotational grazing; Wisconsin.

As native tallgrass prairies in the midwestern United States have all but disappeared, grassland birds nesting in the region have been forced to adopt a variety of secondary habitats that usually are associated closely with agriculture. Although cultivated row crops do not usually provide suitable nesting habitat for most grassland birds (Basore et al. 1986), other agricultural lands can accommodate many of their needs. The most attractive of the secondary habitats for grassland birds in the Midwest are lands managed intensively to produce forage for animals (Sample 1989). Several types of managed grasslands are found, among them grass/legume hayfields that are mowed regularly to provide food for confined livestock, pastures that are grazed continuously by free-ranging stock, and pastures that are grazed rotationally by animals that are moved regularly within a network of small paddocks.

The attractiveness and suitability of these managed grasslands for nesting birds vary. Hayfields can be attractive to birds selecting habitat in the spring, but birds that nest there may have poor reproductive success when mowing cycles are shorter than nesting cycles and many nests are destroyed (Bollinger et al. 1990, Frawley and Best 1991). Continuously grazed pastures are less attractive to most birds early in the nesting season when there is little vegetative cover, and the continuous presence of livestock causes nest disturbances and failures (Kirsch et al. 1978, Jensen et al. 1990). It has been suggested that rotationally grazed pastures, which are becoming increasingly popular (Undersander et al. 1991), could benefit nesting birds (Barker et al. 1990, Severson 1990). There have been few studies, however, of how birds respond to rotational grazing in the Midwest, and optimism regarding its benefits for birds has been largely speculative.

We studied the diversity, density, nesting success, and productivity of birds nesting in ungrazed pastures, continuously grazed pastures, and rotationally grazed pastures. Our goal was to use this information to design grassland management systems that accommodate the needs both of grazing livestock and nesting birds.

METHODS

Our study sites were located on privately owned dairy and beef farms in southwestern Wisconsin in a region (Green, Iowa, and Lafayette Counties) featuring an open landscape in which managed grasslands and row crops are the dominant cover types. We selected previously grazed grassland sites that could be managed according to our guidelines. These sites were in open areas away from trees, buildings, or other landscape features that might create ecological edges, and they were in large landscapes that were similar in topography and land use. Over three seasons (1993–1995), 19 sites totaling 98 ha were managed as ungrazed grasslands which cooperating farmers agreed to neither mow nor graze between 15 May and 1 July. Over the same period, 16 sites totaling 91 ha were managed as continuously grazed pasture on which cattle were stocked at densities of 2.5–4 animals per hectare. Finally, 24 sites totaling 124 ha of grassland were managed as rotationally grazed pasture where stocking densities were typically 40–60 animals per hectare in small paddocks that averaged about 5 ha in size. These paddocks were grazed by livestock for 1–2 d and then left undisturbed, typically for 10–15 d, before being grazed again. Stocking densities, durations of grazing, and intervals between grazing varied primarily as a result of the rate at which forage plants grew. Stocking densities were higher, whereas durations of grazing and intervals between grazing were shorter, when vegetation grew quickly.

All of the sites had similar vegetative composition: 50–75% cool-season grasses, 7–27% legumes, and 8–23% forbs. The structure of the vegetation varied with the grazing treatments. Continuously grazed pastures had little vegetative cover and were kept closely cropped by cattle. Ungrazed grasslands had the most complex structure, with residual debris and vegetation that grew throughout the study periods. Rotationally grazed grasslands varied cyclically through the study periods, with much of the vegetation removed during a grazing episode, and the most complex structure redeveloped just prior to the next grazing period after vegetation had recovered. All sites were on level to slightly rolling land, at least 200 m from stands of trees, and without permanent waterways.

On each site we recorded all bird species detected between 1 May and 1 July. Every 3–5 d we visited each site and used a flush-and-follow territory-mapping technique (Wiens 1969) to determine the densities of territorial birds. We mapped the initial spot where a bird was detected, approached it slowly until it flushed, mapped the spot where it next perched, and continued up to 10 cycles of flushing, following, and mapping. When flushed birds flew long distances and left the study site, we did not follow them and assumed they were transients that did not hold a territory on the site. We mapped territories 4–9 times during each season. At the end of the season we combined maps for each site and circumscribed clusters of perch sites for each species. We assumed that each circumscribed cluster of perch sites represented a territory occupied by at least one pair of birds, and we were reassured

by the fact that mapped clusters were typically confined to areas similar in size to the reported territories for the various species (Wiens 1969).

We plotted the cumulative number of mapped territories on each site over successive visits. The number of territories on most sites seemed to reach an asymptote after about 6 person-hours of mapping. For all sites, and especially for those that did not reach an asymptote, we fitted curves to the data and extrapolated the curves to 10 person-hours of mapping. We used the projected number of territories after 10 person-hours of mapping as our standardized estimate of the number of territories on a site, thus correcting a potential bias introduced by unequal sampling effort.

We located nests of as many birds as possible on each study site. Nest locations were marked with spray paint on vegetation at a recorded direction and distance from the nest. We revisited each nest every 1–5 d to check on its condition. We noted suspected causes of nest failure but acknowledge that few causes could be assigned definitively. We used a modified Mayfield estimator (Johnson 1979) to determine daily nest survival rates for each species. We report results as estimated proportions of nests that would have survived for the reported duration of a normal nesting cycle from egg-laying through fledging for each species (Ehrlich et al. 1988). We estimated the average number of young presumed to have fledged from nests of each species, based on average clutch size and the average daily survival rates for a treatment site.

We made decisions about how nesting success was calculated that were unique to our study. Nests on ungrazed sites that were destroyed as a result of mowing after the 1 July end of our study period were not recorded as failures; they were recorded as successful through the date on which mowing occurred. Hence, when we report nesting success of birds on ungrazed sites, it is based on exposure days during the study period of 15 May–1 July.

There was some between-year variation in measured parameters, but it did not affect the relative values associated with treatments. The only significant between-year difference was in nest success, which was higher overall in 1995 than in 1994. We combined data for all sites and all years of the study when calculating mean values for each of the three treatments. We made comparisons between treatments for four groups of birds: all species combined, Red-winged Blackbirds (*Agelaius phoeniceus*), Savannah Sparrows (*Passerculus sandwichensis*), and other less abundant species combined. We compared treatments using analysis of variance and the Tukey test. Significant differences had a probability of 0.05 or less.

RESULTS

We found differences in the numbers and types of species recorded on different treatment sites. The species associated with each type of grassland site are shown in Table 1. Mean number of species per site varied ($F_{2,56} = 3.6$, $P < 0.05$): ungrazed grasslands ("refuges") averaged 8.2, continuously grazed pastures averaged 5.2, and rotationally grazed pastures averaged 7.7. Ungrazed grasslands and rotationally grazed

TABLE 1. OCCURRENCE AND ABUNDANCE (TERRITORIES PER 40 HA) OF BIRDS ON UNGRAZED GRASSLANDS, CONTIN-UOUSLY GRAZED PASTURES, AND ROTATIONALLY GRAZED PASTURES IN WISCONSIN

	Treatment		
Species	Ungrazed (N = 19)	Continuously grazed (N = 16)	Rotationally grazed (N = 24)
Killdeer	A[a]	4.1	A
Charadrius vociferus			
Upland Sandpiper	A	A	–
Bartramia longicauda			
Eastern Kingbird	A	–	A
Tyrannus tyrannus			
Horned Lark	–	A	A
Eremophila alpestris			
Sedge Wren	4.3	1.3	9.4
Cistothorus platensis			
Eastern Bluebird	A	–	–
Sialia sialis			
Brown Thrasher	A	1.9	6.5
Toxostoma rufum			
Field Sparrow	A	–	A
Spizella pusilla			
Vesper Sparrow	1.9	3.2	1.4
Pooecetes gramineus			
Savannah Sparrow	153.7	107.6	122.5
Passerculus sandwichensis			
Grasshopper Sparrow	5.2	8.7	6.5
Ammodramus savannarum			
Henslow's Saprrow	2.9	3.0	3.9
A. henslowii			
Dickcissel	31.8	6.7	8.9
Spiza americana			
Bobolink	20.2	21.2	22.3
Dolichonyx oryzivorus			
Red-winged Blackbird	103.6	16.2	103.8
Agelaius phoeniceus			
Eastern Meadowlark	7.6	–	A
Sturnella magna			
Western Meadowlark	4.0	2.3	3.2
S. neglecta			
Brown-headed Cowbird	A	A	A
Molothrus ater			

[a] A = individuals observed but not territorial.

grasslands supported significantly more species than continuously grazed sites (Tukey's test, P < 0.05, respectively). Some species were associated primarily with certain treatments. Killdeer (*Charadrius vociferus*) and Horned Larks (*Eremophila alpestris*), for example, were most common on continuously grazed pastures.

We also found differences in densities of territorial birds (Table 1, Fig. 1) which were significant for all species ($F_{2,56}$ = 4.6, P < 0.05), for Red-winged Blackbirds ($F_{2,56}$ = 5.4, P < 0.05), and for other less abundant species ($F_{2,56}$ = 4.9, P < 0.05). There were significantly more territorial individuals of all species and of Red-winged Blackbirds in ungrazed grasslands ("refuges") and rotationally grazed pastures than in continuously grazed pastures, and more Savan-

nah Sparrows in ungrazed grasslands than in rotationally or continuously grazed pastures (Tukey's test, P < 0.05, respectively).

Nesting success varied significantly between the three grassland types for all species combined ($F_{2,56}$ = 5.5, P < 0.05), for Red-winged Blackbirds ($F_{2,56}$ = 6.1, P < 0.05), for Savannah Sparrows ($F_{2,56}$ = 4.8, P < 0.05), and for other less abundant species ($F_{2,56}$ = 5.1, P < 0.05; Table 2, Fig. 2). In each case, nesting success was significantly higher on ungrazed grasslands ("refuges") than on continuously grazed pastures (Tukey's test, P < 0.05), and it was significantly higher on continuously grazed pastures than on rotationally grazed pastures (Tukey's test, P < 0.05). Many of the losses on grazed grasslands were apparently caused by

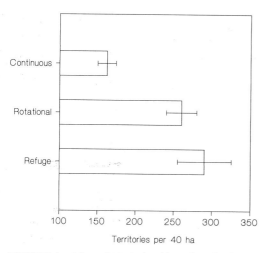

FIGURE 1. Mean (± SE) densities of territories on three types of Wisconsin grasslands: ungrazed grasslands ("refuges"; N = 36 site-years), continuously grazed pastures (N = 32 site-years), and rotationally grazed pastures (N = 48 site-years).

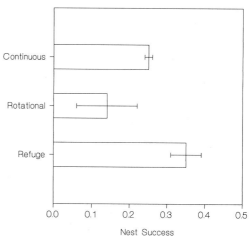

FIGURE 2. Mean (± SE) nesting success for nests on three types of Wisconsin grasslands: ungrazed grasslands ("refuges"; N = 74 nests), continuously grazed pastures (N = 31 nests), and rotationally grazed pastures (N = 87 nests). Nesting success is calculated using a modified Mayfield estimator.

cattle trampling nests and by desertion after cattle grazed the cover around the nest.

We estimated avian productivity of different grasslands by multiplying the density of territories of each group of species on sites by the predicted number of young fledged per nest (Fig. 3). There were significant differences between grasslands for all species combined ($F_{2,56} = 6.4$, $P < 0.05$), for Red-winged Blackbirds ($F_{2,56} = 5.1$, $P < 0.05$), for Savannah Sparrows ($F_{2,56} = 5.5$, $P < 0.05$), and for other less abundant species ($F_{2,56} = 4.7$, $P < 0.05$). For all species combined, for Red-winged Blackbirds, and for other

less abundant species combined, ungrazed grasslands ("refuges") produced the most young per unit area; continuously and rotationally grazed pastures produced significantly fewer young (Tukey's test, $P < 0.05$). For Savannah Sparrows, ungrazed grasslands and rotationally grazed pastures produced more young than continuously grazed pastures (Tukey's test, $P <$

TABLE 2. NUMBERS OF NESTS OBSERVED ON UNGRAZED GRASSLANDS, CONTINUOUSLY GRAZED PASTURES, AND ROTATIONALLY GRAZED PASTURES IN WISCONSIN

	Treatment		
Species	Ungrazed (N = 19)	Continuously grazed (N = 16)	Rotationally grazed (N = 24)
Killdeer	0	2	0
Upland Sandpiper	1	1	0
Brown Thrasher	2	0	3
Field Sparrow	0	0	1
Vesper Sparrow	0	0	2
Savannah Sparrow	11	12	13
Grasshopper Sparrow	1	3	0
Bobolink	1	2	6
Red-winged Blackbird	54	5	56
Eastern Meadowlark	2	2	5
Western Meadowlark	2	4	1
All species	74	31	87

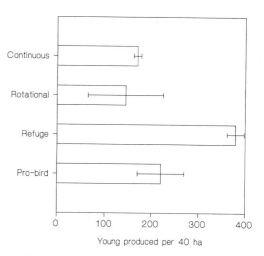

FIGURE 3. Mean productivity (± SE) of four types of Wisconsin grassland: ungrazed grasslands ("refuges"; N = 36 sites), continuously grazed pastures (N = 32 sites), rotationally grazed pastures (N = 48 sites), and a hypothetical system of ungrazed and rotationally grazed grasslands ("pro-bird"; N = 6 sites).

0.05). The "pro-bird" treatment (see Discussion, below) produced more young of all species combined, of Red-winged Blackbirds, and of Savannah Sparrows than did continuously grazed pastures (Tukey's test, $P < 0.05$).

DISCUSSION

Our main findings can be summarized as follows. Of the three grassland types, ungrazed grasslands ("refuges") tended to have the highest diversity, densities, nesting success, and productivity. Continuously grazed pastures tended to have the lowest diversity and densities and intermediate nest success and productivity. Rotationally grazed pastures had intermediate diversity and densities and the lowest nest success and productivity. Overall, ungrazed grasslands were the most productive and rotationally grazed pastures the least productive of the treatments (Fig. 3).

We used these findings and the results of previous studies to explore the possibilities of managing agricultural grasslands to benefit nesting birds. On the basis of previous studies (e.g., Bollinger et al. 1990, Frawley and Best 1991), we concluded that mowing hayfields was the least desirable management practice because birds are often attracted to these grasslands but rarely succeed in rearing young. Early and frequent mowing makes it almost impossible for birds to complete a nesting cycle. Across much of the Midwest, most agricultural grasslands are mowed to provide forage for confined livestock, a situation that some people have blamed for declining grassland bird populations in the region (Sample 1989). Trends in hayfield management are moving toward even earlier and more frequent mowing as new forage crop varieties are developed (Ryan 1986, Ratti and Scott 1991).

Continuous grazing provides mixed opportunities for grassland birds. As our study confirmed, continuously grazed pastures are not very attractive to most grassland birds because they are kept closely cropped by livestock and provide poor nesting cover when migrants arrive and select breeding habitat. They also tend to be near buildings and crop fields. Birds that do settle in continuously grazed pastures experience moderate levels of nesting success, but overall productivity remains low because of the sparse densities of nesting birds. The most obvious management change that might improve avian productivity would be to reduce stocking densities, which would probably increase attractiveness and nesting success. This change, however, would be inconsistent with the ideal agronomic goal of balancing the rates at which forage plants are produced and consumed by livestock.

Rotational grazing also offers advantages and disadvantages for nesting birds. In some cases, rotationally grazed pastures cover much of a farm's area, creating relatively large patches of grassland that are attractive to birds. Because a farm's pasture land is divided into small paddocks, most of which do not have cattle in them at any particular time, much of the total pasture area remains highly attractive to birds. Our results reveal that densities of territorial birds are relatively high in rotationally grazed pastures, reflecting this attractiveness. Eventually, however, each paddock must temporarily support a high density of cattle. When high densities of livestock graze a paddock, there is a high probability of nests being trampled or abandoned (Koerth et al. 1983, Paine et al. 1996). Our results demonstrate that nests in rotational pastures have low overall survival rates because of the brief, but devastating, disturbances caused by concentrated livestock. Many (64%) of the nest losses on our rotationally grazed pastures occurred while cattle were present. Furthermore, nests that survived an initial grazing episode often lost their protective cover and were more vulnerable to predation. Some were also exposed to cattle at least one more time because grazing cycles were much shorter than nesting cycles.

We used these results to design a grassland management system that could accommodate the needs of grazing animals and also produce the largest possible number of fledgling birds. In this paper we discuss the avian aspects of this system; we will discuss the agronomic aspects elsewhere. We based our grassland management system on the premise that it should neither require farmers to sacrifice the livestock carrying capacity of their farms nor reduce the rate of forage consumption by their livestock. Within these constraints, we sought ways to maximize a farm's avian productivity.

Given the results of our study and previous studies, we knew it would be challenging to improve the avian productivity of continuously and rotationally grazed pastures because the most obvious modifications would not satisfy our basic agronomic constraints. Reducing the stocking density of continuously grazed pastures would improve avian productivity but reduce livestock carrying capacity. Making the intervals between grazing events on rotationally grazed pastures long enough to allow nesting cycles to be completed (approximately 25–30 d) would increase avian productivity. But it could also reduce the quality and quantity of forage available to livestock held on paddocks beyond the point at which most new plant growth had been consumed, and it could make grazing cycles so long that cattle would encounter older forage when they were eventually moved to a new paddock.

Instead of modifying the way pastures are grazed, we focused on finding how both grazed and ungrazed grasslands could be included on a farm during the nesting season. By providing an ungrazed "refuge" to complement grazed pastures, we predicted that the overall avian productivity of a farm could be enhanced because of the higher densities and nest success associated with the refuge. Although it proved difficult to incorporate the refuge concept into a continuous grazing system, it was feasible to combine a refuge with a rotational grazing system.

During the peak of the midwestern nesting season (mid-May through June), cool-season forage plants normally grow so vigorously in Wisconsin that it can be difficult for farmers to rotate their livestock rapidly enough through paddocks to keep up with the new growth. In contrast, when plant growth slows later in the summer, farmers need to use all of their rotational pasture area to satisfy their animals' demands. We capitalized on the fact that many rotational grazers seem to maintain more pasture area than they need during the nesting season in order to cope with the bottleneck in forage availability that occurs later in the season. We estimated that during the late spring and early summer up to about a third of rotational pasture area may not be needed, providing an opportunity to set aside a temporary refuge without compromising livestock productivity.

We used our data to predict the avian productivity that might be achieved on a farm that set aside a third of its grassland area as an ungrazed and unmowed refuge from 15 May until 1 July and grazed the remaining grassland area using a rotational system. After 1 July, the refuge area can be mowed and incorporated into the rotational grazing schedule. An example of such a system is shown in Fig. 4. As can be seen in Fig. 3, this "pro-bird" system improves avian productivity over a completely rotational or completely continuous grazing system. At the same time, we can show that carrying capacity and forage availability are adequate to accommodate the needs of livestock (Paine et al. 1996). There may even be additional agronomic benefits associated with our pro-bird system.

Although the pro-bird system has advantages over other grazing systems, it does not allow nesting grassland birds to be productive enough to replace expected annual losses. Because of this deficit, even the birds nesting on a farm managed under a pro-bird grazing system seem to be a population sink, but not to the extent of the other grazing systems.

We conclude that it is feasible to accommo-

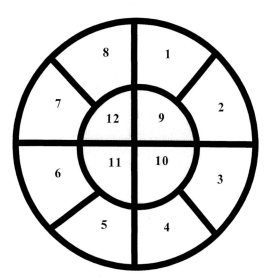

FIGURE 4. An example of a "pro-bird" grassland management system with 12 paddocks, in which a third of a farm's grassland area (paddocks 9–12) has been set aside as a refuge during the peak of the nesting season (15 May–1 July) while the remaining grassland area is managed as rotationally grazed pasture.

date the needs of livestock while modifying grassland management to improve avian productivity. Nonetheless, we are concerned that even the improvements achieved under our pro-bird management system may not be adequate to allow some grassland birds to maintain stable populations. And, of course, some grassland birds have habitat needs that simply cannot be met on the types of agricultural grasslands we studied.

ACKNOWLEDGMENTS

Our research was supported by the University of Wisconsin College of Agricultural and Life Sciences, University of Wisconsin Foundation, Wisconsin Department of Natural Resources, National Fish and Wildlife Foundation, U.S. Fish and Wildlife Service, and Max McGraw Wildlife Foundation. We are grateful to the following farmers who cooperated with us: P. Bickford, D. Long, R. and C. March, D. and D. Nodolf, C. Opitz, T. and M. Payne, D. Popp, and D. Reeson. K. Castelein, K. Burcar, M. Boldt, D. Passi, J. Steichen, and W. Wagner assisted with field work. The Agricultural Ecosystems Research Committee of Wisconsin, and especially G. A. Bartelt, helped coordinate our work.

LITERATURE CITED

BARKER, W. T., K. K. SEDIVEC, T. A. MESSMER, K. F. HIGGINS, AND D. R. HERTEL. 1990. Effects of specialized grazing systems on waterfowl production in southcentral North Dakota. Transactions of the North American Wildlife and Natural Resources Conference 55:462–474.

BASORE, N. S., L. B. BEST, AND J. B. WOOLEY. 1986.

Birds nesting in Iowa no-tillage and tilled cropland. Journal of Wildlife Management 50:19–28.

BOLLINGER, E. K., P. B. BOLLINGER, AND T. A. GAVIN. 1990. Effects of hay-cropping on eastern populations of the Bobolink. Wildlife Society Bulletin 18: 142–150.

EHRLICH, P. R., D. S. DOBKIN, AND D. WHEYE. 1988. The birder's handbook. Simon and Schuster, New York, NY.

FRAWLEY, B. J,. AND L. B. BEST. 1991. Effects of mowing on breeding bird abundance and species composition in alfalfa fields. Wildlife Society Bulletin 19:135–142.

JENSEN, H. P., D. ROLLINS, AND R. L. GILLEN. 1990. Effects of cattle stock density on trampling loss of simulated ground nests. Wildlife Society Bulletin 18:71–74.

JOHNSON, D. H. 1979. Estimating nest success: the Mayfield method and an alternative. Auk 96:651–661.

KIRSCH, L. M., H. F. DUEBBERT, AND A. D. KRUSE. 1978. Grazing and haying effects on habitats of upland nesting birds. Transactions of the North American Wildlife and Natural Resources Conference 43: 487–497.

KOERTH, B. H., W. M. WEBB, F. C. BRYANT, AND F. S. GUTHERY. 1983. Cattle trampling of simulated ground nests under short duration and continuous grazing. Journal of Range Management 36:385–386.

PAINE, L. K., D. J. UNDERSANDER, D. W. SAMPLE, G. A. BARTELT, AND T. A. SCHATTEMAN. 1996. Cattle trampling of simulated ground nests in rotationally grazed pastures. Journal of Range Management 49: 294–300.

RATTI, J. T., AND J. M. SCOTT. 1991. Agricultural impacts on wildlife: problem review and research needs. Environmental Professional 13:263–274.

RYAN, M. R. 1986. Nongame management in grassland and agricultural ecosystems. Pp. 117–136 in J. B. Hale, L. B. Best, and R. L. Clawson (editors). Management of nongame wildlife in the midwest. North-central Section of the Wildlife Society, Grand Rapids, MI.

SAMPLE, D. W. 1989. Grasslands birds in southern Wisconsin: habitat preference, population trends, and response to land use changes. M.S. thesis. University of Wisconsin, Madison, WI.

SEVERSON, K. E. 1990. Can livestock be used as a tool to enhance wildlife habitat? USDA Forest Service Gen. Tech. Rep. RM-194. USDA Forest Service Rocky Mountain and Range Experimental Station, Fort Collins, CO.

UNDERSANDER, D. J., B. ALBERT, P. PORTER, AND A. CROSSLEY. 1991. Wisconsin pastures for profit: a hands on guide to rotational grazing. Publication A3529, University of Wisconsin Cooperative Extension, Madison, WI.

WIENS, J. A. 1969. An approach to the study of ecological relationships among grassland birds. Ornithological Monograph no. 8.

Studies in Avian Biology No. 19:203–210, 1999.

BIRD POPULATIONS OF SEEDED GRASSLANDS IN THE ASPEN PARKLAND OF ALBERTA

DAVID R. C. PRESCOTT AND ANDREW J. MURPHY

Abstract. The conversion of cropland to grasslands providing dense nesting cover is the main program being implemented by the North American Waterfowl Management Plan to restore duck populations in the Aspen Parkland of Alberta. We examined bird richness and abundance in six age classes (0–5 years) of "tame" dense nesting cover and in controls (cropland) in 1994. Our objectives were to describe temporal changes in bird communities as seeded grasslands matured, to relate these changes to structural changes in the grass cover, and to make recommendations on the timing of management of these restored habitats. Eighteen bird species were recorded in seeded grasslands and controls, but only Savannah Sparrows (*Passerculus sandwichensis*) were found in all age classes surveyed. Controls and dense nesting cover less than one year of age contained few breeding species (primarily Horned Larks [*Eremophila alpestris*] and Killdeer [*Charadrius vociferus*]) but were attractive to corvid and icterid species that used these areas for foraging. Older stands supported a variety of sparrows (Emberizinae) and, to a lesser extent, waterfowl (Anatidae), Sedge Wrens (*Cistothorus platensis*), and Northern Harriers (*Circus cyaneus*). Overall, bird species richness and abundance were lowest in controls, increased monotonically until three years after seeding, and declined thereafter. The Robel value and height of vegetation peaked at three and two years of age, respectively. Both vegetation measures were important determinants of bird richness, but abundance was related only to vegetation height.

Seeded grasslands require periodic management to remove lodged vegetation and rejuvenate growth. Although the type and timing of management that maximizes waterfowl production are not well established, we suggest that these habitats could be managed four to five years after establishment, when bird species richness and abundance are declining.

LAS POBLACIONES DE AVES EN PASTIZALES SEMBRADOS EN EL PRADO DE ASPEN DE ALBERTA

Sinopsis. Para restaurar las poblaciones de patos en el Prado de Aspen de Alberta se realiza actualmente el programa principal del Plan para el Control de Aves Acuáticas Norteamericanas, que es la conversión de terrenos sembrados a pastizales que ofrecen cobertura densa para anidaje. En 1994 estudiamos la riqueza y la abundancia de aves en seis clases de edad de cobertura densa no nativa para anidaje (0–5 años) y en controles (terrenos sembrados). Nuestros objetivos fueron describir los cambios temporales en las comunidades de las aves mientras maduraban los pastizales sembrados, relacionar estos cambios a los cambios estructurales en la cobertura de hierbas, y hacer recomendaciones para la coordinación del manejo de estos hábitats restaurados. Se registraron 18 especies de aves en los pastizales sembrados y en los controles, pero se encontraron solamente Gorriones Sabaneros (*Passerculus sandwichensis*) en todas las clases de edades estudiadas. Los controles y la cobertura densa para anidaje que tenía menos de un año de edad contenían pocas especies en reproducción (principalmente las Alondras Cornudas [*Eremophila alpestris*] y los Chorlitos Tildíos [*Charadrius vociferus*]) pero fueron atrayentes para las especies Corvidae e Icteridae que usaban estas áreas para forrajear. Los lugares con más años mantenían una variedad de gorriones (Emberizinae) y, en menor medida, aves acuáticas (Antidae), los Saltaparedes Sabaneros (*Cistothorus platensis*), y los Gavilanes Rastreros (*Circus cyaneus*). En total, la riqueza y la abundancia de las especies de aves fueron menores en los controles, aumentaron monotónicamente hasta tres años después del sembrado, y luego disminuyeron. El valor Robel y la altura de la vegetación alcanzaron su máximo grado a los tres y a los dos años de edad, respectivamente. Las dos mediciones de vegetación fueron factores determinantes en la riqueza de aves, pero la abundancia fue relacionada únicamente con la altura de la vegetación.

Los pastizales sembrados requieren un manejo periódico para quitar la vegetación fija y para renovar el crecimiento. Aunque no se haya establecido apropiadamente el tipo de manejo y la coordinación del manejo que intensifique la producción de aves acuáticas, recomendamos el control de estos hábitats entre cuatro y cinco años después de su establecimiento, cuando la riqueza y la abundancia de especies de aves estén decreciendo.

Key Words: Alberta; Aspen Parkland; dense nesting cover; seeded grasslands.

Waterfowl populations have been in serious decline in North America since the early 1970s. The primary reasons for this decline appear to be a degradation of nesting habitat caused by wetlands drainage and intensive cultivation of upland nesting habitats. These factors are especially prominent on the Canadian prairies, where 50% of the continental population of dabbling ducks breed. In this region, almost 60% of wetland basins and 80% of wetland margins have been affected to some degree by agricultural practices (Turner et al. 1987), and more than 80% of uplands are intensively cultivated (Adams and Gentle 1978, Rounds 1982, Sugden and Beyersbergen 1984).

In 1986 the North American Waterfowl Management Plan (NAWMP) was implemented with the goal of restoring continental waterfowl populations to 1970s levels. NAWMP programs employ a wide variety of techniques to secure, restore, and enhance wetlands and adjacent upland habitats critical for nesting waterfowl. In the Aspen Parkland of Alberta, waterfowl production is limited primarily by the loss of upland nesting habitats to intensive agriculture (Alberta Prairie Habitat Joint Venture Technical Committee, unpubl. data). Accordingly, NAWMP programs in this area have focused on restoring permanent cover to upland sites in areas of high wetland density. The primary way of accomplishing this has been to establish permanent forages on land previously used for the production of annual crops. This forage is referred to as "dense nesting cover" (DNC) and is of two general types. Most cover seeded during early years of the NAWMP program in Alberta was composed of "tame" cultivars, dominated by alfalfa (*Medicago sativa*), brome grass (*Bromus* spp.), and introduced species of wheat grasses (*Agropyron* spp.). Increased availability of native grass seed has permitted a recent shift toward a "native" DNC mix that contains green needlegrass (*Stipa viridula*) and native wheat grasses. Collectively, DNC has been established on approximately 6,300 ha in the Aspen Parkland of Alberta and on more than 39,000 ha across the Canadian prairies.

DNC is planted as breeding habitat for waterfowl, but it is used by a wide variety of other wildlife species as well. Of particular interest are grassland songbirds, which have been declining at alarming rates over the past 25 yr (Peterjohn and Sauer 1993). Many of these species have colonized restored grasslands on the Canadian prairies (Dale 1993; Prescott et al. 1993, 1995; Hartley 1994; Jones 1994), suggesting that NAWMP programs are providing valuable habitat for these species in this area.

This study documents bird use of tame DNC established in the Aspen Parkland of Alberta over a 6-yr period. This duration is significant because it represents the approximate management interval of restored grasslands in this area; older grasslands must be rejuvenated to restore vigor (Duebbert et al. 1981). Our goals were to (1) document changes in the relative abundance and species composition of bird communities in tame DNC over time; (2) relate temporal changes in bird community structure to vegetational

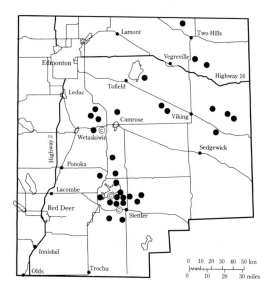

FIGURE 1. Location of DNC study plots (filled circles) and controls (open circles with "c") in the Aspen Parkland of Alberta.

changes in seeded cover; and (3) make recommendations on the timing of rejuvenation of restored grasslands based on knowledge of temporal changes in bird community structure.

METHODS

Thirty-one treatment properties in the central Aspen Parkland of Alberta that were seeded with tame DNC between 1989 (stand age = 5 yr) and 1994 (0 yr) were selected for study (Fig. 1). Thirteen different plant species were used in tame DNC mixtures during this period, and five to seven species were present in any one mix (Table 1). The relative proportion of major seed types in these mixes was not constant over time. Recently restored properties tended to be seeded with a higher proportion of wheat grasses and a lower percentage of brome/fescue (*Festuca*) and legumes than properties seeded in the early years of the NAWMP program in this region (Fig. 2). Three properties subjected to conventional agricultural rotation (spring-seeded grain crops) were selected as controls (Fig. 1).

Bird censuses were conducted between 24 May and 17 June 1994 using fixed-radius point counts (Hutto et al. 1986). A 75-m radius was used for all counts, and count centers were at least 200 m apart to minimize the possibility of counting the same bird in adjacent circles (Prescott et al. 1993). Circles were also positioned so their perimeters were at least 30 m from wetland margins and property boundaries. The observer counted all individuals seen or heard in the count circle during a 3-min interval. Flying birds were excluded unless they were foraging in the air column within the bounds of the circle. All counts were conducted between 0600 and 1000 hours mountain daylight time under calm (winds < 19 km/hr), rainless conditions.

We measured vegetation height and density in each

TABLE 1. OVERALL COMPOSITION OF DNC MIXES USED TO RESTORE PERMANENT COVER ON STUDY PROPERTIES IN THE ASPEN PARKLAND OF ALBERTA

Species		Average % by mass
alfalfa	*Medicago sativa*	12.29 (0–25)
sweet clover	*Melilotus* sp.	0.45 (0–4)
crested wheat grass	*Agropyron cristatum*	4.17 (0–17)
intermediate wheat grass	*A. intermedium*	4.08 (0–23)
pubescent wheat grass	*A. trichophorum*	7.39 (0–22)
slender wheat grass	*A. trachycaulum*	3.05 (0–7)
western wheat grass	*A. smithii*	11.84 (0–29)
northern wheat grass	*A. dasystachyum*	3.34 (0–15)
streambank wheat grass	*A. riparium*	4.90 (0–9)
tall wheat grass	*A. elongatum*	24.04 (12–54)
smooth brome grass	*Bromus inermis*	7.73 (0–35)
meadow brome grass	*B. biebersteinii*	14.98 (0–32)
tall fescue	*Festuca arundinacea*	4.00 (0–17)

Note: Individual seed mixes contained 5–7 of these species; numbers in parentheses are range of percentages in individual seed mixtures.

count circle following the methodology of Robel et al. 1970. A wooden pole, marked in decimeter increments, was placed in a vertical position at each sample location. The observer viewed the pole from a distance of 4 m and a height of 1 m from each of four cardinal directions and recorded the lowest decimeter that was completely obstructed by vegetation (hereafter "ROBEL"). We also recorded the highest decimeter ("HIGHDM") that was intersected by vegetation. Each set of measurements was taken at four randomly chosen locations 10–30 m from the center of the point-count circle.

Analyses of variance were used to test for differences in species richness, relative abundance, and vegetation readings among treatment (six age classes) and control habitats (Sokal and Rohlf 1981). Following significant overall F tests, Dunnett's multiple compar-

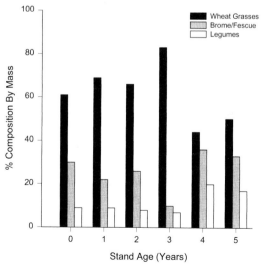

FIGURE 2. Mean composition (percent by mass in seed mix) of major vegetation types in DNC mixes used on study areas in the Aspen Parkland of Alberta.

ison procedure was used to test for differences in mean values of dependent variables between year classes and the control (Dunnett 1955, Miller 1981). Spearman rank correlations (Conover 1980) and multiple regression analyses (Sokal and Rohlf 1981) were used to test for associations of ROBEL and HIGHDM values with species richness and relative abundance across year classes and controls. All analyses were conducted using PC-SAS/STAT (SAS Institute 1990).

RESULTS

Bird censuses were conducted in 162 count circles (137 treatment, 25 control) in 1994. Sample sizes were greater than 21 point counts for every control and age class except 5-yr-old stands (N = 5). A total of 18 bird species were observed in seeded grasslands and control fields during the study (Tables 2 and 3).

Bird species composition changed over time as grasslands matured (Tables 2 and 3). Controls and DNC less than 1 yr of age tended to contain species that were not found in older age classes. Although Killdeer (*Charadrius vociferus*) and Horned Larks (*Eremophila alpestris*) were undoubtedly breeding in the upland areas, corvid and icterid species probably used these uplands only for feeding. Savannah Sparrows (*Passerculus sandwichensis*) were found in all age classes but were most frequently encountered, and most abundant, in 1- to 3-yr-old stands. Clay-colored Sparrows (*Spizella pallida*), Le Conte's Sparrows (*Ammodramus leconteii*), and Nelson's Sharp-tailed Sparrows (*A. nelsoni*) were rare or absent in grasslands less than 2 yr of age; these species were more frequently encountered as stand age increased, although a decline in average abundance was observed in the oldest age class. Gadwall (*Anas strepera*), Northern Harriers (*Circus cyaneus*), Common Snipe (*Gallinago gallinago*), and Sedge Wrens (*Cistothorus pla-*

TABLE 2. FREQUENCY OF OCCURRENCE (PERCENT OF POINTS) OF BIRD SPECIES IN TREATMENT AND CONTROL PLOTS IN THE ASPEN PARKLAND OF ALBERTA, 1994

Species	Control (N = 25)	Stand age (years)					
		0 (N = 23)	1 (N = 27)	2 (N = 21)	3 (N = 30)	4 (N = 31)	5 (N = 5)
Mallard *Anas platyrhynchos*		8.7				3.2	
Blue-winged Teal *A. discors*				4.8			
Gadwall *A. strepera*					3.3	3.2	
Northern Harrier *Circus cyaneus*					10.0		
Killdeer *Charadrius vociferus*	8.0						
Marbled Godwit *Limosa fedoa*			3.7				
Common Snipe *Gallinago gallinago*						3.2	
Horned Lark *Eremophila alpestris*	4.0	17.4					
Black-billed Magpie *Pica pica*	4.0						
American Crow *Corvus brachyrhynchos*	4.0	4.3					
Sedge Wren *Cistothorus platensis*					6.7	3.2	
Clay-colored Sparrow *Spizella pallida*				52.4	66.7	77.4	80.0
Vesper Sparrow *Pooecetes gramineus*		4.3			3.3	3.2	
Savannah Sparrow *Passerculus sandwichensis*	65.6	65.2	92.6	95.2	86.7	64.5	20.0
Le Conte's Sparrow *Ammodramus leconteii*		4.3		95.2	96.7	87.1	80.0
Nelson's Sharp-tailed Sparrow *A. nelsoni*			7.4	4.8	10.0	9.7	
Red-winged Blackbird *Agelaius phoeniceus*	16.0	17.4	14.8		3.3		
Yellow-headed Blackbird *Xanthocephalus xanthocephalus*	4.0						

tensis) also showed a preference for mature cover, although the frequency of occurrence and mean abundance of these species were relatively low.

Overall, count circles contained 1.94 ± 0.08 (SE) species and 3.93 ± 0.18 individuals. The number of species ($F = 24.7$; df = 6, 155; $P < 0.0001$) and relative abundance of individuals ($F = 21.3$; df = 6, 155; $P < 0.0001$) differed across treatment and control properties. Dunnett's test indicated that the numbers of species observed in 2- to 4-yr-old stands were significantly higher than in controls ($P < 0.05$), with the largest difference between controls and treatment means occurring in 3-yr-old stands. Avian abundance in DNC was significantly higher than in controls for all but the 0-yr stand (Dunnett's test, $P < 0.05$), with the largest difference between treat-

ment and control means occurring in 3-yr-old cover (Fig. 3). Overall, species richness and relative abundance were lowest in controls, increased monotonically with age of DNC until 3 yr of age, and then declined (Fig. 3).

ROBEL ($F = 561.7$; df = 6, 2569; $P < 0.0001$) and HIGHDM ($F = 744.2$; df = 6, 2569; $P < 0.0001$) values varied significantly across treatment and control habitats. All treatment years had significantly higher mean values than controls for both vegetation measures (Dunnett's tests, $P < 0.05$), with the greatest difference between treatment and controls occurring in 2-yr-old stands for ROBEL values and in 3-yr-old stands for HIGHDM values (Fig. 3).

There was a high correlation between ROBEL and HIGHDM values ($N = 161$, $r = 0.82$, $P < 0.0001$) and significant associations of bird spe-

TABLE 3. MEAN (± SE) ABUNDANCE OF BIRD SPECIES IN TREATMENT AND CONTROL PLOTS IN THE ASPEN PARKLAND OF ALBERTA, 1994

Species	Control (N = 25)	Stand age (years)					
		0 (N = 23)	1 (N = 27)	2 (N = 21)	3 (N = 30)	4 (N = 31)	5 (N = 5)
Mallard		0.13 ± 0.10					
Blue-winged Teal				0.05 ± 0.05		0.03 ± 0.03	
Gadwall					0.03 ± 0.03	0.03 ± 0.03	
Northern Harrier					0.13 ± 0.08		
Killdeer	0.08 ± 0.06						
Marbled Godwit			0.04 ± 0.04				
Common Snipe						0.03 ± 0.03	
Horned Lark	0.04 ± 0.04	0.18 ± 0.08					
Black-billed Magpie	0.08 ± 0.08						
American Crow	0.04 ± 0.04	0.09 ± 0.09					
Sedge Wren					0.17 ± 0.19	0.13 ± 0.13	
Clay-colored Sparrow				0.62 ± 0.15	1.00 ± 0.16	1.52 ± 0.21	0.40 ± 0.19
Vesper Sparrow	0.92 ± 0.18	0.04 ± 0.04	0.04 ± 0.04		0.03 ± 0.03	0.03 ± 0.03	
Savannah Sparrow		1.48 ± 0.31	2.96 ± 0.40	2.52 ± 0.33	2.20 ± 0.28	1.74 ± 0.27	
Le Conte's Sparrow		0.04 ± 0.04		1.52 ± 0.18	1.77 ± 0.20	1.84 ± 0.20	0.08 ± 0.08
Nelson's Sharp-tailed Sparrow					0.17 ± 0.11	0.10 ± 0.05	0.44 ± 0.21
Red-winged Blackbird	0.28 ± 0.15	0.17 ± 0.08	0.07 ± 0.05	0.05 ± 0.05	0.03 ± 0.03		
Yellow-headed Blackbird	0.16 ± 0.16		0.26 ± 0.14				

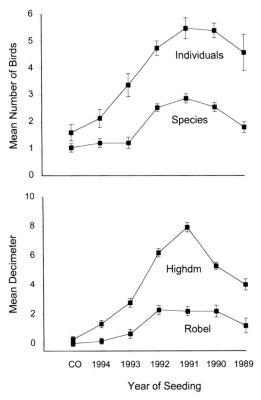

FIGURE 3. Changes in bird species richness and abundance (top) and vegetation profile (bottom) across age classes of DNC and controls in the Aspen Parkland of Alberta. Plotted values are mean ± SE.

cies richness and abundance with average RO-BEL and HIGHDM values across count circles (all r > 0.60, all P < 0.0001). To determine the relative importance of vegetation measures to bird communities in DNC, multiple linear regressions of ROBEL and HIGHDM on bird species richness and abundance were performed. Both HIGHDM (partial F = 5.1; df = 1, 158; P < 0.03) and ROBEL (partial F = 15.1; df = 1, 158; P < 0.0001) values were important determinants of species richness in count circles, but relative abundance was influenced only by HIGHDM values (partial F = 26.5; df = 1, 158; P < 0.0001) after the effects of ROBEL were removed.

DISCUSSION

The structure of seeded grasslands in the Aspen Parkland of Alberta changes substantially over a 6-yr period. Grass height and visual obstruction increase rapidly during the first 2–3 yr, peak, and then decline in older stands. This general pattern has been found in other studies. Higgins et al. (1984) reported that the height and

density of seeded cover increased monotonically during a 4-yr study in North Dakota. Blankespoor (1980) noted a decrease in growth during the fifth year of establishment, although this trend could be attributed partly to local drought and grazing pressure. Higgins and Barker (1982) studied DNC up to 9 yr of age and found that growth declined after a maximum that occurred 3–5 yr after seeding; the authors noted that annual trends in height and density of vegetation were due not only to growth but to successional changes in species composition (see also Blankespoor 1980) and to "lodging" of decadent vegetation in older stands. Although we did not measure compositional changes in the upland cover, matting of vegetation was clearly evident in DNC stands older than 4 yr (pers. obs.). We acknowledge that some of the observed "changes" in vegetation structure over time may be due to annual differences in seed mixes. For example, HIGHDM values in 3- to 5-yr-old stands (Fig. 3) paralleled the amounts of wheat grass in associated seed mixtures (Fig. 2). RO-BEL values, however, exhibited a different pattern. They remained high in 4-yr-old stands but then declined in the oldest age class. Furthermore, the high percentage of brome/fescue and legume in older seed mixes should have meant higher ROBEL values in 4- and 5-yr-old stands. The decline in ROBEL values in the oldest age class therefore appears to be independent of the composition of the seed mix, suggesting a major role of stand decadence in the annual trends in vegetation structure we observed.

Changes in the structure of seeded cover between years are accompanied by changes in the resident bird community. In the Aspen Parkland of Alberta, bird species richness and abundance peaked 3 yr after establishment, and count circles with the greatest vegetation cover, regardless of year class, supported the most species and individuals. Species that breed in short-grass or bare-ground habitats (Horned Lark, Killdeer) are displaced when permanent cover is planted (Owens and Myres 1973, Dale 1993, Johnson and Schwartz 1993), as are icterids and corvids that use these habitats for foraging. Because neither Horned Larks nor Killdeer are declining on a regional or continental basis (Robbins et al. 1986, Peterjohn and Sauer 1993), the conversion to permanent cover should not seriously affect breeding populations of these species. Well-established (>2 yr) DNC in Alberta, and in other areas of the northern Great Plains, is dominated by Le Conte's, Clay-colored, and Savannah sparrows (Duebbert 1981, Renken and Dinsmore 1987, Dale 1993, Hartley 1994, Prescott et al. 1995) and attracts Northern Harriers, Sedge Wrens, and Nelson's Sharp-tailed Sparrows.

Most of these species have stable populations on a continental scale. Clay-colored Sparrows have been declining over the last 25 yr (Peterjohn and Sauer 1993), however, so seeded grasslands might be providing valuable habitat for this species. The same is true of Sedge Wrens. Although this species is currently increasing on a continental scale (Peterjohn and Sauer 1993), sharp declines were noted in all regions, including the Canadian prairies, between 1966 and 1979 (Robbins et al. 1986). This species is at the edge of its range in our study area and was only encountered in three count circles. Sedge Wrens are common inhabitants of seeded cover elsewhere in the prairie region (Higgins et al. 1984, Renken and Dinsmore 1987, Dale 1993, Hartley 1994), however, and the establishment of tame DNC in the parkland of Alberta may provide habitat for the establishment of Sedge Wren colonies in previously unoccupied areas.

In general, the conversion of cropland to permanent cover results in a replacement of several common and stable species with other species of similar attributes. It is notable that Western Meadowlarks (*Sturnella neglecta*), Sprague's Pipits (*Anthus spragueii*), and to a lesser extent, Baird's Sparrows (*Ammodramus bairdii*), which are endemic to grasslands in the Aspen Parkland of Alberta (Semenchuk 1992, Prescott et al. 1995) and which have experienced long-term declines in numbers (Robbins et al. 1986, Peterjohn and Sauer 1993, Sauer et al. 1997), were not encountered during our study. Thus, tame DNC does not provide habitat for some declining grassland songbirds. Even so, restored grasslands may be valuable because nest success is higher in perennial cover than in the cropland it replaces (Dale 1993, Hartley 1994). Future study will determine if the recent shift to more "native" DNC mixes in the Aspen Parkland will provide habitat for species that require undisturbed native prairie.

Previous studies have suggested that seeded grasslands may be productive as waterfowl habitat for a period of 8–10 yr (Duebbert et al. 1981, Higgins and Barker 1982). We did not specifically census waterfowl, and it is difficult to objectively determine how long these habitats would remain "productive" breeding areas for these species. Kirsch et al. (1978), however, reported that the density and success of duck nests are related to the height and density of the surrounding vegetation. The relationship we observed between vegetation structure and bird species richness and abundance therefore suggests that DNC management for waterfowl and for avifauna in general is complementary. Accordingly, habitat managers may consider mowing, burning, or grazing (Duebbert 1981, Hig-

gins and Barker 1982) to rejuvenate seeded grasslands that are losing vertical structure. We suggest that 4–5 yr be the minimum age at which such management occurs. However, stand decadence is known to be influenced by plant composition, climatic conditions, and soil type, so rejuvenation schedules should be determined on a field-by-field basis (Higgins and Barker 1982).

ACKNOWLEDGMENTS

We thank Alberta Prairie Care staff in the Aspen Parkland for assistance with site selection, B. Dale (Canadian Wildlife Service) for advice on census techniques, B. Bishop (Ducks Unlimited Canada) for providing seeding information, and B. Calverley (Ducks Unlimited Canada) for providing acreage figures for DNC on the prairies. We also thank E. Ewaschuk (Land Stewardship Centre of Canada), B. Dale, P. D. Vickery, and an anonymous reader for critically reviewing the manuscript. The study was generously supported with financial assistance from Wildlife Habitat Canada.

LITERATURE CITED

ADAMS, G. D., AND G. C. GENTLE. 1978. Spatial changes in waterfowl habitat, 1964–74, on two land types in the Manitoba Newdale Plain. Canadian Wildlife Service Occasional Papers no. 38.

BLANKESPOOR, G. W. 1980. Prairie restoration: effects on nongame birds. Journal of Wildlife Management 44:667–672.

CONOVER, W. J. 1980. Practical nonparametric statistics. John Wiley and Sons, Toronto, ON.

DALE, B. C. 1993. Saskatchewan non-game bird evaluation of North American Waterfowl Management Plan. DNC and short grass cover—1992. Saskatchewan Wetland Conservation Corporation, Regina, SK.

DUEBBERT, H. F. 1981. Breeding birds on waterfowl production areas in northeastern North Dakota. Prairie Naturalist 13:19–22.

DUEBBERT, H. F., E. T. JACOBSON, K. F. HIGGINS, AND E. B. PODOLL. 1981. Establishment of seeded grasslands for wildlife habitat in the prairie pothole region. U.S. Fish and Wildlife Service Special Scientific Report—Wildlife no. 234. U.S. Fish and Wildlife Service, Washington, D.C.

DUNNETT, C. W. 1955. A multiple comparison procedure for comparing several treatments with a control. Journal of the American Statistical Association 50:1096–1121.

HARTLEY, M. J. 1994. Passerine abundance and productivity indices in grasslands managed for waterfowl nesting cover in Saskatchewan, Canada. M.S. thesis. Louisiana State University, Baton Rouge, LA.

HIGGINS, K. F., T. W. ARNOLD, AND R. M. BARTA. 1984. Breeding bird community colonization of sown stands of native grasses in North Dakota. Prairie Naturalist 16:177–182.

HIGGINS, K. F., AND W. T. BARKER. 1982. Changes in vegetation structure in seeded nesting cover in the prairie pothole region. U.S. Fish and Wildlife Service Special Scientific Report—Wildlife no. 242. U.S. Fish and Wildlife Service, Washington, D.C.

HUTTO, R. L., S. M. PLETSCHET, AND P. HENDRICKS. 1986. A fixed-radius point count method for non-breeding and breeding season use. Auk 103:593–602.

JOHNSON, D. H., AND M. D. SCHWARTZ. 1993. The Conservation Reserve Program and grassland birds. Conservation Biology 7:934–937.

JONES, R. E. 1994. Non-waterfowl evaluation of Manitoba's North American waterfowl management program. Wildlife Branch, Management Department, Natural Resources, Winnipeg, MB.

KIRSCH, L. M., H. F. DUEBBERT, AND A. D. KRUSE. 1978. Grazing and haying effects on habitats of upland nesting birds. Transactions of the North American Wildlife and Natural Resources Conference 43: 486–497.

MILLER, R. G., JR. 1981. Simultaneous statistical inference. Springer-Verlag, New York, NY.

OWENS, R. A., AND M. T. MYRES. 1973. Effects of agriculture upon populations of native passerine birds of an Alberta fescue grassland. Canadian Journal of Zoology 51:697–713.

PETERJOHN, B. G., AND J. R. SAUER. 1993. North American Breeding Bird Survey annual summary 1990–1991. Bird Populations 1:1–15.

PRESCOTT, D. R. C., R. ARBUCKLE, B. GODDARD, AND A. MURPHY. 1993. Methods for the monitoring and assessment of avian communities on NAWMP landscapes in Alberta, and 1993 results. Alberta North American Waterfowl Management Plan Centre, Edmonton, AB.

PRESCOTT, D. R. C., A. J. MURPHY, AND E. EWASCHUK. 1995. An avian community approach to determining biodiversity values of NAWMP habitats in the aspen parkland of Alberta. Alberta North American Waterfowl Management Plan Centre, Edmonton, AB.

RENKEN, R. B., AND J. J. DINSMORE. 1987. Nongame bird communities on managed grasslands in North Dakota. Canadian Field-Naturalist 101:551–557.

ROBBINS, C. S., D. BYSTRAK, AND P. H. GEISSLER. 1986. The Breeding Bird Survey: its first fifteen years, 1965–1979. U.S. Fish and Wildlife Service Resource Publication 157.

ROBEL, R. J., J. N. BRIGGS, A. D. DAYTON, AND L. C. HULBERT. 1970. Relationships between visual obstruction measurements and weight of grassland vegetation. Journal of Range Management 23:295–297.

ROUNDS, R. C. 1982. Land use changes in the Minnedosa pothole region of southwestern Manitoba 1948–1970. Blue Jay 40:6–12.

SAS INSTITUTE, INC. 1990. SAS/STAT user's guide, version 6. SAS Institute, Cary, NC.

SAUER, J. R., J. E. HINES, G. GOUGH, I. THOMAS, AND B. G. PETERJOHN. 1997. The North American Breeding Bird Survey results and analysis. Ver. 96.4: www.mbr-pwrc.usgs.gov/bbs/bbs.html. U.S. Geological Survey, Patuxent Wildlife Research Center, Laurel, MD.

SEMENCHUK, G. P. 1992. The atlas of breeding birds of Alberta. Federation of Alberta Naturalists, Edmonton, AB.

SOKAL, R. R., AND F. J. ROHLF. 1981. Biometry. 2d ed. W. H. Freeman, New York, NY.

SUGDEN, L. G., AND G. W. BEYERSBERGEN. 1984. Farming intensity on waterfowl breeding grounds in Saskatchewan parklands. Wildlife Society Bulletin 12: 22–26.

TURNER, B. C., G. S. HOCHBAUM, F. D. CASWELL, AND D. J. NIEMAN. 1987. Agricultural impacts on wetland habitats on the Canadian prairies, 1981–1985. Transactions of the North American Wildlife and Natural Resources Conference 52:206–215.

Studies in Avian Biology No. 19:211–218, 1999.

GRASSLAND SONGBIRD OCCURRENCE IN NATIVE AND CRESTED WHEATGRASS PASTURES OF SOUTHERN SASKATCHEWAN

STEPHEN K. DAVIS AND DAVID C. DUNCAN

Abstract. We examined grassland songbird occurrence in native pasture and in seeded pastures comprising pure crested wheatgrass (*Agropyron cristatum*), crested wheatgrass/grass mix, and crested wheatgrass/legume mix in southern Saskatchewan, Canada, to determine (1) if grassland songbirds are equally attracted to native and crested wheatgrass pastures; (2) if grassland songbirds are equally attracted to different types of crested wheatgrass pastures; and (3) what habitat variables are important in predicting the occurrence of grassland songbirds. Bird occurrence was quantified using 100-meter fixed-radius point counts. Sprague's Pipit (*Anthus spragueii*), Chestnut-collared Longspur (*Calcarius ornatus*), and Clay-colored Sparrow (*Spizella pallida*) occurred more frequently in native pasture than in any of the crested wheatgrass pastures. Baird's Sparrow (*Ammodramus bairdii*), Savannah Sparrow (*Passerculus sandwichensis*), Vesper Sparrow (*Pooecetes gramineus*), Horned Lark (*Eremophila alpestris*), and Western Meadowlark (*Sturnella neglecta*) were recorded as frequently in each of the crested wheatgrass pasture types as in native pasture. Grasshopper Sparrow (*Ammodramus savannarum*) was the only species detected more often in one or more of the crested wheatgrass pasture types than in native pasture. Among the various types of crested wheatgrass pasture examined, Sprague's Pipit and Grasshopper Sparrow were recorded more often in pure crested wheatgrass than in crested wheatgrass/legume-mix pastures. Habitat variables associated with songbird occurrence differed among species and generally supported findings in other studies. Our results show that vegetative structure is more important than plant-species composition in grassland bird habitat selection, as crested wheatgrass pastures were as attractive as native pastures to many of the species studied. Because previous studies have shown that most grassland songbirds rarely inhabit cropland, the conversion of cropland to pure crested wheatgrass pastures in southern Saskatchewan would likely benefit this avian community.

LA INCIDENCIA DE AVES PASERIFORMES DE PASTIZAL EN LOS PASTOS NATIVOS Y EN LOS PASTOS DE *AGROPYRON CRISTATUM* DEL SUR DE SASKATCHEWAN

Sinopsis. Examinamos la incidencia de aves paseriformes de pastizal en pasto nativo y en pastos sembrados que comprenden *Agropyron cristatum* puro, una mezcla de *Agropyron cristatum* y hierba, y una mezcla de *Agropyron cristatum* y legumbres en el sur de Saskatchewan, Canadá, para determinar (1) si los pastos nativos y los pastos de *Agropyron cristatum* atraen en igual medida a las aves paseriformes de pastizal; (2) si los diferentes tipos de pastos de *Agropyron cristatum* atraen en igual medida a las aves paseriformes de pastizal; y (3) cuáles son las variables importantes de hábitat para predecir la incidencia de aves paseriformes de pastizal. Se cuantificó la incidencia de aves aplicando conteos desde un punto y por un radio fijo de 100 metros. La Bisbita de Sprague (*Anthus spragueii*), el Escribano Cuellicastaño (*Calcarius ornatus*) y el Gorrión Pálido (*Spizella pallida*) se encontraron más frecuentemente en el pasto nativo que en ninguno de los pastos de *Agropyron cristatum*. El Gorrión de Baird (*Ammodramus bairdii*), el Gorrión Sabanero (*Passerculus sandwichensis*), el Gorrión Coliblanco (*Pooecetes gramineus*), la Alondra Cornuda (*Eremophila alpestris*) y el Pradero Occidental (*Sturnella neglecta*) se registraron en cada uno de los tipos de pasto de *Agropyron cristatum* con la misma frecuencia que en los pastos nativos. El Gorrión Chapulín (*Ammodramus savannarum*) fue la única especie detectada con más frecuencia en uno o más de los tipos de pasto de *Agropyron cristatum* que en pasto nativo. Entre los distintos tipos de pasto de *Agropyron cristatum* que examinamos, se registraron la Bisbita de Sprague y el Gorrión Chapulín con más frecuencia en *Agropyron cristatum* puro que en pastos de una mezcla de *Agropyron cristatum* y legumbres. Las variables de hábitat asociadas con la incidencia de aves paseriformes difirieron entre especies y generalmente ratificaron las conclusiones de otros estudios. Nuestros resultados revelan que la estructura vegetativa es más importante que la composición de plantas y especies en la selección de hábitat de las aves de pastizal, ya que los pastos de *Agropyron cristatum* fueron tan atrayentes como los pastos nativos para muchas de las especies estudiadas. Dado que estudios anteriores han comprobado que la mayoría de las aves paseriformes de pastizal habita raramente en terreno cultivado, la conversión de terreno cultivado a pastos de *Agropyron cristatum* puro en el sur de Saskatchewan probablemente beneficiaría a esta comunidad de aves.

Key Words: crested wheatgrass; grassland songbirds; habitat selection; native pasture.

The loss and degradation of native prairie in North America have been cited as primary factors in the decline of many grassland songbird species (Peterjohn and Sauer 1993, Herkert 1994, Knopf 1994). In Saskatchewan only 23% of the original 16.3 million ha of native grassland remains (Samson and Knopf 1994). Recent changes to Canadian agricultural policies have eliminated the major subsidies that previously encouraged the conversion of native prairie to cropland (Reimer 1994). As a result of these changes, agricultural economists predict that up to 4 million ha of cropland in prairie Canada may be converted to permanent forages (i.e., seeded grassland or hayland). A large proportion of the land is expected to be seeded to crested wheatgrass (*Agropyron cristatum*) because it is inexpensive, easy to establish, and hardy (Holt 1994). More than 1 million ha of crested wheatgrass presently exist in prairie Canada (Dormaar et al. 1995).

Although bird response to crested wheatgrass in sagebrush (*Artemisia tridentata*) communities has been examined (Reynolds and Trost 1980, McAdoo et al. 1989), information on grassland songbird use of crested wheatgrass pastures in mixed-grass prairie is almost nonexistent. The purpose of this study was to compare grassland songbird occurrence on native and crested wheatgrass pastures in southern Saskatchewan. We also compared three types of seeded pastures (pure crested wheatgrass, crested wheatgrass/ grass mix, and crested wheatgrass/legume mix) to determine if grassland songbirds are more attracted to a particular type of crested wheatgrass pasture. Lastly, we examined physiognomic and plant-species variables to gain additional insight into habitat selection by grassland songbirds.

STUDY AREA

The study was conducted in the Missouri Coteau region of southern Saskatchewan, Canada, from 24 May to 17 June 1995. This area was selected because a large portion of it consists of native and crested wheatgrass pasture. Classification of the type of crested wheatgrass pasture was initially made by subjective observation and subsequently checked following quantification of plant-species cover (see below).

Native pastures comprised primarily *Stipa* species, June grass (*Koeleria gracilis*), northern wheatgrass (*Agropyron dasystachyum*), blue grama grass (*Bouteloua gracilis*), upland sedges (*Carex* spp.), club moss (*Selaginella densa*), and pasture sage (*Artemisia frigida*). Pastures classified as pure crested wheatgrass had no other plant species with more than 5% cover. Crested wheatgrass/grass-mix pastures were characterized by crested wheatgrass, smooth brome (*Bromus inermis*), and bluegrass (*Poa* spp.), whereas crested wheatgrass/legume-mix pastures consisted of crested wheatgrass and alfalfa (*Medicago sativa*). All other plant species quantified in each of these pastures were present in trace amounts (< 5% cover).

METHODS

FIELD METHODS

Two surveyors quantified the occurrence of singing male grassland songbirds within 100-m-radius 5-min point-count circles (Ralph et al. 1993). Surveys were conducted between 0425 and 0825 central standard time on days with no precipitation and winds less than 20 km/hr. Because roadside counts in grassland have inherent biases (G. Sutter, unpubl. data), the periphery of each point-count circle was situated 50–100 m from roads and fence lines. The periphery of each point count was also located more than 300 m from adjacent point counts. A total of 395 point counts were randomly selected along 30 survey routes, each of which was designed to sample both native and crested wheatgrass pastures. To reduce the influence of grazing intensity on songbird occurrence, we sampled only lightly and moderately grazed pastures.

Habitat variables were quantified for each point count using a 100- × 50-cm quadrat placed randomly in each quadrant of the 100-m circle. Percent cover for each plant species, standing dead vegetation, and bare ground was estimated visually in the quadrat. Litter depth and vegetation height were measured at the northeast corner of each quadrat using a 10-cm and 1-m rule, respectively. Means were calculated for each habitat variable in each circle for use in subsequent analyses.

DATA ANALYSIS

Analyses were conducted on the frequency of occurrence (i.e., presence/absence) of the nine most frequently recorded songbird species (> 10% occurrence) using the SAS/STAT package (SAS Institute 1990). Frequency of occurrence was analyzed because observers seldom recorded more than one individual per species in a point count, thus making normalization of the data problematic. We compared the occurrence of each songbird species inside point-count circles in native and crested wheatgrass pastures using chi-square contingency analyses, or Fisher's exact test if 25% of the cells had expected counts less than 5 (PROC FREQ).

Stepwise logistic regression (PROC LOGISTIC, α = 0.05) was used to identify important habitat variables associated with the occurrence of individual grassland songbird species. If a species showed no preference for any pasture type, data from all pasture types were used in the analyses. Analyses were restricted to within-pasture types for those species that exhibited a habitat preference, to avoid confounding results with habitat variables important in predicting bird occurrence and those variables associated with a particular pasture type. Structural variables included in the analyses were vegetation height, standing dead vegetation, litter depth, and bare ground. Of the 82 plant species quantified in the study, only the 13 species with a mean cover value greater than 1% were used in the analyses (see Appendix). None of these independent variables were strongly correlated (Spearman rank, r < 0.69; PROC CORR).

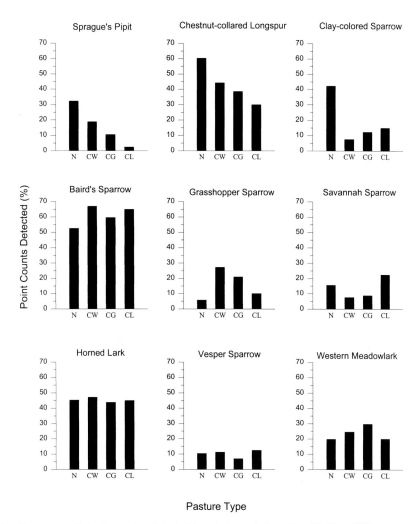

FIGURE 1. Frequency of singing males detected in point counts in native (N; N = 193), pure crested wheatgrass (CW; N = 103), crested wheatgrass/grass mix (CG; N = 60), and crested wheatgrass/legume mix (CL; N = 40) pastures in southern Saskatchewan.

RESULTS

FREQUENCY OF OCCURRENCE

The frequency of occurrence of Horned Lark, Vesper Sparrow, Savannah Sparrow, Baird's Sparrow, and Western Meadowlark was not significantly different among pasture types (χ^2 = 0.054–6.652, df = 3, P > 0.084; Fig. 1). Significant differences in the frequency of occurrence among habitat types were found for Clay-colored and Grasshopper sparrows, Chestnut-collared Longspur, and Sprague's Pipit (χ^2 = 18.194–53.545, df = 3, P < 0.001). Pair-wise comparisons of each pasture type revealed that Sprague's Pipits, Clay-colored Sparrows, and Chestnut-collared Longspurs were recorded more often in native pasture than in any of the crested wheatgrass pastures (χ^2 = 7.307–18.527, df = 1, P < 0.007; Fig. 1). In addition, Sprague's Pipits were detected more often in pure crested wheatgrass than in crested wheatgrass/legume-mix pastures (χ^2 = 5.608, df = 1, P = 0.018; Fig. 1). Clay-colored Sparrows exhibited a trend toward higher occurrence in crested wheatgrass/legume-mix pastures than in pure crested wheatgrass pastures (Fisher's exact test, P = 0.057; Fig. 1). Grasshopper Sparrows were recorded significantly more often in pure crested wheatgrass and crested wheatgrass/grass-mix pastures than in native pastures (χ^2 = 27.099, df = 1, P < 0.001; χ^2 = 13.591, df = 1, P < 0.001, respectively), and they occurred more often in pure crested wheatgrass than in crested wheat-

TABLE 1. SUMMARY OF STEPWISE LOGISTIC REGRESSION ANALYSES OF GRASSLAND SONGBIRD-HABITAT RELATION-
SHIPS IN NATIVE AND CRESTED WHEATGRASS PASTURES

Species	Variable	Estimate (β)	P	Model concordance
Horned Lark	Vegetation height	−0.110	< 0.001	76.8%
	Bare ground	0.031	0.001	
	Litter depth	−0.118	0.016	
	Pasture sage	0.077	0.002	
	Western snowberry	−0.125	0.018	
	Northern wheatgrass	−0.048	0.049	
Sprague's Pipit	Standing dead	0.025	0.011	60.6%
Clay-colored Sparrow	Western snowberry	0.131	0.004	71.3%
	Standing dead	0.029	0.003	
	Pasture sage	0.067	0.016	
Vesper Sparrow	Vegetation height	−0.143	< 0.001	73.0%
	Club moss	−0.107	0.007	
Savannah Sparrow	Alfalfa	0.046	0.002	71.0%
	Standing dead	0.047	< 0.001	
	Vegetation height	0.095	< 0.001	
	Upland sedges	0.056	0.025	
Baird's Sparrow	Vegetation height	0.138	< 0.001	73.2%
	Bare ground	−0.024	0.004	
	Upland sedges	−0.040	0.047	
Grasshopper Sparrow	Vegetation height	0.086	0.005	75.3%
	Crested wheatgrass	0.040	0.004	
	Bluegrass	0.066	0.015	
Chestnut-collared Longspur	Western snowberry	−0.121	0.009	68.2%
	June grass	0.069	0.004	
	Pasture sage	−0.061	0.033	
Western Meadowlark	June grass	−0.079	0.003	46.7%
	Stipa spp.	0.041	0.018	

Note: Variables are listed in order of their entry into the model.

grass/legume-mix pastures (χ^2 = 4.898, df = 1, P = 0.027).

HABITAT VARIABLE ASSOCIATIONS

All pasture types were used in the logistic regression analyses of habitat variables for the five species that showed no habitat preference. Logistic regression analyses for Sprague's Pipit, Clay-colored Sparrow, and Chestnut-collared Longspur were conducted in native pastures, whereas the analyses for Grasshopper Sparrow were restricted to pure crested wheatgrass and crested wheatgrass/grass-mix pastures. The models for Horned Lark and Clay-colored, Vesper, Savannah, Baird's, and Grasshopper sparrows had fair explanatory power (71–76.8% concordance), whereas the Sprague's Pipit and Chestnut-collared Longspur models had somewhat poorer predictive power (Table 1). Variables entered into the Western Meadowlark model failed to explain more than 50% of the variation. Of the habitat variables we examined, structural variables were entered into the models

for seven of nine songbird species and were the first variables entered in five of those species (Table 1). Vegetation height was an important predictor for five species; Baird's, Grasshopper, and Savannah sparrows were positively associated with vegetation height, whereas Horned Lark and Vesper Sparrow were negatively associated with this variable. Percent cover of standing dead vegetation was also an important predictor of songbird occurrence, with Sprague's Pipit and Clay-colored and Savannah sparrows positively associated with this variable. Baird's Sparrows were negatively associated with cover of bare ground, whereas Horned Larks were positively associated with bare ground and negatively associated with litter depth.

Plant species were selected for inclusion in the logistic regression model for eight of nine bird species. Clay-colored Sparrows were positively associated with cover of western snowberry (*Symphoricarpos occidentalis*), whereas Horned Larks and Chestnut-collared Longspurs were negatively associated with this shrub.

Grasshopper Sparrows were positively associated with cover of introduced grasses (crested wheatgrass and bluegrass species), whereas Chestnut-collared Longspurs were positively associated with June grass. Forb species were entered into four of the models. Horned Lark and Clay-colored Sparrows were positively associated with cover of pasture sage, whereas Chestnut-collared Longspurs were negatively associated with this forb. Savannah Sparrow was the only species positively associated with alfalfa.

DISCUSSION

Horned Lark, Vesper Sparrow, Savannah Sparrow, Baird's Sparrow, and Western Meadowlark were recorded as frequently in native pasture as in each type of crested wheatgrass pasture. This lack of discrimination between native pasture and the relative monoculture of crested wheatgrass pastures suggests that these species responded to vegetative structure rather than plant-species composition. Horned Larks and Vesper Sparrows were associated with pastures with low vegetative height. Horned Larks, however, preferred more sparsely vegetated pastures (see also Dubois 1935, Stewart and Kantrud 1972, Owens and Myres 1973, Wiens 1973, Kantrud 1981, Dale 1983). In comparison, Savannah Sparrows occupied pastures with taller, denser vegetation as indicated by the positive association with alfalfa, standing dead vegetation, and vegetation height (Table 1). Lein (1968) and Dale (1983) also found Savannah Sparrows to be associated with tall, dense vegetation in Saskatchewan, and Renken and Dinsmore (1987) found the species most abundant on alfalfa-wheatgrass habitats (but see Johnson and Schwartz 1993a). Baird's Sparrows occurred more often on pastures with greater amounts of vegetative cover as evidenced by their positive association with vegetation height and negative association with cover of bare ground. Dale (1983) and Sutter (1996) also found this species to be associated with taller and denser vegetation in Saskatchewan. The response of Baird's Sparrow to vegetation structure rather than to plant-species composition (see also Mahon 1995, Madden 1996) may allow this species to be more flexible in its habitat requirements than previously thought (Cartwright et al. 1937). The habitat variables measured in this study provided little predictability as to the occurrence of Western Meadowlarks (see also Johnson and Schwartz 1993a, Sutter 1996). These results are supported by previous studies which indicated that all five of these species are not native prairie specialists and are found in a variety of habitats (Owens and Myres 1973, Wiens and Dyer 1975, Rotenberry and Wiens 1980, Basore et al. 1986,

Camp and Best 1993, Johnson and Schwartz 1993a, Davis et al. 1996).

Clay-colored Sparrows, Chestnut-collared Longspurs, and Sprague's Pipits were recorded more frequently in native pasture than in any of the crested wheatgrass pasture types. Because Clay-colored Sparrows were positively associated with native pastures with greater coverage of western snowberry, standing dead vegetation, and pasture sage, their preference for native pastures over crested wheatgrass pastures may be explained by the higher values for these three variables in native pasture (Appendix). The well-known attraction of Clay-colored Sparrows to shrub coverage (see also Knapton 1978, Kantrud 1981, Dale 1983, Arnold and Higgins 1986) may help explain their higher occurrence in crested wheatgrass/legume-mix pastures than in the other crested wheatgrass pastures. Clay-colored Sparrows may have been more attracted to crested wheatgrass pastures with alfalfa because alfalfa likely provides a structural substitute for shrubs (Johnson and Schwartz 1993a).

Our results for Sprague's Pipit are consistent with previous studies which have documented this species' preference for native over introduced vegetation (Wilson and Belcher 1989, Hartley 1994, Sutter et al. 1995, Madden 1996, Sutter 1996). In native pasture, Sprague's Pipit showed a positive association with cover of standing dead vegetation. Thus, the pipit's preference for native pastures may have resulted from the greater coverage of residual vegetation in these pastures than in crested wheatgrass pastures (Appendix). Dale (1983) found Sprague's Pipit to be positively associated with dead vegetation and density of vegetation 10 cm or less in height. Thus, the taller vegetative height and increased amount of bare ground in crested wheatgrass pastures (Appendix) may also have contributed to the pipit's greater occurrence in native pastures. Although previous studies have found Sprague's Pipit to be negatively associated with shrub cover (Dale 1983, Madden 1996), we detected no such association, possibly because native pastures examined in this study had few shrubs (Appendix).

Previous studies have found that Chestnut-collared Longspurs are associated with open and sparsely vegetated native prairie (Harris 1944, Stewart and Kantrud 1972, Owens and Myres 1973, Kantrud and Kologiski 1982, Dale 1983). In our study, this species was negatively associated with western snowberry and pasture sage but positively associated with June grass cover (Appendix). Interpretation of the significance of these three plant species in habitat selection by Chestnut-collared Longspurs is uncertain, with the strongest suggestion being an avoidance of shrubs. Insight into why Chestnut-collared Longspurs preferred native over crested wheatgrass pastures is also difficult to determine from these results.

Grassland birds in Saskatchewan may benefit significantly if the amount of cropland that is predicted to be converted into crested wheatgrass pasture is realized. Six of the nine songbird species were detected in crested wheatgrass pasture in an equal or greater frequency than in native pastures, and the three species that preferred native pasture occurred in varying frequency in crested wheatgrass pastures. Thus, the conversion of cropland to crested wheatgrass pasture should benefit grassland songbirds, as cropland is unattractive to most bird species (Stewart and Kantrud 1972, Owens and Myres 1973, Hartley 1994). In addition, agricultural programs that have converted cultivated land to perennial cover have been shown to provide important habitat for grassland songbirds. The Conservation Reserve Program, for example, has been found to provide habitat that is attractive to many grassland bird species (Johnson and Schwartz 1993a, King and Savidge 1995) and has been suggested as one of the factors contributing to the recovery of some species (Johnson and Schwartz 1993b, Reynolds et al. 1994).

Landowners who seed their land to crested wheatgrass typically seed pure crested wheatgrass or crested wheatgrass/alfalfa to supplement native range and enhance forage quality (Campbell 1963, Hart et al. 1983). The crested wheatgrass/grass-mix pastures in this study were likely pure crested wheatgrass pastures that were subsequently invaded by exotic and native grasses. Of the two types of crested wheatgrass pasture intentionally seeded, pure crested wheatgrass pastures will likely have the greatest benefit for grassland songbirds in Saskatchewan; Sprague's Pipit and Grasshopper Sparrow were least attracted to crested wheatgrass/legume-mix pastures, whereas all other songbird species occurred in similar frequency in pure crested wheatgrass pastures and in those with alfalfa.

We caution that the relative abundance of singing males as we examined here is only one indicator of habitat quality. The reproductive consequences of selecting alternative nesting habitat must also be considered when assessing habitat quality (Van Horne 1983, Johnson and Temple 1986, Vickery et al. 1992). Few studies have examined nesting success of grassland songbirds (e.g., Hill 1976, Elliott 1978, Basore et al. 1986, Johnson and Temple 1986, Davis and Sealy in press), and to our knowledge, no research has been conducted in crested wheatgrass pastures. Research on the reproductive success of grassland songbirds in crested wheat-

grass and native pastures is required to determine definitively the relative value of these pastures.

Although crested wheatgrass pastures were unexpectedly attractive to many grassland songbirds, they were less attractive than native pasture to three songbird species. Hence, preservation of existing native grasslands and restoration of grasslands that more closely mimic the native prairie community should continue to be priorities.

ACKNOWLEDGMENTS

Funding for this study was provided by the National Fish and Wildlife Foundation, Endangered Species Recovery Fund (World Wildlife Fund Canada and Canadian Wildlife Service of Environment Canada), and Saskatchewan Wetland Conservation Corporation (SWCC). We are grateful to J. Pollock and R. Shaw for their competent and dedicated field work and to T. Harrison for assistance in plant identification. D. H. Johnson (Northern Prairie Research Centre) and D. Anstey (SWCC) provided statistical advice. Thanks to D. Prescott, B. Dale, G. McMaster, K. Mazur, and J. Herkert for helpful comments on the manuscript. We especially thank the many landowners who allowed us access to their property.

LITERATURE CITED

ARNOLD, T. W., AND K. F. HIGGINS. 1986. Effects of shrub coverages on birds of North Dakota mixed-grass prairies. Canadian Field-Naturalist 100:10–14.

BASORE, N. S., L. B. BEST, AND J. B. WOOLEY. 1986. Bird nesting in Iowa no-tillage and tilled cropland. Journal of Wildlife Management 50:19–28.

BUDD, A. C. 1987. Budd's flora of the Canadian prairie provinces. Publication no. 1662, Canadian Department of Agriculture, Ottawa, ON.

CAMP, M., AND L. B. BEST. 1993. Bird abundance and species richness in roadsides adjacent to Iowa row-crop fields. Wildlife Society Bulletin 21:315–325.

CAMPBELL, J. B. 1963. Grass-alfalfa versus grass alone pastures grazed in a repeated-seasonal pattern. Journal of Range Management 16:78–81.

CARTWRIGHT, B. W., T. M. SHORTT, AND R. D. HARRIS. 1937. Baird's Sparrow. Transactions of the Royal Canadian Institute 46:153–198.

DALE, B. C. 1983. Habitat relationships of seven species of passerine birds at Last Mountain Lake, Saskatchewan. M.S. thesis. University of Regina, Regina, SK.

DAVIS, S. K., D. C. DUNCAN, AND M. SKEEL. 1996. The Baird's Sparrow: status resolved. Blue Jay 54:185–191.

DAVIS, S. K., AND S. G. SEALY. In press. Cowbird parasitism and nest predation in fragmented grasslands of southwestern Manitoba. In J. N. Smith, T. L. Cook, S. I. Rothstein, S. G. Sealy, and S. K. Robinson (editors). Ecology and management of cowbirds. University of Texas Press, Austin, TX.

DORMAAR, J. F., M. A. NAETH, W. D. WILLMS, AND D. S. CHANASYK. 1995. Effect of native prairie, crested wheatgrass (Agropyron cristatum (L.) Gaertn.) and Russian wildrye (Elymus junceus Fisch.) on soil chemical properties. Journal of Range Management 48:258–263.

DUBOIS, A. D. 1935. Nests of Horned Larks and long-spurs on a Montana prairie. Condor 37:56–72.

ELLIOTT, P. F. 1978. Cowbird parasitism in the Kansas tallgrass prairie. Auk 95:161–167.

HARRIS, R. D. 1944. The Chestnut-collared Longspur in Manitoba. Wilson Bulletin 56:105–115.

HART, R. H., J. W. WAGGONER, JR., D. H. CLARK, C. C. KALTENBACH, J. A. HAGER, AND M. B. MARSHALL. 1983. Beef cattle performance on crested wheatgrass plus native range vs. native range alone. Journal of Range Management 36:38–40.

HARTLEY, M. J. 1994. Passerine abundance and productivity indices in grasslands managed for waterfowl nesting cover. Transactions of the North American Wildlife and Natural Resources Conference 59: 322–327.

HERKERT, J. R. 1994. The effects of habitat fragmentation on midwestern grassland bird communities. Ecological Applications 4:461–471.

HILL, R. A. 1976. Host-parasite relationships of the Brown-headed Cowbird in prairie habitat of west-central Kansas. Wilson Bulletin 88:555–565.

HOLT, N. W. 1994. Management of seeded forage for pasture in southwest Saskatchewan. Pp. 216–223 *in* F. K. Tahan, Z. Abouguendia, and P. R. Horton (editors). Managing Canadian rangelands for sustainability and profitability. Grazing and Pasture Technology Program, Regina, SK.

JOHNSON, D. H., AND M. D. SCHWARTZ. 1993a. The Conservation Reserve Program: habitat for grassland birds. Great Plains Research 3:273–295.

JOHNSON, D. H., AND M. D. SCHWARTZ. 1993b. The Conservation Reserve Program and grassland birds. Conservation Biology 7:934–937.

JOHNSON, R. G., AND S. A. TEMPLE. 1986. Assessing habitat quality for birds nesting in fragmented tallgrass prairie. Pp. 245–249 *in* J. Verner, M. L. Morrison, and C. J. Ralph (editors). Wildlife 2000: modeling habitat relationships of terrestrial vertebrates. University of Wisconsin Press, Madison, WI.

KANTRUD, H. A. 1981. Grazing intensity effects on the breeding avifauna of North Dakota native grasslands. Canadian Field-Naturalist 95:404–417.

KANTRUD, H. A., AND R. L. KOLOGISKI. 1982. Effects of soils and grazing on breeding birds of uncultivated upland grasslands of the northern great plains. U.S. Fish and Wildlife Service Wildlife Report no. 15, Washington, D.C.

KING, J. W., AND J. A. SAVIDGE. 1995. Effects of the Conservation Reserve Program on wildlife in southeast Nebraska. Wildlife Society Bulletin 23:377–385.

KNAPTON, R. W. 1978. Breeding ecology of the Clay-colored Sparrow. Living Bird 17:137–157.

KNOPF, F. L. 1994. Avian assemblages on altered grasslands. Studies in Avian Biology 15:247–257.

LEIN, M. R. 1968. The breeding biology of the Savannah Sparrow, *Passerculus sandwichensis* (Gmelin) at Saskatoon, Sask. M.S. thesis. University of Saskatchewan, Saskatoon, SK.

MADDEN, E. M. 1996. Passerine communities and bird-habitat relationships on prescribed-burned, mixed-grass prairie in North Dakota. M.S. thesis. Montana State University-Bozeman, Bozeman, MT.

MAHON, C. L. 1995. Habitat selection and detectability of Baird's Sparrows in southwestern Alberta. M.S. thesis. University of Alberta, Edmonton, AB.

MCADOO, J. K., W. S. LONGLAND, AND R. A. EVANS. 1989. Nongame bird community responses to sagebrush invasion of crested wheatgrass seedings. Journal of Wildlife Management 53:494–502.

OWENS, R. A., AND M. T. MYRES. 1973. Effects of agriculture upon populations of native passerine birds of an Alberta fescue grassland. Canadian Journal of Zoology 51:697–713.

PETERJOHN, B. G., AND J. R. SAUER. 1993. North American Breeding Bird Survey annual summary 1990–1991. Bird Populations 1:1–15.

RALPH, C. J., G. R. GEUPEL, P. PYLE, T. E. MARTIN, AND D. F. DESANTE. 1993. Handbook of field methods for monitoring landbirds. USDA Forest Service Gen. Tech. Rep. PSW-GTR-144. USDA Forest Service Pacific Southwest Research Station, Albany, CA.

REIMER, G. E. 1994. Agricultural policy impacts on rangeland and options for reform: an overview and evaluation. Pp. 321–327 *in* F. K. Tahan, Z. Abouguendia, and P. R. Horton (editors). Managing Canadian rangelands for sustainability and profitability. Grazing and Pasture Technology Program, Regina, SK.

RENKEN, R. B., AND J. J. DINSMORE. 1987. Nongame bird communities on managed grasslands in North Dakota. Canadian Field-Naturalist 101:551–557.

REYNOLDS, R. E., T. L. SHAFFER, J. R. SAUER, AND B. G. PETERJOHN. 1994. Conservation Reserve Program: benefit for grassland birds in the northern plains. Transactions of the North American Wildlife and Natural Resources Conference 59:328–336.

REYNOLDS, T. D., AND C. H. TROST. 1980. The response of native vertebrate populations to crested wheatgrass planting and grazing by sheep. Journal of Range Management 33:122–125.

ROTENBERRY, J. T., AND J. A. WIENS. 1980. Habitat structure, patchiness, and avian communities in North American steppe vegetation: a multivariate analysis. Ecology 61:1228–1250.

SAMSON, F. B., AND F. L. KNOPF. 1994. Prairie conservation in North America. BioScience 44:418–421.

SAS INSTITUTE INC. 1990. SAS/STAT user's guide. Ver. 6, 4th ed. Vols. 1 and 2. SAS Institute Inc., Cary, NC.

STEWART, R. E., AND H. A. KANTRUD. 1972. Population estimates of breeding birds in North Dakota. Auk 89:766–788.

SUTTER, G. C. 1996. Habitat selection and prairie drought in relation to grassland bird community structure and the nesting ecology of Sprague's Pipit, *Anthus spragueii*. Ph.D. dissertation. University of Regina, Regina, SK.

SUTTER, G. C., T. TROUPE, AND M. FORBES. 1995. Abundance of Baird's Sparrows, *Ammodramus bairdii,* in native prairie and introduced vegetation. Ecoscience 2:344–348.

VAN HORNE, B. 1983. Density as a misleading indicator of habitat quality. Journal of Wildlife Management 47:893–901.

VICKERY, P. D., M. L. HUNTER, JR., AND J. V. WELLS. 1992. Use of a new reproductive index to evaluate relationship between habitat quality and breeding success. Auk 109:697–705.

WIENS, J. A. 1973. Patterns and process in grassland bird communities. Ecological Monographs 43:237–270.

WIENS, J. A., AND M. I. DYER. 1975. Rangeland avifaunas: their composition, energetics, and role in the ecosystem. Pp. 146–182 *in* D. R. Smith (editor). Symposium on management of forest and range habitats for nongame birds. USDA Forest Service Gen. Tech. Rep. WO-1. USDA Forest Service, Washington, D.C.

WILSON, S. D., AND J. W. BELCHER. 1989. Plant and bird communities of native prairie and introduced Eurasian vegetation in Manitoba, Canada. Conservation Biology 3:39–44.

APPENDIX. VEGETATIVE-STRUCTURE AND PLANT-SPECIES VARIABLES IDENTIFIED BY LOGISTIC REGRESSION ANALYSIS AS IMPORTANT PREDICTORS OF THE OCCURRENCE OF GRASSLAND SONGBIRDS[a]

Variable	Pasture type			
	Native	Crested wheatgrass	Crested wheatgrass/ grass mix	Crested wheatgrass/ legume mix
Standing dead	27.2 ± 1.1	14.1 ± 1.1	14.8 ± 1.5	11.2 ± 1.4
Bare ground	11.2 ± 0.8	27.9 ± 1.6	22.6 ± 1.5	26.2 ± 2.5
Litter depth (m)	3.1 ± 0.3	3.4 ± 0.4	3.8 ± 0.7	1.4 ± 0.3
Vegetation height (cm)	8.6 ± 0.4	13.9 ± 0.7	15.1 ± 0.8	15.7 ± 0.8
Northern wheatgrass	4.5 ± 0.4	0.1 ± 0.0	0.5 ± 0.2	0.00
June grass	8.4 ± 0.5	0.1 ± 0.0	0.7 ± 0.5	0.00
Stipa spp.	8.7 ± 0.6	0.3 ± 0.1	0.9 ± 0.4	0.00
Upland sedges	5.6 ± 0.5	0.3 ± 0.1	1.5 ± 0.4	0.00
Club moss	6.8 ± 0.5	1.3 ± 0.3	0.8 ± 0.3	0.00
Crested wheatgrass	0.2 ± 0.1	47.1 ± 1.5	29.8 ± 1.7	34.0 ± 2.5
Pasture sage	5.3 ± 0.4	3.8 ± 0.6	2.7 ± 0.6	1.1 ± 0.5
Western snowberry	2.2 ± 0.3	0.7 ± 0.2	1.3 ± 0.4	0.2 ± 0.1
Bluegrass	2.4 ± 0.4	0.4 ± 0.2	6.1 ± 1.4	0.4 ± 0.4
Alfalfa	0.00	0.1 ± 0.0	1.2 ± 0.4	21.9 ± 2.3

Note: Mean (± SE) values are percent cover except where indicated. Plant-species nomenclature follows Budd 1987.

[a] Three plant species used in the logistic regression analyses not entered into any bird species' models were *Agropyron smithii*, blue grama grass, and smooth brome.

Studies in Avian Biology No. 19:219–229, 1999.

MONITORING GRASSLAND BIRDS IN NOCTURNAL MIGRATION

WILLIAM R. EVANS AND DAVID K. MELLINGER

Abstract. We censused vocalizations of night-migrating birds by making continual audio recordings of the night sky from a transect of seven recording stations across New York State in fall 1991–1993 and at one recording station in south Texas in spring 1995. Bird calls on these audio recordings were later detected by human listening and by automatic sound-detection software. Vocalizations of several migratory bird species that breed in North American grasslands were found on these recordings. We present basic evidence for the identification of nocturnal flight calls of migrant grassland birds east of the Rocky Mountains, and we introduce a method for quantifying nocturnal flight-calling that theoretically derives a minimum number of individuals passing over a recording station from analysis of calling data. Our recordings show that large numbers of certain grassland species can be detected by monitoring their nocturnal flight calls and that using a transect of recording stations can reveal migration corridors. Such information illustrates this monitoring technique's potential as an independent means of assessing population trends and migration pathways. Also evident is the potential for monitoring secretive species and species that nest in remote areas or regions difficult to census by other techniques. Information gained from monitoring nocturnal flight calls can be useful in determining locations for other avian monitoring operations, in making decisions regarding long-term habitat management, and in considering such questions as where to site communications towers and wind-turbine generator farms.

SUPERVISIÓN DE LAS AVES DE PASTIZAL EN MIGRACIÓN NOCTURNA

Sinopsis. Realizamos un censo de las vocalizaciones de aves que migran de noche haciendo grabaciones de audio continuas en el cielo nocturno desde un transecto de siete estaciones de grabación a lo largo del estado de Nueva York durante los otoños de 1991–1993 y en una estación de grabación en el sur de Texas en la primavera de 1995. Posteriormente, los reclamos de aves en estas grabaciones de audio fueron detectados a través de personas y a través de software de detección automática de sonidos. Se encontraron en estas grabaciones las vocalizaciones de varias especies de aves migratorias que se reproducen en pastizales norteamericanos. Ofrecemos pruebas fundamentales para la identificación de los reclamos nocturnos de vuelo de aves migratorias de pastizal del este de las Montañas Rocosas, y presentamos un método para la cuantificación de los reclamos nocturnos de vuelo en el que teóricamente se obtiene un número mínimo de individuos que están pasando encima de una estación de grabación a través de un análisis de los datos de reclamos. Nuestras grabaciones revelan que se pueden detectar grandes números de ciertas especies de pastizal controlando sus reclamos nocturnos de vuelo y que se pueden descubrir pasillos de migración utilizando un transecto de estaciones de grabación. Tal información ilustra el potencial de esta técnica de supervisión como una manera independiente de evaluar las tendencias poblacionales y los pasillos de migración. También es evidente el potencial para la supervisión de especies sigilosas y especies que anidan en áreas remotas o en regiones difíciles de empadronar con otras técnicas. La información recolectada por la supervisión de los reclamos nocturnos de vuelo puede ser útil para determinar lugares para otras actividades de supervisión de aves, para hacer decisiones con respecto al manejo a largo plazo de hábitat, y para considerar preguntas relacionadas con la ubicación de torres de comunicación y de haciendas con generadores de turbinas eólicas.

Key Words: grassland birds; migration; monitoring; nocturnal flight calls.

Many species of North American grassland birds migrate at night, and most of these species are known to vocalize while they fly (Appendix). Calling in night migration may help birds maintain in-flight associations (Hamilton 1962) and organize their spacing to minimize collisions (Graber 1968). Such calling can be monitored from ground-based audio recording stations (Graber and Cochran 1959). When species identities are known, analysis of audio data allows the number of calls for each species to be tallied and the passage of individual birds to be interpreted from sequences of successive calls.

In this paper we present information on nocturnal flight calls of North American grassland migrants and data from recent nocturnal flight-call monitoring studies. We discuss basic concepts behind this monitoring technique and its potential use for studying migration patterns and populations of many migratory grassland birds.

METHODS

We recorded nocturnal flight calls of migrating birds with two monitoring goals in mind: to determine which species migrate over a site and to evaluate each species' quantity of calling for comparison across time and place.

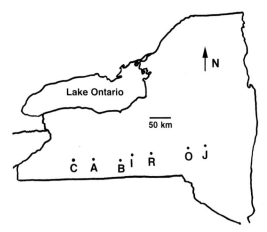

FIGURE 1. Approximate locations of nocturnal flight-call monitoring stations in New York State. Letter designations stand for the town nearest to the monitoring site (C = Cuba, A = Alfred, B = Beaver Dams, I = Ithaca, R = Richford, O = Oneonta, J = Jefferson).

RECORDING STATIONS

The technical goal of recording nocturnal flight calls is to receive sound from the airspace above a recording site while minimizing the reception of environmental ground noise. To achieve this goal, microphones must have directional sensitivity patterns and be aimed at the sky. Depending on their monitoring goals and the recording environment, researchers have used a variety of different microphone and recording-station designs (Graber and Cochran 1959, Dierschke 1989, Evans 1994). In this study we used various pressure-zone microphone designs. In Texas, for example, we surface mounted a Knowles EK3024 hearing-aid microphone element to the center of a 25-cm-diam plastic dinner plate. The simple electronic circuit that powered the microphone element was attached to the bottom of the plate, and clear plastic wrap was stretched and sealed across the upturned edges of the plate as a sound-permeable waterproof membrane. This microphone mount theoretically doubled the sound pressure (for sound frequencies > 1,500 kilohertz [kHz]) in the direction that the face of the plate was pointed. The plate was mounted 23 cm deep inside a 42-cm-deep plastic flowerpot that had a 48-cm-diam top aperture. The inside walls of the flowerpot were lined with acoustic foam to absorb sound reflections, and cheesecloth was fastened over the top to keep out debris. The flowerpot structure helped block out ground-born environmental noise. The overall microphone system provided an approximately 300 km of the Rocky Mountains. east-west transect of up to seven recording stations spanning approximately 300 km across central New York State (Fig. 1). In spring 1995, from mid-March through late May, we operated a re-

expensive, highly directional microphone that was very sensitive in the 2–9 kHz band, which is the frequency range of most avian nocturnal flight calls east of the Rocky Mountains.

In fall 1991–1993, from late July through October, we operated an east-west transect of up to seven recording stations spanning approximately 300 km across central New York State (Fig. 1). In spring 1995, from mid-March through late May, we operated a re-

cording station at Laguna Atascosa National Wildlife Refuge (NWR), about 30 km north of Brownsville, Texas. All of these recording stations consisted of pairs of pressure-zone microphones mounted on the roofs of buildings. The audio signals were recorded on soundtracks of high-fidelity video-cassette recorders. Video tapes recorded 8–9 hr of sound per evening. The equipment was operated by refuge staff in Texas and by volunteers in New York.

NOCTURNAL FLIGHT-CALL ANALYSIS

Nocturnal flight calls were detected on the recordings by listening with headphones and by automatic extraction with signal-analysis software written in the Bioacoustics Research Program at the Cornell Laboratory of Ornithology. This software is designed to detect short, high-pitched sounds in the 5–10 kHz frequency range. Stereo recordings were analyzed from New York. Single-channel and stereo recordings were analyzed from Texas.

Identification of the extracted nocturnal flight calls was performed by aural comparison or by visual comparison of spectrograms to calls of verified identity for each species. Recordings of the known calls had been made in daytime while the species was visually identified. All spectrographic analysis was carried out using the software program Canary (Charif et al. 1995). Spectrograms of calls presented in this paper were made from calls digitized with a 22,254-hertz (Hz) sampling rate and were processed using a 256-point fast Fourier transform (FFT), 128-point frame size, 87.5% overlap, and Hanning window (frequency resolution 86 Hz, time resolution 0.72 ms, analysis bandwidth 700 Hz).

After a night's calls were detected and identified to species, the calling data were analyzed by interpreting call sequences to derive a minimum number of individuals passing (MIP). This interpretive technique considers information such as time delays in calling, amplitude differences between closely occurring calls, stereo spatial separation, the species of the caller, expected flight speeds, and the pickup pattern of the microphone(s). The MIP technique is a conservative estimate that is likely to be more accurate for quantitative population studies than counting the total number of calls because it compensates for the variable calling rates of individual birds.

An example of how we used the MIP technique in this study is illustrated with Grasshopper Sparrow (*Ammodramus savannarum*) and Savannah Sparrow (*Passerculus sandwichensis*) data from a single audio channel recorded at Laguna Atascosa NWR. The formula used to calculate MIP counts for these two species was based on the assumption that migrating individuals were moving toward some distant location on a horizontal plane so that nearly all individuals were passing on a relatively straight-line course through the zone of microphone sensitivity. In addition, we applied previously determined information on the pickup pattern of the microphone and a conservative estimate of the birds' flight speed on the evening of 5–6 April 1995.

The pickup pattern of a microphone design was determined using a ground-based eight-channel microphone array. Eight microphones were laid out in a 75-

× 75-m area—four at the corners of the area and four at the corners of a 30- × 30-m square centered inside the large square. This layout enabled calls from birds flying in the vicinity of the array to be picked up by all eight microphones. It also enabled the approximate point of origin of a nocturnal flight call to be determined by analyzing its varying arrival times at the different microphones. By plotting such locations for hundreds of nocturnal flight calls, the shape of a microphone's detection pattern and its range of detection for different species became evident. The detection range is defined here as the distance in which a call could be picked up by the microphone and still be identified to species by spectrographic analysis. This range varied because of differing call loudness among species, the distinctiveness of the species' acoustic signatures, and variables in a recording site's environmental noise. The eight-channel study revealed that the microphone design used in Texas had a maximum detection range above ground of less than 300 m for a wide range of different warblers and sparrows, including Savannah Sparrow. Furthermore, the maximum horizontal cross-section of sky a single microphone had for detecting such calls was less than 250 m.

In calculating MIP counts through the region of sensitivity from a single microphone, the detection range determined by the eight-channel study was modified to make the estimate a conservative one. The minimum ground speed of passing migrants was assumed to be 20 km/hr, a likely underestimate for average small-passerine ground speed when these birds have a following wind. We also assumed that the longest horizontal cross-section of the microphone sensitivity region was 300 m, a conservative revision of the eight-channel measurement. A Grasshopper or Savannah sparrow flying at 20 km/hr travels about 330 m/min and would typically pass through the region of microphone sensitivity in less than 1 min. Therefore, the first factor used in calculating the MIP for Grasshopper or Savannah sparrows was that calls from one of these species occurring more than 1 min apart were considered to be different individuals of that species.

The second factor used to calculate MIPs was based on 80 hr of listening to stereo recordings containing hundreds of sparrow calls. These data showed that Savannah and Grasshopper sparrow calls occurring within 3 sec of one another in a single microphone recording were almost certainly from two different individuals and not the same individual calling twice. We determined this because the stereo resolution of the microphones allowed a rough spatial assessment of call location (i.e., off to the right or off to the left). If the same bird called twice within 3 sec, these calls would sound as if they came from roughly the same stereo-resolved position and were of similar amplitude. This type of occurrence was quite rare. Such adjacent temporal calls almost always sounded as if they were from birds widely separated in space and often were of different amplitude. The second MIP criterion, therefore, was that calls from the same species occurring within 3 sec of one another were tallied as separate individuals.

A separate statistical analysis used correlations to examine the relationship between the observed hourly detections of Bobolinks (*Dolichonyx oryzivorous*) at all New York recording stations. Differences were considered significant at P = 0.05. The Bonferroni correction for multiple inference was used to correct for multiple tests to ensure an experiment-wide significance level of 0.05.

RESULTS

IDENTIFICATION OF NOCTURNAL FLIGHT CALLS

Confirming the identity of nocturnal flight calls for certain species of grassland birds (e.g., Upland Sandpiper [*Bartramia longicauda*], Long-billed Curlew [*Numenius americanus*], Dickcissel [*Spiza americana*], Bobolink) is simple because they give the same distinctive calls at night that they give during the day. In many species of grassland sparrows, however, the short, high-pitched nocturnal flight calls are not commonly given during the day, making verification difficult. Many of these sparrows' calls also sound similar to one another and can be hard to discriminate by ear. The diurnal counterpart of a sparrow's nocturnal flight call is termed a "flight note" for some species because it is often heard while the bird is flying. For other species, this diurnal counterpart is often called a "location call," as it may not be given in flight as much as while the bird is on the ground in dense grasses. These short notes are often called "tseep notes," a phoneticization of the way many sparrow calls sound. In all cases, whether given at night or during the day, these calls apparently serve to make or maintain contact with other birds.

A primary step in establishing the identity of an unidentified sparrow nocturnal flight call is to obtain recordings of diurnal tseep notes for spectrographic comparison. Figs. 2 and 3 compare nocturnal flight calls from the evening of 5–6 April 1995 with diurnal recordings of verified identity. We classified these nocturnal flight calls as Grasshopper and Savannah sparrow calls based on the similarity of their time-frequency contour with that of the diurnal tseep notes given by these two species, and also because no other species migrating in the Laguna Atascosa NWR region are known to give such call types. Fig. 4 illustrates diurnal tseep notes for five other grassland sparrows and diurnal flight calls of verified identity for four other grassland species. Such call types have been recorded at night in this study or in studies not discussed here. The appendix provides further information on what is known about the nocturnal flight calls of grassland birds east of the Rocky Mountains.

TEXAS

During 5–15 April 1995, four species of North American grassland migrants were acoustically detected by the recording station at La-

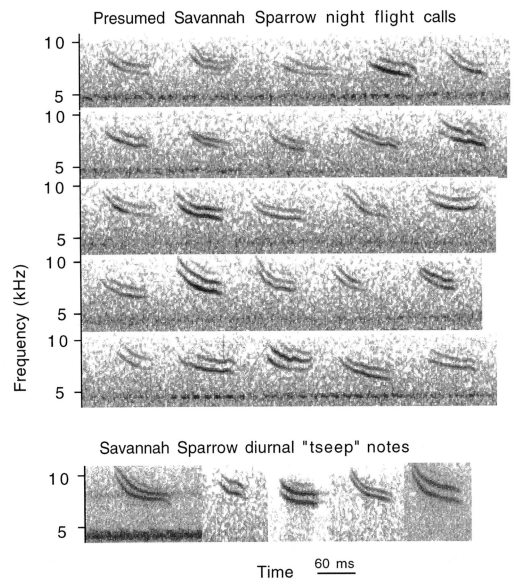

FIGURE 2. Comparison of Savannah Sparrow diurnal and presumed nocturnal flight-call spectrograms. Diurnal flight notes were recorded in south Texas (first two), west Texas (third), Oklahoma (fourth), and North Dakota (fifth). Presumed Savannah Sparrow nocturnal flight calls were recorded on the night of 5–6 April 1995 at Laguna Atascosa NWR, Texas.

guna Atascosa NWR. Most of the identifiable calls were spectrographically classified as Grasshopper or Savannah sparrow calls. For example, of the 385 calls automatically detected on one audio channel during 8 hr of monitoring on the evening of 5–6 April, 78 (22%) were classified as Grasshopper Sparrow and 89 (25%) as Savannah Sparrow (Fig. 5). The MIP technique estimated that at least 54 Grasshopper Sparrows and 57 Savannah Sparrows flew over the recording station during this night's monitoring period.

On most nights in the study period, only small numbers of sparrow calls were recorded (< 50 calls in 8 hr). These low-calling nights corresponded with evenings of east to southeast winds over this part of Texas. Wind data from Brownsville, Texas, indicated that the large sparrow-calling event on the night of 5–6 April occurred when there was a shift from calm con-

Presumed Grasshopper Sparrow night flight calls

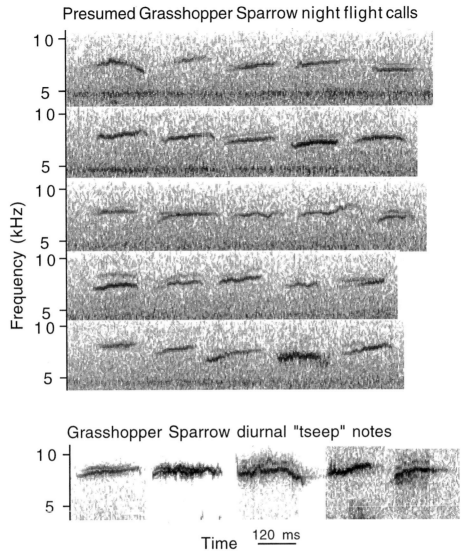

FIGURE 3. Comparison of Grasshopper Sparrow diurnal and presumed nocturnal flight-call spectrograms. Diurnal flight notes were recorded in Florida (first two), Texas (third and fourth), and Alabama (fifth). Presumed Grasshopper Sparrow nocturnal flight calls were recorded on the night of 5–6 April 1995 at Laguna Atascosa NWR, Texas. Note that the time scale is more condensed than in Fig. 2.

ditions to a steady wind out of the southwest during the evening (Fig. 6).

Listening to recordings and using the MIP technique to analyze data also revealed that at least 26 Upland Sandpipers and 28 Long-billed Curlews passed over the recording station during 5–15 April 1995. Later in April and in early May 1995, thousands of Dickcissel calls and five incidences of Black Rail (*Laterallus jamaicensis*) nocturnal flight calls were recorded. The MIP method has not yet been applied to the Dickcissel calling data.

NEW YORK

The transect of New York recording stations revealed calls from Upland Sandpipers, Bobolinks, and several grassland sparrows. Upland Sandpiper counts were detected in larger numbers toward the west end of the monitoring array than the east end, with an average of 13.3 and 12.0 per year detected over 3 yr at the western stations A and B, respectively. In the same period, the eastern station O averaged only 4.0 Upland Sandpiper calls per season (Table 1). In contrast to Upland Sandpipers, Bobolinks passed

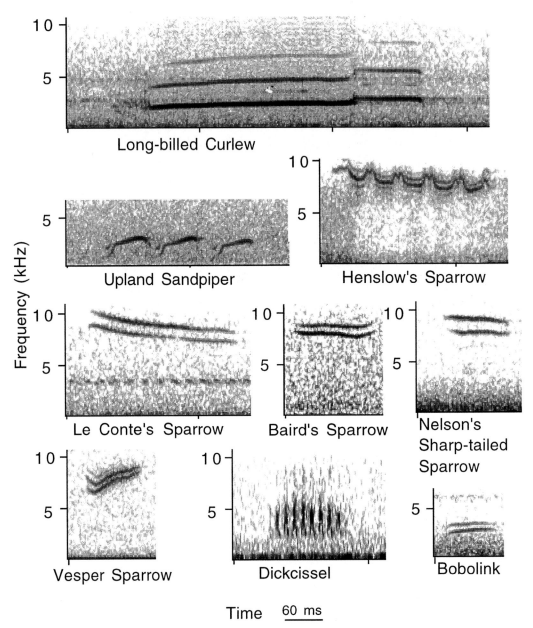

FIGURE 4.   Diurnal calls from a variety of grassland breeders in eastern North America. All recordings were made during the day when the species' identities were observed. Calls similar to these have often been recorded at night during migration.

over the east end of the array in larger numbers than they did over the west end (Table 1). Station O recorded the four largest nights of Bobolink passage during 3 yr of monitoring and consistently had the highest season total. From 1991 to 1993, data from stations in the New York transect indicated the period of fall Bobolink migration, with a peak from the last week in August through the first week of September (Fig. 7). Nights with southerly winds were not monitored, as previous experience had shown that very few calls are detected on such nights in this region.

Because of differences in coverage between stations and seasons, statistical comparison of the Upland Sandpiper and Bobolink season total

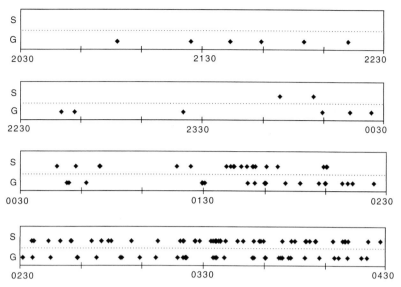

FIGURE 5. Temporal occurrence of Grasshopper and Savannah sparrow calls detected from one audio channel at Laguna Atascosa NWR, Texas, on the night of 5–6 April 1995 (1930–0330 central standard time). S = Savannah Sparrow calls, G = Grasshopper Sparrow calls.

data is not possible. The number of nights recorded at each location per season varied depending on weather and occasional equipment failure. The data are presented to give a rough count of the minimum number of these species that may be detected from recording stations in this region.

Bobolink data from the recording stations across New York revealed correlations in the hourly density patterns between stations (Table 2). Five of the seven stations had their highest correlation with a neighboring station. Patterns

of hourly counts at the two eastern stations, O and J, were correlated (r = 0.87, significant at P < 0.05) and appeared to have relatively large, similar counts, with a peak in the fifth hour. Stations in the middle of the array (B, I, and R) had a highly correlated but uniformly smaller passage, with a density peak in the fourth hour (I-B: r = 0.99; I-R: r = 0.89; R-B: r = 0.93; all significant at P < 0.05). Stations A and C, at the west end of the array, had a less correlated temporal pattern (r = 0.57, not significant at P < 0.05) but also showed the density peak in the fourth hour.

DISCUSSION

An important facet of nocturnal flight-call identification is that certainty in call identification is based partly on the process of elimina-

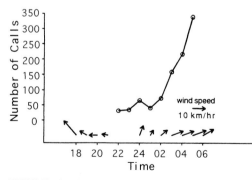

FIGURE 6. Hourly wind direction and speed at Brownsville, Texas, indicated by the direction and length of arrows (lower) compared with the rate of nocturnal flight calls detected per hour by ear (upper) from a stereo recording at Laguna Atascosa NWR, Texas. Data are from the night of 5–6 April 1995 between 2100 and 0500 central standard time.

TABLE 1. NUMBER OF UPLAND SANDPIPERS AND BOBOLINKS DETECTED DURING FALL MIGRATION AT RECORDING STATIONS IN NEW YORK STATE, 1991–1993

Species	Station	Year			Mean
		1991	1992	1993	
Upland Sandpiper	A	12	15	13	13.3
	B	6	19	11	12.0
	O	2	2	8	4.0
Bobolink	A	ND[a]	126	140	130
	B	ND	75	85	80
	O	162	140	418	240

[a] ND = no data.

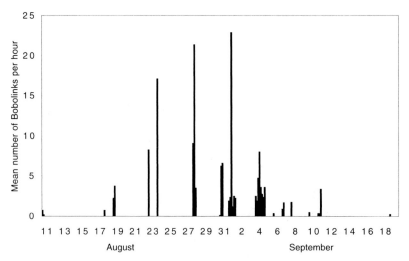

FIGURE 7.   Mean number of Bobolinks per hour detected by the MIP technique at stations A, B, and O in New York State during fall migration 1991–1993. Each migration night was monitored for 8 hr. Nights with southerly winds were not monitored. The three highest hourly rates were documented from station O. Because all years and station data are plotted together, the plot illustrates variability on a particular recording date. Since major migration happened to occur on the same nights in several seasons, data have a clumped appearance.

tion. One cannot know that a certain nocturnal flight call is given by a particular species until one knows that other species do not give a similar call. An archive of diurnal tseep notes and flight calls is nearly complete for passerines that migrate east of the Rocky Mountains (W. R. Evans and M. O'Brien, unpubl. data). This body of evidence, some of which is illustrated in Figs. 2–4, is a primary tool that we used to support the nocturnal flight-call species identifications in this paper. Such call types are believed to be the same ones given in night migration by these species.

Our five diurnal-call examples of Grasshopper and Savannah sparrows (Figs. 2 and 3) are not a sufficiently large dataset to define the range of variation of these species' tseep calls. They do, however, give an idea of the basic time-frequen-

cy contour of these calls, and it appears unlikely that these two species could be confused because their call types are so distinct from one another. The calls of the other migratory species common in the Laguna Atascosa NWR region of Texas are known and are distinct from the basic time-frequency contours of Savannah and Grasshopper sparrow calls.

Identification of other species of grassland sparrows is not as clear. For example, spectrographic analysis of diurnal tseep calls of Baird's Sparrow (*Ammodramus bairdii*), Le Conte's Sparrow (*A. leconteii*), and Nelson's Sharptailed Sparrow (*A. nelsoni*) show that although the calls appear to have distinctive characteristics, they are similar enough that variations of their nocturnal flight calls could overlap (Fig. 4). Larger diurnal datasets and study of nocturnal datasets from different geographic regions are necessary to define variations in these species' calls before they can be distinguished at night in regions where the species migrate together. Calls illustrated in this paper are not meant to definitively identify nocturnal flight calls but to provide preliminary identification characteristics and to illustrate the concept of nocturnal flight-call identification.

Our Texas data illustrate the type of information that can be gathered from a single monitoring station operated through a migration season. A calling record can be obtained that yields a minimum number of individuals passing over the recording site through time. The Texas data

TABLE 2.   HOURLY TOTALS OF BOBOLINKS DETECTED AT RECORDING STATIONS ACROSS NEW YORK STATE ON THE NIGHT OF 28–29 AUGUST 1993

Hour	Recording station						
	C	A	B	I	R	O	J
1930–2030	3	14	0	0	2	12	0
2031–2130	5	23	0	0	0	4	0
2131–2230	19	7	4	7	2	37	6
2231–2330	33	25	14	18	17	32	27
2331–0030	10	2	3	4	9	63	38
0031–0130	3	1	0	2	0	21	8
0131–0230	1	1	0	0	0	1	0
0231–0330	0	0	0	0	0	1	0

produced evidence that at least six species of North American grassland breeders migrated over Laguna Atascosa NWR. Baseline information was gathered on the volume of calling from Black Rail, Upland Sandpiper, Long-billed Curlew, Savannah and Grasshopper sparrows, and Dickcissel. The Black Rail detections were significant because the species was not known to currently winter or migrate through southernmost Texas. The significance of the acoustic data for the other species will not be revealed until future use of the acoustic-monitoring technique produces comparative data from other regions or seasons. For example, there may be no other region of North America where dozens of Long-billed Curlews can be detected in nocturnal migration.

The timing of calls within evenings also revealed interesting patterns. On 5–6 April 1995 at Laguna Atascosa NWR, the rate of calling of Grasshopper and Savannah sparrows increased greatly after 0130 central standard time (Fig. 5). This increase is thought to be due to a change from calm conditions to a steady wind from the southwest (Fig. 6). Such a change would tend to wind-drift migrating passerines toward the Gulf Coast. As birds reached the coast, many probably adjusted their northerly heading to avoid getting carried out over the water, resulting in an increased number of birds migrating in the coastal region.

The formula used to tabulate the MIP for Grasshopper and Savannah sparrows gives a conservative estimate and is meant to illustrate a basic example of this new method for interpreting nocturnal flight-calling data. In cases where three or more calling birds pass over a single microphone at about the same time, the MIP technique counts at least one individual passing but may not be able to distinguish two or more. Such distinctions depend on the number and sequence of calls by each individual and the birds' positions in space. Use of radar to characterize small-passerine flight speeds in relation to varying weather conditions could improve the accuracy of the ground-speed component in the MIP formula. Further research on MIP methods could reveal distinctive calling patterns characteristic of three or more birds passing in 1 min. In addition, analysis of factors such as varying call amplitude could be incorporated. Such advancements could be reapplied to the data presented here to produce a more accurate MIP count.

Our Texas data illustrate the limitations of operating a single monitoring station. The recording station at Laguna Atascosa NWR was within 8 km of the southeast coast of Texas. Data from the station showed a low number of passerine calls detected on nights when winds were from the southeast—the region's most common spring wind direction. More calls were detected on nights of relatively rare southwesterly winds. This coastal recording location, where the density of migrating passerines appears to be dependent on wind direction, therefore may not be a reliable location for quantitative studies of migrant passerines aimed at population monitoring. One way to compensate for the effects of wind and geographic location on the consistency of nocturnal flight-call monitoring would be to set up a line of inland recording stations, as we did in southern New York.

The New York transect revealed many interesting results. Interpretations of these data, however, raise further questions. For example, the cause of the fall Bobolink density pattern (Table 1) across the New York transect is unknown. One possibility is that the pattern reflects breeding distributions to the north. Another is that the pattern is caused by birds flying around Lake Ontario. The hourly density pattern on the night of 28–29 August 1993 suggests passage around Lake Ontario because of the larger density at the east and west ends of the transect compared with smaller passages across the middle stations (Table 2). The uniform density increase across the transect during the fourth hour indicates that a wave of Bobolinks may have crossed Lake Ontario. Night migrants typically take off 0.5–1 hr after sunset (Hebrard 1971; Richardson 1972; W. R. Evans, unpubl. data), which was at approximately 1840 eastern standard time. Ground speed in small passerines is variable, but with following winds, speeds of 40–80 km/hr have been measured (Cochran et al. 1967, Cochran 1987, Berthold 1993). The northern shoreline of Lake Ontario is roughly 240 km north of the recording transect, so migrants would cross the transect 3–6 hr after takeoff, or at approximately 2210–0110. The observed peak hour was in fact 2230–2330, within the expected arrival period.

Regarding the broad-front correlation in Bobolink detections on 28–29 August 1993, weather factors were probably not involved because clear skies and light northerly winds prevailed across the region. The parallel, east-west geographic position of Lake Ontario in relation to the recording transect may have aided this correlation. The relatively similar hourly counts between neighboring stations suggest a broad-front character to Bobolink migration in this region. Because stations are 51 km apart on average, the acoustically detected Bobolink flight on 28–29 August 1993 tended to cross the transect in broad, related density fronts at least 50 km wide. This phenomenon raises the possibility that for certain species, if a monitoring transect is positioned appropriately, the flight density between stations may be interpolated and an estimate of the minimum number of birds crossing a transect may be calculated. Local topography, which may affect migration patterns, would need to be considered in this interpolation. Such potential greatly increases the population-estimation power of this monitoring method. Detecting a greater fraction of individuals in a given area theoretically makes a monitoring operation's estimates more sensitive to population change through time.

The Bobolink and Upland Sandpiper data from New York illustrate a basic idea of nocturnal flight-call monitoring: by recording calling through a migration season for several years, baseline data are established on the number of acoustic detections expected in a region. Even with only three seasons of monitoring, certain acoustically determined density patterns appear to be indicated across central New York. Continued monitoring may reveal population trends.

An ideal monitoring operation for grassland birds might consist of several east-west lines of recording stations stacked north-south, perhaps 50–100 km apart. Research on the appropriate interstation distance in such transects is still needed. Our results suggest that an interstation distance of 50 km may be suitable for broadfront detection of some species; however, this distance may vary in different geographic regions. A multi-tiered network would allow broad waves of migrants to be tracked as they move north or south, providing a means for acoustic monitoring to validate its results. Waves of birds crossing one line of stations could be resampled crossing second and third lines.

One of the impediments to such monitoring is the large quantity of acoustic data to be analyzed. Developing signal-processing software to facilitate data analysis is a key step in handling this volume of data. Automatic call-detection technology has already greatly assisted data analysis. Research on automatic-processing technology is in progress (e.g., Mellinger and Clark 1993, Fristrup and Watkins 1994) and holds great promise for the nocturnal flight-call monitoring technique.

ACKNOWLEDGMENTS

We thank S. Gauthreaux and D. Kroodsma for comments that greatly improved the manuscript; A. Finney for editorial assistance; J. Wells, P. D. Vickery, and J. Herkert for encouragement in reporting our research; M. O'Brien for sharing information on Sharp-tailed Sparrow notes; and M. T. Green for providing recordings and information on Baird's Sparrow tseep notes. We also thank K. Rosenberg, J. Fitzpatrick, B. Howe, S. Jones, the Klingensmith family, E. Brooks, and the staff at Laguna Atascosa NWR. We especially thank C. W. Clark, H. Mills, and the Bioacoustics Research Program at the Cornell Laboratory of Ornithology. Funding was provided by the U.S. Fish and Wildlife Service and by U.S. Department of Agriculture Hatch Grant NYC-171404.

LITERATURE CITED

AVERY, M. L., P. F. SPRINGER, AND J. F. CASSEL. 1978. The composition and seasonal variation of bird losses at a tall tower in southeastern North Dakota. American Birds 32:1114–1121.

BAUMGARTNER, F. M. 1961. The fall migration: southern Great Plains. Audubon Field Notes 15:54–56.

BERTHOLD, P. 1993. Bird migration: a general survey. Oxford University Press, Oxford, U.K.

CHARIF, R. A., S. MITCHELL, AND C. W. CLARK. 1995. Canary 1.2 user's manual. Cornell Laboratory of Ornithology, Ithaca, NY.

COCHRAN, W. W. 1987. Orientation and other migratory behavior of a Swainson's Thrush followed for 1500 km. Animal Behavior 35:927–929.

COCHRAN, W. W., G. G. MONTGOMERY, AND R. R. GRABER. 1967. Migratory flights of *Hylocichla* thrushes. Living Bird 6:213–225.

DIERSCHKE, V. 1989. Automatisch-akustische Erfassung des nächtlichen Vogelzuges bei Helgoland im Sommer 1987. Die Vogelwarte 35:115–131.

EVANS, W. R. 1994. Nocturnal flight call of Bicknell's Thrush. Wilson Bulletin 106:55–61.

FRISTRUP, K. M., AND W. A. WATKINS. 1994. Marine animal sound classification. Technical Report WHOI-94-13, Woods Hole Oceanographic Institute, Woods Hole, MA.

GRABER, R. R. 1968. Nocturnal migration in Illinois—different points of view. Wilson Bulletin 80:36–71.

GRABER, R. R., AND W. W. COCHRAN. 1959. An audio technique for the study of nocturnal migration of birds. Wilson Bulletin 71:220–236.

HAMILTON, W. J., III. 1962. Evidence concerning the function of nocturnal call notes of migratory birds. Condor 64:390–401.

HEBRARD, J. J. 1971. The nightly initiation of passerine migration in spring: a direct visual study. Ibis 113:8–18.

MELLINGER, D. K., AND C. W. CLARK. 1993. A method for filtering bioacoustic transients by spectrogram image convolution. Pp. 122–127 *in* Proceedings Oceans '93, Victoria, BC [no editor]. Institute of Electrical and Electronics Engineers, Piscataway, NJ.

RICHARDSON, W. J. 1972. Autumn migration and weather in eastern Canada: a radar study. American Birds 26:10–17.

APPENDIX. MIGRANT GRASSLAND BIRDS EAST OF THE ROCKY MOUNTAINS, WITH AN INDICATION OF WHETHER THEY ARE KNOWN TO CALL IN NIGHT MIGRATION AND A DESCRIPTION OF THEIR FLIGHT CALL

Species	Nocturnal flight-call information
Yellow Rail *Coturnicops noveboracensis*	No. A night migrant based on tower-kill data (e.g., Baumgartner 1961), but no nocturnal flight call is known.
Black Rail *Laterallus jamaicensis*	Yes. *Kee kee kerr* or *kee kerr*. Similar to distinctive diurnal calls.
Upland Sandpiper *Bartramia longicauda*	Yes. A strident chatter series similar to alarm chatter given on breeding ground (Fig. 4). May also migrate diurnally.
Long-billed Curlew *Numenius americanus*	Yes. *Ker-lee* series or variations. Similar to diurnal calls (Fig. 4). May also migrate diurnally.
Horned Lark *Eremophila alpestris*	Yes. Distinctive diurnal flight note has occasionally been detected at night. Thought to be primarily a diurnal migrant.
Sprague's Pipit *Anthus spragueii*	No. Distinctive *squeet* diurnal flight note has not been detected at night. May be primarily a diurnal migrant.
Sedge Wren *Cistothorus platensis*	No. A night migrant based on tower-kill data (e.g., Graber 1968), but no nocturnal flight call is known.
Dickcissel *Spiza americana*	Yes. A low *bzrrt* note. Similar to diurnal flight call (Fig. 4). Also migrates diurnally.
Cassin's Sparrow *Aimophila cassinii*	No. Diurnal location call is not known. No nocturnal flight call is known.
Vesper Sparrow *Pooecetes gramineus*	Yes. A high, thin *tseep*. Similar to diurnal flight note or location call (Fig. 4).
Lark Sparrow *Chondestes grammacus*	Yes. A dry *tsip*. Similar to diurnal flight note.
Lark Bunting *Calamospiza melanocorys*	No. Distinctive *tew* flight note has not been recorded in night migration. May be a diurnal migrant. Some tower-kill data (e.g., Avery et al. 1978) suggest night migration.
Savannah Sparrow *Passerculus sandwichensis*	Yes. A high *tsew*. Similar to diurnal flight note or location call (Fig. 2).
Grasshopper Sparrow *Ammodramus savannarum*	Yes. A high *tsee*. Similar to diurnal location call (Fig. 3).
Baird's Sparrow *A. bairdii*	No. Believed to give a high *tsee* note based on diurnal recordings by M. T. Green (Fig. 4). Call is similar to that of certain other sparrows and has not yet been distinguished at night.
Henslow's Sparrow *A. henslowii*	Yes. A high descending *tzeee*. Similar to diurnal location call (Fig. 4).
Le Conte's Sparrow *A. leconteii*	Yes. A high descending *tseew*. Similar to diurnal location call (Fig. 4).
Nelson's Sharp-tailed Sparrow *A. nelsoni*	Yes. A high sibilant *tsew* or *tsee*. Similar to diurnal location call (Fig. 4).
Eastern Meadowlark *Sturnella magna*	No. Diurnal flight note (*klee*) has not been detected in night migration. May be primarily a diurnal migrant.
Western Meadowlark *S. neglecta*	No. Diurnal flight note (*klee*) has not been detected in night migration. May be primarily a diurnal migrant.
Lapland Longspur *Calcarius lapponicus*	Yes. A *tew* note similar to calls occasionally heard during the day amidst more common rattle calls. Night migration may be initiated by snowstorms (S. Seltman, pers. comm.). Other longspur species may exhibit similar behavior, though they are thought to be primarily diurnal migrants.

Studies in Avian Biology No. 19:230–236, 1999.

DESIGN AND DURATION OF PERTURBATION EXPERIMENTS: IMPLICATIONS FOR DATA INTERPRETATION

Kenneth L. Petersen and Louis B. Best

Abstract. Studies of effects of habitat perturbations on birds sometimes lack adequate controls, pre-treatment data, or long-term postdisturbance data. We studied the effects of a prescribed fire on a bird community in shrubsteppe habitat in southeastern Idaho. The study comprised two years preburn and seven years postburn data collection on experimental and control plots. Interpretation of our results varies, depending on inclusion or exclusion of data from control plots, inclusion or exclusion of preburn data, and the number of years of postburn data incorporated in the analysis. For example, the Brewer's Sparrow (*Spizella breweri*) population declined the first two years after burning but subsequently showed a neutral response. Without control data, we would have concluded that fire had a negative impact on Sage Sparrow (*Amphispiza belli*) numbers when in fact the population also declined on unburned controls. Several fire-induced changes in nest-site selection by Brewer's and Sage sparrows would not have been detected without preburn data. Inadequate study design and duration can lead to inaccurate conclusions and misdirected conservation efforts.

EL DISEÑO Y LA DURACIÓN DE EXPERIMENTOS DE PERTURBACIÓN: EFECTOS EN LA INTERPRETACIÓN DE DATOS

Sinopsis. A veces los estudios de los efectos de las perturbaciones de hábitat en las aves carecen de controles adecuados, de datos previos, o de datos a largo plazo posteriores al cambio. Estudiamos los efectos de un fuego programado en una comunidad de aves en un hábitat de estepa arbustiva en el sureste de Idaho. El estudio comprendió dos años de recolección de datos antes del fuego, y siete años después del fuego en parcelas experimentales y de control. La interpretación de nuestros resultados varía según la inclusión o la exclusión de los datos de las parcelas de control, según la inclusión o la exclusión de datos previos al fuego, y según el número de años de datos posteriores al fuego que se incluyan en el análisis. Por ejemplo, la población del Gorrión de Brewer (*Spizella breweri*) disminuyó durante los primeros dos años después de la quema pero luego registró una respuesta neutra. Sin datos de control habríamos concluido que el fuego tenía un efecto negativo en los números del Gorrión de Artemisia (*Amphispiza belli*), cuando de hecho la población disminuyó también en los controles sin quema. El fuego produjo varios cambios en la selección de los Gorriones de Brewer y de Artemisia de los sitios de nidos que no habríamos descubierto sin los datos previos al fuego. Un estudio con diseño y duración inadecuados puede traducirse en conclusiones erróneas y en tentativas de conservación mal encaminadas.

Key Words: *Amphispiza belli*; Brewer's Sparrow; data interpretation; experimental design; prescribed fire; Sage Sparrow; shrubsteppe; *Spizella breweri*.

Because so many grasslands have been destroyed or altered, studies of how various habitat perturbations affect grassland bird populations play an important role in bird conservation. The most powerful design for such studies is to collect pre- and postdisturbance data from control and disturbed areas (Stewart-Oaten et al. 1986) over a sufficiently long period to reveal the dynamics of the system (Wiens 1989). Historically, however, many studies have been deficient in one or more of these requirements. For example, we surveyed the 1994 and 1995 issues of the *Auk, Journal of Field Ornithology, Condor, Wilson Bulletin,* and *Journal of Wildlife Management.* We identified 35 papers that investigated effects of natural or artificial habitat alterations (including food additions or deletions) on some aspect of bird biology. Of these, 33 (94%) either did not sample predisturbance conditions, had no control sites, or were brief (< 5 yr) in duration. Twenty-five (71%) of the 35 studies were

deficient in at least two of these design aspects. The most common weakness was short-term data collection; 21 of the studies spanned 2 yr or less, and 12 were based on only 1 yr of data collection.

These shortcomings occur not necessarily because investigators are unaware of the elements of study design but because they often are faced with unavoidable limitations and therefore have few options in planning their studies. For example, a disturbance such as a fire, storm, or human-caused disaster may afford an unexpected opportunity for study, but unless the site is already being monitored, no predisturbance data are available (e.g., Bowman et al. 1995, Latta et al. 1995). Or a study may be of limited duration because of funding constraints. Although investigators should not forego the opportunity to study habitat perturbations in such situations, they must exercise caution in interpreting the results. This paper demonstrates potential errors that may occur in data interpretation when any one of the aforementioned requirements of research design is not met.

STUDY AREA AND METHODS

We studied the effects of prescribed fire on a bird community in shrubsteppe habitat in southeastern Idaho (Petersen and Best 1987). The study area was about 11 km south of Howe, Butte County, Idaho, and the vegetation was dominated by big sagebrush (*Artemisia tridentata*) and bunchgrasses (e.g., *Agropyron, Oryzopsis, Sitanion*). The study comprised 2 yr (1980–1981) of preburn data and 7 yr (1982–1988) of postburn data collected on two experimental and two control plots. Each plot measured 250 × 250 m, was gridded at 25-m intervals to facilitate recording bird observations and nest locations, and was large enough to encompass 6–12 average-sized territories of most of the songbird species that inhabited the study area. Plots were positioned far enough apart (200–300 m) so that bird territories on one plot did not overlap those on another.

The fire substantially reduced mean coverage of sagebrush on experimental plots and moderately stimulated development of herbaceous vegetation (Petersen and Best 1987). Even 7 yr after burning, there was no evidence of sagebrush recovery on burned sites. Big sagebrush does not resprout after fire, and fire-induced changes in coverage may persist for more than 10 yr (Wright and Bailey 1982). In contrast, coverage of shrubs and herbaceous vegetation on control plots did not vary significantly over the course of the study. Thus, we were confident that the significant variations we documented in the bird community, even several years after the fire, could reasonably be attributed to burning.

We censused bird populations in June each year by delineating territories either by spot mapping (International Bird Census Committee 1970) or by using the "flush" technique (Wiens 1969). Both techniques involved recording positions and movements of individuals on maps of the grids. Each plot was visited at least five times in each year, typically for 3–4 hr each visit. In 1980–1984 we captured and color-banded Sage Sparrows (*Amphispiza belli*) and Brewer's Sparrows (*Spizella breweri*) to facilitate individual identification (Petersen and Best 1987); we banded 50–100% of the territorial Sage Sparrow males and 30–75% of the territorial Brewer's Sparrow males in each of these years. By the end of each season's census, we were confident that we had accounted for every territorial male. Population densities were determined by counting territories (and fractions thereof) lying within plot boundaries.

We also systematically searched all plots for nests during the first 5 yr (1980–1984) of the study (Petersen and Best 1985a, b, 1991), but only two species—Sage and Brewer's sparrows—were present in sufficient numbers to afford analysis of nest success and nest-site selection in response to fire. Active nests were visited at 1- to 2-d intervals, and nest success was calculated by Mayfield's (1975) method. Nest-site characteristics were measured after nests (either successful or failed) had been abandoned. These measurements included nest height, height of the shrub supporting the nest, and coverage and average height of sagebrush within a 5-m radius of the nest.

We employed one-way analysis of variance (ANOVA) to ascertain whether, within each treatment, a parameter (e.g., population density or nest success) of a given species varied significantly among years of the study. In analyses of nest success, a significant ANOVA result was followed by Duncan's multiple range test to determine which years differed significantly from each other. We used t-tests to determine the significance of between-treatment differences in population parameters of a given species in each year of the study. Statistical significance was set at $P \leq 0.05$.

RESULTS AND DISCUSSION

IMPLICATIONS OF SHORT-TERM DATA COLLECTION

Drawing firm conclusions about bird responses to habitat perturbation from only one or a few years of postdisturbance data may be unwise. Analyses of our population data for Brewer's Sparrows in 2 yr pre- and 2 yr postburn (1980–1983) show that fire had an immediate negative impact on this species, reducing densities on experimental plots by about 50% (ANOVA: $F_{(3,4)}$ = 21.51; Fig. 1). Brewer's Sparrow densities on control plots did not vary significantly over these years. Examination of all 9 yr of data, however, shows that the negative effect of fire was short-lived; densities increased substantially on experimental plots (ANOVA: $F_{(8,9)}$ = 21.66) after 1983 but did not vary significantly on controls. Moreover, in 1985 and 1988 densities on experimental plots averaged significantly higher than on controls (t_{1985} = 121.00, df = 2; t_{1988} = 6.00, df = 2), a seeming reestablishment of the preburn pattern in which densities on experimental plots also exceeded those on controls. Thus, the long-term impact of fire seemed to be neutral for this species.

Similarly for the Sage Thrasher (*Oreoscoptes montanus*), short-term (1980–1982) data suggest that fire had no impact after two pre- and one postburn seasons (Fig. 2). There were no significant variations in densities on either treatment over these 3 yr, nor did densities differ significantly between treatments. When the long-term data are included in the analysis, however, densities were consistently higher on the burned plots (although the difference between treatments was significant only in 1985 [t = 9.00, df = 2]), suggesting that the effects of fire stimulated the population.

Vesper Sparrows (*Pooecetes gramineus*) were not present on the study area in the first 4 yr of the study (two pre- and two postburn years) and then abruptly appeared on burned plots in the third postburn year and were present thereafter (Fig. 3). Thus, a study of as much as 4 yr duration would not have led to an accurate conclusion about the composition of this postburn bird

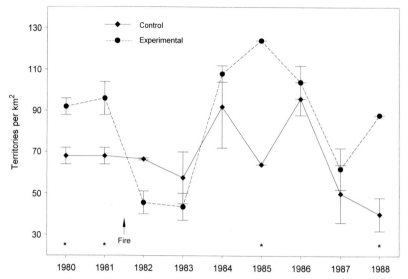

FIGURE 1. Population densities of Brewer's Sparrows on experimental and control plots in southeastern Idaho. Experimental plots were burned in the fall of 1981. Each data point and associated error bars represent values from two study plots ($\bar{X} \pm$ SE). Asterisks signify that treatments differed significantly ($P \leq 0.05$, t-test) in particular years.

community. In our survey of 35 papers, only 7 (20%) examined data from 5 yr or more of study. We can be confident that the pattern observed in this instance reflected a perturbation effect because Vesper Sparrows consistently settled on burned plots after 1983 yet never did so on unburned controls. Furthermore, because the two treatments were close enough to each other to be influenced by the same range of natural phenomena, it is difficult to imagine a factor other than the fire that would have produced this effect.

Our data on Western Meadowlarks (*Sturnella neglecta*) show that even 5 yr may not be suf-

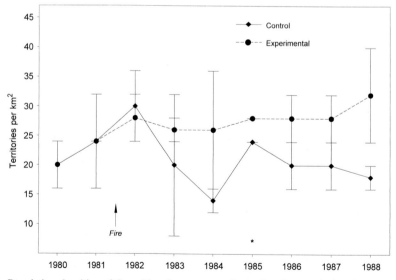

FIGURE 2. Population densities of Sage Thrashers on experimental and control plots in southeastern Idaho. Experimental plots were burned in the fall of 1981. Each data point and associated error bars represent values from two study plots ($\bar{X} \pm$ SE). Control and experimental means were identical in 1980 and 1981. The asterisk signifies that treatments differed significantly ($P \leq 0.05$, t-test) in 1985.

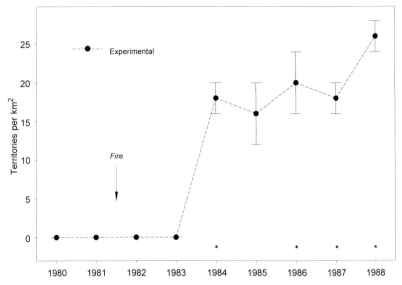

FIGURE 3. Population densities of Vesper Sparrows on experimental plots in southeastern Idaho, burned in the fall of 1981. Each data point and associated error bars represent values from two study plots ($\bar{X} \pm$ SE). Asterisks signify that experimental means differed significantly ($P \leq 0.05$, t-test) from controls in particular years. Control plots supported no Vesper Sparrows during this time.

ficient to assess the long-term impact of disturbance. If our study had spanned only 5 yr (1980–1984), we likely would have concluded that fire had a mildly positive effect on Western Meadowlarks (Fig. 4). Population densities increased significantly (ANOVA: $F_{(4,5)} = 6.22$) on experimental plots over this time but did not vary significantly on controls. And in 1984, mean density on burned plots was nearly significantly greater ($P = 0.09$) than on controls ($t = 3.00$, df = 2). Analysis of all 9 yr of data, however, does not seem to suggest a long-term in-

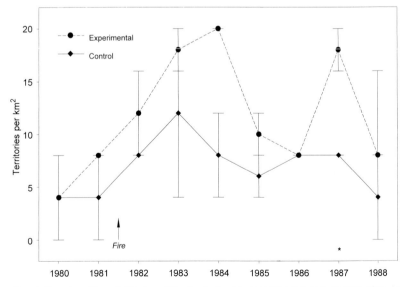

FIGURE 4. Population densities of Western Meadowlarks on experimental and control plots in southeastern Idaho. Experimental plots were burned in the fall of 1981. Each data point and associated error bars represent values from two study plots ($\bar{X} \pm$ SE). Control and experimental means were identical in 1980 and 1986. The asterisk signifies that treatments differed significantly ($P \leq 0.05$, t-test) in 1987.

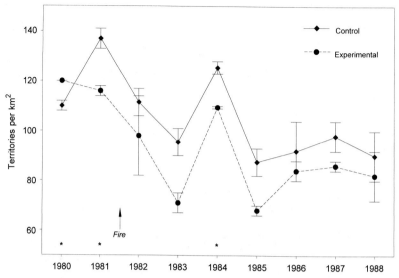

FIGURE 5. Population densities of Sage Sparrows on experimental and control plots in southeastern Idaho. Experimental plots were burned in the fall of 1981. Each data point and associated error bars represent values from two study plots ($\bar{X} \pm$ SE). Asterisks signify that treatments differed significantly ($P \leq 0.05$, t-test) in particular years.

fluence of fire. Although mean density on experimental plots was greater than on controls in 1987 ($t = 5.00$, df = 2), density did not vary significantly on plots of either treatment when all 9 yr were incorporated in the analysis.

IMPLICATIONS OF NO CONTROLS

Although most (26 of 35) studies we surveyed included data from control areas, control data may occasionally be absent. For example, a

TABLE 1. DAILY SURVIVAL PROBABILITIES ($\bar{X} \pm$ SE, N = 2 PLOTS)[a] FOR BREWER'S SPARROW NESTS ON CONTROL AND EXPERIMENTAL (BURNED) PLOTS IN SOUTHEASTERN IDAHO

Year	Plots	
	Control	Experimental
1980	0.958 ± 0.042 (41%)[c]	0.992 ± 0.008 A[b] (84%)
1981	0.926 ± 0.046 (20%)	0.970 ± 0.018 AB (53%)
-------------- Fire --------------		
1982	0.978 ± 0.022 (63%)	0.932 ± 0.009 C (23%)
1983	0.992 ± 0.008 (84%)	1.000 ± 0.000 A (100%)
1984	0.955 ± 0.015 (38%)	0.956 ± 0.002 BC (39%)

[a] Number of nests sampled per year per treatment ranged from 6 to 18.
[b] Means in the same column with no letters in common are different (P $\leq$ 0.05, one-way ANOVA, Duncan's multiple range test).
[c] Estimated nest success based on a nesting-cycle length of 21 d.

change or disturbance may occur unexpectedly on an area from which some data had already been collected (e.g., Miller et al. 1994, Hestbeck 1995, Wunderle 1995).

From an examination of Sage Sparrow densities on experimental plots alone, we would be strongly inclined to conclude that fire had a negative impact, at least in the short term (Fig. 5). Except for a spike in 1984, this conclusion could be drawn from the long-term data as well; densities varied significantly over 9 yr (ANOVA: $F_{(8,9)} = 8.19$). When control data are included, however, it is clear that, after the fire, changes in densities on control and experimental plots paralleled each other (9-yr ANOVA on controls: $F_{(8,9)} = 6.66$). Although mean density on controls exceeded that on burned plots in 1984 ($t = 6.28$, df = 2), this pattern also existed in 1981 before the fire ($t = 4.70$, df = 2). Therefore, the conclusion to be drawn from examination of both control and experimental data is that fire had no effect.

Similarly, patterns of change in Brewer's Sparrow nest success show that lack of control data might lead to an incorrect conclusion. Success declined on experimental plots immediately after burning, but there was also a decline on experimental plots between the two preburn years (Table 1). Nest success rebounded strongly in 1983 but then declined again. Without control data, one would be uncertain as to how much of this variation was attributable to fire. When data

TABLE 2. NEST-SITE CHARACTERISTICS ON CONTROL AND EXPERIMENTAL (BURNED) PLOTS IN SOUTHEASTERN IDAHO

	Sage Sparrow				Brewer's Sparrow			
	Control		Experimental		Control		Experimental	
	Preburn	Postburn	Preburn	Postburn	Preburn	Postburn	Preburn	Postburn
Nest height (cm)	32	29	38*a	28	34	34	41*	32
Substrate height (cm)	61**b	60	72*	61	61	65	74	64
Sagebrush height (cm)	43	40	52*	39	49	47	58	44
Sagebrush coverage (%)	24	24	32*	18	31	26**	32	15

Note: Each value is a mean from two plots. Standard errors have been omitted for clarity. The number of nests sampled preburn and postburn per treatment ranged from 23 to 60 for Sage Sparrows and from 11 to 28 for Brewer's Sparrows.
[a] A single asterisk signifies that preburn differs significantly ($P \leq 0.05$, t-test) from postburn in either control or experimental.
[b] Double asterisks signify that control differs significantly ($P \leq 0.05$, t-test) from experimental in either pre- or postburn.

from control plots are included, however, the pattern becomes clearer. Now, because of the immediate postburn increase (although statistically insignificant) on controls, it seems likely that the decline on experimental plots was fire induced. And it is evident that the pattern of the subsequent 2 yr (1983–1984) was independent of fire.

IMPLICATIONS OF NO PRE-ALTERATION DATA

Some habitat perturbations may occur unexpectedly on sites not previously studied. Although one would have no predisturbance data, the investigator still might wish to take advantage of the opportunity to collect postdisturbance data (e.g., Bowman et al. 1995). In our survey, 24 studies (69%) lacked pre-alteration data.

Analysis of Sage and Brewer's sparrow nest-site selection provides a good example of potential misinterpretation. In comparing controls against burned plots (postburn data only), nest height, substrate height, and height of sagebrush around the nest were virtually the same (Table 2). We might conclude from postburn data alone that, with the possible exception of sagebrush coverage, fire had essentially no effect on nest-site selection. When we include preburn data, however, we draw a different conclusion. On experimental plots, postburn means were significantly smaller than preburn means in several instances, but there were no significant postburn changes on control plots. Thus, fire did seem to influence nest-site selection.

CONCLUSIONS

We must design perturbation experiments as any good scientific experiment is designed: with adequate controls, with pre- as well as postdisturbance data, with replicated treatments, and with a time scale that is as long as we can reasonably make it. Then we may draw conclusions with some confidence, and we may be able to develop and apply management if it is needed. Deciding what "long-term" means may be difficult, but in general, the duration of a pertur-

bation study should be proportional to the life span of the birds being studied (Calder 1984, Wiens 1984). We showed that even 2–3 yr of postdisturbance data collection may be insufficient for short-lived passerines. The term of a perturbation study also will depend on the rate of habitat change after disturbance. If an altered site changes quickly toward the predisturbance condition or some other stable configuration (as may be the case in some eastern North American grasslands), comparatively few years will be required to assess the effects of the perturbation on the bird community. Where disturbance cycles and recovery times are long (as, for example, in sagebrush shrubsteppe), longer-term study is required.

Determining what constitutes an appropriate control also is not always straightforward. In a perturbation study aimed at generalizing average or "usual" effects of a disturbance to a large set of possible instances, treatments should be randomly assigned to study plots. Otherwise the experiment is controlled only in a subjective and approximate way (Hurlbert 1984). This was a limitation of our own study as well as of many others because, realistically, such randomization is often not possible. Random allocation of treatments to study plots may not be necessary, however, if the concern is with a particular impact in a particular place resulting from a particular disturbance (i.e., impact assessment; Stewart-Oaten et al. 1986).

Similarly, establishing replication in a perturbation experiment is not necessarily simple. First, care must be taken to avoid pseudoreplication, in which, for example, nests might be replicated but the actual experimental units (e.g., study plots) are not (Hurlbert 1984). Second, the number of replicates must be sufficient to enable investigators to infer treatment effects when such effects occur. The power of most inferential statistical tests to detect treatment effects increases as sample size increases, and determination of sample sizes adequate to ensure detection of treatment effects requires power analysis. Such analysis should occur before beginning a study because the role and utility of power analysis after data have been collected and analyzed are controversial (Thomas 1997). The consequences of failing to statistically detect a positive or negative perturbation effect may be as critical for bird conservation as the consequences of inferring perturbation effects when none exist. In our study, the necessity of accurately and comprehensively sampling all study sites, given available time and personnel, constrained us to two replicate plots per treatment. Because of this small sample size, we possibly failed to detect some fire effects that did in fact occur. Nevertheless, we were able to observe several significant trends and differences that we could not have documented without replication of study plots.

Our limited literature survey suggests that it is frequently difficult to incorporate all of the aforementioned aspects of study design. When this is true, however, it is not necessarily wise to abandon plans to collect data. Because opportunities to conduct well-designed perturbation experiments are scarce, we should take advantage of any situation (e.g., an unexpected wildfire) that can provide some information. Surely even studies that lacked predisturbance data, were short term, etc., have contributed to our understanding of bird biology in a disturbed landscape. As we have shown, however, such situations require caution in data interpretation. We cannot afford, for example, to conclude that a disturbance had a positive impact when in fact there was no effect or perhaps even a negative effect. This, of course, would lead to an inappropriate stewardship strategy that would waste time, energy, and money and might even be detrimental to the species or community we were trying to conserve. Unfortunately, regardless of the soundness of the design, there will always be uncertainty in data interpretation. This is so because, in the natural world, many factors cannot be controlled even by the most careful design. At best, we can design research in such a way as to minimize the probability of reaching false conclusions.

ACKNOWLEDGMENTS

P. Sievert and L. Erickson-Eastwood contributed substantially to field data collection. Field work was funded by the Office of Health and Environmental Research, U.S. Department of Energy. We thank O. D. Markham for the opportunity to use facilities and field sites of the Idaho National Engineering Laboratory. This paper benefited greatly from the comments of two anonymous reviewers.

LITERATURE CITED

BOWMAN, T. D., P. F. SCHEMPF, AND J. A. BERNATOWICZ. 1995. Bald Eagle survival and population dynamics in Alaska after the Exxon Valdez oil spill. Journal of Wildlife Management 59:317–324.

CALDER, W. A., III. 1984. How long is a long-term study? Auk 101:893–894.

HESTBECK, J. B. 1995. Response of Northern Pintail breeding populations to drought, 1961–92. Journal of Wildlife Management 59:9–15.

HURLBERT, S. H. 1984. Pseudoreplication and the design of ecological field experiments. Ecological Monographs 54:187–211.

INTERNATIONAL BIRD CENSUS COMMITTEE. 1970. Recommendations for an international standard for a mapping method in bird census work. Audubon Field Notes 24:723–726.

LATTA, S. C., J. M. WUNDERLE, JR., E. TERRANOVA, AND M. PAGAN. 1995. An experimental study of nest predation in a subtropical wet forest following hurricane disturbance. Wilson Bulletin 107:590–602.

MAYFIELD, H. F. 1975. Suggestions for calculating nesting success. Wilson Bulletin 87:456–466.

MILLER, C. K., R. L. KNIGHT, L. C. MCEWEN, AND T. L. GEORGE. 1994. Responses of nesting Savannah Sparrows to fluctuations in grasshopper densities in interior Alaska. Auk 111:962–969.

PETERSEN, K. L., AND L. B. BEST. 1985a. Brewer's Sparrow nest-site characteristics in a sagebrush community. Journal of Field Ornithology 56:23–27.

PETERSEN, K. L., AND L. B. BEST. 1985b. Nest-site selection by Sage Sparrows. Condor 87:217–221.

PETERSEN, K. L., AND L. B. BEST. 1987. Effects of prescribed burning on nongame birds in a sagebrush community. Wildlife Society Bulletin 15:317–329.

PETERSEN, K. L., AND L. B. BEST. 1991. Nest-site selection by Sage Thrashers in southeastern Idaho. Great Basin Naturalist 51:261–266.

STEWART-OATEN, A., W. W. MURDOCH, AND K. R. PARKER. 1986. Environmental impact assessment: "pseudoreplication" in time? Ecology 67:929–940.

THOMAS, L. 1997. Retrospective power analysis. Conservation Biology 11:276–280.

WIENS, J. A. 1969. An approach to the study of ecological relationships among grassland birds. Ornithological Monographs 8:1–96.

WIENS, J. A. 1984. Editorial. The place of long-term studies in ornithology. Auk 101:202–203.

WIENS, J. A. 1989. The ecology of bird communities. Vol. 2. Processes and variations. Cambridge University Press, New York, NY.

WRIGHT, H. A., AND A. W. BAILEY. 1982. Fire ecology: United States and southern Canada. J. Wiley and Sons, New York, NY.

WUNDERLE, J. M., JR. 1995. Responses of bird populations in a Puerto Rican forest to Hurricane Hugo: the first 18 months. Condor 97:879–896.

Studies in Avian Biology No. 19:237–243, 1999.

SAMPLING CONSIDERATIONS FOR ESTIMATING DENSITY OF PASSERINES IN GRASSLANDS

JAY J. ROTELLA, ELIZABETH M. MADDEN, AND ANDREW J. HANSEN

Abstract. Researchers often use fixed-radius point counts to estimate density (absolute or relative) of territorial male grassland birds, but in doing so they must assume that detectability of birds is constant (or nearly so) among habitats, years, and/or species. If the assumption is violated, comparisons of density among species and/or habitats are invalid because counts are confounded by changes in both detectability and density. Recent advances in the theory and methods of distance sampling allow biologists to estimate detection probabilities and may provide more accurate estimates of density than other techniques. We conducted 450 point counts at 150 points in Lostwood National Wildlife Refuge, North Dakota, in 1994, estimated the distance to each male detected aurally, and estimated density for the 10 most abundant species with two methods: (1) using data from 50- or 75-meter-radius plots (estimates based on the average number of males heard per point count) and (2) using program DISTANCE and a maximum detection distance of 400 meters (estimates based on number of males heard and the detectability of males). We felt we were able to meet the assumptions of distance sampling and reliably estimate absolute density. Results generated by program DISTANCE suggested that males of some species went undetected on 50- and/or 75-meter plots. Density estimates from the two analysis methods were similar, however, and did not differ for any species ($P > 0.05$). Estimates from fixed-radius point counts in our study thus appeared to provide valid estimates of density (absolute and relative). In other habitats or for other species, the problem of undetected males may be more pronounced. In such cases, distance-sampling techniques may provide an important alternative for collecting and analyzing density data if adequate samples are obtained and unbiased distance data can be collected.

CONSIDERACIONES PARA LA TOMA DE MUESTRA DE LAS ESTIMACIONES DE LA DENSIDAD DE AVES PASERIFORMES EN PASTIZALES

Sinopsis. A menudo los investigadores utilizan conteos desde un punto y por un radio fijo para estimar la densidad (absoluta o relativa) de machos territoriales de aves de pastizal, pero al hacerlo tienen que presumir que la posibilidad de detectar aves es constante (o prácticamente constante) entre hábitats, años y/o especies. Si la suposición no es correcta, las comparaciones de densidad entre especies y/o hábitats son inválidas porque los cambios de la posibilidad de detección y de la densidad confunden los conteos. Recientes avances en la teoría y en los métodos de la toma de muestra a distancias diferentes permiten que los biólogos estimen las probabilidades de detección y también pueden proveer estimaciones de densidad más precisas que otras técnicas. En 1994, en el Refugio Nacional de Fauna Lostwood, Dakota del Norte, hicimos 450 conteos desde 150 puntos, estimamos la distancia a cada macho detectado auditivamente, y estimamos la densidad para las 10 especies más abundantes con dos métodos: (1) utilizando datos de parcelas de 50 ó 75 metros de radio (estimaciones basadas en el número promedio de machos oídos por conteo) y (2) utilizando el programa DISTANCE y una distancia de detección máxima de 400 metros (estimaciones basadas en el número de machos oídos y en la posibilidad de detección de los machos). Pensamos que logramos satisfacer las suposiciones de la toma de muestra a distancias diferentes y estimar fidedignamente la densidad absoluta. Los resultados que produjo el programa DISTANCE indicaron que no se hallaron los machos de algunas especies en parcelas de 50 y/o 75 metros. Sin embargo, las estimaciones de densidad hechas con los dos métodos de análisis fueron similares, y no se diferenciaron para ninguna especie ($P > 0,05$). Así parecía que las estimaciones de los conteos desde un punto y por un radio fijo en nuestro estudio entregaron estimaciones válidas de densidad (absoluta y relativa). En otros hábitats o para otras especies, el problema de machos no detectados puede ser mayor. En esos casos, las técnicas de toma de muestra a distancias diferentes pueden proporcionar una alternativa importante para la recolección y el análisis de datos de densidad si se obtienen muestras adecuadas y se recolectan datos imparciales de distancia.

Key Words: density estimation; detectability; grasslands; point counts.

Density of passerines and numerous other land-birds is most commonly estimated from point-based counts of birds on fixed-radius plots (Hutto et al. 1986; Ralph et al. 1993, 1995). Because point counts may provide incomplete counts of birds present on survey plots (e.g., Burnham 1981, Hutto et al. 1986, Barker and Sauer 1995), point counts are typically considered estimates of relative density (Hutto et al. 1986). Because researchers do not usually estimate the proportion of birds counted (i.e., bird detectability; Barker and Sauer 1995), however, point counts provide an untested index that may be unreliable (Burnham 1981, Rotella and Ratti 1986). In particular, factors other than density (e.g., observers, habitat) can affect counts (see numerous articles *in* Ralph and Scott 1981), and thus variation in counts among habitats, years, and/or species may represent variation in detectability rather than variation in actual density (Pendleton 1995).

Although survey conditions are typically constrained to reduce variation in detectability among counts, it is unlikely that all factors influencing detectability can be controlled (Burnham 1981, Pendleton 1995). Consequently, Burnham (1981) concluded that it is necessary to adjust point counts by detection probabilities if reliable estimates of density are desired. Similarly, Johnson (1995:123) stated that "we need to better understand the role of the detection probabilities if we are to draw inferences from the counts about bird populations."

Distance sampling, which has recently undergone important advances in estimation methods, provides a rigorous means of estimating detection probabilities (Buckland 1987, Buckland et al. 1993). Although the technique requires that distances to detected birds be estimated, distances can be recorded in categories. Furthermore, "provided distance estimation is unbiased on average, measurement errors must be large to be problematic" (Buckland et al. 1993:171). In distance sampling, the distance from the sampling point to each bird detected (seen and/or heard, depending on the study) is recorded; distances are analyzed to estimate the detectability of birds as a function of the distance from the sampling point to a bird; and the detection function (based on distance data) is used to correct for birds that went undetected. Using distance sampling, it is possible to produce unbiased maximum likelihood estimates of density and variance despite missing the majority of the birds on a plot if the following assumptions are met: (1) birds on points (distance = 0) are always detected; (2) birds are detected at their initial locations before any movement is made in response to observers; and (3) distances are accurately measured or assigned to the correct distance category (Buckland et al. 1993). Because detection functions can be estimated for each species and habitat type, valid comparisons of density can be made among species and/or habitats even though detectability may vary.

Although distance sampling has been used effectively to estimate density of numerous inanimate objects (e.g., bird nests, burrows) and vertebrates (e.g., birds, terrestrial and marine mammals; Buckland et al. 1993), it has not been used or evaluated in studies of grassland birds. Although others have commented on the logistical difficulties of estimating detection probabilities

(e.g., Hutto et al. 1986, Pendleton 1995), we suspected we could meet the assumptions of distance sampling in open grassland habitat. Furthermore, distance sampling may more efficiently sample grassland birds than do fixed-radius plots. Because birds often occur at lower densities in grasslands than in structurally complex habitats (Cody 1985), point counts of grassland birds often yield small sample sizes. Distance sampling precludes the need to constrain plot sizes such that all birds on a plot can be detected and thus can sample a larger area per point than can fixed-radius plots.

We designed this study to evaluate the feasibility of using distance-sampling techniques and, if distance sampling proved effective, to test the validity of estimating density (absolute or relative) from fixed-radius point counts. To meet these objectives, we simultaneously collected data using fixed-radius point counts and distance sampling and estimated passerine density with both methods. Our study was conducted as part of a larger study investigating fire management and habitat ecology of grassland birds in North Dakota (Madden 1996).

STUDY AREA

We conducted bird sampling at Lostwood National Wildlife Refuge (NWR) in Mountrail and Burke Counties, North Dakota (48°37′ N, 102°27′ W). Lostwood NWR is 109 km² of undulating mixed-grass prairie interspersed with more than 4,000 wetland basins and many clumps of quaking aspen (*Populus tremuloides*). Major vegetation is a needlegrass (*Stipa* spp.)/wheatgrass (*Agropyron* spp.) association (Coupland 1950) with diverse forbs and scattered shrubs. Since the 1970s, the U.S. Fish and Wildlife Service has used prescribed fire and short-duration grazing to reduce woody vegetation and restore natural diversity of successional stages to Lostwood NWR.

METHODS

BIRD SAMPLING

We randomly selected 150 sampling points from a grid of 265 potential points that encompassed the study area. Grid points were 250 m or more apart to provide statistical independence (Hutto et al. 1986, Ralph et al. 1993). Selected points met the following criteria: (1) located in "upland prairie" as delineated by the National Wetland Inventory (NWI) map of cover types of Lostwood NWR (NWI Project 1989); (2) more than 100 m from aspen trees; (3) more than 100 m from roads or firebreaks; (4) more than 50 m from any seasonally flooded wetland zone; and (5) ungrazed by livestock in 1994.

We conducted three replicate bird counts at each sampling point between 26 May and 24 June 1994. During each point count, an observer stood at a point for 10 min and recorded the distance to each bird heard singing. Distance to each bird when first detected was categorized as 0–14.9 m, 15–29.9 m, 30–49.9 m, 50–74.9 m, or more than 75 m. We chose these categories so we could compare detectability in different bands (see "Data Analysis," below) and could test whether the probability of detecting a singing male declined in outer portions (30–49.9 m and/or 50–74.9 m) of 50- or 75-m-radius plots typically used for point counts or varied among species. We did not count birds we saw fly on to plots during counts.

To meet critical assumptions of distance sampling (Buckland et al. 1993:30–37), we spent 2 wk prior to the field season practicing bird identification by song, point-count techniques, and distance measurements (Reynolds et al. 1980), with emphasis on estimating distances to aurally detected birds; we observed each point from 100–200 m away and recorded distance categories for birds detected within 75 m of the point before approaching the point; and we used flagging placed 30, 50, and 75 m from each point in cardinal directions to ensure accurate distance estimation. When assignment to a distance category was uncertain, we confirmed distances by pacing to observed locations after the 10-min count was completed.

Point counts were conducted only on mornings when weather conditions did not impede detection of birds (i.e., no rain, fog, or wind >15 km/hr). Counts began 30 min before sunrise and continued until 0900 central daylight time. Assignment of observers (E. Madden and one technician) to points and the order in which points were surveyed were rotated among replicate counts to minimize sampling bias. We recorded data only for passerines and upland-nesting shorebirds.

DATA ANALYSIS

For species detected 10 or more times within 50 m of sampling points, we estimated density of territorial males (males/100 ha) using a fixed-radius method (Hutto et al. 1986) and distance-sampling methods (Buckland et al. 1983). Hutto et al. (1986) reviewed two commonly used methods of analyzing data from fixed-radius point counts: (1) calculating the average number of birds detected per point count (relative density) and (2) calculating the average number of birds detected per unit area censused by each point count (converting relative density to absolute density). We used the second method to calculate estimates of territorial males per 100 ha for each of two plot sizes; we calculated the average number of territorial males detected per point count (based on three replicate surveys of 150 50- or 75-m-radius plots) and divided the average count by the area of each plot (0.79 ha for 50-m plots, 1.77 ha for 75-m plots). Brown-headed Cowbirds (*Molothrus ater*) were treated differently because male cowbirds do not sing and defend territories in the same manner as other passerines. For cowbirds, we divided the number of male and female detections (aural and visual) per point count by two to estimate the number of breeding males detected. We note that Hutto et al. (1986) cautioned that presenting average detections per unit area of each fixed-radius plot may be misleading because the effective area sampled by each point count is unknown. Accordingly, most recent studies only present relative density. We made the conversion to detections per unit area, however, so that comparisons with density estimates from distance sampling, which are estimated on a per-unit-area basis,

could be made using estimates presented on the same scale.

To estimate density from distance data, we used program DISTANCE (Laake et al. 1993) and the methods of Buckland et al. (1993) as reviewed above. Program DISTANCE requires an entry for maximum detection distance for each species. Therefore, we set the maximum detection distance to 400 m for all species, which we felt encompassed all detections. We note that distance sampling does not assume that birds are only counted from one point (Buckland et al. 1993). Thus, 400 m was an appropriate distance despite points being within 250 m of each other. Also, more than 90% of birds were detected less than 250 m from points. Accuracy of the maximum distance was not critical because estimates from program DISTANCE are not highly sensitive to data in the most distant category (J. Laake, pers. comm.). To verify this, we conducted analyses using a maximum distance of 1,000 versus 400 m and, as expected, found that the two analyses generated virtually identical density estimates.

We modeled the probability of detecting territorial males as a function of the distance from the sampling point to a male and estimated density using the model to adjust for undetected males. The probability of detecting each species was modeled using one of the following functions: uniform model with cosine adjustment terms, uniform model with polynomial adjustment terms, half-normal model with hermite polynomial adjustment terms, hazard-rate model with cosine adjustment terms, or a negative-exponential model (Buckland et al. 1993:46–49). We determined the number of adjustment terms to add to each function type based on the results of likelihood ratio tests between sequential versions of each function type, e.g., uniform model with and without a cosine adjustment term. We then chose among models using Akaike's Information Criterion (AIC; Akaike 1973, Burnham and Anderson 1992). Finally, we calculated the χ^2 goodness-of-fit statistic for the chosen model and visually inspected histograms of the distance data and the fit of detection function, with special emphasis on model fit for birds near sampling points. If an adequate fit was not achieved for any model for a given species, we pooled data from two adjacent distance categories and reanalyzed the data for that species. We chose which categories to pool based on visual inspection of distance data as suggested by Buckland et al. 1993. Standard errors were estimated using 399 bootstrap samples (Buckland et al. 1993). The detection-function model for each species was used to estimate the probability of detecting territorial males of each species that were 50 or 75 m from sampling points.

We tested whether the probability of detecting territorial males that were 50 or 75 m from sampling points was less than 1.0 for any species or differed among species by examining 95% confidence intervals for detection probabilities. We tested for a difference between estimates generated by the two analysis methods across all species with the Wilcoxon signed-ranks test (Conover 1980:280–283). This method considered density estimates from the two methods as species-specific matched pairs. We also tested whether the two methods produced different density estimates for any species using z-tests (z = [DISTANCE estimate—

TABLE 1.   DENSITY (TERRITORIAL MALES/100 HA) OF GRASSLAND BIRDS AT LOSTWOOD NWR, NORTH DAKOTA, ESTIMATED FROM POINT COUNTS CONDUCTED MAY–JUNE 1994

Species	N (50)[a]	N (400)[b]	50-m-radius plot		75-m-radius plot		Distance sampling	
			D[c]	SE	D	SE	D	SE
Sprague's Pipit	11	81	3.1	0.9	2.6	0.6	3.1	0.9
Common Yellowthroat	24	601	6.8	1.7	7.3	1.2	7.6	1.1
Clay-colored Sparrow	271	1,149	76.7	6.2	71.9	4.2	72.1	4.4
Savannah Sparrow	223	1,226	63.1	4.2	60.5	3.0	60.5	9.1
Baird's Sparrow	28	424	10.2	2.0	11.8	1.7	11.8	1.4
Grasshopper Sparrow	65	336	18.4	2.8	15.3	1.8	19.0	2.3
Le Conte's Sparrow	15	58	4.2	1.1	2.8	0.7	3.6	1.0
Bobolink	48	609	13.6	2.3	15.3	1.8	17.0	1.9
Western Meadowlark	14	808	4.0	1.2	4.0	0.8	3.6	0.7
Brown-headed Cowbird	30	350	4.2	1.4	4.9	1.0	6.7	2.1

Note: Density was estimated from three replicate counts at 150 sampling points using (1) numbers detected on 50-m-radius plots, (2) numbers detected on 75-m-radius plots, and (3) birds detected out to 400 m. For distance sampling, program DISTANCE (Laake et al. 1993) and distances to birds on 400-m-radius plots were used to estimate density.
[a] Total number of singing males detected on 450 counts on 50-m-radius plots.
[b] Total number of singing males detected on 450 counts on 400-m-radius plots.
[c] Density of territorial males/100 ha.

fixed-radius estimate]/[SE of DISTANCE estimate]; Steel and Torrie 1980).

RESULTS

DENSITY ESTIMATES

Ten species were detected 10 or more times within 50 m of sampling points and were used to compare density estimates from different analysis methods: Sprague's Pipit (*Anthus spragueii*), Common Yellowthroat (*Geothlypis trichas*), Clay-colored Sparrow (*Spizella pallida*), Savannah Sparrow (*Passerculus sandwichensis*), Baird's Sparrow (*Ammodramus bairdii*), Grasshopper Sparrow (*A. savannarum*), Le Conte's Sparrow (*A. leconteii*), Bobolink (*Dolichonyx oryzivorus*), Western Meadowlark (*Sturnella neglecta*), and Brown-headed Cowbird (Table 1).

We felt we were able to meet the assumptions of distance sampling (discussed above) for all species except Clay-colored Sparrow. Program DISTANCE successfully fit models to the distance data for nine species and marginally fit a model for Clay-colored Sparrow (Table 2, Fig. 1). We pooled data from two distance categories for 3 of 10 species to achieve acceptable model fit (Table 2). Clay-colored Sparrows apparently moved away from points in response to observers before we detected them (Fig. 1). Hence, the best model marginally fit the distance data for this species (P = 0.04), and the density estimate is likely biased low. Bibby and Buckland (1987) calculated that the bias in density estimates would be −30 and −55% if birds moved 20 and 40 m, respectively, before being detected. Such fleeing distances seem reasonable for Clay-colored Sparrows based on inspection of histograms of the distance data.

COMPARISON OF ESTIMATES FROM DIFFERENT ANALYSES

Analysis of distance data indicated that the probability of detecting all territorial males present was less than 1.0 at 50 and 75 m for 6 of 10 species (Table 2); i.e., we did not detect all males of all species on 50- and 75-m plots. Despite this problem, the fixed-radius method of analyzing data from 50-m plots did not yield different density or standard-error estimates than program DISTANCE (P = 0.68; Table 1). The fixed-radius method of analyzing data from 75-m plots, however, tended to yield smaller estimates of density and standard error than program DISTANCE (P = 0.04 and 0.02, respectively), although differences between the estimate types were relatively small (mean differences for density and standard error were 0.86 and 1.13 males/100 ha, respectively).

Single-species comparisons of density estimates also indicated that the two analysis methods produce consistent results. Point estimates of density from fixed-radius methods of analysis (50- or 75-m plots) and program DISTANCE differed by 27–60% but were not significantly different for any species (z < 1.8, P > 0.07). Percentage differences between the two estimate types were greatest for Brown-headed Cowbirds, but estimates were not significantly different because of the large standard error produced by the negative-exponential model used.

DISCUSSION

Based on our field experiences, we felt we were able to meet the assumptions of distance sampling for 9 of 10 grassland species that were common on our study area. Accordingly, we be-

TABLE 2. DENSITY OF 10 SPECIES OF GRASSLAND BIRDS AT LOSTWOOD NWR, NORTH DAKOTA, ESTIMATED FROM DISTANCE SAMPLES, 1994

Species	N	Pooled categories[b]	Estimator[c]	G-O-F $(P > \chi^2)$[d]	Density (males/100 ha) $\bar{X}$	Density (males/100 ha) SE[e]	Probability of detection $(\bar{X})$[a] 50 m	Probability of detection $(\bar{X})$[a] 75 m
Sprague's Pipit	81	none	HN (0)	0.12	3.1	0.9	0.87*	0.74*
Common Yellowthroat	601	none	UN (1)	0.85	7.6	1.1	0.96*	0.91*
Clay-colored Sparrow	1,149	3 & 4	HZ (0)	0.04	72.1	4.4*	1.00	1.00
Savannah Sparrow	1,226	2 & 3	HZ (0)	0.21	60.5	9.1*	1.00	1.00
Baird's Sparrow	424	none	HZ (0)	0.14	11.8	1.4	1.00	1.00
Grasshopper Sparrow	3636	none	HN (0)	0.10	19.0	2.3	0.82*	0.64*
Le Conte's Sparrow	58	none	HN (0)	0.24	3.6	1.0	0.80*	0.61*
Bobolink	609	none	HN (0)	0.06	17.0	1.9	0.91*	0.80*
Western Meadowlark	808	none	UN (0)	0.12	3.6	0.7*	1.00	1.00
Brown-headed Cowbird	350	3 & 4	NE (0)	0.51	6.7	2.1*	0.73*	0.63*

Note: Density was estimated from three replicates of 150 point-centered distance samples.

[a] Estimated probability of detecting a singing male exactly 50 or 75 m away from a sampling point. Probabilities marked with an asterisk differed (P < 0.05) from 1.0 based on z tests. Upper and lower 95% confidence limits for probabilities that were different from 1.0 at 50 and 75 m, respectively, are Sprague's Pipit (0.91–0.80; 0.81–0.61), Common Yellowthroat (0.97–0.94; 0.93–0.87), Grasshopper Sparrow (0.84–0.78; 0.68–0.58), Le Conte's Sparrow (0.86–0.71; 0.71–0.46), Bobolink (0.92–0.89; 0.83–0.77), and Brown-headed Cowbird (0.78–0.68; 0.68–0.56).

[b] Categories used to estimate the distance from sampling points to singing males were (1) 0–14.9 m, (2) 15–29.9 m, (3) 30–49.9 m, (4) 50–74.9, and (5) 75–400 m. During analysis, pooling of data from distance categories 1 and 2, 2 and 3, or 3 and 4 was conducted based on examination of histograms of the distance data that were generated by program DISTANCE (Laake et al. 1993) as suggested by Buckland et al. 1993.

[c] The estimator with the lowest Akaike Information Criteria value was used for density estimation. Estimators considered were UN (uniform model with cosine adjustment terms), HN (half-normal model with hermite polynomial adjustment terms), HZ (hazard rate model with cosine adjustment terms), and NE (negative-exponential model; Buckland et al. 1993). Numbers in parentheses represent the number of adjustment terms, if any, that were added to the model.

[d] Goodness-of-fit tests were conducted to determine how well the best model fit the observed data (Buckland et al. 1993).

[e] Standard errors marked with an asterisk were generated with bootstrapping techniques (Buckland et al. 1993) and represent cases where standard errors generated by program DISTANCE were underestimates.

lieve that distance sampling produced reliable estimates of absolute density for 9 of 10 species. Our distance data show that point counts did not detect all males of all species on 50- or 75-m plots and that detectability varied by species. Most males on 50-m plots were detected, however, and undetected males did not cause estimates from fixed-radius plots to differ significantly from estimates generated from distance sampling. Thus, it appears that the typical plot size used for point counts of grassland birds (50 m; Ralph et al. 1993) provides reasonable density estimates (absolute or relative). The greater percentage of males undetected on 75-m plots caused a slight negative bias in density estimates. Thus, when estimates of absolute density are desired, we caution against using analysis of fixed-radius data on plot sizes larger than 50 m in radius without examining species detectability as a function of distance. If the trade-off between plot size and number of detections per plot causes researchers to choose larger plots (smaller plots yield fewer detections/plot, and their use may necessitate sampling large numbers of plots to detect rare species), investigators should realize that average detections per point on plots larger than those evaluated here represent an untested index of relative density and should consider the potential problems of using

such an index (Burnham 1981, Rotella and Ratti 1986).

It is important to note that we only worked on one study area in one year. Other species/habitat combinations may have steeper detection functions, i.e., detection probability drops off more quickly with increasing distance from sampling points. For example, detection functions for House Wrens (*Troglodytes aedon*) in Colorado were quite steep and indicated that only a small percentage of individuals present were detected beyond 25 m (Buckland et al. 1993:396–403). Steeper detection functions will cause fixed-radius analyses to underestimate density and may occur in habitats with denser vegetation or for species with subtle songs. Thus, we recommend that researchers collect distance data, examine detection functions, and consider whether estimates are biased by birds that flee before detection or are difficult to detect within 50 m of a point. This recommendation is especially important for researchers intending to compare density estimates among species/habitat combinations that may have different detection functions. Under such circumstances, using the average number of birds detected per point count as an index to density is "neither scientifically sound nor reliable" (Burnham 1981: 325).

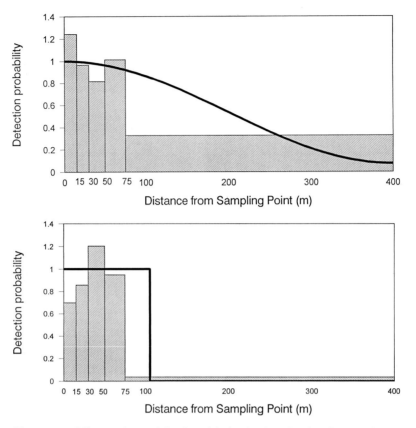

FIGURE 1.   Histograms of distance data and fitted models for the detection function $g(x)$ for point-count data collected at Lostwood NWR, 1994. Top: uniform model with one cosine term fitted to data for Common Yellowthroat showing an acceptable fit (P = 0.85) and slight decline in detectability within 75 m. Bottom: hazard function model with no adjustment terms fitted to data for Clay-colored Sparrow showing a marginal fit (P = 0.04) and evidence of movement away from sampling points before detection.

Based on our experience and recommendations in Buckland et al. 1993, we believe that the following distance categories are appropriate for grassland work: 0–20 m, 20–30 m, 30–40 m, 40–50 m, 50–65 m, 65–100 m, and more than 100 m. These intervals are likely to have equal sample sizes in each category and to allow for data truncation, which may occasionally be necessary to achieve adequate fit of detection functions to the data (Buckland et al. 1993). If researchers are uncomfortable assigning birds to categories that are 10 m wide, they can establish larger categories following guidelines in Buckland et al. 1993.

Although the methods of Buckland et al. (1993) seem to provide an excellent alternative for estimating density from point-count data, distance sampling will not reliably allow density estimation in all situations. Not all species will be detected frequently enough to provide adequate sample sizes in each stratum for which estimates are desired. Buckland et al. (1993:

301–308) suggest that 75–100 detections are needed to produce reliable estimates. Furthermore, the behavior of some species will cause assumptions of distance sampling to be violated. For example, despite our efforts to the contrary, Clay-colored Sparrows apparently fled from points before being detected, which probably caused our estimate to be biased low. Similar problems with fleeing from or being attracted toward observers before detection have been discussed by others (e.g., Hutto and Mosconi 1981, Bibby and Buckland 1987). Simulations, as conducted by Bibby and Buckland (1987), can be used to estimate the bias resulting from assumption violations and can be used to adjust estimates.

We caution that we did not know true density for any species. Future studies should estimate true density from work with banded birds and should validate estimates from point counts and distance sampling. It will be extremely difficult, however, to band adequate samples of multiple species at spatial scales of interest to most studies.

ACKNOWLEDGMENTS

Financial support was provided by Region 6 of the U.S. Fish and Wildlife Service (Refuges and Wildlife; Migratory Bird Program). We gratefully acknowledge D. R. Anderson and J. L. Laake for their helpful thoughts. G. M. Shriver and R. K. Murphy provided helpful comments on an earlier draft of the manuscript. L. J. DeMoss and R. K. Murphy assisted with data collection.

LITERATURE CITED

AKAIKE, H. 1973. Information theory and an extension of the maximum likelihood principle. Pp. 26–281 *in* B. N. Petran and F. Csaaki (editors). International symposium on information theory. 2d ed. Akadeemiai Kiadi, Budapest, Hungary.

BARKER, R. J., AND J. R. SAUER. 1995. Statistical aspects of point count sampling. Pp. 125–130 *in* C. J. Ralph, J. R. Sauer, and S. Droege (editors). Monitoring bird populations by point counts. USDA Forest Service Gen. Tech. Rep. PSW-GTR-149. USDA Forest Service, Albany, CA.

BIBBY, C. J., AND S. T. BUCKLAND. 1987. Bias of bird census results due to detectability varying with habitat. Acta Ecologica 8:103–112.

BUCKLAND, S. T. 1987. On the variable circular plot method of estimating animal density. Biometrics 43:363–384.

BUCKLAND, S. T., D. R. ANDERSON, K. P. BURNHAM, AND J. L. LAAKE. 1993. Distance sampling: estimating abundance of biological populations. Chapman and Hall, New York, NY.

BURNHAM, K. P. 1981. Summarizing remarks: environmental influences. Studies in Avian Biology 6:324–325.

BURNHAM, K. P., AND D. R. ANDERSON. 1992. Data-based selection of an appropriate biological model: the key to modern data analysis. Pp. 16–30 *in* D. R. McCullough and R. H. Barrett (editors). Wildlife 2001: populations. Elsevier Scientific Publishers, London, U.K.

CODY, M. L. 1985. Habitat selection in grassland and open-country birds. Pp. 191–226 *in* M. L. Cody (editor). Habitat selection in birds. Academic Press, Orlando, FL.

CONOVER, W. J. 1980. Practical nonparametric statistics. 2d ed. John Wiley and Sons, New York, NY.

COUPLAND, R. T. 1950. Ecology of mixed prairie in Canada. Ecological Monographs 20:271–315.

HUTTO, R. L., AND S. L. MOSCONI. 1981. Lateral detectability profiles for line transect bird censuses:

some problems and an alternative. Studies in Avian Biology 6:382–387.

HUTTO, R. L., S. M. PLETSCHET, AND P. HENDRICKS. 1986. A fixed-radius point count method for non-breeding and breeding season use. Auk 103:593–602.

JOHNSON, D. H. 1995. Point counts of birds: what are we estimating? Pp. 117–123 *in* C. J. Ralph, J. R. Sauer, and S. Droege (editors). Monitoring bird populations by point counts. USDA Forest Service Gen. Tech. Rep. PSW-GTR-149. USDA Forest Service, Albany, CA.

LAAKE, J. L., S. T. BUCKLAND, D. R. ANDERSON, AND K. P. BURNHAM. 1993. DISTANCE user's guide V2.0. Colorado Cooperative Fish and Wildlife Research Unit, Colorado State University, Fort Collins, CO.

MADDEN, E. M. 1996. Passerine communities and bird-habitat relationships on prescribe-burn, mixed-grass prairie in North Dakota. Master's thesis. Montana State University, Bozeman, MT.

NATIONAL WETLANDS INVENTORY PROJECT. 1989. Cover types of Lostwood National Wildlife Refuge: a digital map. U.S. Fish and Wildlife Service, St. Petersburg, FL.

PENDLETON, G. W. 1995. Effects of sampling strategy, detection probability, and independence of counts on the use of point counts. Pp. 131–133 *in* C. J. Ralph, J. R. Sauer, and S. Droege (editors). Monitoring bird populations by point counts. USDA Forest Service Gen. Tech. Rep. PSW-GTR-149. USDA Forest Service, Albany, CA.

RALPH, C. J, G. R. GEUPEL, P. PYLE, T. E. MARTIN, AND D. F. DESANTE. 1993. Handbook of field methods for monitoring landbirds. USDA Forest Service Gen. Tech. Rep. PSW-GTR-144. USDA Forest Service, Albany, CA.

RALPH, C. J., J. R. SAUER, AND S. DROEGE (EDITORS). 1995. Monitoring bird populations by point counts. USDA Forest Service Gen. Tech. Rep. PSW-GTR-149. USDA Forest Service, Albany, CA.

RALPH, C. J., AND J. M. SCOTT (EDITORS). 1981. Estimating numbers of terrestrial birds. Studies in Avian Biology 6.

REYNOLDS, R. T., J. M. SCOTT, AND R. A. NUSSBAUM. 1980. A variable circular-plot method for estimating bird numbers. Condor 82:309–313.

ROTELLA, J. J., AND J. T. RATTI. 1986. Test of a critical density index assumption: a case study with Gray Partridge. Journal of Wildlife Management 50:532–539.

STEEL, R. G. D., AND J. H. TORRIE. 1980. Principles and procedures of statistics: a biometrical approach. 2d ed. McGraw-Hill, New York, NY.

Studies in Avian Biology No. 19:244–249, 1999.

BIRD SPECIES RICHNESS AND CONSERVATION IN THE CERRADO REGION OF CENTRAL BRAZIL

Roberto B. Cavalcanti

Abstract. The Cerrado biome of central Brazil comprises one of the most biologically diverse savannas in the world. Modern agricultural practices have led to a large-scale conversion of the region for high-yield grain production. This paper presents a preliminary analysis of among-site variation in bird species richness and turnover. Species lists for six sites ranged from 202 to 263 species per site, with the Jaccard similarity index varying from 0.326 to 0.611. All six site lists added up to 519 species, more than 50 percent of which occurred at only one or two sites. Most among-site turnover was associated with forest and aquatic faunas. Savanna and other open habitats also had substantial turnover, however, with similarity indices in the range of 0.434 to 0.734. Eighteen endemic species were recorded; those at risk were associated primarily with open grasslands. The high avian diversity and substantial human impact in this region indicate that the Cerrado should be a major priority for conservation action.

LA RIQUEZA DE ESPECIES DE AVES Y LA CONSERVACIÓN EN LA REGIÓN DEL CERRADO DEL CENTRO DE BRASIL

Sinopsis. El bioma del Cerrado del centro de Brasil comprende una de las sabanas más diversas del mundo biológicamente. Los sistemas agrícolas modernos han producido en la región una conversión en grande escala hacia una alta producción de granos. Este informe presenta un análisis preliminar de las variaciones de la riqueza y la renovación de las especies de aves. Las listas de especies para seis localidades de estudio tenían entre 202 y 263 especies por localidad, con una variación en el índice de similaridad de Jaccard de 0,326 a 0,611. La totalidad de las seis listas sumaron 519 especies, donde más del 50 por ciento de las especies estaba sólo en una o dos de las localidades. La mayoría de la renovación entre localidades se asocia con las faunas forestales y acuáticas. Sin embargo, hubo una renovación importante también en las sabanas y en otros hábitats abiertos, con índices similares de alrededor de 0,434 a 0,734. Dieciocho especies endémicas fueron registradas; aquellas en riesgo se asociaron principalmente con pastizales abiertos. La alta diversidad de aves y el considerable impacto humano en esta región indican que las actividades de conservación en el Cerrado deberían ser una prioridad.

Key Words: Brazil; Cerrado; grassland birds; species richness.

The Cerrado biome is an extensive savannalike biome extending over 1.8 million km² in central Brazil, with a small extension into Bolivia (Dias 1992; Fig. 1). It is dominated by open grasslands (campo limpo) interspersed with scattered trees and shrubs (campo sujo) and dense woodlands (cerradão woodland; Eiten 1972, 1984). Beginning in the eighteenth century, this region was sparsely inhabited by Europeans, mainly prospectors seeking gold and diamonds and ranchers who grazed cattle on an extensive scale using native pasture. Intensive agriculture was not important because of the low nutrient content and high acidity of the soils and the lack of highway or railroad access.

Since the 1950s, however, mechanization of agriculture and construction of major highways through central Brazil have dramatically increased the impact of humans in the Cerrado. The use of lime and of new fertilization techniques has made cerrado soils suitable for crops, and the deep soils on rolling terrain are easily developed for mechanized agriculture. As a result, more than 35% of the Cerrado has been converted to agriculture, forestry, or pastureland. In São Paulo state, the cerrado vegetation has been reduced from 14 to 1.17% of the state's area (Secretaria do Meio Ambiente–SP 1997).

Further impacts on the Cerrado may result from pressure by national and international organizations to halt destruction of forests in Amazonia. The Cerrado has been viewed as a favorable area in which to develop alternative sites for intensive agriculture, especially for planting forests to produce pulp or to act as carbon sinks (Ab'Sáber et al. 1990).

The existence of scrubby vegetation in the Cerrado has been erroneously assumed to be correlated with low species diversity. In fact, these savannas are some of the richest in the world, with more than 600 woody plant species (Rizzini 1971). The bird fauna is also diverse. More than 420 species have been recorded in or near the Federal District, a 5,000-km² unit in the core of the Cerrado (Negret et al. 1984). However, fewer than 32,000 km²—in fewer than 100 parks, sanctuaries, or scientific reserves—have been protected in the Cerrado (Dias 1990).

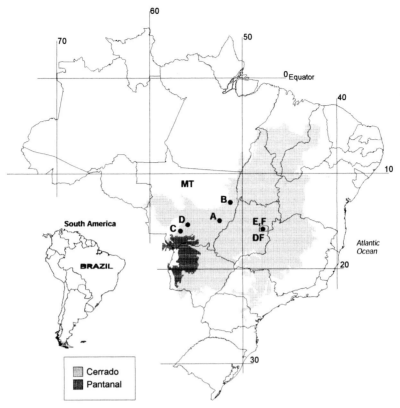

FIGURE 1. Map showing Cerrado region of central Brazil and locations of the six bird-survey sites (A–F; for references for each site, see Table 1). MT = Mato Grosso state, DF = Federal District.

Large subregions of the Cerrado, such as the newly created state of Tocantins, have only one or two reserves.

Birds are sensitive indicators of environmental degradation. Concern for South American grasslands, including the Cerrado, has been sparked by recent reports of the rarity and low numbers of grassland-dependent species (Goriup 1988, Collar et al. 1992). The disappearance of natural grasslands in South America has led to alarming declines in nesting birds associated with these habitats. Species of concern (Collar and Andrew 1988) include Lesser Nothura (*Nothura minor*), Dwarf Tinamou (*Taoniscus nanus*), Crowned Eagle (*Harpyhaliaetus coronatus*), White-winged Nightjar (*Caprimulgus candicans*), Sickle-winged Nightjar (*Eleothreptus anomalus*), Black-and-white Monjita (*Xolmis dominicana*), Strange-tailed Tyrant (*Yetapa risoria*), Bearded Tachuri (*Polystictus pectoralis*), Sharp-tailed Tyrant (*Culicivora caudacuta*), Chaco Pipit (*Anthus chacoensis*), Ochre-breasted Pipit (*A. nattereri*), Rufous-rumped Seedeater (*Sporophila hypochroma*), Marsh Seedeater (*S. palustris*), Chestnut Seedeater (*S. cinnamomea*), Black-masked Finch (*Coryphaspiza melanotis*), Saffron-cowled Blackbird (*Xanthopsar flavus*), and Pampas Meadowlark (*Sturnella defilippii*).

These poorly known species face numerous threats, including habitat fragmentation, isolation, trapping for the cagebird trade, hunting, and environmental degradation from pesticides (Bucher and Nores 1988, Cavalcanti 1988, Willis and Oniki 1988). Because little natural habitat remains in many areas, there is serious concern whether these native birds will be able to survive in human-influenced environments. Several species may be adapting temporarily to secondary habitats but may be unable to reproduce successfully in such marginal sites.

The purpose of this paper is to review data on species richness and turnover in the Cerrado and to discuss the conservation needs of the region's avifauna.

METHODS

I conducted a review of published and unpublished data to examine the following questions: what is the species richness at individual sites in the Cerrado biome, and how similar are nearby sites?

TABLE 1. BIRD SPECIES RICHNESS FOR SIX SITES IN THE CERRADO REGION OF BRAZIL

Site	Reference	State	Species count
A	Sick 1955	Mato Grosso	245
B	Fry 1970	Mato Grosso	263
C	Silva and Oniki 1988	Mato Grosso	233
D	R. Cavalcanti and M. Marini, unpubl. data	Mato Grosso	202
E	Negret 1983	Federal District	260
F	Antas 1995	Federal District	262

Data were obtained from six lists. Four lists came from Mato Grosso state and two from the Federal District. A site was defined as an area in the range of 1,000–50,000 ha, surveyed by one or two observers. Sampling effort was not known for all sites. I considered all species recorded for species richness (Table 1). Comparisons among sites were done only for species that had been positively identified, however; hence the differences in species numbers in Tables 1 and 3.

Similarities among sites were analyzed through a cluster analysis on the Euclidean distance matrix using the UPGMA method (Kovach 1990). The Jaccard similarity index was also calculated (Kovach 1990). Birds were classified according to their habitats as mostly cerrado and open landscapes, forest, or aquatic/riverine, based on the habitat preferences cited by the authors of individual species lists and by Silva 1995a. Cerrado-region endemics were also analyzed, based on the list of Silva (1995a), to which I added three species (Rufous-sided Pygmy-Tyrant [*Euscarthmus rufomarginatus*], White-rumped Tanager [*Cyspnagra hirundinacea*], and White-banded Tanager [*Neothraupis fasciata*]) with distributions in the cerrados of central Brazil plus Amapá state and its neighboring areas.

RESULTS

SPECIES RICHNESS AND SIMILARITIES

Species richness data were remarkably consistent. All counts fell within the range of 200–270 species per site (Table 1). A total of 519 species were identified at these six sites. By comparison, Silva (1995a) listed 837 species for the entire Cerrado region, and Negret et al. (1984) found 429 species in the Federal District. These data indicate that each of the six sites for which I examined data held about 20–30% of the Cerrado regional avifauna.

TABLE 2. SPECIES DISTRIBUTION AMONG SIX SITES IN THE CERRADO REGION OF CENTRAL BRAZIL (TOTAL SPECIES 519)

Number of species	Number of sites recorded
164	1
108	2
75	3
74	4
39	5
59	6

Similarities in species composition between sites were fairly low, with a Jaccard index ranging from 0.326 between sites C and F to 0.611 between sites E and F. More than 50% of all species were recorded at only one or two sites (Table 2). In general, the similarities were related to geographical proximity and position in the Cerrado region. The cluster dendrogram grouped both sites in the Federal District apart from the Mato Grosso sites (Fig. 2). Two sites in the middle of the Cerrado, in Mato Grosso, were grouped apart from sites at the edge of the region (Fig. 2). Edge sites B and C were influenced by Amazonian forest species, as indicated by Fry 1970 and Silva and Oniki 1988.

TURNOVER AND HABITAT EFFECTS

The Cerrado is a complex mixture of habitat types. In addition to the various forms of savanna and grassland that dominate the landscape in the core of the region, several types of forest are

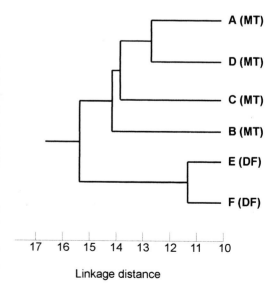

FIGURE 2. Cluster analysis dendrogram of the relationship between sites in the Cerrado region of central Brazil, based on presence/absence data of 519 bird species. All sites from Mato Grosso state (MT) are distinct from those of the Federal District (DF).

TABLE 3.   BETWEEN-SITE TURNOVER IN BIRD SPECIES COMPOSITION FOR SIX SITES IN CENTRAL BRAZIL

| | | Site-specific species per habitat | | |
Site	All species	Cerrado	Forest and aquatic	% cerrado site specific
A	245	2	13	0.8
B	263	6	43	2.2
C	230	5	28	2.1
D	190	3	4	1.5
E	260	12	17	3.8
F	262	9	22	3.5

TABLE 4.   BETWEEN-SITE SIMILARITY (JACCARD INDEX) FOR OPEN-HABITAT AVIFAUNA AND FOREST- AND AQUATIC-HABITAT AVIFAUNAS IN CENTRAL BRAZIL

Sites	Cerrado/Open	Forest/Aquatic
A–B	0.562	0.412
A–C	0.493	0.308
A–D	0.518	0.414
A–E	0.489	0.258
A–F	0.480	0.310
B–C	0.493	0.313
B–D	0.529	0.283
B–E	0.464	0.178
B–F	0.438	0.206
C–D	0.481	0.352
C–E	0.460	0.201
C–F	0.494	0.178
D–E	0.515	0.248
D–F	0.515	0.255
E–F	0.734	0.462

widespread, occurring most densely on rich soils or in areas of high humidity. As a result, the avifauna at any site is composed of both open-habitat and forest species. To determine whether variation among sites was due to non-savanna habitat effects, I compared the number of site-specific species per habitat.

Forest- and aquatic-associated species were the main site-specific component (Table 3). The cerrado and open-habitat species were fairly constant and in lower proportion than the site-specific birds, which ranged from 0.8 to 3.8% of the avifauna (Table 3). Similarity between sites, as measured by the Jaccard index, was always higher for the cerrado and open-habitat avifauna than for the forest and aquatic avifauna (Table 4). These results indicate that most of the turn-over among sites can be attributed to variation in the forest- and aquatic-habitat components of the avifauna.

OCCURRENCE OF CERRADO-REGION ENDEMICS

Eighteen of the 32 Cerrado-region endemic species that Silva (1995a) and I considered were found at the six study sites (Table 5). Six species were recorded at only one site. With the exceptions of Blue-eyed Ground-Dove (*Columbina cyanopis*) and Brasilia Tapaculo (*Scytalopus novacapitalis*), however, most of these species do not have particularly restricted distributions; thus, one would not expect such high site specificity. It is likely that habitat and abundance factors contributed substantially to this variation. Fifteen species occurred at the Federal District sites, whereas only 10 were found at the Mato Grosso sites. Eight species were largely restricted to open grasslands or areas with scattered trees, five occurred in tree and scrub cerrado, and five were restricted to forests (Table 5).

The degree of risk to the survival of these species is correlated with the human impact on their habitats. Open grasslands are preferred sites for mechanized agriculture, and this habitat is almost gone from central Brazil. Tree and scrub cerrado on deep, well-drained soils is also prime agricultural land. Remnants of this native vegetation survive in areas of rough terrain and in small fragments throughout the region. Gallery forests are protected by law and by natural barriers such as flooded soil. Grassland and cerrado species are of particular conservation concern; these include Lesser Nothura, Dwarf Tinamou, Campo Miner (*Geobates poecilopterus*), Blue-eyed Ground-Dove, and Yellow-faced Parrot (*Amazona xanthops*). As a group, gallery-forest species are fairly stable.

DISCUSSION

Planning a conservation strategy for a regional avifauna requires detailed knowledge of its richness, endemism, and spatial distribution. In the Cerrado region of Brazil, however, large areas remain unexplored (Silva 1995b). Under these circumstances, where habitat conversion is occurring rapidly and little is known about the spatial heterogeneity of bird distributions, a preliminary analysis of existing inventories can be useful in informing initial conservation actions and designing future surveys. Because site lists were comparable in species numbers across several locations, the present analysis suggests that comparatively small sites, in the order of tens of thousands of hectares, can harbor about a third of the Cerrado-region avifauna.

Because of the exceptional species richness and habitat diversity in the Cerrado, there were substantial turnover rates among sites at the local and regional level. I discerned effects in turnover rate attributable to local habitat composition (forest, aquatic, and cerrado) and regional (influence of Amazonian fauna) as well as other factors. In addition to demonstrating

TABLE 5. DISTRIBUTION OF CERRADO-REGION ENDEMICS AMONG SIX SITES IN CENTRAL BRAZIL

Family	Species	Habitat	Site
Tinamidae	*Nothura minor*	Cerrado	E
	Taoniscus nanus	Cerrado	E
Columbidae	*Columbina cyanopis*	Cerrado	C
Psittacidae	*Amazona xanthops*	Cerrado	E, F
Furnariidae	*Geobates poecilopterus*	Cerrado	E, F
	Phylidor dimidiatus	Forest	E
Formicariidae	*Herpsilochmus longirostris*	Forest	A, D
Rhinocryptidae	*Melanopareia torquata*	Cerrado	A, B, C, D, E, F
	Scytalopus novacapitalis	Forest	E, F
Tyrannidae	*Euscarthmus rufomarginatus*	Cerrado	A
Pipridae	*Antilophia galeata*	Forest	A, B, C, D, E, F
Corvidae	*Cyanocorax cristatellus*	Cerrado	B, C, D, E, F
Parulidae	*Basileuterus leucophrys*	Forest	E, F
Emberizidae	*Charitospiza eucosma*	Cerrado	B, D, E, F
	Saltator atricollis	Cerrado	A, C, D, E, F
	Porphyrospiza caerulescens	Cerrado	F
	Neothraupis fasciata	Cerrado	C, E, F
	Cypsnagra hirundinacea	Cerrado	C, E, F

turnover attributable to habitat mix (i.e., relative importance of aquatic habitats), I also found substantial turnover among sites in a given habitat (Tables 3 and 4). Further studies will be necessary to determine the relative importance of ecological and biogeographical effects in species turnover patterns among sites. For example, Silva (1996) has suggested that the distribution of Atlantic and Amazonian elements in the gallery-forest avifauna of the Cerrado was influenced by altitude and distance from the species' centers of distribution. Silva (1995c) also identified seven major patterns of biogeographic distribution for the avifauna associated with the Cerrado savanna vegetation.

The high local bird richness in the Cerrado region and the strong habitat preferences of many species exacerbated apparent turnover among sites that was not accounted for simply by changes in habitat. In this survey, additional sources of variation were the number of observers and different sampling methods. To rectify this problem, future studies should use a standard range of habitat types and sampling methods, and trained observers.

Grasslands and savannas are preferred habitats for human occupation. Changes in patterns of use have far-reaching consequences for species diversity as well as for other factors of importance to humans, such as frequency and intensity of fires and availability of groundwater during the dry season. Survival of Cerrado birds will depend on bringing together many forces to support the maintenance of natural landscapes and biological communities.

ACKNOWLEDGMENTS

I am grateful to P. D. Vickery for the invitation to participate at the International Conference and Training Workshop on Conservation and Ecology of Grassland Birds and for the encouragement to write this paper. The Association for Field Ornithologists supported my attendance at the meeting. I am indebted to many people for insights and discussions on this subject, especially A. Negret, J. M. C. da Silva, E. Willis, P. T. Z. Antas, and E. Bucher. Two anonymous referees made substantial improvements to the manuscript. I appreciate the help of R. B. Machado with the figures and tables. My research on the Cerrado has benefited from support from the University of Brasília, Brazilian National Research Council, and Federal District Foundation for Research Support.

LITERATURE CITED

AB'SÁBER, A., J. GOLDEMBERG, L. RODÉS, AND W. ZU-LAUF. 1990. Identificação de áreas para o florestamento no espaço total do Brasil. Estudos Avançados 4(9):63–119.

ANTAS, P. T. Z. 1995. Aves do Parque Nacional de Brasília. Instituto Brasileiro do Meio Ambiente e dos Recursos Naturais Renováveis. Centro de Pesquisas para Conservação das Aves Silvestres, Brasília, D.F., Brazil.

BUCHER, E. H., AND M. NORES. 1988. Present status of birds in steppes and savannas of northern and central Argentina. Pp. 71–79 in P. D. Goriup (editor). Ecology and conservation of grassland birds. ICBP Technical Publication no. 7. International Council for Bird Preservation, Cambridge, U.K.

CAVALCANTI, R. B. 1988. Conservation of birds in the *cerrado* of central Brazil. Pp. 59–66 in P. D. Goriup (editor). Ecology and conservation of grassland birds. ICBP Technical Publication no. 7. International Council for Bird Preservation, Cambridge, U.K.

COLLAR, N. J., AND P. ANDREW. 1988. Birds to watch:

the ICBP world list of threatened birds. ICBP Technical Publication no. 8. Smithsonian Institution Press, Washington, D.C.

COLLAR, N. J., L. P. GONZAGA, N. KRABBE, A. MADROÑO NIETO, L. G. NARANJO, T. A. PARKER III, AND D. WEGE. 1992. Threatened birds of the Americas: the ICBP/IUCN red data book. International Council for Bird Preservation, Cambridge, U.K.

DIAS, B. F. S. 1990. Conservação da natureza no cerrado. Pp. 583–640 *in* M. Novaes Pinto (editor). Cerrado: caracterização, ocupação e perspectivas. Editora Universidade de Brasília e SEMATEC, Brasília, D.F., Brazil.

DIAS, B. F. S. 1992. Cerrados: uma caracterização. Pp. 11–25 *in* B. Dias (editor). Alternativa de Desenvolvimento dos Cerrados: Manejo e Conservação dos Recursos Naturais Renováveis. Fundação Pró-Natureza, Brasília, D.F., Brazil.

EITEN, G. 1972. The cerrado vegetation of Brazil. Botanical Review 38(2):201–341.

EITEN, G. 1984. Vegetation of Brasília. Phytocoenologia 12:271–292.

FRY, C. H. 1970. Ecological distribution of birds in north-eastern Mato Grosso state, Brazil. Anais da Academia Brasileira de Ciências 42(2):275–318.

GORIUP, P. D. (EDITOR). 1988. Ecology and conservation of grassland birds. ICBP Technical Publication no. 7. International Council for Bird Preservation, Cambridge, U.K.

KOVACH, W. L. 1990. Multivariate statistical package plus version 2.0: users' manual. Kovach Computing Services, Anglesey, Wales, U.K.

NEGRET, A. 1983. Diversidade e abundância da avifauna da Reserva Ecológica do IBGE, Brasília–D.F. Master's thesis. Universidade de Brasília, Brasília, D.F., Brazil.

NEGRET, A., J. TAYLOR, R. C. SOARES, R. B. CAVALCANTI, AND C. JOHNSON. 1984. Aves da região geopolítica do Distrito Federal (check list) 429 espécies. Ministério do Interior, Secretaria do Meio Ambiente, Brasília, D.F., Brasil.

RIZZINI, C. T. 1971. A flora do cerrado. Pp. 107–153 *in* M. G. Ferri (editor). Simpósio sobre o Cerrado. Editora Edgard Blucher, Editora USP, São Paulo, Brazil.

SICK, H. 1955. O aspecto fisionômico da paisagem do médio Rio das Mortes, Mato Grosso, e a avifauna da região. Arquivos do Museu Nacional 42:541–576.

SILVA, J. M. C. 1995a. Birds of the cerrado region, South America. Steenstrupia 21:69–92.

SILVA, J. M. C. 1995b. Avian inventory of the cerrado region, South America: implications for biological conservation. Bird Conservation International 5:291–304.

SILVA, J. M. C. 1995c. Biogeographic analysis of the South American cerrado avifauna. Steenstrupia 21:49–67.

SILVA, J. M. C. 1996. Distribution of Amazonian and Atlantic birds in gallery forests of the cerrado region, South America. Ornitologia Neotropical 7:1–18.

SILVA, J. M. C., AND Y. ONIKI. 1988. Lista preliminar da avifauna da Estação Ecológica Serra das Araras, Mato Grosso, Brasil. Boletim do Museu Paraense Emílio Goeldi, Série Zoologia 4(2):123–143.

SECRETARIA DO MEIO AMBIENTE–SP. 1997. Cerrado: bases para conservação e uso sustentável das áreas de cerrado do Estado de São Paulo. Secretaria de Estado do Meio Ambiente, São Paulo, SP, Brazil.

WILLIS, E. O., AND Y. ONIKI. 1988. Bird conservation in open vegetation of São Paulo state, Brazil. Pp. 67–70 *in* P. D. Goriup (editor). Ecology and conservation of grassland birds. ICBP Technical Publication no. 7. International Council for Bird Preservation, Cambridge, U.K.

Studies in Avian Biology No. 19:250–257, 1999.

THE DECLINE OF THE PAMPAS MEADOWLARK: DIFFICULTIES OF APPLYING THE IUCN CRITERIA TO NEOTROPICAL GRASSLAND BIRDS

PABLO LUIS TUBARO AND FABIÁN MARCELO GABELLI

Abstract. The current status of the Pampas Meadowlark (*Sturnella defilippii*) was analyzed in terms of the new criteria adopted by the World Conservation Union. Estimated values of the species' Extent of Occurrence and Area of Occupancy were 8,000 square kilometers and 150 square kilometers, respectively. The total population size of the species was estimated to be approximately 7,500 adults. Considering its Extent of Occurrence and population size, this species qualified as Vulnerable by World Conservation Union criteria, but because of its small Area of Occupancy and possible fluctuations in its preferred habitat—natural grasslands—the species should be placed in the Endangered category.

LA DECLINACIÓN DE LA LOICA PAMPEANA: DIFICULTADES PARA LA APLICACIÓN DE LOS CRITERIOS DE LA UICN A LAS AVES NEOTROPICALES DE PASTIZAL

Sinopsis. Se analizó el estatus actual de la Loica Pampeana (*Sturnella defilippii*) en función de los nuevos criterios adoptados por la UICN. Los valores estimados para la Extención de Ocurrencia y el Área de Ocupación son 8.000 km² y 150 km², respectivamente. El tamaño total de la población fue estimado en 7.500 adultos. Por su Extención de Ocurrencia y tamaño poblacional la especie califica como Vulnerable, pero considerando su pequeña Área de Ocupación y posibles fluctuaciones en el hábitat preferido (pastizales naturales) la especie debe ser ubicada en la categoría En Peligro.

Key Words: Argentina; grasslands; IUCN; pampas; Pampas Meadowlark; *Sturnella defilippii*; World Conservation Union.

Neotropical grasslands in South America are widespread and include a variety of types. For example, high-altitude grasslands can be found in the Andes, Sierras Pampeanas, and Puna plateau. Low-altitude grasslands occur in the Venezuelan llanos, pampas of Argentina, and campos of Uruguay and southern Brazil (Cabrera and Willink 1980). Lowland grasslands such as the Pampas have experienced extensive pressure from agriculture and cattle-farming (Soriano et al. 1991), and concern about the conservation of Argentine grassland birds is growing (Bucher and Nores 1988).

The Pampas Meadowlark (*Sturnella defilippii*) is typical of many bird species living in lowland grasslands. This is a highly dimorphic species, especially during the austral spring and summer when mature males exhibit a red throat and breast contrasting with a dark body. Females are much duller, with a reduced, paler red breast area. Pampas Meadowlarks are gregarious, even during the breeding season, which typically extends from October to December. Males' territories are small and tightly packed in areas of suitable habitat, forming what we call reproductive groups. The nest consists of an open cup built on the ground and concealed under grasses. In January, at the end of the breeding season, individuals congregate in large flocks, hereafter referred to as nonreproductive groups, until the following spring.

Formerly distributed from southern Brazil and Uruguay to central Argentina, the Pampas Meadowlark has declined since the beginning of the twentieth century. In this paper we describe the species' present status. We also discuss the applicability of the new criteria of the World Conservation Union (IUCN) for assigning threat status (Mace and Stuart 1994) to neotropical grassland species in general and to the Pampas Meadowlark in particular.

METHODS

This study is based on field work done in Argentina in November 1992 and 1993 and in January, May, and December 1996 in the southwest of the province of Buenos Aires and adjacent areas of the province of La Pampa.

Field work took place on an 11,800-km route on primary and secondary roads. We looked for Pampas Meadowlarks from a vehicle moving at low speed (< 50 km/hr) and with windows down. Pampas Meadowlarks were easily detected because males have a conspicuous flight display and flight song. We made numerous stops along the route, as many as one every 0.5–1.5 km, in areas where previous information or research suggested the species might be present, as well as at any site judged to be appropriate habitat.

The minimum geographical area (hereafter referred to as Extent of Occurrence, or EO; Mace and Stuart 1994) covered by the Pampas Meadowlark was estimated using a grid of 100 km² superimposed on a map (Mercator projection) with the location of reproductive groups found during field work. We drew a minimum convex polygon, which included the outermost points of distribution of reproductive groups, and counted the number of squares included inside the polygon. The number of squares multiplied by 100 yielded the EO in square kilometers. The Area of Occupancy, or AO (the fraction of the EO effectively occupied by the species; Mace and Stuart 1994), was calculated as the sum of the areas of the sites where the species was found or estimated to be present.

We used additional sources of information to determine the species' original distribution and the timing of its range contraction. These included ornithological collections at the Museo Argentino de Ciencias Naturales "Bernardino Rivadavia" in Buenos Aires and at the National Museum of Natural History, Smithsonian Institution, Washington, D.C; the database of the grassland birds of eastern Argentina, Asociación Ornitológica del Plata (R. Fraga, pers. comm.); and a bibliographic survey, including the complete collection of the journal *El Hornero* from 1918 to 1995. The International Council for Bird Preservation (ICBP)/IUCN book *Threatened Birds of the Americas* (Collar et al. 1992) also provided useful information.

In areas where we detected Pampas Meadowlarks during field work, we conducted a point count using a visual scanning method (Lehner 1979, Bibby et al. 1992) and estimated the area used by the reproductive group. The frequency of vocal and flight displays increased with the size of the reproductive group (Gochfeld 1978), so small groups were less detectable, or appeared smaller in size than they were.

To assess the relationship between the visual scanning count and the real size of a reproductive group, at four sites we made exhaustive searches coupled with song recordings and territory mapping. These searches revealed that our scanning method underestimated the size of reproductive groups by about 50%. We therefore applied a correction factor, which consisted of doubling the number of counted birds, to estimate the number of individuals per site.

The procedure for estimating the total Pampas Meadowlark population size was as follows. First we divided the EO into four subareas (Villa Iris, Chasicó, Felipe Solá, and Napostá) based on maps (scale 1: 100,000) from the Instituto Geográfico Militar. Inside each subarea we counted the number of potential sites (NPS) judged to be suitable habitat for Pampas Meadowlarks. We then multiplied the NPS by the proportion of sites occupied by the species and by the mean number of Pampas Meadowlarks per site.

For the study of habitat preferences, we considered three types of habitats differing in species composition and structure: natural grasslands, planted pastures, and croplands. Planted pastures and croplands revert to natural grasslands when abandoned for periods ranging from 5 to ≥ 15 yr. It is important to note that natural grasslands are not natural in a strict sense because all of them have been cultivated or grazed at some point (Soriano et al. 1991). We studied plant species composition by collecting herbarium specimens in most areas where Pampas Meadowlarks were detected. This material was identified at the Darwinion Institute in San Isidro City. Natural grasslands were dominated by a variety of *Stipa* and *Piptochaetium* species, among

them *S. ambigua, S. trichotoma, S. neesiana, S. clarazi, P. montevidense,* and *P. stipoides.* We also found *Bromus unioloides* and *Hordeum parodii.* The structure of natural grasses had a typical "tussock" physiognomy. Planted pastures and croplands typically included *Avena barbata, A. sativa, Bromus mollis, Lolium multiflorum,* alfalfa (*Medicago sativa*), *Trifolium repens, Vicia angustifolia, V. sativa,* and wheat (*Triticum aestivum*) as dominant species. The main difference between planted pastures and croplands is that planted pastures are not cropped at the end of the annual growing cycle but remain in place for several years.

We used a graduated ruler to assess the height of the vegetation at 25 sample points inside each habitat type. These samples were located along a transect crossing the area and were separated by 10 m. At each sample point we measured the height of the vegetation touching the ruler to the nearest centimeter.

We compared vegetation height between habitat types using the Student t-test. Paired t-tests on vegetation height were performed between preferred sites that were occupied by Pampas Meadowlarks and adjacent unoccupied sites, or when we compared the same sites at different times. All statistical tests were two-tailed.

RESULTS

RANGE CONTRACTION

The former range of the Pampas Meadowlark included most of the Pampas grasslands from the southern part of Brazil (Rio Grande do Sul, Santa Catarina, and Paraná states), Uruguay (departments of Canelones, Paysandú, Cerro Largo, Flores, San José, Tacuarembó, and Montevideo), and eastern and central Argentina (including the provinces of Entre Ríos, Buenos Aires, Santa Fe, Córdoba, San Luis, and La Pampa; Fig. 1).

Since 1900 the distribution of this species has decreased by 90%. It is now virtually extinct in Brazil, Uruguay, and most of the northern and central Argentine pampas (Fig. 1). Pampas Meadowlarks were very common near the city of Buenos Aires until 1925, but now they are found almost exclusively on the margins of their former distribution, mainly in the southwestern part of the province of Buenos Aires.

Although the range contraction of this species has been rapid and extensive, the pace of the contraction has not been steady; most of the local extinction occurred between 1890 and 1950, coincident with the period of extensive agricultural transformation of natural grasslands (Soriano et al. 1991). Since 1950, Pampas Meadowlarks have been seen regularly in the marginal areas of the southwestern Pampas (Short 1968; Gochfeld 1978, 1979a, b; Tubaro et al. 1994).

EXTENT OF OCCURRENCE AND AREA OF OCCUPANCY

In 1992 and 1993 we found 41 sites occupied by reproductive groups of Pampas Meadow-

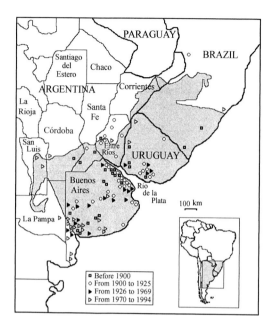

FIGURE 1. Sites where Pampas Meadowlarks were collected or sighted during different time periods. For simplicity, the 59 sites where Pampas Meadowlarks were recorded during field work in 1992–1996 are excluded. The shaded area indicates the extent of the Rio de la Plata Grasslands (Soriano et al. 1991) which include the Argentine pampas and the campos of Uruguay and southern Brazil. The present distribution of the Pampas Meadowlark is restricted to the margins of the original area, mainly in the southwestern part of the province of Buenos Aires.

larks. All of the sites were located in the southwestern part of the province of Buenos Aires and neighboring areas of the province of La Pampa (Fig. 2). Based on these findings, we estimated the EO of the species to be approximately 8,000 km^2. In 1996 we found 18 additional sites supporting reproductive and nonreproductive groups inside the EO. In the same year, however, we found a similar number of sites that had been occupied by the species in previous years unoccupied.

Based on the area used by 41 reproductive groups studied in 1992 and 1993, and assuming a population size of about 7,500 individuals (see "Population Size," below), we estimated the AO of the Pampas Meadowlark to be less than 150 km^2.

WINTER GROUNDS

We saw Pampas Meadowlarks most commonly in the northern part of their range during the nonreproductive season (Fig. 3), supporting Hudson's (1920) idea that this species, or at least

some of its members, moves northward during the winter. In May 1996, however, we found six nonreproductive groups containing a total of 516 individuals (range 9–173 individuals/group) in areas used by reproductive groups during the breeding season. This suggests that the Pampas Meadowlark, or at least a part of its population, is resident year-round.

POPULATION SIZE

In November 1993 we counted a total of 533 individuals (mostly males). In January 1996 we counted a total of 1,645 individuals. The number declined to 414 in November 1996. These differences reflect, at least in part, a change in the social behavior of these meadowlarks because at the end of the breeding season (January) they concentrate in large flocks where females and juveniles are more easily seen. Although an estimate of population size must be considered speculative given the information presently available, we think it is valuable to assist in conservation planning. Based on the estimated number of appropriate sites inside the EO and the number of such sites supporting reproductive groups of the species in the studied area, we extrapolated a population size of approximately 7,500 individuals (Table 1).

We also observed that the proportion of potential sites supporting reproductive groups of Pampas Meadowlark was low—less than 29% in the most suitable subarea. Pampas Meadowlarks were particularly abundant in the Chasicó and Naposta subareas (Table 1).

HABITAT PREFERENCE

We found 31 of the 41 reproductive groups (76%) on natural grasslands, even though this habitat represented less than 10% of the land in the study area. The remaining 10 groups (24%) occupied planted pastures and cultivated fields. No less than 89% (16/18) and 83% (5/6) of the nonreproductive flocks preferred natural grasslands during January and May 1996, respectively. This contrasted with 11% (2/18) and 17% (1/6) of the groups found over planted pastures in January and May 1996, respectively.

Height of the vegetation appeared to be another important factor for Pampas Meadowlarks. The height of the vegetation in sites supporting reproductive groups was 34.52 ± 5.79 cm ($\bar{X}$ ± SD, range 29–45 cm, N = 11 sites) for natural grasslands and 44.29 ± 17.83 cm (range 25–67 cm, N = 4 sites) for planted pastures. To assess the importance of vegetation height in Pampas Meadowlark settlement, we measured this variable at occupied and adjacent unoccupied sites supporting similar habitat. Occupied sites had higher vegetation than unoccupied areas (32.83

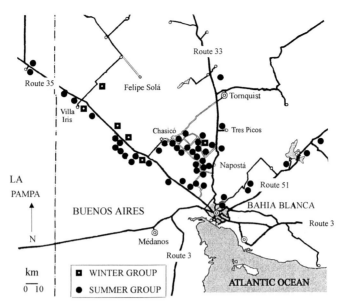

FIGURE 2. Detail of the southwestern portion of the province of Buenos Aires, showing sites where Pampas Meadowlarks were recorded during field work in 1992–1996. Summer groups included reproductive and non-reproductive groups detected between November and January. Winter groups consisted of nonreproductive groups found in May 1996.

± 14.85 cm vs. 9.54 ± 6.15 cm, t = 6.87, df = 10, P < 0.001).

Pampas Meadowlarks can coexist with cattle. About 26% of the natural grasslands supporting reproductive groups also supported cattle, but no planted pasture supported cattle and meadowlarks simultaneously. In the southwestern Pampas we found that grazed natural grasslands had higher vegetation than grazed planted pastures (28.00 ± 9.53 cm vs. 12.60 ± 11.54 cm, t = 3.19, df = 17, P < 0.01).

In 1993 Pampas Meadowlarks disappeared from 3 of the 11 sites where they had occurred in 1992. At all three sites the natural or planted grasslands had been replaced by wheat (*Triticum* spp.) fields. This suggests that habitat alteration is an important cause of local extinction. By December 1996, 18 natural grassland sites that supported Pampas Meadowlarks had been totally or partially converted. An additional six sites with planted pastures had been replaced by agriculture. Thus, 46% of the sites supporting Pampas Meadowlarks had suffered some kind of alteration by the end of our study period. Between 1993 and 1996 we also detected a substantial reduction in the height of the vegetation layer in the remaining sites (34.67 ± 6.20 cm vs. 12.95 ± 7.41 cm, t = 9.88, df = 9, P < 0.001). This was probably the result of extreme drought affecting the region, which reduced vegetation growth and increased the cattle load on natural

grasslands. Although the effect of these habitat changes on Pampas Meadowlark populations cannot be assessed presently, we suspect a negative impact because of the species' preference for taller natural grasslands.

DISCUSSION

In the early twentieth century, Pampas Meadowlarks were abundant throughout the Pampas region (Hudson 1920). Hudson considered the name Military Starling appropriate for this species because it referred to the huge numbers and coordinated movements of individuals in nonreproductive groups. The current status of the Pampas Meadowlark is clearly different. We could find it only in the southernmost part of its former distribution. Some recent records seem to confirm that the species is still present in other marginal areas of its former distribution, including southern Brazil (M. Pearman *in* Collar et al. 1992), Uruguay (Pearman 1994; A. Azpiroz and J. Cravino, pers. comm.), and Argentina in the provinces of Entre Ríos (C. Bertonatti and S. Heinonnen, pers. comm.), San Luis and Córdoba (Nellar Romanella 1993), and the southern tip of Buenos Aires (A. Di Giacomo, pers. comm.). Some of these records may reflect wintering migrants, although the migratory behavior of this species has never been clearly demonstrated. In contrast, our finding of six nonreproductive groups wintering in grasslands in the south-

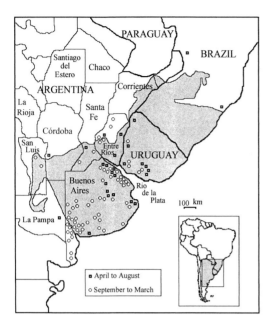

FIGURE 3. Sites where Pampas Meadowlarks were recorded according to time of year. For simplicity, the groups found during field work in 1992–1996 are excluded. The shaded area indicates the extent of the Rio de la Plata Grasslands (Soriano et al. 1991) which include the Argentine pampas and the campos of Uruguay and southern Brazil. Most of the fall and winter records (April–August) are from the northern half of the species' range, suggesting that at least part of the population is, or was, migratory.

eas of the Pampas have been rapidly transformed by agriculture since 1890, with a corresponding range contraction of Pampas Meadowlarks. Only marginal areas of low productivity, with reduced rainfall and poor soils, have escaped transformation. The limited availability of water is one of the environmental factors limiting productivity of temperate grassland ecosystems (Sala et al. 1981), and there is a clear trend of decreasing rainfall from north to south and from east to west in the Pampas (Prohaska 1952). Consequently, the southwestern Pampas are not suitable for agriculture, and natural grasslands continue to persist in this area.

A possible explanation for the existence of taller vegetation in natural grasslands than in planted pastures lies in differences of cattle use. Natural grasslands support fewer cattle (< 1 head/ha), so the disruptive effects of cattle-grazing and cattle movement (cover loss, disappearance of large tussocks, changes in species composition, and changes in the vertical distribution of verdant material [Sala et al. 1986]) are not as acute. Planted pastures are more palatable, support greater cattle densities, and are typically grazed until the grass is very low.

The habitat preferred by Pampas Meadowlarks is scarce, and its availability varies annually because of the management decisions of landowners. During the 4 yr of this study, we documented the conversion of 46% of the areas used by this species. At the same time, new areas were regenerating where pastures and croplands had been abandoned. It is important to remember that "natural grasslands" are in fact lands that have been abandoned for periods ranging from 5 to ≥15 yr. In the past, these sites were not always available for the settlement of Pampas Meadowlarks, and some of them will be unavailable in the near future. This dynamic balance between habitat loss and gain may be critical for Pampas Meadowlark survival. Because the habitat preferred by Pampas Meadowlarks is ephemeral, this species may be unable to colonize all available sites. This may explain the low

western portion of the province of Buenos Aires demonstrates that at least part of the population is resident year-round in the same general area.

Evidence suggests that the primary cause of the Pampas Meadowlark's decline is habitat destruction or degradation. In our study, Pampas Meadowlarks clearly preferred sites with taller grasses. This vegetative structure was found mainly in natural grasslands and to a lesser extent in planted pastures without cattle. Core ar-

TABLE 1. ESTIMATED NUMBERS OF PAMPAS MEADOWLARKS, 1992–1993

Subarea	Number of potential sites scanned	Proportion of potential sites with S. defilippii	Estimated number of potential sites	Expected number of potential sites with S. defilippii	Mean number of individuals per site	Total number of individuals
Villa Iris	210	0.048 (10/210)	1,600	76.8	14.8	1,137
Chasicó	116	0.138 (16/116)	840	115.9	33.0	3,825
Felipe Solá	20	0.050 (1/20)	1,008	50.4	16.0	806
Naposta	28	0.286 (8/28)	180	51.5	33.1	1,705
All subareas	374	0.1305	3,628	294.6	24.2	7,473

proportion of apparently appropriate sites occupied by the species (Table 1). In addition, we think the social behavior of Pampas Meadowlarks may play a role in the local pattern of distribution. We always saw these birds in groups, so it is possible that some males may use suboptimal habitats (e.g., planted pastures and croplands) because they are stimulated by social interactions of displaying males in adjoining natural grasslands.

OTHER POSSIBLE THREATS

Although there is a general correlation between the degree of habitat transformation in the Pampas and the range contraction of the Pampas Meadowlark, there are other possible causes of this species' decline. Some of these causes may interact with habitat loss.

The southern Pampas is the only place in the Americas where three *Sturnella* species coexist. Such coexistence increases the possibility that interspecific competition may adversely affect one or more of the species, as has been documented with Pampas Meadowlarks and White-browed Blackbirds (*S. superciliaris*; Gochfeld 1979b). We also recorded interspecific aggression between Pampas Meadowlarks and Long-tailed Meadowlarks (*S. loyca*; see also Gochfeld 1979b). White-browed Blackbirds are particularly abundant in modified agroecosystems, and Long-tailed Meadowlarks are expanding northward because farmers have supplied elevated song perches (fences, poles, and planted rows of trees), which this species requires (Gochfeld 1978). In this circumstance, habitat transformation could have compounded negative effects on Pampas Meadowlark populations, both by reducing the extent of its preferred habitat (natural grasslands) and by favoring increases in competitor species.

Another factor may be illegal capture for the pet trade. Pampas Meadowlarks were sold as cagebirds in Uruguay until 1920 (R. Vaz Ferreira, pers. comm.), and they are still captured illegally in Argentina. In 1985, 12 individuals were exported to the United States, and in 1986 at least 10 individuals were offered on the local market; in 1988 the latter number exceeded 100 individuals (Bertonatti and Tubaro 1993). Although we have no further data on the illegal trade of Pampas Meadowlarks, it seems that commercial exploitation is not extensive at present. Because the estimated population is so small, however, any extractive activity may be significant.

CURRENT STATUS OF THE PAMPAS MEADOWLARK AND PROBLEMS OF APPLYING THE IUCN CRITERIA

Recent efforts have been made by the IUCN to standardize criteria used in the evaluation of a species' status (Mace and Lande 1991, Mace and Stuart 1994). The use of such criteria not only helps establish a common priority agenda for conservation efforts but also describes the current status of a species in terms that are relevant for conservation. For example, listing a species as Endangered requires at least one of the following conditions: (1) a population decline greater than 50% in 10 yr or three generations; (2) an EO and AO smaller than 5,000 km^2 and 500 km^2, respectively; (3) a declining population with fewer than 2,500 mature (i.e., capable of reproducing) individuals; (4) a stable population of fewer than 250 mature individuals; or (5) a population viability analysis suggesting a probability of extinction greater than 20% in the next 20 yr.

Collar et al. (1994) considered the Pampas Meadowlark to be Endangered because of its extensive range contraction, which implies an equivalent decline in population. We do not think the available evidence supports this contention, however. The Pampas Meadowlark's geographic range has not changed substantially since 1950, although it declined rapidly in the first half of the twentieth century (Fig. 1).

The Pampas Meadowlark can also be classified as Vulnerable, as its EO is smaller than 20,000 km^2 and its population size is below 10,000 mature individuals. The species should be considered Endangered, however, because of its extremely small AO of about 150 km^2, which is substantially smaller than the threshold of 500 km^2 required by this category. In addition, two of the following three subcriteria are also required for a species to be considered Endangered: (1) a population that is severely fragmented, (2) a continuous decline (observed or inferred) in the EO and AO, and (3) an extreme fluctuation in the EO, AO, or number of locations in which the species is found. We detected important changes in the extent and quality of the Pampas Meadowlark's preferred habitat, natural grasslands, which is affected by agriculture and cattle-grazing. By the end of our study, most of the sites supporting Pampas Meadowlarks on the margins of its EO had been abandoned. For example, between 1993 and 1996 no reproductive groups were found north or east of the city of Tornquist in the province of Buenos Aires (Fig. 2). Thus, we think that subcriteria 1 and 2 are met and that the species should be classified as Endangered.

According to Collar et al. (1994), 6.3% of the world's threatened bird species occur in grasslands; habitat loss and alteration are identified as main threats. Some Critical or Endangered species live in the Pampas, among them Saffron-cowled Blackbird (*Xanthopsar flavus*), Ochre-breasted Pipit (*Anthus natereri*), Marsh Seedeater (*Sporophila palustris*), and Entre Rios Seedeater (*S. zelichi*). With the exception of the Ochre-breasted Pipit, the main criterion used for the inclusion of these species in the Endangered category was the rapid decline in their population sizes. Although most of the Pampas bird species depending on natural grasslands suffered extensive range contractions, this process probably occurred primarily between 1870 and 1950, when the Pampas were altered by agriculture and increasingly intensive cattle-farming (Soriano et al. 1991). As in the case of the Pampas Meadowlark, there is no clear evidence that the ranges of the above species have contracted further since 1950, which would be required by the IUCN for them to be considered Endangered. Thus, other factors should be considered in assessing their present status.

We have found that the main problems in applying the IUCN criteria to neotropical grassland birds are the scarcity of data about the species' biology, uncertainties about the actual distribution and population numbers, and dearth of historical information (see also Bucher and Nores 1988). This situation makes it very difficult to decide, or even to project on a reasonable basis, the future conservation status of a particular species. In the case of Pampas grassland birds, this situation is aggravated by the fact that they live on the margins of the main agricultural area of the Neotropics. There is still no protection against the rapid conversion of this land, which could happen again if costs of supplies fall and/or crop prices rise.

ACKNOWLEDGMENTS

We thank R. Fraga, E. Haskell, A. Lemoine, J. Pierson, J. Reboreda, S. Talía, and P. Vickery for their comments on previous versions of the manuscript. We also thank E. Bucher, R. Cavalcanti, V. Malán, and H. Ribicini for their help. R. Pozner of the Darwinion Institute identified herbarium specimens. J. Navas and R. Banks provided access to the collections of the Museo Argentino de Ciencias Naturales "Bernardino Rivadavia" and the National Museum of Natural History, respectively. The Asociación Ornitológica del Plata provided access to unpublished data sources. Field work was supported by the ICBP Panamerican Continental Section, American Bird Conservancy, U.S. Fish and Wildlife Service, University of Buenos Aires (UBACyT PS-045), and Consejo Nacional de Investigaciones Científicas y Técnicas. We also thank the Association of Field Ornithologists and the Sutton Avian Research Center in Oklahoma for financial support to attend the International Conference and Training Workshop on Conservation and Ecology of Grassland Birds and the 1995 annual meeting of the Association of Field Ornithologists.

LITERATURE CITED

BERTONATTI, C., AND P. L. TUBARO. 1993. Loica Pampeana. Vida Silvestre 34:21–22.

BIBBY, C. J., N. D. BURGESS, AND D. A. HILL. 1992. Bird census techniques. Harcourt Brace, New York, NY.

BUCHER, E. H., AND M. NORES. 1988. Present status of birds in steppes and savannas of northern and central Argentina. Pp. 71–79 in P. D. Goriup (editor). Ecology and conservation of grasslands birds. ICBP Technical Publication no 7. International Council for Bird Preservation, Cambridge, U.K.

CABRERA, A. L., AND A. WILLINK. 1980. Biogeografía de América Latina. Secretaría General de la Organización de los Estados Americanos, Washington, D.C.

COLLAR, N. J., M. J. CROSBY, AND A. J. STATTERSFIELD. 1994. Birds to watch 2: the world list of threatened birds. BirdLife International, Cambridge, U.K.

COLLAR, N. J., L. P. GONZAGA, N. KRABBE, A. MADROÑO NIETO, L. G. NARANJO, T. A. PARKER III, AND D. C. WEGE. 1992. Threatened birds of the Americas: the ICBP/IUCN red data book. International Council for Bird Preservation. 3d ed. Cambridge, U.K.

GOCHFELD, M. 1978. Social facilitation of singing: group size and flight song rates in the Pampas Meadowlark *Sturnella defilippii*. Ibis 120:338–339.

GOCHFELD, M. 1979a. Brood parasite and host coevolution: interactions between Shiny Cowbirds and two species of meadowlarks. American Naturalist 113:855–870.

GOCHFELD, M. 1979b. Interspecific territoriality in Red-breasted Meadowlarks and a method for estimating the mutuality of their participation. Behavioral Ecology and Sociobiology 5:159–170.

HUDSON, W. H. 1920. Birds of La Plata. J. M. Dent & Sons, New York, NY.

LEHNER, P. N. 1979. Handbook of ethological methods. Garland STPM Press, New York, NY.

MACE, G., AND R. LANDE. 1991. Assessing extinction threats: toward a re-evaluation of IUCN threatened species categories. Conservation Biology 5:148–157.

MACE, G., AND S. STUART. 1994. Draft IUCN red list categories, version 2.2. Species 21–22:13–24.

NELLAR ROMANELLA, M. M. 1993. Aves de la Provincia de San Luis. Museo Privado de Ciencias Naturales Investigaciones Ornitológicas "Guillermo E. Hudson," San Luis, Argentina.

PEARMAN, M. 1994. Neotropical notebook. Cotinga 2:26–31.

PROHASKA, F. J. 1952. Regímenes estacionales de precipitación de Sudamérica y mares vecinos. Meteoros 2:66–100.

SALA, O. E., V. A. DEREGIBUS, T. SCHLICHTER, AND H. ALIPPE. 1981. Productivity dynamics of a native temperate grassland in Argentina. Journal of Range Management 34:48–51.

SALA, O. E., M. OESTERHELD, R. J. C LEÓN, AND A. SORIANO. 1986. Grazing effects upon plant community structure in subhumid grasslands of Argentina. Vegetatio 67:27–32.

SHORT, L. L. 1968. Sympatry of Red-breasted Meadowlarks in Argentina, and the taxonomy of meadowlarks (Aves: *Leistes, Pezites,* and *Sturnella*). American Museum Novitates 2349:1–30.

SORIANO, A., R. J. C. LEON, O. E. SALA, R. S. LAVADO, V. A. DEREGIBUS, M. A. CAUHEPE, O. A. SCAGLIA, C. A. VELAZQUEZ, AND J. H. LEMCOFF. 1991. Rio de la Plata grasslands. Pp. 367–407 *in* R. T. Coupland (editor). Ecosystems of the world. Vol. 8A. Natural grasslands. Elsevier, Amsterdam, Netherlands.

TUBARO, P. L., F. M. GABELLI, AND D. GALLEGOS-LUQUE. 1994. Pampas Meadowlark. World Birdwatch 16:18–19.

Studies in Avian Biology No. 19:258–262, 1999.

A PRELIMINARY ASSESSMENT OF DISTRIBUTIONS AND CONSERVATION NEEDS OF GRASSLAND BIRDS IN MEXICO

A. Townsend Peterson and Mark B. Robbins

Abstract. We examined distributional patterns of grassland birds in three major grassland biomes in Mexico: the grasslands of northern Mexico, the pine (*Pinus*) grasslands of central Mexico, and the tropical savannas of southern Mexico. Although results are preliminary, we identified the grasslands of northern Mexico and the pine grasslands of central Mexico as important areas of endemism for grassland birds. We also found that a sizeable component of North American grassland birds depends heavily on grasslands in northern Mexico. The tropical savannas of southern Mexico, although lacking endemic species, support the only Mexican populations of several species.

UNA EVALUACIÓN PRELIMINAR DE LAS DISTRIBUCIONES Y DE LAS NECESIDADES DE CONSERVACIÓN DE LAS AVES DE PASTIZAL EN MÉXICO

Sinopsis. Examinamos los modelos de distribución de las aves de pastizal en tres biomas principales de pastizal en México: los prados del norte de México, los prados de pino (*Pinus*) del centro de México y las sabanas tropicales del sur de México. Aunque los resultados son preliminares, identificamos los prados del norte de México y los prados de pino del centro de México como áreas importantes para las aves endémicas de pastizal. Descubrimos también que una parte importante de las aves de pastizal norteamericanas depende mucho de los prados en el norte de México. Las sabanas del sur de México, aunque carecen de especies endémicas, mantienen las únicas poblaciones de varias especies.

Key Words: endemism; grassland birds; Mexico.

Grassland habitats, although originally extensive across central North America, are now among the continent's most degraded and threatened habitats (Dinerstein et al. 1995, Stotz et al. 1996). A review of the distribution and diversity of grassland birds in Mexico is challenging because at least three distinct types of grasslands can be identified. In northern Mexico, grasslands are continuous with and similar to those of the southern Great Plains of the United States; in the Transverse Volcanic Belt of central Mexico, open pine (*Pinus*) woodlands are interspersed with extensive grasslands; and in lowland portions of southern Mexico, tropical savannas extend south and east into Guatemala and Belize (Fig. 1). We examined distributional patterns of grassland birds in each of these three major grassland biomes.

We defined grasslands as large expanses of open areas dominated by grass and without a closed tree canopy cover. Bird distributions were determined in part from specimens in scientific collections (American Museum of Natural History, New York, New York; Field Museum, Chicago, Illinois; Museo de Zoología, Universidad Nacional Autónoma de México, México, D.F.; University of Kansas Natural History Museum, Lawrence, Kansas; and U.S. National Museum of Natural History, Washington, D.C.) but principally from summaries of Mexican bird distributions. The latter included Friedmann et al. 1950, Miller et al. 1957, Mengel 1970, Binford

1989, Howell and Webb 1995, Stotz et al. 1996, and American Ornithologists' Union (AOU) 1998. We excluded from consideration species found only in trees or in shrub edges.

SPECIES DISTRIBUTIONS

We identified 71 species of birds that make significant use of grassland habitats in Mexico (Table 1; note that there is some overlap between sections). Compared with avifaunas in other habitats in Mexico, the grassland avifauna is not especially diverse (Escalante et al. 1993). Still, several interesting and distinctive forms are represented, and it is clear that Mexican grasslands are important to a broad spectrum of North American grassland birds, especially during the winter months (Stotz et al. 1996).

Of the 71 grassland species we identified, 3 are endemic and 2 are nearly endemic to the country (Table 1, sec. I). Among the 23 major habitat types represented in Mexico, this level of endemism ranks thirteenth (Escalante et al. 1993). Botteri's Sparrow (*Aimophila botterii*) and Rufous-winged Sparrow (*A. carpalis*) range from just north of the U.S. border south into central Mexico and thus are almost endemic to Mexico. Striped Sparrow (*Oriturus superciliosus*) and Sierra Madre Sparrow (*Xenospiza baileyi*), both representing monotypic genera, are endemic to the highlands of the Transvolcanic Belt. Masked Bobwhite (*Colinus* [*virginianus*] *ridgwayi*) is a distinctive form that is restricted to northwestern Mexico and is probably recog-

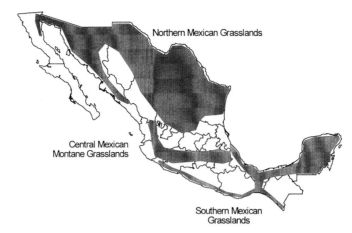

FIGURE 1. Major grassland biomes of Mexico.

nizable as a species (Phillips et al. 1964). All five of these species appear to be ecologically restricted to grassland habitat.

Seven species are broadly distributed, ranging from the United States south through Mexico into South America (Table 1, sec. II). Only one of these seven species (Burrowing Owl [*Athene cunicularia*]) uses grassland habitats almost exclusively, however.

Another component of Mexico's grassland avifauna breeds from Canada and the United States south into northern Mexico, where geographic distributions frequently end at the southern terminus of the Chihuahuan Desert, in the states of Jalisco, Guanajuato, and Querétaro. Of the 14 species in this category, 8 are ecologically restricted to grasslands (Table 1, sec. III). Interestingly, Horned Lark (*Eremophila alpestris*) ranges from northern North America south to the Isthmus of Tehuantepec, where its range terminates, in spite of the existence of apparently similar habitats to the south; there is a disjunct population in the vicinity of Bogotá, Colombia (AOU 1998).

A very different set of species, 20 in total, resides in the tropical grasslands and savannas of Central America and ranges north into the tropical lowlands of southern Mexico (Table 1, sec. IV). Most of these species (e.g., Spot-tailed Nightjar [*Caprimulgus maculicaudus*], Blue-black Grassquit [*Volatinia jacarina*]) inhabit grassy openings in tropical rain forest, although one (Ocellated Quail [*Cyrtonyx ocellatus*]) is found in grassy montane pine forests and another (Sedge Wren [*Cistothorus (platensis) stellaris*]) in grassy marsh habitats. Seven of the 20 species are restricted to grassland habitats.

A fifth component of Mexico's grassland avifauna consists of species that nest in Canada and the United States and migrate south to winter in

Mexican grasslands (Table 1, sec. V). Most of the 20 species we include in this category spend the winter in northern Mexico. Four of the species (Ferruginous Hawk [*Buteo regalis*], Mountain Plover [*Charadrius montanus*], Sprague's Pipit [*Anthus spragueii*], and Lark Bunting [*Calamospiza melanocorys*]) winter principally in Mexico, and another (Baird's Sparrow [*Ammodramus bairdii*]) is nearly endemic to the country in winter.

The entire populations of another 10 species (Table 1, sec. VI) migrate through Mexico on their way to points farther south, including the savannas of northern South America (e.g., Dickcissel [*Spiza americana*]) and the pampas of southern South America (e.g., Buff-breasted Sandpiper [*Tryngites subruficollis*]; Eskimo Curlew [*Numenius borealis*], spring only; Upland Sandpiper [*Bartramia longicauda*]). Most of the species in this category are ecologically restricted habitat specialists (Stotz et al. 1996; Table 1, sec. VI).

CONSERVATION STATUS AND RECOMMENDATIONS

The conservation status and needs of Mexican grasslands and their avifaunas vary. Although conservation of grassland birds and habitats has intensified in the United States, little or no progress has been made in Mexico.

NORTHERN GRASSLANDS

The grasslands of northern Mexico were originally extensive, but fragmentation through encroachment of woody vegetation and overgrazing has been nearly ubiquitous; isolated portions of this region, such as the coastal plain of Sonora state, are most seriously threatened (Phillips et al. 1964, Howell and Webb 1995). At least six species of grassland birds depend

TABLE 1.   PRELIMINARY CLASSIFICATION OF BIRDS THAT COMMONLY OCCUR ON GRASSLANDS IN MEXICO

Species		Habitat restricted	Endemism[a]
I. Endemic or nearly endemic to Mexico			
Masked Bobwhite	*Colinus [virginianus] ridgwayi*	✓	E
Botteri's Sparrow	*Aimophila botterii*	✓	N
Rufous-winged Sparrow	*A. carpalis*	✓	N
Striped Sparrow	*Oriturus superciliosus*	✓	E
Sierra Madre Sparrow	*Xenospiza baileyi*	✓	E
II. Occur north and south of Mexico			
Harris's Hawk	*Parabuteo unicinctus*		
Crested Caracara	*Polyborus plancus*		
American Kestrel	*Falco sparverius*		
Common Ground-Dove	*Columbina passerina*		
Burrowing Owl	*Athene cunicularia*		
Lesser Nighthawk	*Chordeiles acutipennis*		
Cassin's Kingbird	*Tyrannus vociferans*		
III. Breed from Canada and U.S. south into northern Mexico			
Swainson's Hawk	*Buteo swainsoni*	✓	
Golden Eagle	*Aquila chrysaetos*	✓	
Prairie Falcon	*Falco mexicanus*		
Scaled Quail	*Callipepla squamata*	✓	
Sandhill Crane	*Grus canadensis*		
Common Poor-will	*Phalaenoptilus nuttallii*		
Western Kingbird	*Tyrannus verticalis*		
Horned Lark	*Eremophila alpestris*		
Chihuahuan Raven	*Corvus cryptoleucus*		
Cassin's Sparrow	*Aimophila cassinii*	✓	
Savannah Sparrow	*Passerculus [sandwichensis] sandwichensis*	✓	
Grasshopper Sparrow	*Ammodramus savannarum*	✓	
Baird's Sparrow	*A. bairdii*	✓	
"Lilian's" Meadowlark	*Sturnella [neglecta] lilianae*	✓	
IV. Breed north into tropical lowlands of southern Mexico from Central America			
Lesser Yellow-headed Vulture	*Cathartes burrovianus*	✓	
Roadside Hawk	*Buteo magnirostris*		
White-tailed Hawk	*B. albicaudatus*	✓	
Aplomado Falcon	*Falco femoralis*	✓	
Ocellated Quail	*Cyrtonyx ocellatus*		
Black-throated Bobwhite	*Colinus nigrogularis*		
Double-striped Thick-knee	*Burhinus bistriatus*		
Striped Owl	*Asio clamator*		
Spot-tailed Nightjar	*Caprimulgus maculicaudus*	✓	
Tropical Kingbird	*Tyrannus melancholicus*		
Fork-tailed Flycatcher	*T. savana*		
Sedge Wren	*Cistothorus [platensis] stellaris*		
Gray-crowned Yellowthroat	*Geothlypis poliocephala*		
Blue-black Grassquit	*Volatinia jacarina*	✓	
Variable Seedeater	*Sporophila aurita*		
White-collared Seedeater	*S. torqueola*		
Ruddy-breasted Seedeater	*S. minuta*		
Grassland Yellow-Finch	*Sicalis luteola*	✓	
Stripe-headed Sparrow	*Aimophila ruficauda*		
Peten Sparrow	*A. [botterii] petenica*	✓	
V. Migrate south into Mexico (winter residents)			
Northern Harrier	*Circus cyaneus*		
Ferruginous Hawk	*Buteo regalis*	✓	
Prairie Falcon	*Falco mexicanus*		
Merlin	*F. columbarius* (*F. c. richardsonii* only)		
Sandhill Crane	*Grus canadensis*		
Mountain Plover	*Charadrius montanus*	✓	

TABLE 1. CONTINUED

Species		Habitat restricted	Endemism[a]
Long-billed Curlew	*Numenius americanus*	√	
Short-eared Owl	*Asio flammeus*	√	
Scissor-tailed Flycatcher	*Tyrannus forficatus*	√	
Sedge Wren	*Cistothorus [platensis] platensis*		
Sprague's Pipit	*Anthus spragueii*	√	
Vesper Sparrow	*Pooecetes gramineus*	√	
Lark Sparrow	*Chondestes grammacus*	√	
Sage Sparrow	*Amphispiza belli*	√	
Lark Bunting	*Calamospiza melanocorys*	√	
Baird's Sparrow	*Ammodramus bairdii*	√	
McCown's Longspur	*Calcarius mccownii*	√	
Chestnut-collared Longspur	*C. ornatus*	√	
Eastern Meadowlark	*Sturnella magna*	√	
Western Meadowlark	*S. [neglecta] neglecta*	√	
VI. Passage migrants			
Swainson's Hawk[b]	*Buteo swainsoni*	√	
Mississippi Kite	*Ictinia mississippiensis*		
American Golden-Plover	*Pluvialis dominica*		
Buff-breasted Sandpiper	*Tryngites subruficollis*	√	
Upland Sandpiper	*Bartramia longicauda*	√	
Eskimo Curlew	*Numenius borealis*	√	
Franklin's Gull	*Larus pipixcan*		
Common Nighthawk[b]	*Chordeiles minor*	√	
Dickcissel	*Spiza americana*	√	
Bobolink	*Dolichonyx oryzivorus*	√	

[a] E = endemic, N = near endemic.
[b] Small numbers breed in northern Mexico.

heavily on the grasslands in this region; two are effectively endemic to Mexico, two are near endemics (Escalante et al. 1993), and two are near endemics as far as wintering populations. Hence, a sizeable component of North American grassland birds depends heavily on grasslands of northern Mexico.

TRANSVOLCANIC BELT

The open, grassy pine woodlands that are concentrated in the Transvolcanc Belt of central Mexico comprise the most unusual Mexican grassland habitat. This habitat extends north in the Sierra Madre Occidental and Sierra Madre Oriental (Escalante et al. 1993) and south in the mountains, such as Cerro San Felipe (Binford 1989), of interior Oaxaca state. Two endemic species (Striped and Sierra Madre sparrows) and two near-endemic species (Botteri's and Rufous-winged sparrows) are found only in the grassland habitats of this region; included are the two monotypic genera (*Oriturus* and *Xenospiza*) representing distinctive phylogenetic lineages. Several species of small mammals, including the unusual volcano rabbit (*Romerolagus diazi*), are also endemic to this habitat. Hence, this grassland habitat clearly supports many distinctive animals (Escalante et al. 1993).

The Transvolcanic Belt grasslands are becoming critically endangered. There are several large cities, including Cuernavaca, Guadalajara, Morelia, and Mexico City, in the region. People seeking to fulfill subsistence needs (e.g., collecting firewood, planting corn fields) have destroyed large expanses of this habitat. Additional areas, especially between Cuernavaca and Mexico City, are being consumed by urban sprawl, and still more habitat is being affected by air pollution from large population centers (Flores-Villela and Pérez 1988). The once-extensive high-elevation grasslands in the mountains around Mexico City are especially critical; they include the volcanoes El Ajusco, Popocatépetl, and Nevado de Toluca as well as other nearby volcanoes. Some of these peaks have been the focus of conservation efforts, yet little concrete progress has been achieved. Continued rapid reduction and fragmentation of this high-elevation habitat could lead to several avian extinctions in a short period of time.

TROPICAL SAVANNAS

The tropical savannas and grassy openings of southern Mexico are being converted to agricultural uses; indeed, almost all lowland tropical habitats in the country are degraded. Although no endemic species are found in these habitats, further perturbation of this ecosystem could well eliminate species from Mexico that are dependent on it, such as the Grassland Yellow-Finch (*Sicalis luteola*). Identifying sizeable patches of remaining undisturbed lowland habitat will be a major challenge.

RECOMMENDATIONS

Developing an action plan for effective conservation of grassland habitats and their birds is critical. First steps should include identifying the largest remaining patches of grasslands in the Chihuahuan Desert, Sonoran Coastal Plain, and Transvolcanic Belt (preferably in the states of México, Michoacán, and Morelos). Basic inventories need to be conducted throughout the year to ensure that species of special concern are included in the area, and effective steps for conservation must be implemented. It is critical that active grassland preservation efforts in the United States be coordinated with such efforts in Mexico, providing expertise and enthusiasm to preserve habitats that in Mexico have received little attention.

In conclusion, Mexican grasslands are a heterogeneous assemblage of habitats that overlap little in the composition of bird species they support. Habitat restriction is high among the northern migrants that winter in or pass through Mexico. Year-round endemism is focused in the grassy pine woodlands of the Transvolcanic Belt, but many species that move into Mexican grasslands on migration are nearly endemic to the country. Hence, even though grasslands were not emphasized in a previous evaluation of avian diversity and endemism in Mexico (Escalante et al. 1993), a more careful inspection reveals considerable numbers of interesting forms in these distinctive habitats in Mexico.

ACKNOWLEDGMENTS

We thank G. Escalona-Segura, P. D. Vickery, and M. Carter for helpful comments on the manuscript and A. Navarro-Sigüenza and H. Benítez-Díaz for their assistance in collaborative projects related to this work. For providing access to specimens and data, we thank the staffs of the American Museum of Natural History; Field Museum; Museo de Zoología, Facultad de Ciencias, Universidad Nacional Autónoma de México; University of Kansas Natural History Museum; and U.S. National Museum of Natural History.

LITERATURE CITED

AMERICAN ORNITHOLOGISTS' UNION. 1998. Check-list of North American birds. 7th ed. American Ornithologists' Union, Washington, D.C.

BINFORD, L. C. 1989. A distributional survey of the birds of the Mexican state of Oaxaca. Ornithological Monographs no. 43.

DINERSTEIN, E., D. M. OLSON, D. J. GRAHAM, A. L. WEBSTER, S. A. PRIMM, M. P. BOOKBINDER, AND G. LEDEC. 1995. A conservation assessment of the terrestrial ecosystems of Latin America and the Caribbean. World Bank, Washington, D.C.

ESCALANTE, P., A. G. NAVARRO, AND A. T. PETERSON. 1993. A geographic, historical, and ecological analysis of avian diversity in Mexico. Pp. 281–307 *in* T. P. Ramamoorthy, R. Bye, A. Lot, and J. Fa (editors). The biological diversity of Mexico: origins and distribution. Oxford University Press, New York, NY.

FLORES-VILLELA, O., AND P. PÉREZ. 1988. Conservación en México: sintesis sobre vertebrados terrestres, vegetación y uso del suelo. INIREB, Xalapa, Veracruz, Mexico.

FRIEDMANN, H., L. GRISCOM, AND R. T. MOORE. 1950. Distributional check-list of the birds of Mexico, part 1. Pacific Coast Avifauna 29:1–202.

HOWELL, S. N. G., AND S. WEBB. 1995. A guide to the birds of Mexico and northern Central America. Oxford University Press, Oxford, U.K.

MENGEL, R. M. 1970. The North American central plains as an isolating agent in bird speciation. Pp. 279–340 *in* W. Dort and J. K. Jones, Jr. (editors). Pleistocene and recent environments of the central great plains. University of Kansas Press, Lawrence, KS.

MILLER, A. H., H. FRIEDMANN, L. GRISCOM, AND R. T. MOORE. 1957. Distributional check-list of the birds of Mexico, part 2. Pacific Coast Avifauna 33:1–436.

PHILLIPS, A. R., J. T. MARSHALL, AND G. MONSON. 1964. The birds of Arizona. University of Arizona Press, Tucson, AZ.

STOTZ, D. F., J. W. FITZPATRICK, T. A. PARKER III, AND D. K. MOSKOVITZ. 1996. Neotropical birds: ecology and conservation. University of Chicago Press, Chicago, IL.

Studies in Avian Biology No. 19:263–271, 1999.

GRASSLAND BIRDS IN PRAIRIE-DOG TOWNS IN NORTHWESTERN CHIHUAHUA, MEXICO

PATRICIA MANZANO-FISCHER, RURIK LIST, AND GERARDO CEBALLOS

Abstract. From November 1994 to December 1995 we studied the species composition, distribution, seasonality, and abundance of grassland birds in the prairie dog (*Cynomys ludovicianus*) towns of northwestern Chihuahua state, Mexico. We recorded 71 species of birds on the grasslands, 22 of which were grassland specialists. Most (52 percent) of the 71 species were residents, followed by winter migrants, summer migrants, and transients. Horned Larks (*Eremophila alpestris*) and Lark Buntings (*Calamospiza melanocorys*) were the most abundant species. The abundance of all species was generally low, possibly because of a prolonged drought. The low abundance could also reflect a decline in grassland birds in North America, however. Because there were no data on grassland birds in this area prior to our study, it was not possible to assess population trends. On the basis of our study, we suggest conservation measures to enhance maintenance of grassland-bird habitat and of biodiversity in general.

LAS AVES DE PASTIZAL EN COLONIAS DE PERROS LLANEROS DEL NOROESTE DE CHIHUAHUA, MÉXICO

Sinopsis. Se estudió la composición de especies, distribución, temporalidad y abundancia de aves de pastizal en colonias de perros llaneros (*Cynomys ludovicianus*) del noroeste de Chihuahua, México. Se registraron 71 especies en los pastizales, de las cuales 22 se consideran como aves exclusivas de pastizal. La mayoría de las especies fueron residentes (un 52 por ciento), seguidas de las migratorias de invierno, las migratorias de verano y las transitorias. La Alondra Cornuda (*Eremophila alpestris*) y el Gorrión Alipálido (*Calamospiza melanocorys*) fueron las especies más abundantes. La abundancia de todas las especies fue en general baja, probablemente debido a la prolongada sequía. Sin embargo, la baja abundancia observada podría ser un reflejo de la disminución de este grupo en Norteamérica. Desafortunadamente, no existe información previa sobre aves de paztizal en el área, para determinar las tendencias en la variación de las poblaciones. Basados en nuestro estudio, se sugieren medidas regionales de conservación para apoyar el mantenimiento de hábitat para las aves de pastizal en particular y de la biodiversidad en general.

Key Words: Chihuahua; grassland birds; prairie-dog towns.

North American prairies, considered one of the most biologically diverse grasslands in the world (Mountfort 1988), once stretched almost continuously from Mexico to Canada (Shelford 1963). These grasslands, however, have suffered the most extensive fragmentation and transformation of the natural communities in North America (Marsh 1984, Miller et al. 1994). Habitat fragmentation and destruction have become leading causes of species extinctions (Ehrlich and Ehrlich 1981). Habitat fragmentation usually reduces the number of populations and population sizes and increases the risk of extinction because of demographic, genetic, or stochastic processes (Wilcove et al. 1986, Robinson et al. 1995). The impact of fragmentation can be viewed as a combination of the percentage of habitat left and the isolation and connectivity of habitat fragments (Wilcove et al. 1986, McCullough 1996).

In the nineteenth century, prairie dogs (*Cynomys* spp.) occupied up to 100 million ha of native grasslands in North America (Merriam 1902, Nelson 1919). The expansion of human activities early in the twentieth century, how-

ever, led to extensive eradication campaigns, and the area occupied by prairie dogs has been reduced to approximately 2% of the original range (Marsh 1984, Miller et al. 1994).

The largest complex of prairie-dog towns left in North America is found in northwestern Chihuahua state, Mexico (Ceballos et al. 1993). This area is important for the maintenance of regional biodiversity because it holds populations of many endangered vertebrate species, is a wintering ground for many grassland birds (Manzano-Fischer 1996), and is one of the last relatively well preserved grasslands in Mexico (Miller et al. 1994).

Since the late 1980s there has been growing concern about North America's grassland birds, which have shown consistent, sharp declines (Knopf 1994). Although many species are threatened or of conservation concern in the United States and Canada (McNicholl 1988, Knopf 1994), their status in Mexico has not been assessed (see Peterson and Robbins 1999). Birds in general, however, are quite threatened in Mexico, where approximately 35% of all avian species are considered at risk of extinction (Ce-

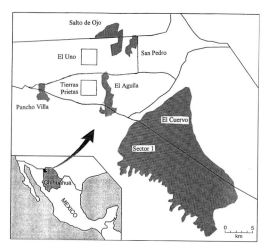

FIGURE 1. Location of the Janos-Nuevo Casas Grandes prairie-dog complex, Chihuahua, Mexico, showing the distribution of bird localities studied in 1994–1995 (modified from Moehrenschlager and List 1996).

ballos and Márquez in press). The purpose of this study was to determine the composition, distribution, seasonality, and abundance of grassland birds in northwestern Mexico. The grasslands in this region provide critical habitat for resident and migrant grassland birds (Manzano-Fischer 1996), among them Mountain Plover (*Charadrius montanus*), Long-billed Curlew (*Numenius americanus*), and Ferruginous Hawk (*Buteo regalis*).

STUDY AREA

The study was carried out from November 1994 to December 1995 in the Janos-Nuevo Casas Grandes (JNCG) prairie-dog complex in northwestern Mexico (Ceballos et al. 1993). The complex is located approximately 75 km south of the Mexico–United States border, on the grasslands and scrublands southeast of the

Sierra Madre Occidental in Chihuahua state (approximately 30°50' N, 108°25' W; Fig. 1). The area extends west and north to the arid scrub of the Chihuahuan Desert and south and east of the foothills of the Sierra Madre Occidental. The climate is arid, with hot summers and cold winters. Mean annual precipitation is 307 mm, with most precipitation in July and August and scattered showers in winter (Rzedowsky 1981). The mean temperature is 15.7 C (García 1973), with a range from −15 C in winter to 50 C in summer.

Grasslands dominate the area and are characterized by grasses and annual herbs, including *Bouteloua gracilis, B. curtipendula, B. hirsuta, Aristida hamulosa, Fouqueria splendens, Prosopis laevigata, Festuca imbricata,* and toboso (*Hilaria mutica*). Isolated patches of cholla (*Opuntia* spp.), yucca (*Yucca* spp.), ephedra (*Ephedra trifurca*), and mesquite (*Prosopis* spp.) scrub occur in the grasslands. From mid-1993 to January 1996 the region suffered one of the worst droughts in recent decades. This drought, combined with overgrazing and dust burial, resulted in a great reduction of vegetation cover and created extensive areas of bare ground in the prairie-dog complex.

METHODS

We used point counts on fixed transects to determine the abundance of birds in the JNCG prairie-dog complex. Transects were carried out in the fall (8–28 Nov) and winter (17 January–26 February) of 1994 and in the spring (12 May–13 June), summer (18 July–7 August), early fall (27 September–17 October), and late fall (20 November–4 December) of 1995.

We selected eight study sites: six sites with prairie dogs, one site where the prairie dogs were poisoned in 1989 and were no longer present, and one toboso grassland site without prairie dogs (Table 1). Two transects were established at each site. Each transect was 2,500 m long with 10 point counts at 250-m intervals. Point counts had a fixed radius of 50 m and were conducted according to Hutto et al. 1986. We recorded all birds within the 50-m radius, beyond the 50-m radius, and between point counts. Point counts were conducted for 10 min. Censuses began 30 min after sunrise and lasted 3 hr. Censuses were not carried out when it rained or when wind velocities exceeded 24 km/hr.

We identified bird species using the field guides of

TABLE 1. DESCRIPTION OF GRASSLAND LOCALITIES STUDIED IN THE JANOS-NUEVO CASAS GRANDES PRAIRIE-DOG COMPLEX, CHIHUAHUA, MEXICO, 1994–1995

Locality	Coordinates	Land ownership	Vegetation
San Pedro (dog town)	30°53'N, 108°22'W	Communal	*Ephedra* spp. and annual plants
Pancho Villa (dog town)	30°48'N, 108°37'W	Communal	*Aristida* spp. and annual plants
Salto de Ojo (dog town)	30°54'N, 108°26'W	Private	*Hilaria mutica* and annual plants
El Aguila (dog town)	30°49'N, 108°26'W	Private	*Aristida* spp., *Bouteloa* spp., *Hilaria mutica,* and annual plants
Sector 1 (dog town)	30°42'N, 108°21'W	Communal	*Prosopis* spp. and annual plants
El Cuervo (dog town)	30°43'N, 108°17'W	Communal	*Opuntia* spp., *Yucca* spp., and annual plants
El Uno (poisoned town)	30°51'N, 108°27'W	Private	*Bouteloa* spp. and *Muhlembergia utilis*
Tierras Prietas (toboso grassland)	30°46'N, 108°30'W	Private	*Hilaria mutica* and *Opuntia* spp.

TABLE 2. GRASSLAND BIRD ABUNDANCE DURING EACH SEASON IN THE JANOS-NUEVO CASAS GRANDES PRAIRIE-DOG COMPLEX, CHIHUAHUA, MEXICO, 1994–1995

Species	Abundance[a]					
	Fall 1994	Winter 1994	Spring 1995	Summer 1995	Early fall 1995	Late fall 1995
Northern Harrier	13	4	0	0	3	0
Swainson's Hawk	0	0	7	10	0	0
Ferruginous Hawk	38	22	0	0	8	19
Prairie Falcon	1	3	0	0	1	0
Mountain Plover	0	3	0	0	0	0
Long-billed Curlew	1	32	1	73	156	0
Burrowing Owl	2	0	37	42	21	7
Horned Lark	2,017	662	126	141	391	903
Grasshopper Sparrow	0	0	5	6	0	0
Vesper Sparrow	0	0	0	0	18	0
Lark Sparrow	0	0	1	20	1	0
Cassin's Sparrow	0	0	0	4	0	0
Brewer's Sparrow	0	0	2	1	20	1
longspur sp.	144	12	0	0	60	4
Lark Bunting	105	0	0	2	183	674
meadowlark sp.	61	33	60	32	29	59
Total no. individuals	2,382	771	234	325	891	1,667
Total no. species	9	8	8	10	12	7

[a] Total number of birds observed in the 16 transects per season.

the National Geographic Society (1983), Robbins et al. (1983), Edwards (1989), and Howell and Webb (1995). Species names follow the check-list of the American Ornithologists' Union (AOU 1983, 1991).

The seasonality of each species was determined from our field records and from Howell and Webb 1995. We classified species as belonging to one of four seasonal groups: (1) resident (species found year-round), (2) summer migrant (species that breed and summer), (3) winter migrant (species that winter), and (4) transient (species that pass by on migration).

We determined abundance only for the 18 species of grassland birds we observed on transects, but we noted observations of other significant species (e.g., Golden Eagle [*Aquila chrysaetos*]). Species that we observed in the grassland during the study period but did not record on transects (including four grassland species) were listed as present in the area and were included in our inventory of species; we provided no information on their abundance, however. Waterfowl were not included in the study because they were associated primarily with reservoirs.

The conservation statuses of species in Mexico, the United States, and Canada were determined from government and scientific lists (McNicholl 1988, Knopf 1994, SEDESOL 1994, U.S. Fish and Wildlife Service 1996a, b).

RESULTS

SPECIES COMPOSITION, DISTRIBUTION, SEASONALITY, AND ABUNDANCE

We observed 71 bird species representing 11 orders, 24 families, and 57 genera in the grasslands of the JNCG complex (Appendix). As expected, the order Passeriformes and the family Emberizidae had the highest species richness. A few species were abundant (> 500 individuals), but most species were relatively scarce (Table 2). The temporal and spatial distribution of species was very heterogeneous. Most species (52%) were residents, followed by winter migrants (24%), summer migrants (17%), and transients (7%). The number of species present in the JNCG complex at one time varied from 21 to 29, with the highest number in early fall, when both resident and transient species were present simultaneously.

GRASSLAND BIRDS

Twenty-two (31%) of the 71 species we recorded at the JNCG complex were grassland specialists (Mengel 1970). They represented 4 orders, 8 families, and 17 genera. We classified 45% of the grassland specialists as residents, 45% as winter migrants, 5% as summer migrants, and 5% as transients.

We observed 18 of the 22 grassland specialists on transects. Savannah Sparrows (*Passerculus sandwichensis*), Short-eared Owls (*Asio flammeus*), Sprague's Pipits (*Anthus spragueii*), and Baird's Sparrows (*Ammodramus bairdii*) were recorded only in grasslands outside our transects.

Two of the grassland specialists we observed on transects—Horned Larks (*Eremophila alpestris*) and Lark Buntings (*Calamospiza melanocorys*)—were abundant (> 500 individuals) and accounted for 65% of all individuals recorded (Tables 2 and 3). Six species were common (≥

STUDIES IN AVIAN BIOLOGY

NO. 19

TABLE 3. SPATIAL VARIATION IN RELATIVE ABUNDANCE OF GRASSLAND BIRDS IN EIGHT LOCALITIES IN THE JANOS-NUEVO CASAS GRANDES PRAIRIE-DOG COMPLEX, CHIHUAHUA, MEXICO, 1994–1995

Species	Localities[a]							
	SP	PV	SO	EA	S1	EC	EU	TP
Northern Harrier	5	0	7	1	0	2	4	1
Swainson's Hawk	0	8	5	1	0	2	1	0
Ferruginous Hawk	9	4	39	6	12	14	3	0
Prairie Falcon	1	0	0	0	1	0	2	1
Mountain Plover	0	0	0	3	0	0	0	0
Long-billed Curlew	15	28	75	11	0	100	33	1
Burrowing Owl	8	31	25	8	16	11	10	0
Horned Lark	599	215	841	958	98	309	889	331
Grasshopper Sparrow	0	0	0	2	0	0	4	5
Vesper Sparrow	10	0	0	0	0	7	0	1
Lark Sparrow	0	22	0	0	0	0	0	0
Cassin's Sparrow	4	0	0	0	0	0	0	0
Brewer's Sparrow	0	1	0	1	21	0	0	1
longspur sp.	0	1	0	45	0	0	173	1
Lark Bunting	0	105	0	0	0	859	0	0
meadowlark sp.	30	109	33	25	3	12	24	38
Total no. species	9	10	7	11	6	9	10	9

[a] SP = San Pedro, PV = Pancho Villa, SO = Salto de Ojo, EA = El Aguila, S1 = Sector 1, EC = El Cuervo, EU = El Uno, TP = Tierras Prietas.

100 individuals), and 10 species were uncommon (< 100 individuals; Tables 2 and 3). Mountain Plovers were common in the region but were recorded on only three transects.

The abundance of each species varied among seasons (Table 2), and the number of individual birds increased from spring to fall (Fig. 2). The total number of grassland species recorded per locality varied from 6 to 11 (Table 3). El Aguila had the highest number of grassland species (11) and Sector 1 the lowest (6).

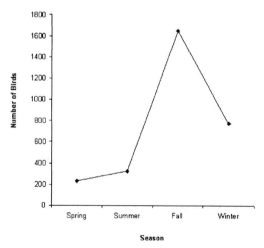

FIGURE 2. Seasonal variation in the number of grassland birds at the Janos-Nuevo Casas Grandes prairie-dog complex, Chihuahua, Mexico, 1994–1995.

SPECIES OF CONSERVATION CONCERN

Of the 71 species we recorded in the JNCG complex, 29 are considered to be of conservation concern in Mexico, the United States, or Canada; 21 of the 29 species are grassland specialists (Appendix). In Mexico, 11 of these 29 species have formal conservation status: 9 (all grassland specialists) are Threatened and 2 (Golden Eagle and Bald Eagle [*Haliaeetus leucocephalus*]) are Endangered. Six of the 11 species are residents, and 5 are migrants. In the United States, 1 of the 29 species of concern (Bald Eagle) is formally listed as Threatened, and an additional 22 species (19 of which are grassland specialists) are declining. In Canada, three species (Ferruginous Hawk, Burrowing Owl [*Athene cunicularia*], and Loggerhead Shrike [*Lanius ludovicianus*]) are formally listed as Threatened, and an additional three species (Grasshopper Sparrow [*Ammodramus savannarum*], Baird's Sparrow, and Western Meadowlark [*Sturnella neglecta*]) are declining.

All together, six species—Ferruginous Hawk, Burrowing Owl, Loggerhead Shrike, Grasshopper and Baird's sparrows, and Western Meadowlark—have formal conservation status in the United States and Canada. Four species—Northern Harrier (*Circus cyaneus*), Mountain Plover, Burrowing Owl, and Lucy's Warbler (*Vermivora luciae*)—are listed as Threatened in Mexico and are declining in the United States; Bald Eagle is listed as Endangered in Mexico and as Threatened in the United States. Finally, Burrowing

Owl is listed as Threatened in Canada and Mexico and is declining in the United States.

SPECIES ACCOUNTS

Raptors

Northern Harriers were observed on transects in fall and winter (Table 2) and outside transects throughout the year. The latter was of particular interest because the JNCG complex is located in an area that had previously been considered to be in this species' wintering range only (Howell and Webb 1995). Harriers occurred in five of the eight localities and accounted for 8% of all raptors observed along transects. Golden Eagles feed on prairie dogs regularly and were seen in prairie-dog towns year-round. A pair of Golden Eagles nested near a small prairie-dog colony in March 1996 and produced two chicks, one of which fledged. Prairie Falcons (*Falco mexicanus*) were observed mainly in fall and winter, in small numbers, at four of the eight localities (Tables 2 and 3).

Ferruginous Hawks were common and comprised 41% of all raptors recorded (Tables 2 and 3). They were observed from October into February, mainly near prairie-dog towns, as prairie dogs are their main prey in the JNCG complex. They occurred at all but one locality (Tierras Prietas). Swainson's Hawks (*Buteo swainsoni*) were summer migrants and accounted for 8% of all raptors seen on transects. Recorded in five of the eight localities, they bred in mesquite scrub and spent the summer feeding on small mammals and grasshoppers.

Bald Eagles were present in winter and were observed hunting prairie dogs and sometimes fighting with Golden Eagles for prey. Remains of prairie dogs (bones, skulls, and even entire bodies) were found in Bald Eagle pellets. Burrowing Owls were both resident and migratory and bred in the JNCG complex. They were recorded in seven of the eight localities and were most abundant in summer, decreasing in winter when part of the population migrated south (Tables 2 and 3). Great Horned Owls (*Bubo virginianus*) were also residents. They roosted and nested in riparian areas but foraged in prairie-dog towns, probably hunting kangaroo rats (*Dipodomys* spp.) and other nocturnal rodents. Great Horned Owls were usually observed at night perching on the fence posts near El Uno and El Aguila.

Shorebirds

We were particularly interested to find Mountain Plovers wintering in the JNCG complex (Tables 2 and 3). Although we observed only three individuals on transects, we observed approximately five groups outside transects in Salto de Ojo and Sector 1. Groups contained approximately 30 individuals, and one group had more than 120. These observations constituted new records for Mountain Plovers in Chihuahua state and are of special interest because the wintering range of this species in Mexico is unknown.

Long-billed Curlews were generally observed in groups and were most abundant in Salto de Ojo and El Cuervo (Table 3). We recorded the highest numbers of this species in early fall (Table 2).

Passerines

Horned Lark was the most abundant species in the JNCG complex (Table 2). Individuals were present year-round but were most abundant in fall and winter, probably because of their migratory habits. They migrate south early in fall and return north before spring. This species occurred at all eight localities (Table 3).

Lark Buntings were the most abundant sparrows in the area (Table 2). They were recorded mainly in fall and had a local distribution; they were present in only two localities, El Cuervo, where they accounted for 66% of all individual birds observed, and Pancho Villa, where they comprised 14% of all individual birds observed (Table 3).

McCown's Longspurs (*Calcarius mccownii*) and Chestnut-collared Longspurs (*C. ornatus*) were most numerous in two localities, El Aguila and El Uno (Table 3). These localities previously formed a single prairie-dog town before they were fragmented by poisoning in 1989. Nevertheless, even in the absence of prairie dogs, these localities had the same vegetation type. The longspurs were probably present throughout the original area covered by the prairie-dog town. Longspurs were observed mainly in fall (Table 2), generally near reservoirs.

Brewer's Sparrows (*Spizella breweri*), Lark Sparrows (*Chondestes grammacus*), and Cassin's Sparrows (*Aimophila cassinii*) were locally distributed in the complex (Tables 2 and 3). Brewer's Sparrows were most abundant in fall and in Sector 1, with just one sighting in each of three other localities. Lark Sparrows were observed only in Pancho Villa and almost exclusively in summer. Cassin's Sparrows were observed in ephedra plants in San Pedro, in very low numbers and only in summer. Vesper Sparrows (*Pooecetes gramineus*) were also observed in low numbers, mainly in San Pedro and El Cuervo and only in early fall (Tables 2 and 3). Grasshopper Sparrows were recorded in spring and summer, mainly in grasslands without prairie dogs, except for two that were observed in El Aguila (Tables 2 and 3). Meadowlarks (*Stur-*

nella spp.) were present in all seasons and in all localities (Tables 2 and 3); their abundance was highest in Pancho Villa, Tierras Prietas, and Salto de Ojo, all of which had mesquite scrub or tall grasses such as toboso.

DISCUSSION

Grasslands in northwestern Chihuahua provide important habitat for birds in general and for grassland birds in particular. In North America, populations of grassland birds have declined more than any other group of birds since the early 1970s (Knopf 1994). This decline is probably related to the massive decrease, fragmentation, and degradation of grasslands across the continent, which has resulted in habitat loss on breeding and wintering grounds as well as a shortage of nest sites (McNicholl 1988, Johnson and Schwartz 1993, Herkert 1994, Knopf 1994). Grasslands in the JNCG region support the largest remaining prairie-dog complex in North America (Ceballos et al. 1993, Miller et al. 1994). This complex has been severely affected since the late 1980s, however. Prairie-dog poisoning, overgrazing, urbanization, and agriculture are the main environmental problems in the region (List 1997). It is important to assess how these factors may be affecting grassland birds in the JNCG complex, especially when considering that many of these species are declining throughout North America.

Many species whose breeding populations are declining were observed in the JNCG complex, generally in low numbers, with the exception of Horned Larks and Lark Buntings. We lack sufficient data to determine causal factors of these small numbers, however. There are at least two possible explanations. First, it is likely that the low bird abundance we observed in 1994–1995 was caused by the prolonged drought that affected the region from 1993 to 1996. Droughts can profoundly affect species diversity and abundance of grassland bird communities (George et al. 1992). It is also possible, however, that the low abundance was the result of the general decline that grassland birds in North America have been experiencing. Most likely, our results reflect natural variation on population numbers related to environmental factors such as food availability and to anthropogenic factors such as habitat degradation and fragmentation. For example, since the late 1980s more than 10,000 ha of prairie-dog towns in the JNCG complex have been converted to croplands and cattle ranches (List 1997; J. Pacheco and G. Ceballos, pers. comm.). Such changes undoubtedly have negative impacts on some species of grassland birds. It is important to develop monitoring schemes for grassland birds in the JNCG region

to properly evaluate long-term temporal and spatial population changes, and to understand these changes in relation to human disturbances.

Preserving the prairie-dog ecosystem will benefit and protect declining bird species as well as other grassland birds and vertebrates that use prairie-dog towns (Agnew et al. 1986, Ceballos et al. 1993, Miller et al. 1994). It is not feasible, of course, to eliminate established human settlements, but it may be feasible to control and limit the number of people and livestock in the JNCG complex.

Some measures that may help decrease the impact of humans and livestock in the area include the following.

1. Establish a protected area or nature reserve. This would prevent further decline of prairie dogs and other species that depend on their ecosystem (Miller et al. 1994). It would also reinforce the law and stop illegal hunting. Additionally, it would prevent future changes in land use and help control the expansion of human settlements. The JNCG region is considered to be a priority area for the conservation of Mexico's biological diversity (SEMARNAP 1996). We are presently working with the Mexican government to have this region recognized as a biosphere reserve.

2. Stop poisoning prairie dogs. Prairie dogs are protected in Mexico, so their poisoning is forbidden by Mexican law. Poisoning affects all vertebrate species that use prairie-dog burrows. Some grassland birds, such as Burrowing Owls, are especially vulnerable to poisoning because they nest in prairie-dog burrows and use them to escape from predators. Changes in habitat heterogeneity and vegetation associated with prairie-dog disappearance may have major impacts on grassland birds (e.g., Miller et al. 1994). Eradication of prairie dogs usually results in increased mesquite scrub cover; prairie dogs inhibit mesquite growth (Koford 1958). In addition, mesquite seed propagation by livestock could have a detrimental effect on the preservation of grasslands and grassland bird species. Finally, poisoning can also affect raptors, such as eagles and Ferruginous Hawks, that feed on prairie dogs.

3. Encourage technical support and training. Overgrazing is a serious problem on the JNCG complex. Livestock grazing affects bird communities by influencing food supply, food availability, plant growth, and plant diversity (McNicholl 1988, Brady et al. 1989). Technical training and support should include improving grazing techniques and herd management in order to reduce the effects of overgrazing in the JNCG complex.

4. Encourage education programs. Establish-

ing an environmental education program would increase awareness of the importance of the prairie-dog ecosystem and its conservation. The main goal should be to promote an integrated view of wildlife conservation and sustainable use of resources. Education programs should be aimed at local residents, ranchers, and school children, as well as at visitors from neighboring towns and cities.

5. Conduct scientific research in the area. There are few data on grassland birds in Mexico. Further research is needed, especially in relation to the habitat requirements, abundance, and distribution of declining, threatened, and endangered species in the JNCG complex and the rest of the country.

The long-term survival of the JNCG complex and its biological diversity clearly depend on establishing and implementing a well-designed conservation strategy. Success will depend on the understanding and cooperation of local people, the scientific community, and the government. The long-term maintenance of one of the largest relatively pristine grasslands in the continent represents a major challenge for Mexico.

ACKNOWLEDGMENTS

We thank the Instituto de Ecología and Universidad Nacional Autónoma de México (DGAPA Project IN213694), CONABIO (project no. BO43), and National Fish and Wildlife Foundation for supporting this project. We also thank M. Eaton and J. Pacheco, who helped with field work, and P. D. Vickery, G. Barreto, B. Howe, C. Melcher, L. Harrington, and an anonymous reviewer for their critical comments on the manuscript.

LITERATURE CITED

AGNEW, W., D. W. URESK, AND R. M. HANSEN. 1986. Flora and fauna associated with prairie dog towns and adjacent ungrazed mixed-grass prairie in western South Dakota. Journal of Range Management 39:135–139.

AMERICAN ORNITHOLOGISTS' UNION. 1983. Check-list of North American birds. 6th ed. American Ornithologists' Union, Washington, D.C.

AMERICAN ORNITHOLOGISTS' UNION. 1991. Thirty-eighth supplement to the American Ornithologists' Union check-list of North American birds. Auk 108: 750–754.

BRADY, W. W., M. R. STROMBERG, E. F. ALDON, C. D. BONHAM, AND S. H. HENRY. 1989. Response of a semidesert grassland to 16 years of rest from grazing. Journal of Range Management 42:284–288.

CEBALLOS, G., E. MELLINK, AND L. R. HANEBURY. 1993. Distribution and conservation status of prairie dogs *Cynomys mexicanus* and *Cynomys ludovicianus* in Mexico. Biological Conservation 63:105–112.

CEBALLOS, G., AND L. MÁRQUEZ. In press. Las aves de México en peligro de extinción. CONABIO, México, D.F., Mexico.

EDWARDS, P. E. 1989. A field guide to the birds of Mexico. E. P. Edwards, Sweet Briar, VA.

EHRLICH, P. R., AND A. H. EHRLICH. 1981. Extinctions. Random House, New York, NY.

GARCÍA, E. 1973. Modificaciones al Sistema de clasificación climatica de Köppen. Instituto de Geografía, Universidad Nacional Autónoma de México, México, D.F., Mexico.

GEORGE, L. T., A. C. FOWLER, R. L. KNIGHT, AND L. C. MCEWEN. 1992. Impact of severe drought on grassland birds in western North Dakota. Ecological Applications 2:275–284.

HERKERT, J. R. 1994. The effect of habitat fragmentation on midwestern grassland bird communities. Ecological Applications 4:461–471.

HOWELL, S. N. G., AND S. WEBB. 1995. A guide to the birds of Mexico and northern Central America. Oxford University Press, Oxford, U.K.

HUTTO, R. L., S. PLETSCHET, AND P. HENDRICKS. 1986. A fixed-radius point count method for nonbreeding and breeding season use. Auk 103:593–602.

JOHNSON, D. H., AND M. D. SCHWARTZ. 1993. The Conservation Reserve Program and grassland birds. Conservation Biology 7:934–937.

KNOPF, F. L. 1994. Avian assemblages on altered grasslands. Studies in Avian Biology 15:247–257.

KOFORD, C. B. 1958. Prairie dogs, whitefaces and blue grama. Wildlife Monograph 3:1–78.

LIST, R. 1997. Ecology of the kit fox (*Vulpes macrotis*) and coyote (*Canis latrans*) and the conservation of the prairie dog ecosystem in northern Mexico. Ph.D. dissertation. Oxford University, Oxford, U.K.

MANZANO-FISCHER, P. 1996. Avian communities associated with prairie dog towns in northwestern Mexico. M.S. thesis. Oxford University, Oxford, U.K.

MARSH, R. E. 1984. Ground squirrels, prairie dogs, and marmots as pests on rangelands. Pp. 195–208 in Proceedings of the conference for organization and practice of vertebrate pest control, 30 August–3 September 1982, Hampshire, U.K. ICI Plant Protection Division, Fernherst, U.K.

MCCULLOUGH, D. R. 1996. Metapopulations and wildlife conservation. Island Press, Washington, D.C.

MCNICHOLL, M. K. 1988. Ecological and human influences on Canadian populations of grassland birds. Pp. 1–25 in P. D. Goriup (editor). Ecology and conservation of grassland birds. ICBP Technical Publication no. 7. International Council for Bird Preservation, Cambridge, U.K.

MENGEL, R. M. 1970. The North American Central Plains as an isolating agent in bird speciation. Pp. 280–340 in W. Dort and J. K. Jones (editors). Pleistocene and recent environments of the central Great Plains. University of Kansas Press, Lawrence, KS.

MERRIAM, C. H. 1902. The prairie dog of the Great Plains. Pp. 257–270 in Yearbook of the U.S. Department of Agriculture 1901 [no editor]. U.S. Government Printing Office, Washington, D.C.

MILLER, B., G. CEBALLOS, AND R. READING. 1994. The prairie dog and biotic diversity. Conservation Biology 8:677–681.

MOEHRENSCHALGER, A., AND R. LIST. 1996. Comparative ecology of North American foxes: conservation through collaboration. Pp. 22–28 in D. W. MacDonald and F. H. Tattersall (editors). The Wildcru review. Wildlife Conservation Research Unit, Oxford, U.K.

MOUNTFORT, G. 1988. Rare birds of the world. Penguin Books, London, U.K.

NATIONAL GEOGRAPHIC SOCIETY. 1983. Field guide to the birds of North America. National Geographic Society, Washington, D.C.

NELSON, E. W. 1919. Annual report of chief, Bureau of Biological Survey. Department of Agriculture, U.S. Government, Washington, D.C.

PETERSON, A. T., AND M. B. ROBBINS. 1999. A preliminary assessment of distributions and conservation needs of grassland birds in Mexico. Studies in Avian Biology 19:258–262.

RZEDOWSKY, J. 1981. Vegetación de Mexico. Limusa, México, D.F., Mexico.

ROBBINS, C. S., B. BRUUN, AND H. S. ZIM. 1983. A guide to the identification of the birds of North America. Golden Press, New York, NY.

ROBINSON, S. K., F. R. THOMPSON III, T. M. DONOVAN, D. R. WHITEHEAD, AND J. FAABORG. 1995. Regional forest fragmentation and the nesting success of migratory birds. Science 267:1987–1990.

SEDESOL. 1994. Norma Oficial Mexicana NOM-059-ECOL-1994, que determina las especies y subespecies de flora y fauna silvestre terrestres y acuáticas en peligro de extinción, amenazadas, raras y las sujetas a protección especial, y que establece especificaciones para su protección. Diario Oficial de la Federación 438:2–60.

SEMARNAP. 1996. Programa de áreas naturales protegidas de México 1995–2000. SEMARNAP, México, D.F., Mexico.

SHELFORD, V. E. 1963. The ecology of North America. University of Illinois Press, Urbana, IL.

U.S. FISH AND WILDLIFE SERVICE. 1996a. Endangered and threatened wildlife and plants. 50 CFR 17.11 and 17.12; 31 October 1995. U.S. Government Printing Office, Washington, D.C.

U.S. FISH AND WILDLIFE SERVICE. 1996b. Migratory nongame birds of management concern in the United States: the 1996 list. Office of Migratory Bird Management, Arlington, VA.

WILCOVE, D. S., C. H. McLELLAN, AND A. P. DOBSON. 1986. Habitat fragmentation in the temperate zone. Pp. 237–256 in M. E. Soulé (editor). Conservation biology: the science of scarcity and diversity. Sinauer, Sunderland, MA.

APPENDIX.   SPECIES OBSERVED IN THE GRASSLANDS OF THE JANOS-NUEVO CASAS GRANDES PRAIRIE-DOG COMPLEX, CHIHUAHUA, MEXICO, 1994–1995

Species	Seasonality	Conservation status		
		Mexico	US	Canada
Turkey Vulture (*Cathartes aura*)	Re			
Golden Eagle (*Aquila chrysaetos*)	Re	En		
Bald Eagle (*Haliaeetus leucocephalus*)	Wi	En	Th	
Northern Harrier (*Circus cyaneus*)	Re	Th	De	
*Red-tailed Hawk (*Buteo jamaicensis*)	Re			
Swainson's Hawk (*B. swainsoni*)	Su			
Ferruginous Hawk (*B. regalis*)	Wi		De	Th
Zone-tailed Hawk (*B. albonotatus*)	Su			
*Osprey (*Pandion haliaetus*)	Tr			
American Kestrel (*Falco sparverius*)	Re			
*Merlin (*F. columbarius*)	Wi	Th		
Prairie Falcon (*F. mexicanus*)	Re	Th		
*Peregrine Falcon (*F. peregrinus*)	Re	Th		
Scaled Quail (*Callipepla squamata*)	Re			
Killdeer (*Charadrius vociferus*)	Re			
Mountain Plover (*C. montanus*)	Wi	Th	De	
*Whimbrel (*Numenius phaeopus*)	Tr			
Long-billed Curlew (*N. americanus*)	Re		De	
Mourning Dove (*Zenaida macroura*)	Re			
*Inca Dove (*Columbina inca*)	Re			
Greater Roadrunner (*Geococcyx californianus*)	Re			
*Short-eared Owl (*Asio flammeus*)	Tr	Th		
*Great Horned Owl (*Bubo virginianus*)	Re	Th		
Burrowing Owl (*Athene cunicularia*)	Re	Th	De	Th
*Lesser Nighthawk (*Chordeiles acutipennis*)	Su			
*White-throated Swift (*Aeronautes saxatalis*)	Re			
*Belted Kingfisher (*Ceryle alcyon*)	Wi			
Ladder-backed Woodpecker (*Picoides scalaris*)	Re			
Western Kingbird (*Tyrannus verticalis*)	Su			
Ash-throated Flycatcher (*Myiarchus cinerascens*)	Su			
Say's Phoebe (*Sayornis saya*)	Re			
Horned Lark (*Eremophila alpestris*)	Re		De	

APPENDIX.   CONTINUED

Species	Seasonality	Conservation status		
		Mexico	US	Canada
*Tree Swallow (*Tachycineta bicolor*)	Tr			
Violet-green Swallow (*T. thalassina*)	Su			
*Bank Swallow (*Riparia riparia*)	Tr			
*Northern Rough-winged Swallow (*Stelgidopteryx serripennis*)	Su			
*Cliff Swallow (*Hirundo pyrrhonota*)	Su			
Barn Swallow (*H. rustica*)	Su			
Chihuahuan Raven (*Corvus cryptoleucus*)	Re			
Cactus Wren (*Campylorhynchus brunneicapillus*)	Re			
*Rock Wren (*Salpinctes obsoletus*)	Re			
Eastern Bluebird (*Sialia sialis*)	Re			
Loggerhead Shrike (*Lanius ludovicianus*)	Re		De	Th
Northern Mockingbird (*Mimus polyglottos*)	Re			
Curved-billed Thrasher (*Toxostoma curvirostre*)	Re			
*Sprague's Pipit (*Anthus spragueii*)	Wi		De	
*Lucy's Warbler (*Vermivora luciae*)	Su	Th	De	
Yellow-rumped Warbler (*Dendroica coronata*)	Wi			
Blue Grosbeak (*Guiraca caerulea*)	Su			
Grasshopper Sparrow (*Ammodramus savannarum*)	Wi		De	De
*Baird's Sparrow (*A. bairdii*)	Wi		De	De
Vesper Sparrow (*Pooecetes gramineus*)	Wi		De	
*Savannah Sparrow (*Passerculus sandwichensis*)	Wi		De	
Song Sparrow (*Melospiza melodia*)	Wi			
Lark Sparrow (*Chondestes grammacus*)	Re		De	
Black-throated Sparrow (*Amphispiza bilineata*)	Re		De	
Cassin's Sparrow (*Aimophila cassinii*)	Re		De	
*Chipping Sparrow (*Spizella passerina*)	Wi			
Brewer's Sparrow (*S. breweri*)	Wi		De	
*Dark-eyed Junco (*Junco hyemalis*)	Wi			
McCown's Longspur (*Calcarius mccownii*)	Wi		De	
*Chestnut-collared Longspur (*C. ornatus*)	Wi		De	
Lark Bunting (*Calamospiza melanocorys*)	Re		De	
Eastern Meadowlark (*Sturnella magna*)	Re		De	
Western Meadowlark (*S. neglecta*)	Re		De	De
Yellow-headed Blackbird (*Xanthocephalus xanthocephalus*)	Re			
Red-winged Blackbird (*Agelaius phoeniceus*)	Re			
Northern Oriole (*Icterus galbula*)	Su			
Brown-headed Cowbird (*Molothrus ater*)	Re			
*Pine Siskin (*Carduelis pinus*)	Wi			
House Finch (*Carpodacus mexicanus*)	Re			

Note: Seasonality: Re = resident, Wi = winter migrant, Su = summer migrant, Tr = transient. Conservation Status: De = declining, Th = Threatened, En = Endangered.

* Species not observed on transects.

Studies in Avian Biology No. 19:272–280, 1999.

SEASONAL MOVEMENTS AND CONSERVATION OF SEEDEATERS OF THE GENUS *SPOROPHILA* IN SOUTH AMERICA

José Maria Cardoso da Silva

Abstract. Small seed-eating finches of the genus *Sporophila,* commonly called seedeaters, are among the most characteristic elements of South America's grassland avifauna. Twenty-three species of *Sporophila* seedeaters were classified into three groups according to their seasonal movements. Fourteen species make long-distance movements between at least two major ecological regions in South America, four species make intermediate to long-distance movements within a single ecological region, and five species make short-distance movements between adjacent habitats. The grasslands in the Cerrado region seem to be the most important wintering sites for most of the long-distance migrant *Sporophila.* Mapping the ranges of all threatened or near-threatened *Sporophila* species identified seven critical areas between southern coastal Colombia and southernmost Brazil. Creating reserves in these seven areas would protect at least one population of 23 *Sporophila* species. Mapping the ranges of all species and well-marked subspecies with restricted ranges (350,000 square kilometers or less) identified nine critical areas (five of which were also identified by mapping threatened or near-threatened species) between northern South America and southernmost Brazil. Creating reserves in these nine areas would protect populations of 29 species or well-defined subspecies of *Sporophila.* The conservation of South American grasslands needs urgent action. The areas identified here are important grassland habitats that should be priority areas for organizations and agencies interested in grassland conservation.

LOS MOVIMIENTOS ESTACIONALES Y LA CONSERVACIÓN DE GRANÍVOROS DEL GÉNERO *SPOROPHILA* EN AMÉRICA DEL SUR

Sinopsis. Entre los elementos más característicos de la avifauna de pastizal de América del Sur se encuentran pequeños fringílidos del género *Sporophila* que se alimentan de semillas, llamados comúnmente granívoros. Se clasificaron veintitrés especies de granívoros *Sporophila* en tres grupos según sus movimientos estacionales. Catorce especies realizan movimientos de larga distancia entre, al menos, dos grandes regiones ecológicas en América del Sur; cuatro especies realizan movimientos de distancia media a larga dentro de una sola región ecológica; por último, cinco especies hacen movimientos de corta distancia entre hábitats adyacentes. Los pastizales en la región Cerrado parecen ser los sitios invernales más importantes para la mayoría de los *Sporophila* que migran largas distancias. La delineación de mapas de las extensiones de todas las especies *Sporophila* amenazadas o casi amenazadas identificó siete áreas críticas entre la costa sur de Colombia y el sur de Brasil. La creación de reservas en estas siete áreas protegería por lo menos una población de cada una de las 23 especies de *Sporophila.* La delineación de mapas de las extensiones de todas las especies y subespecies bien definidas con extensiones limitadas (350.000 kilómetros cuadrados o menos) identificó nueve áreas críticas (cinco de las cuales se identificaron también haciendo mapas de las especies amenazadas o casi amenazadas) entre el norte de América del Sur y el sur de Brasil. La creación de reservas en estas nueve áreas protegería poblaciones de 29 especies o subespecies bien definidas de *Sporophila.* La conservación de pastizales sudamericanos requiere medidas inmediatas. Las áreas aquí identificadas son importantes hábitats de pastizal que deberían ser áreas prioritarias para las entidades y organizaciones interesadas en la conservación de pastizales.

Key Words: Cerrado; conservation; grassland birds; seedeaters; *Sporophila.*

Grasslands are among South America's most threatened environments because of the ever-growing expansion of human activities. Large areas of grasslands in the continent have been converted to agricultural fields or pastures. This has led to an impoverished native fauna and flora and large-scale declines in the extent of these ecosystems. Because conservation efforts in South America are directed mainly at the species-rich tropical forests (e.g., Rylands 1991), few measures have been taken to conserve South American grasslands and their biota (Ratter 1995; Silva 1995a, 1996).

In general, knowledge about South American grassland birds is limited. There is little infor-mation about range limits, geographic variation, migratory patterns, and population dynamics of most species. For some species (e.g., Blue-eyed Ground Dove [*Columbina cyanopis*], White-winged Nightjar [*Caprimulgus candicans*], and Gray-backed Tachuri [*Polystictus superciliaris*]), even basic data about their natural history are lacking.

Among the most characteristic elements of the grassland avifauna in South America are the small (8–15 g) seed-eating finches of the genus *Sporophila* (Family Emberizidae), commonly called seedeaters. This genus includes about 30 species that range from the southwestern United States to central Argentina (Paynter 1970,

Ridgely and Tudor 1989, Sibley and Monroe 1990, Ouellet 1992). *Sporophila* species are associated primarily with grasslands, but a few species also inhabit medium and upper levels of tall tropical forests (Sick 1985). Seedeaters feed mostly on seeds, but several species also include small fruits and even insects in their diet, at least seasonally (Sick 1985; J. M. Silva, pers. obs.).

Because seedeaters occur in almost all major grassland regions of South America and appear to be sensitive to human pressures on their habitat, they can be a useful indicator group to assess and monitor the magnitude and distribution of the major threats to South American grassland avifaunas. For instance, in the most recent edition of the "red data" book for American birds (Collar et al. 1992), eight and three *Sporophila* species were classified as threatened and near threatened, respectively.

One of the reasons why so many *Sporophila* species make intermediate to long-distance seasonal movements is that they are stem-gleaner specialists, i.e., they feed primarily on seeds still borne on the stalks (Remsen and Hunn 1979). Because of this behavior, when areas no longer have grasses producing appropriate seeds on stalks, most *Sporophila* species must look for food elsewhere, resulting in seasonal changes in their distributions. In this regard, stem-gleaner specialists contrast with other granivorous species that are able to feed on fallen seeds on the ground, as these species remain in their breeding areas until the stock of fallen seeds is consumed. The few long-term studies that have examined seasonality of grassland birds in South America (Thomas 1979, Cintra and Yamashita 1990) support the hypothesis that feeding behavior may predict whether or not a given granivorous species will migrate during periods when seed production in its breeding area decreases. In the Venezuelan llanos, Thomas (1979) found that some well-known granivorous species that feed on seeds on the ground (e.g., Grassland Sparrow [*Ammodramus humeralis*], Saffron Finch [*Sicalis flaveola*]) were year-round residents, whereas some *Sporophila* species (Lesson's Seedeater [*S. bouvronides*] and Ruddy-breasted Seedeater [*S. minuta*]) were absent for several months. Similarly, in the Pantanal of Poconé in Mato Grosso, Brazil, Cintra and Yamashita (1990) found that ground-feeding finches (e.g., Grassland Sparrow, Saffron Finch, Rufous-collared Sparrow [*Zonotrichia capensis*]) were present year-round whereas all six *Sporophila* species showed marked seasonal movements.

The association between *Sporophila* seedeaters and the native grasses they consume is still poorly understood and deserves investigation. Large areas of natural grasslands in South America have been replaced by artificial pastures, which means native grasses have been replaced by exotic, mostly African, grasses. Although a few *Sporophila* species (e.g., Double-collared Seedeater [*S. caerulescens*]) may adjust their diets to include exotic grass species, it is likely that several other species may suffer population reductions because of the large-scale replacement of native grass species (Sick 1985). Replacing native grasses with exotics may also have a serious impact on the seasonal movements of several *Sporophila* species, as we now know that these movements (either regional or long-distance) are closely tied to the seed production of some critically important grass species (Remsen and Hunn 1979, Silva 1994). To evaluate such impacts, detailed information about the diet of most *Sporophila* species is urgently needed. For instance, a list of grass species and the seedeaters that consume them would help contribute to a database that could be used to monitor populations of *Sporophila* seedeaters and their food sources.

The wintering areas of *Sporophila* seedeaters that make long-distance migrations are incompletely known, and much more study is necessary to accurately determine these ranges. Several species exhibit remarkable seasonal movements in response to fluctuations in food availability on their breeding grounds (Remsen and Hunn 1979, Sick 1985, Ridgely and Tudor 1989). Data on the nature of these movements, however, are scarce.

It is possible that the wintering areas currently mapped in some reference books (e.g., Ridgely and Tudor 1989) are underestimated. For example, Remsen and Hunn (1979) demonstrated how knowledge of wintering distributions of a *Sporophila* seedeater changed dramatically when additional distribution data became available. They recorded migrant Double-collared Seedeaters in southern Colombia, several hundred kilometers north of the species' previously known range. More recently, Dark-throated Seedeater (*S. ruficollis*), a species known to winter in the Cerrado region and northern Bolivia (Ridgely and Tudor 1989), was recorded in Humaitá (07°31′ S, 63°02′ W), Amazonas, Brazil, in upland savannas along the Rio Madeira. Specimens are housed at the Museu Paraense Emílio Goeldi (MPEG) in Belém, Pará, Brazil: one male (MPEG 49606, collected 14 October 1991) and one female (MPEG 49607, collected 15 October 1991).

This paper has two main objectives: (1) to identify, in a preliminary fashion, the general patterns of seasonal movements exhibited by South American *Sporophila* seedeaters and (2) to analyze the distribution of two sets of *Spo-*

TABLE 1. TWENTY-THREE SPECIES OF SOUTH AMERICAN *Sporophila* SEEDEATERS CLASSIFIED ACCORDING TO THEIR SEASONAL MOVEMENTS

Common name	Species	References[a]
Local movements		
Gray Seedeater	*intermedia*	10
Plumbeous Seedeater	*plumbea*	10
Variable Seedeater	*americana*	10
Rusty-collared Seedeater	*collaris*	10
White-bellied Seedeater	*leucoptera*	10
Regional movements		
Buffy-fronted Seedeater	*frontalis*	2, 7
Temminck's Seedeater	*falcirostris*	2, 7
Slate-colored Seedeater	*schistacea*	4
Ruddy-breasted Seedeater	*minuta*	10
Long-distance movements		
Lined Seedeater	*lineola*	8
Lesson's Seedeater	*bouvronides*	5, 10
Yellow-bellied Seedeater	*nigricollis*	1
Double-collared Seedeater	*caerulescens*	4
Capped Seedeater	*bouvreuil*	3, 10
Tawny-bellied Seedeater	*hypoxantha*	6, 7
Rufous-rumped Seedeater	*hypochroma*	6, 10
Dark-throated Seedeater	*ruficollis*	7
Marsh Seedeater	*palustris*	5
Chestnut-bellied Seedeater	*castaneiventris*	7
Chestnut Seedeater	*cinnamomea*	5, 7
Black-bellied Seedeater	*melanogaster*	6, 7
White-throated Seedeater	*albogularis*	9
Narosky's Seedeater	*zelichi*	11

Note: For some species (e.g., Yellow-bellied Seedeater [*S. nigricollis*] or Capped Seedeater [*S. bouvreuil*]), one population may make shorter, regional movements whereas others may make long-distance movements.
[a] 1 = Antas and Cavalcanti 1988; 2 = Collar et al. 1992; 3 = Chesser 1994; 4 = Hilty and Brown 1986; 5 = Ridgely and Tudor 1989; 6 = Rosário 1996; 7 = Sick 1985; 8 = Silva 1995a; 9 = Silva 1995b; 10 = J. M. Silva, pers. obs.; 11 = Stotz et al. 1996.

rophila seedeaters: species regarded as threatened or near threatened and species with restricted ranges. This analysis should help identify priority areas for conserving *Sporophila* seedeaters and other grassland birds, and their habitats, in South America.

METHODS

SEASONAL MOVEMENTS

To classify the movements of *Sporophila* seedeaters, I used data I collected during several years of field work (1982–1995) in Brazil as well as a literature survey (Remsen and Hunn 1979; Sick 1985; Hilty and Brown 1986; Antas and Cavalcanti 1988; Ridgely and Tudor 1989; Fjeldså and Krabbe 1990; Collar et al. 1992; Chesser 1994; Silva 1995a, b; Rosário 1996; Stotz et al. 1996). I identified three major types of movements. The first category includes species that make only local movements, which I defined as short-distance movements (less than a few kilometers) between two or more adjacent habitats in response to seasonal changes. For example, Variable Seedeater (*S. americana*) moves from várzea grasslands to open várzea forests during the seasonal rising of the water level of the Amazon River (J. M. Silva, pers. obs.). The second category includes species that make regional,

intermediate movements (100–1,000 km) within a single large South American ecological region. Examples of this category include Buffy-fronted Seedeater (*S. frontalis*) and Temminck's Seedeater (*S. falcirostris*), which move within the Atlantic Forest region following the seeding of bamboos (primarily *Merostachys* spp. and *Chusquea* spp.; Sick 1985). The third category includes species that make long-distance seasonal movements (>1,000 km) between at least two major ecological regions in South America. For example, Lined Seedeater (*S. lineola*), a species that has two distinct populations breeding in northeastern and southeastern South America, moves north to the Llanos and Amazonia, respectively, during the austral fall and winter (Silva 1994).

CONSERVATION PRIORITIES

I used two methods to identify areas critical to the conservation of *Sporophila* seedeaters in South America. The first method consisted of mapping the breeding ranges of all *Sporophila* species regarded as threatened or near threatened in the "red data" book of American birds (Collar et al. 1992) and then determining where species' distributions overlapped. The second method consisted of mapping the breeding ranges of all species or well-marked subspecies with a restricted range. I considered well-marked subspecies to

TABLE 2. WINTERING AREAS OF LONG-DISTANCE MIGRANT *Sporophila* SEEDEATERS IN SOUTH AMERICA

Common name	Species	Wintering areas
Lined Seedeater	*lineola*	
Caatinga population		Llanos, savannas of northern South America
southern population		Amazonian várzea grasslands
Lesson's Seedeater	*bouvronides*	Amazonian várzea grasslands
Yellow-bellied Seedeater	*nigricollis*	Cerrado region
Double-collared Seedeater	*caerulescens*	Cerrado region
Capped Seedeater	*bouvreuil*	Cerrado region
Tawny-bellied Seedeater	*hypoxantha*	Cerrado region
Rufous-rumped Seedeater	*hypochroma*	Cerrado region, central Brazil
Dark-throated Seedeater	*ruficollis*	Cerrado region, Humaitá
Marsh Seedeater	*palustris*	Cerrado region
Chestnut-bellied Seedeater	*castaneiventris*	Cerrado region
Chestnut Seedeater	*cinnamomea*	Cerrado region
Black-bellied Seedeater	*melanogaster*	Cerrado region
White-throated Seedeater	*albogularis*	Cerrado region
Narosky's Seedeater	*zelichi*	unknown

be any populations that are distinct from other populations of the same species by discrete morphological characters. I made determinations of well-marked taxa by studying museum specimens from the American Museum of Natural History (United States), Museu de Zoologia da Universidade de São Paulo (Brazil), Museu Paraense Emílio Goeldi (Brazil), and Zoological Museum of the University of Copenhagen (Denmark). These subspecies could be regarded as different species under the phylogenetic species concept (Cracraft 1983, McKitrick and Zink 1988). I defined a restricted range as 350,000 km² or smaller.

High-priority areas for the conservation of *Sporophila* seedeaters were determined to be areas that included at least one population of all threatened or near-threatened species (in the first method) or all restricted-range taxa (in the second method). For both methods, I assumed that the taxa whose ranges were mapped were the most likely to go extinct if current trends in habitat modification in South America continue.

RESULTS

PATTERNS OF SEASONAL MOVEMENTS

Based on a literature survey and my own studies, I gathered data about the seasonal movements of 23 species of South American *Sporophila* seedeaters (Table 1). Fourteen species make long-distance movements, five make local movements, and four make regional movements (Table 1).

Eleven of the 14 species that make long-distance movements are part of a larger migration system in South America known as neotropical austral migration, a migration from southern South America to central or northern South America during the austral fall and winter (Table 2; Zimmer 1938, Sick 1983, Chesser 1994, Hayes 1995). An additional three species, al-

TABLE 3. BREEDING DISTRIBUTIONS OF SOUTH AMERICAN *Sporophila* SEEDEATERS REGARDED AS THREATENED OR NEAR THREATENED BY COLLAR ET AL. 1992

Common name	Species	Category[a]	Area[b]						
			NAR	CB	URP	ARA	PAR	SC	ERC
Buffy-fronted Seedeater	*frontalis*	T					√	√	
Temminck's Seedeater	*falcirostris*	T					√		
Hooded Seedeater	*melanops*	T				√			
Black-and-tawny Seedeater	*nigrorufa*	T		√	√				
Tumaco Seedeater	*insulata*	T	√						
Rufous-rumped Seedeater	*hypochroma*	T		√	√		√		√
Dark-throated Seedeater	*ruficollis*	NT	√	√	√				√
Marsh Seedeater	*palustris*	T							√
Chestnut Seedeater	*cinnamomea*	NT							√
Black-bellied Seedeater	*melanogaster*	NT					√		
Narosky's Seedeater	*zelichi*	T							√

[a] T = threatened, NT = near threatened.
[b] NAR = Nariño, CB = central Bolivia, URP = upper Rio Paraguay, ARA = Araguaia, PAR = upper Rio Paraná, SC = Santa Catarina, ERC = Entre Ríos-Corrientes.

STUDIES IN AVIAN BIOLOGY

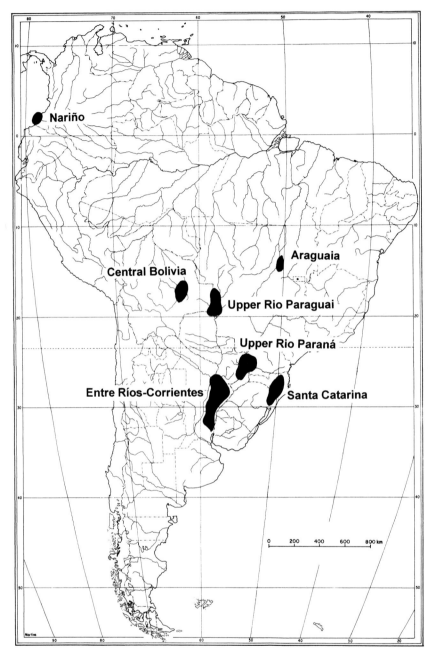

FIGURE 1. Priority areas for conservation of *Sporophila* seedeaters in South America. Areas were identified by mapping the ranges of 11 species regarded as threatened or near threatened by Collar et al. 1992.

though long-distance migrants, are not austral migrants and thus do not fit this migration pattern. Lesson's Seedeater breeds in the Llanos and other grasslands of northern South America between June and December (Thomas 1979) and then moves south to upper and central Amazonia (Ridgely and Tudor 1989; J. M. Silva, unpubl. data); Chestnut-bellied Seedeater (*S. castaneiventris*) breeds mostly in Amazonia but has been recorded in the Cerrado region, on the grasslands along the Rio São Francisco (Sick 1985; but see comments in Ridgely and Tudor 1989);

TABLE 4.   BREEDING DISTRIBUTION OF *Sporophila* SEEDEATERS WITH RESTRICTED RANGES IN SOUTH AMERICA

Common name	Species	Area[a]								
		NSA	NAR	PC	CB	ARA	RJ	SP	SC	ER
Buffy-fronted Seedeater	*frontalis*						√	√	√	
Temminck's Seedeater	*falcirostris*						√	√		
Lesson's Seedeater	*bouvronides*	√								
Hooded Seedeater	*melanops*					√				
White-bellied Seedeater	*leucoptera bicolor*				√					
Parrot-billed Seedeater	*peruviana*			√						
Drab Seedeater	*simplex*			√						
Black-and-tawny Seedeater	*nigrorufa*				√					
Capped Seedeater	*bouvreuil crypta*						√			
Capped Seedeater	*bouvreuil saturata*							√		
Tumaco Seedeater	*insulata*		√							
Marsh Seedeater	*palustris*									√
Chestnut Seedeater	*cinnamomea*									√
Black-bellied Seedeater	*melanogaster*								√	
Chestnut-throated Seedeater	*telasco*	√	√							
Narosky's Seedeater	*zelichi*									√

[a] NSA = northern South America, NAR = Nariño, PC = Peruvian coast, CB = central Bolivia, ARA = Araguaia, RJ = Rio de Janeiro, SP = São Paulo, SC = Santa Catarina, ERC = Entre Ríos-Corrientes.

and White-throated Seedeater (*S. albogularis*) breeds in the Caatinga and possibly moves south to the Cerrado (Silva 1995b).

Even though the wintering distributions of several *Sporophila* species are poorly known, it is clear that grasslands in the Cerrado region are the most important wintering sites for populations of at least 10 species (Table 2). Other important sites for migrant *Sporophila* include Amazonian várzea grasslands, central Bolivian grasslands, some Amazonian upland savannas (e.g., Humaitá, Brazil), and the Llanos (Table 2).

CONSERVATION PRIORITIES FOR *SPOROPHILA* SPECIES

I mapped the ranges of 11 *Sporophila* species regarded as threatened or near threatened (Table 3). Seven critical grassland areas that include at least one population of each of these species were identified: Nariño (defined here as the western portion of the Department of Nariño in southern Colombia and the islands of Tumaco and Boca Grande), central Bolivia, the upper Rio Paraguay, Araguaia (defined as the grasslands along the Rio Araguaia, south of Bananal Island and on the border between the Brazilian states of Mato Grosso and Goiás), the upper Rio Paraná (a region including the province of Misiones in Argentina, southeastern Paraguay, and the western portion of the Brazilian state of Paraná), Santa Catarina (defined as southern Santa Catarina and northern Rio Grande do Sul states, Brazil), and Entre Ríos-Corrientes (the vast wet grassland region located in the Argentine provinces of Entre Ríos and Corrientes, between the Rios Paraguay and Uruguay; Fig. 1). If reserves

are created in these seven areas, populations of 23 *Sporophila* species would be protected. The seven species (Gray Seedeater [*S. intermedia*], Lesson's Seedeater, Black-and-white Seedeater [*S. luctuosa*], White-throated Seedeater, Parrot-billed Seedeater [*S. peruviana*], Drab Seedeater [*S. simplex*], and Chestnut-bellied Seedeater) that would not be protected in these reserves have adapted successfully to anthropogenic modifications in their habitats and are not likely to become threatened in the future (Stotz et al. 1996).

I regarded 16 species or well-marked subspecies of *Sporophila* seedeaters as having restricted ranges (Table 4). Based on the range overlaps of these 16 taxa, I identified 9 priority areas for conservation of South American *Sporophila* seedeaters: northern South America, Nariño, the Peruvian coast, central Bolivia, Araguaia, Rio de Janeiro (defined here as the Atlantic Forest remnants and natural grasslands around the city of Rio de Janeiro and neighboring towns), São Paulo (the Atlantic Forest remnants and natural grasslands around the city of São Paulo and neighboring towns), Santa Catarina, and Entre Ríos-Corrientes (Fig. 2). If reserves are created in these areas, populations of 29 species (96.6%) of *Sporophila* seedeaters would be protected. The only species that would not be protected, White-throated Seedeater, still is quite common in northeastern Brazil and seems to be expanding its range in other regions (J. M. Silva, pers. obs.)

DISCUSSION

Two major problems affect populations of several South American *Sporophila* species:

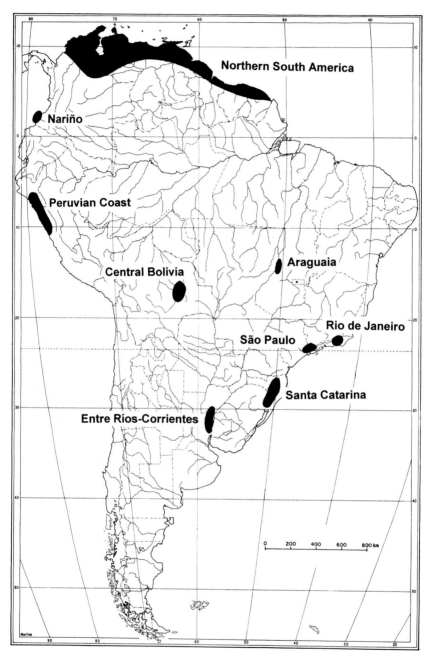

FIGURE 2.   Priority areas for conservation of *Sporophila* seedeaters in South America. Areas were identified by mapping the ranges of 16 species or well-marked subspecies with restricted ranges ($\leq$ 350,000 km²).

widespread capture for the cagebird trade and loss of habitat (Sick 1985, Collar et al. 1992, Willis and Oniki 1993). Although the first problem might be solved by education and enforcement of existing wildlife-protection laws, the second can be addressed only by conserving critical areas of natural grassland ecosystems.

The results of the two methods I used to identify priority areas for the conservation of *Sporophila* seedeaters were only partially congruent. Both methods identified five of the same areas: Nariño, central Bolivia, Araguaia, Santa Catarina, and Entre Ríos-Corrientes. Areas identified by only one method were northern South America, the Peruvian Coast, the upper Rio Paraguay, the upper Rio Paraná, Rio de Janeiro, and São Paulo. The method that focused on threatened and near-threatened species did not identify as many areas or protect as many species as the method based on restricted-range taxa. Many more *Sporophila* species will be protected if conservation areas are determined by the restricted-range method.

The International Council for Bird Preservation (ICBP; 1992) identified several endemic bird areas (EBAs) worldwide by mapping all species that had ranges of 50,000 km^2 or smaller. Compared with ICBP's study, eight areas identified in this study showed high spatial congruence with previously recognized EBAs: northern South America, Nariño, the Peruvian coast, the upper Rio Paraná, Rio de Janeiro, São Paulo, Santa Catarina, and Entre Ríos-Corrientes. Areas that were not identified by the ICBP study include central Bolivia, Araguaia, and the upper Rio Paraguay.

The methods I used in this study did not take into account several important factors one might use when evaluating and selecting priority areas for conservation, such as levels of habitat modification, population trends of species, and viability of reserves. Therefore, the priority areas I have identified must be viewed as initial recommendations where government agencies and private organizations and institutions can direct their conservation efforts to protect South American grasslands. The need for conservation action is critical because human pressure has been so intense and major environmental modifications have already occurred in some of these areas, notably Entre Ríos-Corrientes, Nariño, the Peruvian coast, Santa Catarina, Rio de Janeiro, and São Paulo.

The methods used in this study and in other efforts (e.g., ICBP 1992) to identify priority conservation areas have not accounted for the wintering areas of migratory birds. Unfortunately, the winter distributions of most South American birds, including several *Sporophila* seedeaters, are not adequately known (Marantz and Remsen 1991). Despite this limitation, my analysis has identified some critical areas that are clearly important for migratory *Sporophila* seedeaters (Table 2). Among these areas, the most important is the Cerrado region, the largest savanna region in South America, which harbors a rich flora and fauna (Silva 1996). Unfortunately, the Cerrado is undergoing rapid environmental degradation, encouraged by the Brazilian government. Approximately 50% of the region has been converted to modern agricultural use, either as "improved" pastures planted with exotic grasses (*Brachiaria, Hyparrhenia rufa*, and *Panicum*

maximum) or as arable land, primarily for the cultivation of annual crops such as soybeans, maize, rice, and cassava (Ratter 1995). To date, only 0.7% of the Cerrado is protected in national parks or ecological stations (Silva 1996). Because conserving wintering areas is as important for migratory birds as is protecting breeding areas (Terborgh 1980, Basili and Temple 1999), creating new reserves in the Cerrado must be regarded as a leading conservation priority for several migratory species of *Sporophila* seedeaters, as well as for other South American grassland birds.

ACKNOWLEDGMENTS

I thank R. B. Cavalcanti, E. Bucher, and P. D. Vickery for suggesting that I present this paper at the Ecology and Conservation of Grassland Birds Conference in Tulsa, Oklahoma, in 1995. I thank D. C. Oren for his invaluable comments on the first draft of the manuscript. J. Fjeldså discussed with me several issues about conservation of South American grasslands. My studies have been supported by the Conselho Brasileiro de Desenvolvimento Científico e Tecnológico, Brasília, Brazil. Field work and collection studies were supported by the National Geographic Society (grant no. 4964-93), Danish Natural Science Research Council (grant j. nr. 11-0390), World Wildlife Fund-US, Frank M. Chapman Memorial Fund, John D. and Catherine T. MacArthur Foundation, Museu Paraense Emílio Goeldi, and Universidade de Brasília.

LITERATURE CITED

ANTAS, P. T. Z., AND R. B. CAVALCANTI. 1988. Aves comuns do Planalto Central. Universidade de Brasília, Brasília, Brazil.

BASILI, G. D., AND S. A. TEMPLE. 1999. Winter ecology, behavior, and conservation needs of Dickcissels in Venezuela. Studies in Avian Biology 19:289–299.

CHESSER, R. T. 1994. Migration in South America: an overview of the austral system. Bird Conservation International 4:91–107.

CINTRA, R., AND C. YAMASHITA. 1990. Habitats, abundância e ocorrência das espécies de aves do Pantanal de Poconé, Mato Grosso, Brasil. Papéis Avulsos de Zoologia 37:1–21.

COLLAR, N. J., L. P. GONZAGA, N. KRABBE, A. MADROÑO NIETO, L. G. NARANJO, T. A. PARKER III, AND D. C. WEGE. 1992. Threatened birds of the Americas: the ICBP/IUCN red data book. International Council for Bird Preservation. 3d ed. Cambridge, U.K.

CRACRAFT, J. 1983. Species concepts and speciation analysis. Current Ornithology 1:159–187.

FJELDSÅ, J., AND N. KRABBE. 1990. Birds of the high Andes. Zoological Museum, University of Copenhagen, Copenhagen, and Apollo Books, Svendborg, Denmark.

HAYES, F. E. 1995. Definitions for migrant birds: what is a neotropical migrant? Auk 112:521–523.

HILTY, S. L., AND W. L. BROWN. 1986. A guide to the birds of Colombia. Princeton University Press, Princeton, NJ.

INTERNATIONAL COUNCIL FOR BIRD PRESERVATION.

1992. Putting biodiversity on the map: priority areas for global conservation. International Council for Bird Preservation, Cambridge, U.K.

MARANTZ, C. A., AND J. V. REMSEN, JR. 1991. Seasonal distribution of the Slaty Elaenia, a little-known austral migrant of South America. Journal of Field Ornithology 62:162–172.

MCKITRICK, M., AND R. ZINK. 1988. Species concepts in ornithology. Condor 90:1–14.

OUELLET, H. 1992. Speciation, zoogeography and taxonomic problems in the neotropical genus *Sporophila* (Aves: Emberizinae). Bulletin of the British Ornithological Club Centenary Suppl. 112A:225–235.

PAYNTER, R. A., JR. 1970. Emberizinae. Pp. 1–214 *in* R. A. Paynter, Jr., and R. W. Storer (editors). Checklist of birds of the world. Vol. 12. Museum of Comparative Zoology, Cambridge, MA.

RATTER, J. A. 1995. Profile of the cerrado (tree savanna biome) of central Brazil: modern agriculture and conservation of biodiversity. Tropical Agriculture Association Newsletter 15:33–34.

REMSEN, J. V., JR., AND E. S. HUNN. 1979. First records of *Sporophila caerulescens* from Colombia; a probable long distance migrant from southern South America. Bulletin of the British Ornithological Club 99:24–26.

RIDGELY, R. S., AND G. TUDOR. 1989. The birds of South America. Vol. 1. University of Texas Press, Austin, TX.

ROSÁRIO, L. A. 1996. As aves em Santa Catarina: distribuição geográfica e meio ambiente. Fundação do Meio Ambiente, Florianópolis, Brazil.

RYLANDS, A. B. 1991. The status of conservation areas in the Brazilian Amazon. World Wildlife Fund, Washington, D.C.

SIBLEY, C. G., AND B. L. MONROE. 1990. Distribution and taxonomy of birds of the world. Yale University Press, New Haven, CT.

SICK, H. 1983. Migrações de aves na América do Sul continental. Publicação Técnica, CEMAVE 2:1–83.

SICK, H. 1985. Ornitologia Brasileira: uma introdução. Universidade de Brasília, Brasília, D.F., Brazil.

SILVA, J. M. C. 1994. Seasonal distribution of the Lined Seedeater *Sporophila lineola.* Bulletin of the British Ornithological Club 115:14–21.

SILVA, J. M. C. 1995a. Avian inventory of the cerrado region, South America: implications for biological conservation. Bird Conservation International 5: 291–304.

SILVA, J. M. C. 1995b. Birds of the cerrado region, South America. Steenstrupia 21:69–92.

SILVA, J. M. C. 1996. Endemic bird species and conservation in the cerrado region, South America. Biodiversity and Conservation 6:435–450.

STOTZ, D. F., J. W. FITZPATRICK, T. A. PARKER III, AND D. K. MOSKOVITS. 1996. Neotropical birds: ecology and conservation. University of Chicago Press, Chicago, IL.

TERBORGH, J. W. 1980. The conservation status of neotropical migrants: present and future. Pp. 21–30 *in* A. Keast and E. S. Morton (editors). Migrant birds in the neotropics: ecology, behavior, distribution and conservation. Smithsonian Institution Press, Washington, D.C.

THOMAS, B. T. 1979. The birds of a ranch in the Venezuelan llanos. Pp. 213–259 *in* J. F. Eisenberg (editor). Vertebrate ecology in the northern neotropics. Smithsonian Institution Press, Washington, D.C.

WILLIS, E. O., AND Y. ONIKI. 1993. New and reconfirmed birds from the state of São Paulo, Brazil, with notes on disappearing species. Bulletin of the British Ornithological Club 113:23–34.

ZIMMER, J. T. 1938. Notes on migrations of South American birds. Auk 55:405–410.

Studies in Avian Biology No. 19:281–288, 1999.

DEMOGRAPHIC CHARACTERISTICS OF DICKCISSELS IN WINTER

GIANFRANCO D. BASILI AND STANLEY A. TEMPLE

Abstract. Populations of breeding Dickcissels (*Spiza americana*) have declined in North America by 40 percent since 1966. One proposed explanation for this decline is female-biased mortality during the nonbreeding season, resulting in a male-dominated breeding population that produces too few offspring to replace annual losses. We tested this hypothesis by examining Dickcissel sex ratios on the species' central wintering grounds in Venezuela. The overall mean sex ratio of 1.53 males per female differed significantly from 1:1. Although the Dickcissel population was male dominated, sex ratios were not sufficiently skewed to support the hypothesis of female-biased mortality in the nonbreeding season. The sex ratio of juveniles, which was also skewed in favor of males, appeared to be determined prior to the juveniles' arrival in Venezuela and not by differential survival during winter. These data, combined with other observations, including the absence of female starvation in Venezuela, appear to indicate that Dickcissels have not undergone major demographic changes since the late 1960s.

LAS CARACTERÍSTICAS DEMOGRÁFICAS DEL ARROCERO AMERICANO EN EL INVIERNO

Sinopsis. Las poblaciones del Arrocero Americano (*Spiza americana*) en reproducción han disminuido en América del Norte en un 40 por ciento desde 1966. Una explicación sugerida para esta disminución es la mortalidad sesgada en las hembras durante la estación no reproductiva, lo que ha resultado en una población reproductiva dominada por machos que produce insuficientes progenies para reemplazar las pérdidas anuales. Comprobamos esta hipótesis examinando las proporciones de sexos en el Arrocero Americano en los terrenos invernales centrales de la especie en Venezuela. La proporción promedio total de sexos de 1,53 machos por cada hembra se diferenció significativamente de 1:1. Aunque la población del Arrocero Americano fue dominada por los machos, las proporciones de sexos no fueron lo suficientemente desiguales para probar la hipótesis de mortalidad sesgada en las hembras durante la estación no reproductiva. La proporción de sexos de los jóvenes, también sesgada a favor de los machos, parecía existir antes de la llegada de los jóvenes a Venezuela y no debido a una sobrevivencia diferencial durante el invierno. Estos datos, en combinación con otras observaciones, entre ellas la ausencia de inanición de las hembras en Venezuela, parecen indicar que los Arroceros Americanos no han experimentado mayores cambios demográficos desde fines de los años 60.

Key Words: Dickcissel; mortality; population demographics; sex ratio; *Spiza americana*.

Populations of breeding Dickcissels (*Spiza americana*) in North America have declined 40% since 1966 (Sauer et al. 1996). One proposed explanation for this decline is female-biased mortality during the nonbreeding season, resulting in a male-dominated breeding population that produces too few offspring to replace annual losses (Fretwell 1977, 1986). The proposed mechanism for this female-biased mortality focuses on the Dickcissel's granivorous winter diet and how the species' diet and survival have been affected by changes in agricultural practices on the winter range.

Because male Dickcissels are larger than females, Fretwell (1986) hypothesized that males are better suited to feed on large-seeded cultivated grains such as rice (*Oryza sativa*) and sorghum (*Sorghum vulgare*). Increased production of rice and sorghum throughout the Dickcissel's winter range therefore may have created more food for males but not for females. To support these ideas, Fretwell (1986) presented evidence for sex-specific foraging strategies and a sex ratio severely skewed in favor of males.

Previous estimates of the population-level sex ratio of the Dickcissel were derived from mistnet samples of wintering birds in Trinidad (ffrench 1967) and from breeding-colony censuses in North America (Fretwell and Calver 1970). These two estimates were obtained using different techniques and therefore are not completely comparable. Both estimates may be biased. The population in Trinidad may not represent the entire winter population because it is on the fringe of the winter range (Fretwell 1986). And estimating sex ratios during the breeding season is complicated by several factors, including detectability differences between the sexes (females are more cryptic than males) and differing degrees of polygyny throughout the range (Zimmerman 1966).

We think a more appropriate estimate of the Dickcissel's sex ratio can be obtained on the species' central wintering grounds in the Venezuelan llanos. The agricultural regions of the Venezuelan llanos harbor most of the world's Dickcissels during the nonbreeding season (Basili 1997). Dickcissels congregate and form large communal roosts that sometimes comprise millions of birds. From 1990 through 1993, and briefly in 1995, we obtained demographic information on Dickcissel populations in Venezuela from November through April. Most of these data were obtained with the same methods employed by ffrench (1967) in Trinidad, allowing us to make spatial and temporal comparisons between these sites and time periods.

We tested Fretwell's (1986) hypothesis that female-biased mortality during the nonbreeding season results in a male-dominated breeding population that ultimately produces too few offspring to replace annual losses. We examined whether several predictions consistent with this hypothesis, such as the presence of underweight females in winter and changes in sex ratios, were supported. We also examined whether winter flocks of Dickcissels in Venezuela were substructured based on sex, age, or breeding location, as is the case in some other migratory passerines (e.g., White-crowned Sparrow [*Zonotrichia leucophrys*; King et al. 1965] and Dark-eyed Junco [*Junco hyemalis*; Ketterson and Nolan 1976]).

METHODS

STUDY AREA

Field research was conducted in 1990–1993 and 1995 in the center of the Dickcissel's winter range on the central llanos of Venezuela (Friedmann and Smith 1955, Basili 1997). The llanos that surround the Orinoco River constitute the largest neotropical savanna north of the equator (Sarmiento 1984). Historically, Dickcissels were distributed widely throughout these llanos, but since the early 1950s a changing agricultural landscape has altered the species' winter distribution. Presently the Dickcissel's center of abundance in winter occurs in farmland in the Venezuelan states of Portuguesa (southeast of the city of Acarigua) and Guárico (south of the city of Calabozo), where approximately 6 million individuals can be found (Basili and Temple 1999). By day Dickcissels forage in large flocks (10,000+ individuals), and at night they come together to roost in even larger aggregations (Basili and Temple 1995). Roost sizes vary from several thousand to several million individuals. From 1990 through 1993 we identified 19 different nocturnal roosts. We collected most of our demographic data at 17 of these roosts. We also sampled the structure of populations at feeding sites and at daytime roosts.

DATA COLLECTION

We obtained demographic data for Dickcissels in Venezuela primarily from mist-net samples. The roosting behavior of Dickcissels greatly facilitates their capture in mist nets. Large numbers of birds were caught at nocturnal roosts by placing 12-m mist nets to intercept birds moving within the roost. Sugarcane (*Saccharum officinarum*) fields, where most Dickcissels roosted, were usually criss-crossed with service roads that provided ideal lanes for net placement. Nets were open in the evenings from the time birds first started arriving until dusk, a period of about 90 min. Morning operations lasted about 45 min, as birds departed from roosts more quickly than they arrived. After capture, birds were placed in holding cages and processed quickly (Bub 1991). We used only mist-net samples in our analysis because early comparisons of mist-net samples and direct observations in 1990–1991 demonstrated that direct observations produced consistently higher estimates of males (68%) than did mist-net surveys (58%; G = 18.35, df = 1, P < 0.001). The brightly colored males are probably easier to detect at long distances, thus biasing samples.

We recorded the sex, age, mass, and wing chord of each captured bird prior to banding it with a U.S. Fish and Wildlife Service aluminum band (size #1B) and releasing it. Dickcissels are sexually dimorphic and can be reliably sexed and aged by wing length and plumage (Pyle et al. 1987). Because they undergo a partial pre-basic molt on the wintering grounds, however, they cannot be reliably aged after February (ffrench 1967); therefore, we only present age data obtained before March of any year. Dickcissels were weighed to the nearest 0.5 g with a Pesola spring balance that was checked periodically for accuracy throughout the study. Wing chord was measured "unflattened," as described by Pyle et al. 1987.

DATA ANALYSIS

We used contingency tables and G-tests (Sokal and Rohlf 1995) to test for independence between observed sex ratios and those expected based on hypotheses of an even sex ratio (1:1) and a sex ratio heavily skewed in favor of males (5:1; Fretwell 1986). Heterogeneity in yearly sex-ratio data was tested using the additive properties of individual G-tests (G_{het} of Sokal and Rohlf 1995). We also used G-tests to test for independence between sex ratios obtained with different sampling methods and for independence of sex ratios and age ratios among years, roosts, and regions.

We used t-tests to compare same-sex mass between sampling periods, ages, and regions. We also used t-tests to compare wing chords between ages and regions. Differences in mass among roosts and years were tested with a one-way analysis of variance (ANOVA; Wilkinson 1992).

RESULTS

Mist-net data from Venezuela revealed a pattern in monthly variations in Dickcissel sex ratios that was similar to what ffrench (1967) observed in Trinidad; males were more abundant in December and less abundant in April because males arrived and departed from the wintering range before females (Fig. 1). To minimize the effect of this seasonal variation on estimates of sex ratios, we excluded December and April data from all of our analyses. Yearly sex ratios were determined from remaining data. In addition, we performed within-year comparisons

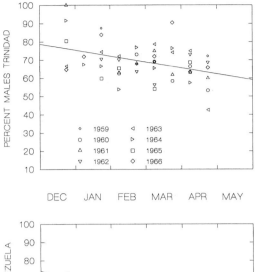

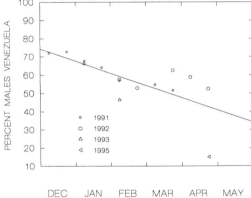

FIGURE 1. Seasonal change in the sex ratios of Dickcissels in Trinidad (N = 2,882; ffrench 1967) and Venezuela (N = 6,326).

only with data from the same 2-wk period, or when appropriate, from the same month.

How Skewed Are Dickcissel Sex Ratios?

The sex ratios of Dickcissels in Venezuela favored males (61%) and were significantly different from 1:1 (one-way G-tests, P < 0.001). Yearly estimates of males ranged from 58 to 65%. There was a mean sex ratio of 1.53 males per female. Although the Dickcissel population was male dominated, sex ratios were not sufficiently skewed to support Fretwell's (1977, 1986) hypothesis of five males per female (G = 1,654, df = 1, P < 0.001). In fact, we rejected the hypothesis of two males for every female (G = 98, df = 1, P < 0.001).

ffrench (1967) also observed a male-biased population of Dickcissels in Trinidad, where from 1959 to 1966 populations averaged 70% males. If Trinidad estimates were representative of the entire Dickcissel population, which is doubtful, and selection continued to operate

against females (Fretwell 1986), we would have expected the proportion of males in the population to have increased over the next three decades. Instead, there were significantly lower proportions of males in Venezuela in the early 1990s than in Trinidad in the 1960s (G = 58.84, df = 1, P < 0.001).

Dickcissel sex ratios in Venezuela were not, however, constant between years. In 1990–1991 and 1991–1992 we found 59 and 60% males, respectively; the 1992–1993 sample contained 65% males, accounting for the significant heterogeneity in the data (G_{het} = 14.63, df = 2, P < 0.001). Likewise, in Trinidad the data were heterogeneous (G_{het} = 42.24, df = 7, P < 0.001), indicating that sex ratios differed among years.

Is the Juvenile Population Dominated by Males?

The juvenile sex ratio in Venezuela did not favor males in 1990–1991 (43%; G = 2.116, df = 1, P > 0.1), but the sex ratios were different in 1991–1992 (66% male, P < 0.001) and 1992–1993 (60% male, P < 0.001). Consequently, juvenile male ratios differed among years (G = 21.06, df = 2, P < 0.001).

Throughout our study, mass of juveniles of each sex was similar to that of adults of the same sex, except in 1990–1991 when juvenile males weighed less than adult males (Table 1). In addition, the proportion of adults that were males in 1991–1992 (53%) was significantly smaller than in 1990–1991 (66%) or in 1992–1993 (67%; G = 44.18, df = 2, P < 0.001), possibly because of poor survival in the 1990–1991 male cohort.

We also examined whether the juvenile sex ratio in Venezuela changed as the season progressed by comparing sex ratios in 2-wk blocks. For all 3 yr, juvenile sex ratios remained constant (1990–1991: G = 3.232, df = 3, P = 0.357; 1991–1992: G = 0.804, df = 1, P = 0.370; 1992–1993: G = 0.719, df = 1, P = 0.396). Thus, the skewed sex ratio of young Dickcissels was likely determined prior to their arrival in Venezuela and not by differential survival during the winter.

How Have Age Ratios Changed?

In the early 1990s adults comprised 74% (range 71–76%) of the Dickcissel population in Venezuela. Differences among years were significant (G = 9.89, df = 2, P < 0.01). In Trinidad the proportion of adults was even more variable. From 1959 to 1966, adults comprised 73% (range 62–87%) of the population. The age structure in Trinidad also differed among years (G = 51.50, df = 7, P < 0.001; ffrench 1967). When data were combined into two time periods

TABLE 1.   MEAN MASS OF JUVENILE AND ADULT DICKCISSELS WINTERING IN VENEZUELA

Year	Sex	Age	N	Mass (g) ± SD	P[a]
1990–1991	male	adult	381	28.50 ± 1.84	
		juvenile	75	27.64 ± 1.77	< 0.001
	female	adult	194	23.49 ± 1.50	
		juvenile	94	23.44 ± 1.48	0.785
1991–1992	male	adult	403	27.18 ± 1.79	
		juvenile	136	27.11 ± 1.59	0.686
	female	adult	363	22.55 ± 1.61	
		juvenile	75	22.41 ± 1.36	0.459
1992–1993	male	adult	24	28.16 ± 1.57	
		juvenile	31	28.04 ± 1.30	0.759
	female	adult	41	23.44 ± 1.47	
		juvenile	17	23.59 ± 1.50	0.731

Note: All measurements were obtained in Portuguesa between December and February.
[a] Within-sex t-test comparing adults and juveniles.

(e.g., the 1960s and 1990s), however, there was no significant difference in age structure between periods (G = 0.961, df = 1, P = 0.327).

ARE FEMALES STARVING IN VENEZUELA?

Evidence of starving females could be revealed in several ways. Their winter mass could be significantly lower than their breeding-season mass. Their mass could also decline during the winter while in Venezuela. In addition, females might have trouble depositing fat in preparation for the northward migration. If selection pressure is strongly sex specific, we would not expect similar trends in body mass of males. Therefore, we used male mass as a control.

To examine whether females were underweight in Venezuela, we compared mass recorded in the winter with that reported from the breeding season (Dunning 1993). Two-tailed t-tests revealed no significant differences in the seasonal mass of females ($t_{[2],1168}$ = 0.860, P > 0.2) or males ($t_{[2],1615}$ = 0.653, P > 0.05). Because we lacked replicated data for all months during each year, and because the one month (February) sampled repeatedly in 1990–1991, 1991–1992, and 1992–1993 revealed no significant differences in the mean mass of females (ANOVA: $F_{[2,591]}$ = 1.535, P = 0.216) or males ($F_{[2,766]}$ = 2.206, P = 0.111) among years, we combined data across years to analyze change in mass over the winter in Venezuela. Trends in male and female mass were similar. Both sexes were heavier early in the season, followed by a period of lower but stable mass until late March. After March, Dickcissels become hyperphagic and rapidly gained mass in preparation for their northward migration. Females and males both increased their mass by 28% during the month of April.

Birds from different nocturnal roosts fed on different types of food because of regional differences in food availability (Basili and Temple 1999). Thus, we were interested in determining if mass varied among regions. The mass of females roosting in Portuguesa (23.00 ± 1.50 g), where rice and sorghum were cultivated, was not significantly different from the mass of females roosting in Guárico (23.25 ± 1.54 g), a predominately rice-growing region ($t_{[400]}$ = −1.46, P < 0.142). Males, however, were significantly heavier in Guárico (28.39 ± 1.74 g) than in Portuguesa (27.47 ± 1.71 g; $t_{[535]}$ = −5.34, P < 0.001).

ARE WINTER ROOSTS SUBSTRUCTURED BY SEX?

To determine whether males and females segregated themselves on the wintering grounds, which could influence sex-ratio estimates, we compared sex ratios at 17 of 19 nocturnal roosts located throughout the study area. Excluding the last half of April, when males had already started migrating north, males constituted a minority at only two roosts (48 and 46%). We never discovered a roost at which females heavily outnumbered males.

Because Dickcissels were concentrated in two agricultural regions of the Venezuelan llanos (Portuguesa and Guárico), and because food availability differed between these two regions, there could be demographic differences between birds occupying these areas. A comparison of roosts in Portuguesa and Guárico, however, revealed that sex ratios between regions did not differ (G = 0.188, df = 1, P = 0.664).

To evaluate whether sex ratios differed in foraging groups and in nocturnal roosts, we compared sex ratios of a nocturnal roost with sex ratios of one of its satellite daytime roosts. In late January 1991, the daytime roost had 68% males, which did not differ from the 61% males

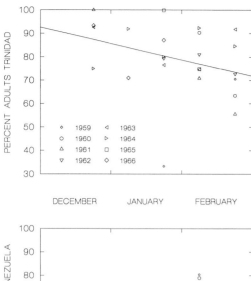

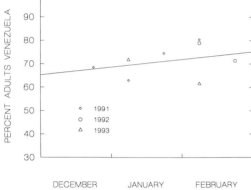

FIGURE 2. Seasonal change in the age ratios of Dickcissels in Trinidad (N = 1,309; ffrench 1967) and Venezuela (N = 3,519).

at the nocturnal roost (G = 2.59, df = 2, P = 0.11).

ARE WINTER ROOSTS SUBSTRUCTURED BY AGE?

We never found a roost in which the majority of birds were juveniles. It appears, at least in Venezuela, that young Dickcissels arriving on the central wintering grounds for the first time do not segregate themselves from the rest of the

population. We did find, however, that age structure varied by region and time. In February 1992 we found different proportions of juveniles in Portuguesa (19%) and Guárico (33%; G = 15.419, df = 1, P < 0.001). In addition, when plotting percent adults over time, it appears that in Trinidad adults arrived earlier than juveniles. This pattern was not observed in Venezuela, however (Fig. 2).

ARE WINTER ROOSTS SUBSTRUCTURED BY BREEDING LOCATION IN NORTH AMERICA?

Fretwell and Shane (1975) proposed that local populations of breeding Dickcissels may overwinter together in discrete subpopulations identifiable by variations in wing length; they presented evidence that birds breeding in Texas winter together in Guárico. Our comparisons of adult and juvenile wing lengths revealed significant age differences in both sexes (Table 2). When we compared adult wing lengths between regions, however, we found no regional differences (Table 2).

DISCUSSION

EVIDENCE FOR DIFFERENTIAL MIGRATION

Many species of nearctic and palearctic migratory passerines have differential migration patterns, depending on sex and age (e.g., Heydweiller 1936, Lack 1944, Balph 1975). For some species, such as Dark-eyed Junco (*Junco hyemalis*; Ketterson and Van Nolan 1976) and White-crowned Sparrow (*Zonotrichia leucophrys*; King et al. 1965), winter populations are segregated by sex, with females wintering farther south than males.

Dickcissels appear to exhibit differential sex migration on both their north- and southbound journeys. In both Venezuela and Trinidad, males were more numerous than females in the early stages of their "winter" residence (Fig. 1). Although differential migration was discernible in these data, we lack samples of the earliest birds arriving in Venezuela. To better understand this pattern, it would be useful to sample roosts in

TABLE 2. WING LENGTHS OF DICKCISSELS WINTERING IN THE VENEZULAN LLANOS, FEBRUARY 1992

	Mean wing length (mm) ± SD (N)	
Group	Males	Females
Adults	81.86 ± 2.01 (504)	74.16 ± 1.98 (453)
Juveniles	79.64 ± 1.93 (200)[a]	72.75 ± 1.61 (104)[b]
Portuguesa adults	81.93 ± 1.96 (406)	74.20 ± 1.96 (363)
Guárico adults	81.58 ± 2.22 (98)[c]	73.99 ± 1.98 (90)[d]

[a] T-test for mean wing length between adult and juvenile males ($t_{[702]}$ = 13.39, P < 0.001).
[b] T-test for mean wing length between adult and juvenile females ($t_{[555]}$ = 6.77, P < 0.001).
[c] T-test for mean wing length between adult males by region ($t_{[502]}$ = 1.54, P = 0.123).
[d] T-test for mean wing length between adult females by region ($t_{[451]}$ = 0.90, P = 0.368).

Mexico and Central America during migration, and also in the fall in Venezuela, when birds first arrive on the wintering grounds.

The proportion of juveniles decreased in the Venezuela population in January and February (Fig. 2). This change could have resulted either from differential mortality of adults and juveniles or from a movement of juveniles out of central Venezuela. ffrench's (1967) data from Trinidad revealed a complementary pattern, wherein the proportion of juveniles increased in January and February. This pattern suggests that juveniles may be leaving the central Llanos during this period, with some movement to peripheral areas such as Trinidad.

POTENTIAL BIASES IN SEX- AND AGE-RATIO ESTIMATES

Sex-ratio estimates of a species can be biased by the method, time, or location of samples (Welty 1962). Biases include different capture probabilities because males and females may (1) behave differently, (2) have different migration patterns (e.g., Howell 1953), or (3) have different geographic wintering areas (e.g., Ketterson and Van Nolan 1976).

When possible, we systematically reduced biases in our sex-ratio estimate. Because male and female Dickcissels exhibit differential migration, our estimates could be affected by time of sample. We addressed this concern by excluding data that were obtained in December and April, when differential migration would be most apparent.

We think our sampling location was most appropriate for a population-level estimate of Dickcissel sex ratios. Among neotropical migratory passerines, Dickcissels present a unique opportunity for study because most of the world's population winters in a small geographic area (Basili and Temple *this volume*). Approximately 6 million Dickcissels converge in this area and form huge roosting aggregations that do not appear to be segregated by sex, age, or breeding location. Because of large sample sizes, however, we did find statistically significant differences in sex ratios between some roosts, and we therefore think the best possible population estimate results from sampling many roosts and pooling information.

The method we employed to sample roosts reduced potential biases in two ways. Mist nets were open from the time birds first arrived and were closed only after nearly all birds had returned to the roost. This reduced potential biases resulting from differential return times for sexes or ages, as has been documented in other communally roosting passerines (Jenni 1992). Nets were also stationed to intercept birds as they moved within the roost. If any substructuring among individuals occurred for preferred roost sites—central or peripheral, high or low—our samples were obtained prior to any intraspecific jockeying for positions. Therefore, we think our samples were representative of birds in a particular roost.

By addressing the above biases, we think our estimate is a good representation of the Dickcissel's overall sex ratio. However, although most Dickcissels winter in Venezuela, we know of a large flock of 250,000 observed in Guatemala in February 1992 (Basili and Temple 1999). It is possible that groups of Dickcissels, "short-stopped" by agriculture on their southward migration, may be segregated by sex or age. Based on our data from wintering Dickcissels in Venezuela and on data from ffrench (1967) in Trinidad, however, we do not think it likely that flocks occupying areas outside the central wintering range would be notably biased in favor of one sex or age group.

INTERPRETATION OF SEX-RATIO DATA

Because we estimated a Dickcissel sex ratio of 1.53 males per female (61% males) in 1990–1993, we rejected the hypothesis that there were five males for every female. We also rejected more conservative estimates of a 3:1 or 2:1 sex ratio. We think these data, combined with other observations, including the lack of starving females in Venezuela, indicate that the Dickcissel population has not undergone marked demographic changes since the late 1960s.

A comparison of data from Venezuela and Trinidad (ffrench 1967) revealed differences in sex ratios by region and decade. This could indicate that males are more likely to wander to the eastern edge of their winter range, which would preclude Trinidad data from being representative of the entire winter population. It could also indicate a trend in the overall sex ratio, which if true, does not support Fretwell's (1977, 1986) hypothesis because selection would have to be operating against males, not females. We cannot be sure why these data differ, and to examine this question will require simultaneous sampling in both regions. Currently, this may be difficult as Dickcissels no longer visit Trinidad regularly (Fretwell 1986; S. Temple, pers. obs.)

A male-biased sex ratio was also apparent among juveniles in Venezuela. In 2 of 3 yr, the juvenile sex ratio upon arrival in Venezuela favored males. Therefore, assuming a 1:1 sex ratio at hatch (e.g., Clutton-Brock 1986), young females either were wintering elsewhere or, more likely, experiencing greater mortality before their arrival in Venezuela.

INTERPRETATION OF AGE RATIOS

Age ratios must be interpreted carefully (Caughley 1974). The age structure of Dickcissels in Venezuela during the early 1990s did not differ from the age structure in Trinidad in the 1960s (ffrench 1967). It is likely that ffrench sampled Dickcissels when the population was in steep decline (Fretwell 1986), whereas our data were collected during a period of relative stability (Sauer et al. 1996). Nevertheless, the age ratios were the same. This suggests that factors responsible for the decline in the 1960s and 1970s were affecting mortality rates in all age classes equally.

Dickcissel age ratios varied among years in Venezuela and Trinidad. It is likely that productivity throughout the Dickcissel's expansive breeding range was variable among years, and that this variability would be apparent in age ratios on the wintering grounds.

FACTORS RESPONSIBLE FOR THE DICKCISSEL'S DECLINE

We agree with Fretwell (1977) that the decline in the Dickcissel population in North America was a result of abnormally high overwinter mortality; however, we suggest a different mechanism. Factors responsible for the decline apparently affected mortality rates of all Dickcissels equally, whether male or female, adult or juvenile.

Basili and Temple (1999) showed that Dickcissels feed on rice and sorghum. They are therefore considered agricultural pests in Venezuela and other countries in their winter range (Slud 1964). To reduce crop damage, some farmers use lethal control and intentionally kill Dickcissels with toxic chemicals. We believe that lethal control was responsible for much of the decline in Dickcissel numbers in the 1960s and 1970s. Chemicals of choice are organophosphates such as parathion and azodrin. Farmers target Dickcissels by poisoning watering holes, spraying feeding areas just prior to morning feeding bouts, and spraying nocturnal roosts with organophosphates from the air or ground. These techniques would not discriminate by sex or age; the spraying of nocturnal roosts in particular has been known to kill hundreds of thousands of birds in minutes (Basili 1997).

Although the population has stabilized in the 1990s (Sauer et al. 1996), Dickcissels are still vulnerable to human-caused catastrophic mortality. Dickcissels continue to roost in huge concentrations—sometimes numbering in the millions at a single roost—and some farmers continue to suffer economic hardship caused by Dickcissels. The conflict persists; a majority (67%) of Venezuelan farmers indicated they would consider using lethal control of Dickcissels if economic damage became severe (Basili and Temple 1998). With single roosting aggregations possibly comprising 30% of the species' entire population (Basili and Temple 1999), Dickcissels are particularly vulnerable to the catastrophic mortality that these control programs can and have caused.

ACKNOWLEDGMENTS

This study was funded by the Wildlife Conservation Society, National Fish and Wildlife Foundation, Lincoln Park Zoo Scott Neotropic Fund, Zoological Society of Milwaukee County, and Agricultural Experiment Station and Department of Wildlife Ecology at the University of Wisconsin-Madison. Field assistance was provided by A. Basili, P. Desenne, M. Goodwin, C. Guglielmo, J. Hansen, R. Israel, M. Lentino, A. Luy, M. Questa, R. Restall, C. Rodner, C. Sanchez, and T. Teal. The Sociedad Conservacionista Audubon de Venezuela, EcoNatura, G. Morales (Instituto de Zoología Tropical, Universidad Central de Venezuela-Caracas), D. Aguerro (FONIAP), M. Ojeda (PROFAUNA), A. Grajal (Wildlife Conservation Society), and S. Strahl provided critical logistic support. We thank P. D. Vickery and J. R. Herkert for editorial comments on the manuscript.

LITERATURE CITED

BALPH, M. H. 1975. Wing length, hood coloration, and sex ratio in Dark-eyed Juncos wintering in northern Utah. Bird Banding 46:126–130.

BASILI, G. D. 1997. Continental-scale ecology and conservation of Dickcissels. Ph.D. dissertation. University of Wisconsin, Madison, WI.

BASILI, G. D., AND S. A. TEMPLE. 1995. A perilous migration. Natural History 9(95):40–47.

BASILI, G. D., AND S. A. TEMPLE. 1998. Dickcissels and crop damage in Venezuela: defining the problem with ecological models. Ecological Applications 9: 732–739.

BASILI, G. D., AND S. A. TEMPLE. 1999. Winter ecology, behavior, and conservation needs of Dickcissels in Venezuela. Studies in Avian Biology 19:289–299.

BUB, H. 1991. Bird trapping and bird banding: a handbook for trapping methods all over the world. Cornell University Press, Ithaca, NY.

CAUGHLEY, G. 1974. Interpretation of age ratios. Journal of Wildlife Management 38:557–562.

CLUTTON-BROCK, T. H. 1986. Sex ratio variation in birds. Ibis 128:317–329.

DUNNING, J. B., JR. 1993. Handbook of avian body masses. CRC Press, Boca Raton, FL.

FFRENCH, R. P. 1967. The Dickcissel on its wintering grounds in Trinidad. Living Bird 6:123–140.

FRETWELL, S. D. 1977. Is the Dickcissel a threatened species? American Birds 31:923–932.

FRETWELL, S. D. 1986. Distribution and abundance of the Dickcissel. Pp. 211–239 in R. F. Johnston (editor). Current ornithology, vol. 4. Plenum Publishing, New York, NY.

FRETWELL, S. D., AND J. S. CALVER. 1970. On territorial behavior and other factors influencing habitat distri-

bution in birds. II. Sex ratio variation in the Dickcissel. Acta Biotheoretica 19:37–44.

FRETWELL, S. D., AND T. G. SHANE. 1975. Ecotypic
variation in wintering Dickcissels. Eastern Bird
Banding Association News 38:125–128.

FRIEDMANN, H., AND F. D. SMITH, JR. 1955. A further
contribution to the ornithology of northeastern Venezuela. Proceedings of the U.S. National Museum
104:463–524.

HEYDWEILLER, A. M. 1936. Sex, age and individual
variation of winter Tree Sparrows. Bird Banding 7:
61–68.

HOWELL, T. R. 1953. Racial and sexual differences in
migration in *Sphyrapicus varius*. Auk 70:118–126.

JENNI, L. 1992. Structure of a Brambling *Fringilla
montifringilla* roost according to sex, age and body
mass. Ibis 135:85–90.

KETTERSON, E. D., AND V. NOLAN, JR. 1976. Geographic variation and its climatic correlates in the sex ratio
of eastern-wintering Dark-eyed Juncos (*Junco hyemalis hyemalis*). Ecology 57:679–693.

KING, J. R., D. S. FARNER, AND L. R. MEWALDT. 1965.
Seasonal sex and age ratios in populations of the
White-crowned Sparrows of the race *gambelii*. Con-
dor 67:489–504.

PYLE, P., S. N. G. HOWELL, R. P. YUNICK, AND D. F.
DESANTE. 1987. Identification guide to North American passerines. Slate Creek Press, Bolinas, CA.

SARMIENTO, G. 1984. The ecology of neotropical savannas. Harvard University Press, Cambridge, MA.

SAUER, J. R., B. G. PETERJOHN, S. SCHWARTZ, AND J.
E. HINES. 1996. The North American Breeding Bird
Survey home page. Ver. 95.1: www.mbr.nbs.gov/
bbs/bbs.html. U.S. Geological Survey, Patuxent
Wildlife Research Center, Laurel, MD.

SLUD, P. 1964. The birds of Costa Rica: distribution
and ecology. Bulletin of the American Museum of
Natural History 128:1–430.

SOKAL, R. R., AND F. J. ROHLF. 1995. Biometry: the
principles and practice of statistics in biological research. 3d ed. W. H. Freeman, New York, NY.

WELTY, J. C. 1962. The life of Birds. W. B. Saunders,
Philadelphia, PA.

WILKINSON, L. 1992. Systat for windows, version 5.02.
Systat, Inc., Evanston, IL.

ZIMMERMAN, J. L. 1966. Polygyny in the Dickcissel.
Auk 83:534–546.

Studies in Avian Biology No. 19:289–299, 1999.

WINTER ECOLOGY, BEHAVIOR, AND CONSERVATION NEEDS OF DICKCISSELS IN VENEZUELA

GIANFRANCO D. BASILI AND STANLEY A. TEMPLE

Abstract. Dickcissels (*Spiza americana*) were studied in 1990–1993, and briefly in 1995, during the nonbreeding season in agricultural regions of the Venezuelan llanos. These llanos comprise the Dickcissel's core wintering area, and birds occurred there for more than seven months, September through April. Dickcissels were gregarious, feeding and roosting together in large flocks. We found that sugarcane (*Saccharum* sp.) fields were the preferred roosting habitat, and we estimated that individual roost sizes could reach three million birds. Dickcissels were mainly granivores in winter, and while in the llanos they fed on wild grass seeds and agricultural crops, especially sorghum (*Sorghum vulgare*) and rice (*Oryza sativa*).

Since the 1950s, increases in cereal agriculture in Venezuela have provided Dickcissels with a superabundant food supply, yet the Breeding Bird Survey has indicated a 40 percent population reduction in North America since monitoring efforts were initiated in 1966. We think this decline has likely resulted from high overwinter mortality induced by lethal control operations. In many areas of Venezuela, farmers consider Dickcissels to be agricultural pests. Although most farmers use nonlethal controls to mitigate damage, some intentionally kill Dickcissels with agricultural chemicals. The Dickcissel's highly gregarious nature and small geographic range make the entire population vulnerable to catastrophic mortality. We propose that further efforts to prevent declines, and possibly to restore Dickcissel populations to historical levels, be aimed at reducing lethal control on the species' central wintering grounds in Venezuela.

ECOLOGÍA, COMPORTAMIENTO Y NECESIDADES DE CONSERVACIÓN DEL ARROCERO AMERICANO DURANTE EL INVIERNO EN VENEZUELA

Sinopsis. Estudiamos los Arroceros Americanos (*Spiza americana*) entre 1990–1993, y brevemente en 1995, durante la estación no-reproductiva en regiones agrícolas de los llanos de Venezuela. Estos llanos contienen el corazón del área invernal del Arrocero Americano, y las aves estuvieron allí por más de siete meses, de septiembre hasta abril. Los Arroceros Americanos eran gregarios, alimentándose y descansando juntos en grandes bandadas. Encontramos que los posaderos preferidos eran los campos de caña de azúcar (*Saccharum* sp.), y estimamos en tres millones de aves las agrupaciones de aves. Los Arroceros Americanos eran principalmente granívoros durante el invierno, y mientras estaban en los llanos se alimentaban con semillas de hierbas silvestres y cosechas agrícolas, especialmente sorgo (*Sorghum vulgare*) y arroz (*Oryza sativa*).

Desde los años 50, el aumento de la agricultura de cereales en Venezuela ha suministrado provisiones alimenticias excesivamente abundantes, pero el Breeding Bird Survey ha indicado una disminución de población de un 40 por ciento en América del Norte desde que se iniciaron los esfuerzos de medición en 1966. Creemos que es probable que esta disminución sea el resultado de la alta mortalidad durante el invierno provocada por operaciones letales de control. En muchas áreas de Venezuela, los agricultores consideran a los Arroceros Americanos como pestes agrícolas. Aunque la mayoría de los agricultores usa controles no letales para mitigar los daños, algunos matan a los Arroceros Americanos intencionalmente con sustancias químicas agrícolas. El carácter gregario del Arrocero Americano y su pequeña extensión geográfica hacen que la población entera sea vulnerable a la disminución del Arrocero Americano y a una mortalidad catastrófica. Proponemos que los futuros esfuerzos para impedir declinaciones y posiblemente para restaurar sus poblaciones a niveles históricos, sean dirigidos a la reducción del control letal en los principales campos invernales de la especie en Venezuela.

Key Words: Dickcissel; feeding behavior; lethal poisoning; mortality; population decline; roosting behavior; *Spiza americana*; winter distribution.

Studying the population dynamics of nearctic-neotropical migrants is complicated because important demographic events take place over huge geographic areas (Maurer and Villard 1996). Most research on migrants, especially grassland species such as the Dickcissel (*Spiza americana*), has taken place during the breeding season (Petit et al. 1995). Although the Dickcissel has been well studied, relatively little is known about its ecology during the nonbreeding season. This dearth of information confounds conservation efforts because it is impossible to implement successful management plans when uncertainties remain concerning the species' geographic distribution, behavioral ecology, and natural history during more than half of its an-

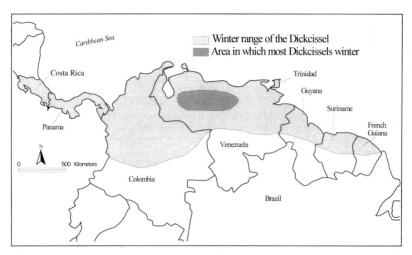

FIGURE 1.   Primary winter range of the Dickcissel in South America.

nual cycle (Petit et al. 1995). Although we agree that existing knowledge of neotropical migrants should be used for immediate conservation action (Martin and Finch 1995), we remain cautious because our experience with Dickcissels, like those of Sherry and Holmes (1995) and Temple (1995), suggests that taking action without a complete understanding of the species' annual cycle may lead to inappropriate and/or inefficient conservation strategies.

We reexamined the Dickcissel's winter range and identified patterns of abundance in this range. In this paper we provide information on natural history, diet and foraging, and habitat use. We also describe conflicts between Dickcissels and Venezuelan farmers that may have catastrophic consequences for the Dickcissel population. Finally, we suggest that conservation efforts focus primarily on the Dickcissel's winter range in Venezuela.

STUDY AREA AND METHODS

Field research was conducted during the nonbreeding season in 1990–1993, and briefly in 1995, in the Venezuelan llanos (Fig. 1). We also reviewed museum specimens and literature and communicated with ornithologists, birdwatchers, and farmers in Trinidad, Venezuela, Colombia, Panama, Costa Rica, Nicaragua, Guatemala, and Mexico. The llanos that surround the Orinoco River in Venezuela and Colombia constitute the largest neotropical savanna north of the equator (Sarmiento 1984). This region is characterized by a rainy season from May through October and a dry season from November through April (Monasterio 1970). Our primary study sites were located in the grain-producing regions of the states of Portuguesa, Cojedes, and Guárico. In Portuguesa and Cojedes, study sites were located in the vicinity of the agriculturally prosperous town of Acarigua. Dominant dry-season crops

there include rice (*Oryza sativa*), sorghum (*Sorghum vulgare*), and sugarcane (*Saccharum* sp.), but tobacco (*Nicotiana* sp.), cotton (*Gossypium* sp.), tomatoes (*Lycopersicon esculentum*), sesame (*Sesamum indicum*), and sunflowers (*Helicanthus* sp.) are also cultivated. Study sites in Guárico were in rice-growing areas south of the town of Calabozo. Rice is currently the only crop cultivated on a large scale in this area.

We located Dickcissels using road surveys. This species' gregarious nature makes it conspicuous, especially in the early morning and late afternoon when flocks move between roosting and feeding areas. Nocturnal roosts were located by following afternoon flights. We plotted locations on topographic maps available from the Cartography Department of the Venezuelan Environmental Ministry (Ministerio de Ambiente). Additional information on Dickcissel distribution in Venezuela and other parts of the winter range was obtained from the literature, personal communication with ornithologists and birdwatchers, and museum skins from the Phelps Collection in Caracas (Venezuela), Field Museum of Chicago (Illinois, USA), American Museum of Natural History (New York, USA), and Smithsonian Institution (Washington, D.C., USA).

We estimated roost size by classifying incoming flocks into size categories based on length, width, and height (e.g., Newton 1972, Lindström 1989). We observed foraging activity of males and females with a window-mounted spotting scope (Litvaitis et al. 1994). Dickcissels are sexually dimorphic, and sex was easily determined by plumage (Pyle et al. 1987). We examined crop and gizzard contents of birds killed in control operations and mist-net sampling. The contents of each sample were sorted by food item, oven-dried at 60 C, and weighed. The proportion of the dry mass represented by each food item was calculated (Litvaitis et al. 1994).

We used focal sampling to document individual feeding behavior. The time between consecutive bites (handling time) for males and females was measured for each food item. An individual's handling time was calculated by measuring the time interval between the first and fourth bites, then dividing by three (the number of seeds handled). These data were then aggregated and averaged by sex and food item.

Fourteen individuals (12 males and 2 females) were fitted with 1.0-g radio transmitters attached with a harness (Rappole and Tipton 1991). Because the range of transmitters was approximately 1 km, these 14 birds were most easily detected at nocturnal roosts. Crop-production data were obtained from the annual agricultural statistics (Anuario Estadistico Agropecuario) published by Venezuela's Agriculture Ministry (Ministerio de Agricultura y Cria).

We made a concerted effort to communicate with farmers throughout the project. Farmers not only provided accurate information on Dickcissel movements but were also candid about their ongoing struggle to reduce damage caused by the birds. This communication was essential to our work, and we recommend that it be an integral component of future Dickcissel research and conservation efforts in the region.

RESULTS

DICKCISSEL MIGRATION AND DISTRIBUTION IN CENTRAL AND SOUTH AMERICA: A REVIEW

Dickcissels begin arriving in Venezuela in September (Fernandez-Yepez 1945, Phelps and Phelps 1963), with the largest numbers occurring from November through April. This 2-mo lag between first arrivals and peak numbers appears to be the result of some birds spending September and October in agricultural regions of Central America. Slud (1964) reported that beginning in September "clouds" of Dickcissels depredated rice fields in the lower Pacific northwest of Costa Rica. Depredations continued through November, with the species diminishing "enormously" from December through April. There are a few instances of Dickcissels staying longer in Central America. One example is a large flock of 250,000 birds observed between 19 and 21 February 1992 on the Pacific Coast of Guatemala, near the village of Montericco (C. Robbins, pers. comm.). Orians and Paulson (1969) reported a flock of 700–800 Dickcissels on 10 December 1966 near Cañas in the Guanacaste province of Costa Rica, and Zimmerman (1965a, b) observed wintering flocks in Panama in January and February 1961.

Museum specimens collected during migration indicate that Dickcissels enter and leave the Venezuelan llanos via valleys in the Andes of western Venezuela (state of Táchira) and the Coastal Corridor range of northern Venezuela (Henri Pittier National Park). Meyer de Schauensee and Phelps (1978) observed 1,000 Dickcissels per hour crossing at Rancho Grande in Henri Pittier National Park in October. More recent studies (1990–1996) of fall migration yielded one Dickcissel captured in a mist net at Rancho Grande on 28 September 1996 (M. Lentino, pers. comm.). Thus, the most heavily used migration routes remain unknown.

Relatively few Dickcissels occur outside the core wintering area in Venezuela. A small flock of about 130 birds was reported near the mouth of Rio Tocuyo, Falcón, on 26 January 1995 (S. Hilty, pers. comm.), and a group of 12 birds was observed in secondary old-field habitat during the third week of January 1995 in the Caño Colorado area east of Maturín, Monagas (C. Rodner, pers. comm.).

The llanos extend into Colombia, and some Dickcissels also winter there. For example, specimens were collected in the department of Meta (Los Micos, 28 February 1957), and Hilty and Brown (1986:642) refer to Dickcissels as a "locally common winter resident but erratic in many places." Fretwell and Shane (1975) surveyed parts of the Colombian llanos near Villavicencio but found few individuals. When information about Dickcissel damage to rice and sorghum in Venezuela was presented to a rice-growing association and rice experimental station in the Colombian llanos in 1995, audiences were surprised to learn that their Venezuelan counterparts were confronted with such huge flocks (J. Botero, pers. comm.). These farmers assured us that Dickcissels are currently not a problem for agriculture in Colombia, confirming our belief that central Venezuela is the main wintering area for the species. Museum specimens collected between 1870 and 1950, however, reveal Dickcissels wintering throughout Venezuelan grasslands, including the states of Zulia (Guayabo, 27 February 1908), Barinas (Santa Barbara, 26 January 1947), Apure (San Fernando, 13 November 1948), Anzoátegui (Santa Rosa, 25 January 1939), and the federal territory of Amazonas (Caño Catamiapo, 8 February 1943).

In Trinidad, ffrench (1967) studied three roosts from 1959 to 1966. Birds generally arrived in Trinidad by December and departed by mid-April. Fretwell (1986:213) stated that Dickcissels begin to leave central Venezuela in December and January and arrive in "Trinidad to the east and Panama to the west by mid-January." Birds arriving in Trinidad undoubtedly do so via Venezuela (ffrench 1967). The origins of January birds in Panama are less certain and do not necessarily indicate a December movement west from Venezuela.

In spring, Orians and Paulson (1967) reported thousands of Dickcissels migrating north in Guanacaste, Costa Rica, between 27 and 30 March 1967, and thousands of individuals were observed flying north past the airport in Managua, Nicaragua, between 21 and 27 March 1996 (R. Purnell, pers. comm.).

DICKCISSEL DISTRIBUTION IN VENEZUELA

The largest Dickcissel concentrations we found in Venezuela (1–6 million) were near the agricultural cities of Acarigua and Calabozo. This confirms that the Venezuelan llanos constitute the species' main wintering area. Smaller populations are known to occur sporadically throughout Venezuela and in agricultural regions on Trinidad (< 50 km north of the Venezuelan coast).

We found few Dickcissels outside the core wintering area in Venezuela. Our surveys of southcentral Guárico, Apure, and Barinas in March 1991, March 1993, and April 1995 revealed only small flocks of Dickcissels (100–700) in rice fields near Sabaneta, Barinas. We did not observe Dickcissels in regions dominated by cattle ranching.

Dickcissels remained in Venezuela after December. A survey between 24 January and 20 February 1993 revealed a population of about 6 million birds distributed among five roosts. Similarly large numbers were present during these months in 1991 and 1993.

Dickcissels occurred in Venezuela for more than 7 mo, and their stay coincided with Venezuela's dry season. In late March and early April, birds began to depart for temperate breeding grounds. Large numbers remained in Venezuela until the third week in April, however, as evidenced by a roost near Caño Seco, Portuguesa, that had an estimated 2,950,000 birds on 15 April 1995. This was the largest roost we encountered during our study. By the end of April, when the rains usually begin (Monasterio 1970), most Dickcissels had migrated north. For example, the Caño Seco roost had nearly 3 million birds on 15 April 1995 but only 20,000 on 24 April 1995. A sample of 40 birds caught there on 25 April 1995 was heavily biased toward females (79%), indicating that males leave Venezuela before females. Our latest records included two males, one singing, at Pozo Blanco, Acarigua, on 15 May 1995.

DIET

Although insects are an important component of the Dickcissel's diet during the breeding season (Gross 1921), the species becomes granivorous on its wintering grounds (Slud 1964, ffrench 1967, Meyer de Schauensee and Phelps 1978). We observed Dickcissels feeding mainly on seeds. Direct observations of foraging individuals revealed five food items: rice, sorghum, and seeds from three wild grasses—*Rottoboellia cochinchinensis, Orizya latifolia,* and *Ischae-*

TABLE 1. AVERAGE PERCENT (BY DRY MASS) AND PERCENT OCCURRENCE OF FOOD ITEMS IN CROPS AND GIZZARDS OF MALE ($N = 35$) AND FEMALE ($N = 26$) DICKCISSELS IN MARCH 1992 IN THE VENEZUELAN LLANOS

Food type	Average % per crop[a]		% occurrence in crops[b]	
	Males	Females	Males	Females
Plant matter				
Rice	50	46	54	58
Sorghum	28	26	46	50
Wild grass seeds[c]	16	16	49	58
Unidentified plant matter	5	11	89	100
Animal matter				
Insect parts	0.04	0.04	14	27
Spiders	0.01	0	6	0
Grit	0.28	0.59	71	81

[a] Proportion of food items in males and females was not significantly different; t-tests using Bonferonni adjustments.
[b] Frequency of occurrence of food items was not significantly different between males and females; $C^2 = 2.516$, df = 6, $P > 0.8$.
[c] Category comprised common grasses *Orizya latifolia* and *Rottoboellia cochinchinensis*. Three less common seed types were found in the crop and gizzard contents and remain unidentified; they are accounted for in the category "Unidentified plant matter."

mum rugosum. Crop and gizzard contents of 61 Dickcissels collected in March 1992 confirmed the species' granivorous diet; 99% of the dry mass was seeds (Table 1). Rice was the most abundant food item, followed by sorghum and wild grasses (*Rottoboellia cochinchinensis* and *Orizya latifolia*). The remains of insects and spiders were found in 23% of all samples; however, their combined dry mass comprised less than 0.05% of the total sample (Table 1). There were no statistically significant differences between crop and gizzard contents (percent dry mass of food items and percent food item occurrence) of males and females.

FORAGING

Dickcissels foraged in flocks that ranged in size from a dozen individuals to enormous aggregations of several hundred thousand. The birds took seeds directly from ripening stalks or from waste grain remaining after harvest (Fretwell 1986; G. Basili, pers. obs.). It was unclear what percentage of the rice and sorghum consisted of waste grain, but the largest feeding aggregations (> 250,000 birds) were observed in recently harvested rice fields. The largest aggregations in sorghum fields were of similar size, but they occurred in fields prior to harvest. Dickcissels also fed in fallow agricultural fields where wild grasses abounded (G. Basili, pers. obs.); aggregations in this habitat, however, were

TABLE 2. DICKCISSEL CROP AND GIZZARD CONTENTS TAKEN AT NOCTURNAL ROOSTS IN THE VENEZUELAN LLANOS, MARCH 1992

Roost	N	Number of individuals						
		Rice only	Sorghum only	Grass only	Rice & sorghum	Rice & grass	Sorghum & grass	Sorghum, rice, & grass
Weiss	11	7	1	1	–	1	1	–
Retejado	10	5	–	1	–	1	3	–
Pepe	15	–	6	1	–	1	5	2
Perez 2	10	9	–	–	–	1	–	–

never as large as those we observed in rice and sorghum.

A typical day of foraging is represented by the following account, recorded 26 January 1993. The site was a 20-ha recently harvested rice field 5 km from a nocturnal roost of 420,000 birds. It was bordered on one side by a strip of trees along a dry stream bed. Old fields with shrubs, grasses, and forbs comprised the remaining habitat mosaic. The first group of birds (1,000) arrived at 0717 and immediately began feeding. Small groups continued to arrive until 0755, bringing the total number of birds at the site to 5,000. During this time, many larger groups passed high overhead and continued to more distant feeding areas. The greatest distance between a roosting and feeding area was 20 km, although Dickcissels have been reported to feed up to 24 km from a roost (ffrench 1967). Birds fed until 1115, with groups (< 1,000 birds) periodically feeding in rice and then moving to rest in cover along the edges of the field. We observed no feeding from 1115 to 1415, but small groups (< 30 birds) moved to different roost sites bordering the rice. Feeding began again at 1415 as several thousand birds emerged from the woods and settled into the rice. In the afternoon, groups (< 1,000 birds) moved periodically between cover and rice, with the longest feeding bouts lasting about 30 min. Feeding continued intermittently until 1735, when birds from more distant areas began flying overhead toward the nocturnal roost. On several occasions, stragglers in high-flying groups spiraled down to the rice field to feed. Finally, small groups (< 500 birds) began to depart, and by 1810 the feeding area was deserted. This schedule was typical in all habitats where Dickcissels fed. In the month before their northward migration, however, Dickcissels became hyperphagic and spent more time foraging as they attempted to build fat reserves.

Birds that shared the same nocturnal roosts did not necessarily feed on the same food items during the day. In Portuguesa and Cojedes, we often observed flocks leaving nocturnal roosts

and dispersing to feed in different habitats, including rice, sorghum, and fallow fields. Variations in crop and gizzard contents in nocturnal roosts confirmed this observation. A single food type predominated at only one of four roosts where we had 10 or more samples on a single evening (Table 2). Crop samples were not obtained in Guárico, but because sorghum was not grown there on a large scale, rice and seeds of wild grasses were the dominant food types.

Foraging Dickcissels exploited certain areas and then shifted to new feeding sites without changing nocturnal roosts. Flight patterns of birds returning to roost often changed over time. For example, in one week most birds entered the roost from the south, but the next week they arrived from the west. In December 1991, morning flights of Dickcissels passed directly over a ranch where we were stationed. For the first 3 d, groups of less than 1,000 birds were present. On day four, numbers increased dramatically as enormous columns of hundreds of thousands of birds appeared, most flying past but thousands landing on the ranch to feed in old fields. Large numbers of Dickcissels persisted in the same flight pattern for 4 d. On day 9, numbers conspicuously diminished, and by day 10 Dickcissels were no longer present. We found that the same nocturnal roost was still active, but foraging sites had shifted just south of the ranch.

We observed feeding activity in a ripening 120-ha sorghum field in March and April 1992. Birds were present for nearly 4 wk, with peak numbers exceeding 100,000 in the final week. Even while the field was being harvested, Dickcissels dodged combines and fed on the remaining seeds. The day before harvesting, there were 100,000 birds feeding in the field; the day after harvesting was completed, the field was deserted, even though waste grain was still abundant. The nocturnal roost remained intact during this period, but foraging flights were directed toward different areas.

We used focal sampling to document individual feeding behavior on four food types (rice, sorghum, *Rottoboellia cochinchinensis*, and

TABLE 3. MEAN TIME REQUIRED FOR FREE-RANGING DICKCISSELS TO HANDLE ONE SEED OF FOUR GRASS SPECIES IN THE VENEZUELAN LLANOS, MARCH 1992

Food item	Mean time (sec) ± SE (N)		Females % slower than males
	Males	Females	
Rice	5.1 ± 0.4 (67)	6.8 ± 0.6 (38)	33.3
Sorghum	6.2 ± 0.4 (57)	8.1 ± 0.7 (25)	30.1
Orizya latifolia	5.9 ± 0.7 (25)	6.7 ± 0.5 (24)	13.6
Rottoboellia cochinchinensis	15.6 ± 0.8 (19)	16.2 ± 1.4 (6)	3.9

Orizya latifolia). Birds consistently fed while perched on stalks, except when eating *Rottoboellia cochinchinensis,* seeds of which were located on the ground. A two-way analysis of variance (ANOVA) to evaluate the effects of sex and food item on bite times revealed that females handled all food types more slowly than males ($F_{1, 3}$ = 5.169, P = 0.019; Table 3). In addition, the type of food item had a significant effect on processing time ($F_{3, 253}$ = 47.552, P < 0.001). Because its seed is encased in a hard capsule, *Rottoboellia cochinchinensis* took longer to process than other seeds. There was no significant interaction between sex and food item, implying that the effect of food items on handling time was the same in both sexes.

When we observed entire feeding bouts, the longest bouts involved immature green sorghum, where a female ate 52 seeds in 241 sec and a male ate 80 seeds in just under 290 sec. Because birds were less conspicuous when feeding on rice and wild grasses, duration of feeding bouts on those items was more difficult to document. The longest bouts in rice (17 seeds in 54 sec) and *Orizya latifolia* (15 seeds in 40 sec) were both for males.

ROOSTING

Dickcissels not only fed in large flocks but roosted together at night in very large aggregations. In Portuguesa and Cojedes they roosted at night almost exclusively in sugarcane, a tall, sturdy grass with numerous horizontal leaves that provide ideal perches and cover from predators. When sugarcane was not available, as in Guárico, the birds roosted in dry cattails (*Typha* sp.), grass, shrubs, small acacia (*Acacia*) trees, and a fallow rice field.

Birds returning to roost in sugarcane did so in an orderly fashion; they wasted little flight time or effort before entering the roost. Birds returning to non-sugarcane roosts, however, appeared more reluctant to settle down and were often observed flying in several directions before finally entering the roost.

The same nocturnal roosts were often used every year. Of the 19 roosts located in our study

area, at least 7 were used in multiple years. One was used for 4 yr (farm of R. Perez, near Caño Seco, Portuguesa) and another for 3 yr (farm of J. Pinero, near Retejado, Cojedes). Three sugarcane fields that were used by Dickcissels for only 1 yr were converted to other crops, thereby precluding their availability as roost sites.

Birds began arriving at nocturnal roosts about 1.5 hr before sunset and began departing 10–30 min after sunrise. In late March, as the migration period approached, birds departed earlier (sometimes before sunrise) and returned later.

It took nearly 1 hr for large roosts to fill in the evening, but in the morning they usually emptied in less than 30 min. Departures were spectacular as hundreds of thousands of birds left together in a burst of noise and wind. Sometimes they spiraled upward, forming tornado-shaped funnels, and at other times broad columns left in serpentine fashion, with the lead birds above those behind. Small roosts (< 100,000 birds) sometimes emptied in one flight, but in large roosts wave after wave emerged until only a few stragglers remained. Departures usually took place from one part of the roost, but in the largest roosts we observed up to three distinct routes and directions of departure.

We observed birds roosting on the ground, both in sugarcane roosts as well as other roosts. On several occasions, large numbers crowded together on furrows in sugarcane roosts. We also observed individual Dickcissels entering the roost after dark, their presence indicated by a distinctive buzzerlike flight call. Although ffrench (1967) found that small roosts were often quiet at night, at large roosts we could hear Dickcissels throughout the night, fleeing from predators such as Barn Owls (*Tyto alba*). In addition, we observed small groups (< 100 birds) returning to the roost at dawn prior to the departure of any individuals. We presumed these birds were unable to reach the roost the previous evening and were returning at first light to rejoin the larger flocks.

Large nocturnal roosts sometimes subdivided into dozens of daytime roosts which varied in size from a few tens of individuals to hundreds of thousands. After foraging for a few hours, Dickcissels entered daytime roosts close to their food source and remained there until late-afternoon feeding bouts. When birds were inactive, we could locate daytime roosts by their loud chatter (when birds were alarmed, chatter immediately stopped, then resumed shortly later). Daytime roosts usually included isolated trees, forest stands, narrow forest strips along canals and streams, hedgerows, grasses, and sugarcane. Only rarely was sugarcane used as a daytime roost, but on several occasions we observed groups of fewer than 100 birds return to their nocturnal sugarcane roost after early morning feeding. Selection of daytime roosts was likely determined by proximity to feeding area and shelter from the sun.

In late March and April, Dickcissels often shared sugarcane roosts with other nearctic-neotropical migrants. Bobolinks (*Dolichonyx oryzivorus*), migrating north from Brazil, formed mixed-species roosting and foraging flocks with Dickcissels in the Venezuelan llanos. Bobolink flocks varied in size from a few to 5,000 individuals. Premigration flocks of thousands of Barn Swallows (*Hirundo rustica*) and Bank Swallows (*Riparia riparia*) were also observed roosting with Dickcissels, although the swallows arrived later and departed earlier than the Dickcissels.

Roost Size

We counted Dickcissels in 16 roosts that ranged in size from 20,000 to 2,950,000 birds. The median count was 580,000, and nearly 40% of all roosts were larger than 1 million birds. In Trinidad, ffrench (1967) reported 66,000 ± 15,000 birds in the Oropuche Lagoon roost in 1962.

Because most Dickcissels overwinter in Venezuela, we think roost counts provide a unique opportunity to estimate the total Dickcissel population. Between 24 January and 20 February 1993, we located and estimated the sizes of all roosts in Portuguesa, Cojedes, and Guárico. We discovered five roosts with a total Dickcissel population estimated at more than 6 million birds. Four roosts in the Acarigua area were estimated to hold 2,370,000; 1,945,000; 590,000; and 420,000 individuals, respectively. One roost near Calabozo contained 1,125,000 individuals. Since these estimates represent a majority of the entire Dickcissel population, approximately 30% of the entire population can be found roosting together in a single sugarcane field.

Radio Telemetry

In January and February 1993 we monitored 14 individuals with radio transmitters. All radios were mounted on birds at the same roost, and at that time the next closest roost was 10 km away. Birds with transmitters were most easily detected at densely populated nocturnal roosts. They were sometimes located in daytime roosts, but this proved more difficult as birds were widely distributed on the landscape. Shortly after we began the telemetry work, the roost where we fitted birds with transmitters began to get smaller and a new roost formed 5 km closer to the main feeding areas. An additional roost was discovered nearby, bringing the total to four nocturnal roosts within 100 km².

Individual birds were not strictly faithful to a single nocturnal roost. All 14 birds with transmitters used multiple nocturnal roosts; eight individuals used two roosts, five individuals used three roosts, and one individual used four roosts. Of the eight birds that used two roosts, five switched roosts once and remained at the new location, whereas three individuals moved back and forth between the two roosts. The exchange of birds between neighboring roosts suggests that individual roosts do not represent distinct subpopulations.

Nocturnal telemetry observations confirmed that Dickcissels made nighttime flights and used several feeding areas. One individual left a roost at 2200 and flew to a neighboring roost 10 km away, where it was detected at 0200. Birds with transmitters did not always return to the same daytime roosts, indicating flexibility in daily choice of feeding areas.

Causes of Mortality

Overwinter mortality is an important factor in the dynamics of the Dickcissel population. We observed 17 species (14 avian, 3 mammalian) preying on Dickcissels in Venezuela: Merlin (*Falco columbarius*), Aplomado Falcon (*F. femoralis*), Peregrine Falcon (*F. peregrinus*), Bat Falcon (*F. rufigularis*), American Kestrel (*F. sparverius*), Pearl Kite (*Gampsonyx swansonii*), White-tailed Kite (*Elanus caeruleus*), Roadside Hawk (*Buteo magnirostris*), Short-tailed Hawk (*B. brachyurus*), Gray Hawk (*B. nitidus*), Harris' Hawk (*Parabuteo unicinctus*), Long-winged Harrier (*Circus buffoni*), Barn Owl, Short-eared Owl (*Asio flammeus*), jaguarundi (*Felis yagouaroundi*), grison/huron (*Galictis vittata*), and tayra (*Eira barbara*). On Trinidad, ffrench (1967) noted three predators, all avian, of Dickcissels.

Merlins, also migrants, were the most common diurnal predators in Venezuela. We generally found one to five Merlins at every roost. Barn Owls were the most conspicuous nocturnal predators. Although Peregrine Falcons were not common in the llanos, they appeared at Dickcissel roosts in March and April, presumably on their migration north. On 15 April 1995, 19 Peregrine Falcons hunted at a large Dickcissel roost near the village of El Cruce southeast of Acarigua. Jaguarundis were the most common mammalian predators we observed.

CONFLICTS BETWEEN DICKCISSELS AND VENEZUELAN FARMERS

The greatest cause of overwinter mortality in Venezuela appears to be deliberate chemical poisoning by farmers, who consider Dickcissels pests. We observed numerous birds that showed signs of pesticide poisoning (e.g., loss of balance, respiratory problems, paralysis), and on one occasion we discovered a roost that 3 d earlier had been fumigated with a cannon sprayer attached to a tractor. Approximately 1,000 Dickcissels and unknown numbers of migratory Bank and Barn swallows were killed. We confirmed that at least five other nocturnal roosts had been chemically targeted since 1989 (G. Basili, pers. comm. with farmers). One farmer acknowledged that every few years he had sprayed a roost on his property with an aerial application of parathion (spraying is done in early morning prior to the birds' departure to feeding areas). The chemical is so effective that most roosting birds are killed. The farmer described dead Dickcissels as "knee-deep." He estimated that control efforts on his property have killed more than 1 million birds over the years, and neighboring farmers and agricultural workers corroborated his statements.

DISCUSSION

WINTER DISTRIBUTION

The present concentration of Dickcissels in the states of Portuguesa and Guárico, Venezuela, is best explained when one reviews the condition of the llanos before mechanized agriculture changed the landscape. We believe Dickcissels historically foraged on the seeds of grasses and forbs, resources that were more uniformly distributed on the landscape (Levey and Stiles 1992). After entering the llanos of northern South America, Dickcissels probably dispersed widely in search of productive feeding areas. Museum specimens support this idea and indicate that until the first half of the twentieth century Dickcissels occurred throughout the llanos of northern South America (Venezuela, Colombia, Brazil, Guyana, and Trinidad), including savannas of the Amazon basin. Since the 1950s, the llanos have become an agricultural region dominated by rice and sorghum. Seeds are no longer distributed uniformly but are superabundant and clumped. Instead of dispersing over a wide area, most Dickcissels remain concentrated, taking advantage of the concentrated food.

A few birds still disperse to historical parts of their winter range (e.g., appearing every few years in Trinidad), but most now congregate in agricultural regions of central Venezuela.

Our research suggests that most Dickcissels overwinter in the vicinity of Acarigua. This may represent a population shift since Fretwell (1977) indicated that most birds wintered near Calabozo, approximately 220 km east of Acarigua. Our research suggests that the agricultural areas around Acarigua and Calabozo remain the center of abundance from November through April. We did not find a December movement of Dickcissels out of Venezuela (cf. Fretwell 1977).

"Short-stopping" (Hestbeck et al. 1991) of Dickcissels may also now be occurring on the species' southward migration through Central America, as evidenced by large roosting flocks in Central American agricultural areas. Early in their fall migration, Dickcissels have been observed flocking with blackbirds (Icteridae) and feeding on rice in the Arkansas Grand Prairie (Meanly 1971). Although few Dickcissels overwinter in the United States, a large proportion of those that do can be found in the rice lands of the alluvial plain of the Mississippi River and coastal prairies of Texas and Louisiana (Root 1988). This suggests that some Dickcissels may be short-stopped before leaving the United States. Dickcissels appear to be able to adapt to rapidly changing agricultural landscapes along their migration route (e.g., Slud 1964). Thus, we think the winter range of Dickcissels will vary as agricultural practices change in Venezuela and elsewhere in northern South America, as well as in the countries through which Dickcissels migrate.

ROOSTING

Nocturnal roosts in Venezuela were much larger than roosts reported from Trinidad (ffrench 1967). Sugarcane, when available, appeared to be the preferred habitat for night roosting. Sugarcane was introduced to Venezuela in 1520 but was not intensively cultivated until the 1920s (Gomez-Alvarez 1975). Dickcissels have quickly selected sugarcane as preferred roosting habitat. When sugarcane was not available, Dickcissels roosted in bamboo, cattail marshes, grasses, and shrubs (ffrench 1967; Orians and Paulson 1969; G. Basili, pers. obs.). We suspect that these latter habitats are similar to preagriculture roost sites.

DICKCISSEL MORTALITY

Humans kill Dickcissels, sometimes accidentally but most often intentionally. Accidental Dickcissel mortality occurred during our study when sugarcane roosts were harvested while they were still occupied by Dickcissels. Prior to harvest, fields were burned to eliminate excess, nonvaluable leaf material. Roosts burned at night have been known to kill some birds (ffrench 1967; G. Basili, pers. comm. with farmers 1991–1994). We only observed one roost being burned; it was in the late afternoon when birds were settling in for the evening, and no mortality was discovered. The impact of roost-burning while birds are present remains unclear but warrants further investigation.

People eat Dickcissels throughout their range in Venezuela. Children hunt them with slingshots and by throwing short stalks of sugarcane into dense flocks arriving at nocturnal roosts. Some people enter roosts at night and club the birds with sticks and bats. When shotguns are used to protect crops from Dickcissel depredation, birds that are shot are eaten. The most unusual hunting method we observed was a vehicle driving rapidly through flocks flying low across farm roads. It seems unlikely that this cause of mortality has a major effect on the Dickcissel population, yet these daily events may be important when summed over the species' 7-mo stay in the llanos.

The fact that Bobolinks, Barn Swallows, and Bank Swallows occupied Dickcissel roosts in March and April is an important conservation issue because these species now share the same risk of intentional chemical poisoning. This became apparent when we discovered dead Barn and Bank swallows among dead Dickcissels following an April control operation. Because Bobolinks feed with Dickcissels in rice, Bobolinks are also susceptible to control operations in feeding areas. These observations, and knowledge of rice and sorghum depredations on the Bobolink's main wintering grounds in Brazil and Argentina (Sick 1986), raise the question of whether Bobolinks are subject to similar threats of chemical poisoning as Dickcissels.

FARMERS AND DICKCISSEL POPULATION TRENDS

Most farmers use nonlethal controls to keep birds out of their fields, but some farmers use toxic agricultural chemicals to kill Dickcissels (Basili and Temple 1998). We think that events on the wintering grounds in Venezuela could have been responsible for most of the 40% Dickcissel population decline reported in North America since the late 1960s (Peterjohn et al. 1995). When the decline was most precipitous (1966–1978), crop production was still limited. At this point there were many Dickcissels but few crops on the landscape, possibly resulting in severe crop depredation. During this period, Dickcissels were considered a major problem for

Venezuelan farmers (J. L. Mèndez-Arrocha, pers. comm.), and lethal control of Dickcissels was most flagrant (G. Basili, pers. comm. with farmers). We think lethal control may have been responsible for the rapid Dickcissel decline observed in North America between 1966 and 1978.

By the early 1980s, crop production in Venezuela had increased dramatically, yet Dickcissel populations in North America were reduced. The impact of Dickcissels on regionwide crop yields probably became less important, but on local scales the threat of Dickcissel depredation remained high and some farmers still suffered substantial economic hardships (Basili and Temple 1998). Because of this history, lethal control persists in Venezuela, and it continues to play a critical role in Dickcissel population dynamics.

If our ideas concerning the dynamics of the Dickcissel population are correct, Dickcissels may be in jeopardy. Because the population has declined rapidly, and because single roosting aggregations sometimes comprise approximately 30% of the species' entire population, Dickcissels continue to be vulnerable to catastrophic mortality. Lethal control of Dickcissels is still practiced (Basili and Temple 1998).

There appears to be a major conservation problem regarding the Dickcissel's central wintering area in Venezuela, and it is reasonable to infer that the entire population may be limited as a result. These results support Sherry and Holmes's (1995:86) statement that "understanding the whole migratory phenomenon is essential for effective conservation and management." Once reasonable inferences can be made about population limitations, that knowledge should be applied to conservation action. In the case of the Dickcissel, we recommend that conservation efforts be directed primarily toward reducing lethal control in the Venezuelan llanos while also addressing the concerns of local farmers. If the predicament of Dickcissels wintering in Venezuela is ignored, a critical opportunity for effective and efficient management and conservation of Dickcissels, and other migratory birds, will be lost.

ACKNOWLEDGMENTS

This study was funded by the Wildlife Conservation Society, National Fish and Wildlife Foundation, Lincoln Park Zoo Scott Neotropic Fund, Zoological Society of Milwaukee County, and Agricultural Experiment Station and Department of Wildlife Ecology at the University of Wisconsin-Madison. Field assistance was provided by A. Basili, P. Desenne, C. Guglielmo, J. Hansen, R. Israel, M. Lentino, C. Rodner, C. Sanchez, and T. Teal. We thank G. Aymard of Unellez-Guanare for help in botanical identification, S. McWilliams for help in interpreting diet information, and

J. Cary for assisting with data analysis. The Sociedad Conservacionista Audubon de Venezuela, EcoNatura, G. Morales (Instituto de Zoología Tropical, Universidad Central de Venezuela-Caracas), E. Lander (Universidad Central de Venezuela-Maracay), D. Aguerro (FONIAP), and A. Grajal (Wildlife Conservation Society) provided critical logistical support. We thank P. D. Vickery and J. R. Herkert for reviewing and improving the manuscript. We thank P. Bichier, P. Desenne, and S. Strahl for their support and encouragement. Finally, we thank the people of the llanos for their hospitality and for opening their doors for hot meals, cold drinks, showers, and wonderful company.

LITERATURE CITED

ANUARIO ESTADISTICO AGROPECUARIO. 1996. República de Venezuela. Ministerio de Agricultura y Cria, Dirección General Sectorial de Planificación del Sector Agricola. Dirección de Estadistica. Caracas, Venezuela.

BASILI, G. D., AND S. A. TEMPLE. 1998. Dickcissels and crop damage in Venezuela: defining the problem with ecological models. Ecological Applications 9: 732–739.

FERNANDEZ-YEPEZ, A. J. 1945. El Problema del Pajaro Arrocero. Ph.D. dissertation. Universidad Central de Venezuela, Caracas, Venezuela.

FFRENCH, R. P. 1967. The Dickcissel on its wintering grounds in Trinidad. Living Bird 6:123–140.

FRETWELL, S. D. 1977. Is the Dickcissel a threatened species? American Birds 31:923–932.

FRETWELL, S. D. 1986. Distribution and abundance of the Dickcissel. Pp. 211–239 in R. F. Johnston (editor). Current ornithology, vol. 4. Plenum Press, New York, NY.

FRETWELL, S. D., AND T. G. SHANE. 1975. Ecotypic variation in wintering Dickcissels. Eastern Bird Banding Association News 38:125–128.

GOMEZ-ALVAREZ, F. 1975. Caña de Azucar. Fondo Nacional de Investigaciones Agropecuarias. Caracas, Venezuela.

GROSS, A. O. 1921. The Dickcissel (Spiza americana) of the Illinois prairies. Auk 38:163–184.

HESTBECK, J. B., J. D. NICHOLS, AND R. A. MALECKI. 1991. Estimates of movement and site fidelity using mark-resight data of wintering geese. Ecology 72: 523–533.

HILTY, S. L., AND W. L. BROWN. 1986. A guide to the birds of Colombia. Princeton University Press, Princeton, NJ.

LEVEY, D. J., AND F. G. STILES. 1992. Evolutionary precursors of long distance migration: resource availability and movement patterns in neotropical landbirds. American Naturalist 140:447–476.

LINDSTRÖM, Å. 1989. Finch flock size and risk of hawk predation at a migratory stopover site. Auk 106: 225–232.

LITVAITIS, J. A., K. TITUS, AND E. M. ANDERSON. 1994. Measuring vertebrate use of terrestrial habitats and foods. Pp. 254–274 in T. A. Bookout (editor). Research and management techniques for wildlife and habitats. 5th ed. Wildlife Society, Bethesda, MD.

MARTIN, T. E., AND D. M. FINCH. 1995. Importance of knowledge and its application in neotropical migratory birds. Pp. xiii–xvi in T. E. Martin and D. M. Finch (editors). Ecology and management of neotropical birds: a synthesis and review of critical issues. Oxford University Press, Oxford, U.K.

MAURER, B. A., AND M. A. VILLARD. 1996. Continental scale ecology and neotropical migratory birds: how to detect declines amid the noise. Ecology 77:1–2.

MEANLEY, B. 1971. Blackbirds and the southern rice crop. U.S. Fish and Wildlife Service Resources Publication 100.

MEYER DE SCHAUENSEE, R., AND W. H. PHELPS, JR. 1978. A guide to the birds of Venezuela. Princeton University Press, Princeton, NJ.

MONASTERIO, M. 1970. Ecología de las sabanas de América tropical. II. Caracterización ecólogica del clima en los llanos de Calabozo, Venezuela. Revista Geográfica 21:5–38.

NEWTON, I. 1972. Finches. Taplinger Publishing, New York, NY.

ORIANS, G. H., AND D. R. PAULSON. 1969. Notes on Costa Rican birds. Condor 71:426–431.

PETERJOHN, B. G., J. R. SAUER, AND C. S. ROBBINS. 1995. Population trends from the North American Breeding Bird Survey. Pp. 3–39 in T. E. Martin and D. M. Finch (editors). Ecology and management of neotropical birds: a synthesis and review of critical issues. Oxford University Press, Oxford, U.K.

PETIT, D. R., J. F. LYNCH, R. L. HUTTO, J. G. BLAKE, AND R. B. WAIDE. 1995. Habitat use and conservation in the neotropics. Pp. 145–200 in T. E. Martin and D. M. Finch (editors). Ecology and management of neotropical birds: a synthesis and review of critical issues. Oxford University Press, Oxford, U.K.

PHELPS, W. H., AND W. H. PHELPS, JR. 1963. Lista de las Aves de Venezuela su distribución. 2d ed. Vol. 1, pt. 2. Boletin de la Sociedad Venezolana Ciencias Naturales 24, no. 104 and 105.

PYLE, P., S. N. G. HOWELL, R. P. YUNICK, AND D. F. DESANTE. 1987. Identification guide to North American passerines. Slate Creek Press, Bolinas, CA.

RAPPOLE, J. H., AND A. R. TIPTON. 1991. New harness design for attachment of radio transmitters to small passerines. Journal of Field Ornithology 62:335–337.

ROOT, T. L. 1988. Atlas of wintering North American birds. University of Chicago Press, Chicago, IL.

SARMIENTO, G. 1984. The ecology of neotropical savannas. Harvard University Press, Cambridge, MA.

SAUER, J. R., B. G. PETERJOHN, S. SCHWARTZ, AND J. E. HINES. 1996. The North American Breeding Bird Survey home page. Ver. 95.1: www.mbr.nbs.gov/bbs/bbs.html. Patuxent Wildlife Research Center, Laurel, MD.

SHERRY, T. W., AND R. T. HOLMES. 1995. Summer versus winter limitation of populations: what are the issues and what is the evidence? Pp. 85–120 in T. E. Martin and D. M. Finch (editors). Ecology and management of neotropical birds: a synthesis and review of critical issues. Oxford University Press, Oxford, U.K.

SICK, H. 1986. Ornitologia Brasileira, Uma Introdução. 2d ed. Vol. 2. Editora Universidade de Brasília, Brasília, D.F., Brazil.

SLUD, P. 1964. The birds of Costa Rica: distribution and ecology. Bulletin of the American Museum of Natural History 128:1–430.

TEMPLE, S. A. 1995. When and where are shrike populations limited? Proceedings of the Western Foundation of Vertebrate Zoology 6:6–10.

ZIMMERMAN, J. L. 1965a. Bioenergetics of the Dick-cissel, *Spiza americana.* Physiological Zoology 38:370–389.

ZIMMERMAN, J. L. 1965b. Carcass analysis of wild and thermal stressed Dickcissels. Wilson Bulletin 77:55–70.

1